Opera House
Act One

David Messent

Published by
DAVID MESSENT PHOTOGRAPHY
Unit 17
28 Roseberry Street
Balgowlah
NSW 2093
Sydney
Australia

First published 1997

Copyright David Messent 1997
National Library of Australia
ISBN No. O 646 32279 6

Cataloguing-in-Publication Data
1. Architecture
2. Engineering
3. Construction
4. Modern history

Acknowledgments for quoted matter are included
in the Author's Note and Acknowledgments which
start on page 7 and in the Notes and References
starting on page 447. These constitute an extension
of this copyright notice.

Typeset by Max Peatman
in Times Ten Roman. Printed by
The Bookprinter, Melbourne.
Platemaking Sinnot Bros. Sydney.

This one is for Dundas Corbet Gore

Contents

Author's note and acknowledgments.

There was a particular photograph that I wanted to take of the Opera House. I had noticed the location one day when flying over the Opera House shells in a helicopter. Between the shells of the Major and Minor Halls there is a narrow walkway. It looks like the base of a canyon, with the great white sails soaring on either side of it, and I thought it would make an interesting picture photographed from the air. The walkway is a passage facing directly north, so it would only receive the sun for about ten minutes at midday, and the light would fall on the shells at the right angle at the beginning of April, when the sun in Sydney is at an angle of 45° from the horizontal.

Everything was prepared. The time was right, the light was right, I had a 'soft' batch of film in the camera that would pick up the detail in the white shells in the glare of the harsh sunlight, and I booked the helicopter. We arrived above the Opera House at the appointed time, and I asked John, the helicopter pilot, to bank low over the shells and circle above the passage between the two shells. I took one or two pictures, then something extraordinary happened that still gives me pins and needles when I think about it. It was like being in an earthquake, where you wonder at first if your senses are playing tricks on you. As we circled tightly over the shells they seemed to move. The movement was in the north shells facing the sun, where the Major and Minor Halls have three shells curling towards the light, with the top two shells overhanging the shell below. At first the movement was like the jumpy frames from an old movie reel, with the top shells seeming to step forward and down, but as we kept circling the movement became smoother and smoother, until finally the shells took on a life of their own, rolling forward in a gentle smooth action like waves breaking on a shore. Not just one movement but a continuous movement, one wave following another like giant waves crashing onto rocks seen from a clifftop on a bright sunny day after a storm.

I wanted to ask John just to stay circling over the shells so I could make the most of the wonderful show, but the helicopter was too expensive to bow to such an indulgence, and besides, we could not stay too long, because the Governor of New South Wales who lived at Government House in the Royal Botanic Gardens just next to the Opera House, would complain about the noise. (He had once before!) So I took my pictures and we were on our way.

This is a summary of acknowledgments, to recognise the help I had along the way to produce this book. But this book would not have been written if it was not for the Opera House, so an acknowledgment must go first and foremost to Jorn Utzon, the extraordinary architect who could seem to make still things move and whose magnificent original inspiration inspired me to undertake this work.

Appreciation is extended to all the staff at the research institutions listed in the abbreviations and the bibliography, but in particular, Barbara Tait and Pauline Shirley of the Arup Library in London and Paul Bentley of the Dennis Wolanski Library in Sydney. Thanks also to Ella Ashworth for permission to use the papers of her late husband, Professor Harry Ashworth, held at the National Library, Canberra, and to Owen Haviland, grandson of the late Stan Haviland, for permission to use family papers relating to the Opera House. Great appreciation is extended to all those who took the time to be interviewed for this book, and shared their experiences, but particular mention should be made of Bob Kelman, John Blanchard, Sir Jack Zunz and John Nutt, who read through the draft, corrected my errors and made suggestions on how it could be improved. John Blanchard pointed out that the story seems confusing (which it does) but then qualified the statement by saying this was not surprising because the nature of the job *was* confusing. John Nutt said the draft read like a series of dramas and disasters, but that the construction of the Opera House in fact went very well, and it is now there completed in its magnificence for all to see. The point is that the language of engineers is drawings, of which they made thousands for the Opera House, and the only reason an engineer will put pen to paper to write a word is if there is a problem, and since the information for the book is taken to a large extent from correspondence too much weight is given to problems because when something is right and works (which it usually did) there was no necessity to commit a word to paper. So the difficulties outlined in the story should not detract from the fact that the construction of the Opera House was a tremendous success.

Even so, participants in the Opera House saga talk of the experience like some tragic, tumultuous event that has taken place in their lives like a war, which they would not have missed for the world but which has left them somehow scarred, and life has never been quite the same since.

This book is a narrative history, which contains numerous extracts from previously published works. Thanks are extended to Waveney Browne, Ava Hubble, George Molnar and Gavin Souter for permission to reproduce extracts from their written works. Also Karen Sturrock of News Ltd for permission to reproduce extracts from the *Daily Telegraph, Sunday Telegraph, Daily Mirror* and *Sunday Mirror*; Lesley Mallett of Fairfax for permission to reproduce extracts from the *Sydney Morning Herald*, and John Digby of Fairfax for permission to reproduce extracts from the *Sun Herald*.

Thanks go to Jill Swart, Sara Paxton and Graham White for proofreading, Louise Edgerton for proofreading and editing, Denise Llewellyn for photocopying and other work and Judy Ireland for typing and her husband Bill for assistance in checking. The index was compiled by Glenda Browne, a registered member of the Australian Society of Indexers. Eric Sierens of Max Dupain Studios produced the prints from Max Dupain's original negatives which are reproduced here.

Mention must also be made here of Corbet Gore, to whom this book is dedicated. Corbet gave his time for interviews, offered words of encouragement and buoyed me up with his wonderful sense of humour. Three years ago he suffered a stroke which left him paralysed down one side and the power of his very nimble mind slightly diminished. But he has still kept his wonderful sense of humour, can still seem to answer any question I ask him about the Opera House and maintained his encouragement to 'keep my nose to the grindstone' until the book was finished.

While writing this book, if ever my interest flagged or I seemed to run out of words, I would go and walk around the Opera House and maybe take a few photos, which seemed to cure the problem. However, when I was part way through one of the chapters on the podium and went on a stroll on the plateau of the real podium to revive my spirits, just at that moment, 500 metres away at Alfred Street on Circular Quay, my one and only sales representative Jack Swart was run over and killed. Jack sold my books, calendars and postcards to shops in Sydney, had just finished his calls at the shops at Circular Quay and was returning to his van on Pitt Street. It was hard for a while, to write anything at all after that.

CHAPTER 1

BENNELONG POINT

On 17th December 1770, the day of Beethoven's birth, the crew of Lieutenant James Cook's ship the *Endeavour* were, according to his diary, 'taking on board provisions, scraping and painting the ship' at Batavia in the Dutch East Indies. Cook had been engaged during 1769 and the earlier part of 1770 in sailing the *Endeavour* on a voyage of exploration and scientific study: he had observed the transit of Venus from Tahiti, spent four months mapping the entire coast of the North and South Islands of New Zealand, and on 19th April he had discovered the east coast of Australia at Cape Everard in Victoria.

On 29th April Cook dropped anchor in Botany Bay where the expedition rested for a week, then weighed anchor early in the morning of 6th May and sailed north up the coast. At noon, according to Cook's diary, 'we were between two and three miles distant from the land, and abreast of a bay or harbour, in which there appeared to be a good anchorage, and which I called Port Jackson.'[1] On 22nd August Cook rowed ashore with a party from the *Endeavour* to Possession Island, two miles off the western shore of Cape York and

> As I was now about to quit the eastern coast of New Holland... which I am confident no European had ever seen before, I... hoisted English colours... (and) took possession of the whole eastern coast... in right of His Majesty King George the Third... with all the bays, harbours, rivers and islands situated upon it.[2]

The party on the island 'fired several volleys of small arms on the occasion, and cheer'd 3 times, which was answer'd from the ship.'[3] Then Cook sailed for Batavia to victual and repair the ship, then on to England, arriving in July 1771 to announce his latest discoveries and additions to the English Empire.

Scant notice was paid by the English authorities to Cook's discoveries until 1779, when Joseph Banks, a botanist who had travelled with Cook's expedition, suggested to a House of Commons committee set up to examine alternative locations for convicts that if America should be lost to the rebels, Botany Bay

11

was eminently suitable for a penal settlement, and could be self-supporting within a year.

In August 1783, England recognised the United States at Versailles, and that month James Matra, a midshipman who had been on Cook's voyage on the *Endeavour*, proposed to the English Government that Australia be colonised to 'atone for the loss of our American colonies.'[4] Later in the year the Home and Colonial Secretary, Lord Sydney, wrote to Thomas Townshend about how convicts could be sent to Australia: 'Give them a few acres of ground as soon as they arrive... they cannot fly from the country... they have no temptation to theft, and... they must work or starve.'[5] Eventually Lord Sydney persuaded Pitt's Cabinet to act on an Admiralty plan 'for effectually disposing of convicts, by the establishment of a Colony in New South Wales', and a fleet was despatched commanded by Governor Phillip containing approximately 1400 souls, half of whom were convicts.

On arrival at Botany Bay in January 1788, Phillip discovered '... it did not afford a shelter from the easterly winds' and where the land around the bay wasn't 'damp and spongy' or 'a perfect swamp' there was no 'no supply of fresh water, except in very small drains.'[6]

While some of the sailors and marines amused themselves in encounters with local Aborigines,[7] Phillip set off to explore Cook's Port Jackson. On arrival:

> The different coves were examined with all possible expedition. I fixed on the one that had the best spring of water, and in which the ships can anchor... close to the shore. This Cove, which I honoured with the name of Sydney,[8] is about a quarter of a mile across at the entrance, and half a mile in length.[9]

The ships of the First Fleet were ordered by Phillip to sail the short distance from Botany Bay to Sydney Cove, and on the evening of 26th January[10] '... the colours were displayed on shore' and the officers 'assembled round the flagstaff (and) drank the King's health and success of the settlement...'.[11] Two days later on an island off the eastern side of the cove called Jubughalee by the Aborigines, two bulls, four cows, one stallion, three mares and three colts were disembarked. The island,[12] separated from the harbour foreshore by flat rocks covered with water at high tide, was first known as Cattle Point[13] or Limeburners Point[14] by the First Fleeters.

Phillip's instructions on being appointed Governor of New South Wales had included protecting the Aborigines, opening a dialogue with them and reporting 'in what manner our intercourse with these people may be turned to the advantage of this Colony'. Phillip was convinced of the necessity to 'attain their language and teach them ours... to reconcile them by showing the many advantages they would enjoy by mixing with us'. An Aborigine called Arabanoo was captured at Manly on 31st December 1788, but died of smallpox five months later. Unable to persuade another adult Aborigine to come and live in the settlement, on 25th November 1789 Lieutenant Bradley, First Lieutenant of the First Fleet flagship the *Sirius*, was despatched by Phillip with an expedition to capture another native. According to Bradley's journal,

> As we went down the harbour we got some fish from the boats that lay off the N'arm (North Harbour) fishing and proceeded up that arm in which we saw a great number of natives... several landed on the beach at the N'cove (Collins Beach, Manly) hauling their canoes up after them. As we got near... we held two large fish up to them and had the good luck to draw two of them away from a very large party by this bait.
>
> These people came round the rocks where they left their spears and met us on the beach near the boat... They eagerly took the fish. Four of the boat's crew were kept in the boat which was winded and backed close to the beach where the two natives and the rest of our people were. They were dancing together when the signal was given by me and the two poor devils were seized and handed into the boat in an instant.
>
> The natives, who were very numerous all round us, on seeing us seize those two, immediately advanced with their spears and clubs, but we were too quick for them... They were entering on the beach just as everybody was in the boat and as she did not take the ground we pulled immediately out without having occasion to fire a musquet.
>
> The noise of the men crying and screaming of the women and children together with the situation of the two miserable wretches in our possession was really a most distressing scene...[15]

At Sydney Cove at that time were living two Aboriginal children who had been staying with the colonists since April 1789 when they were found at a cove near the settlement suffering from smallpox. The children were Nanbarry, a boy aged nine or ten, and Abaroo, a girl aged about fourteen. Nanbarry had been living with the Surgeon-General John White and Abaroo with Mrs Johnson, the wife of the clergyman Richard Johnson. Bradley described the arrival of his expedition with the captives:

> On our landing at Sydney Cove we were met by Nanbarry, the native boy who was much pleased and called them by name Colbey and Benallon (Bennelong). Colbey we have frequently heard spoken of by the boy as a great warrior and a leading man among them; they were taken to the Governor's house where they were soon met by Abooroo (Abaroo), the native girl. She called them by name, the same as the boy had done and was quite frantic with joy.
>
> ... An iron shackle was put on one leg with a rope tied fast to it and a convict charged with each of them. They were very sullen and sulky and continued so several days, yet it did not by any means affect their appetite if we may judge from the quantity they now eat, which is beyond everything incredible (12 lb of fish does but little towards satisfying them for one meal).

Lieutenant Daniel Southwell of the *Sirius* also noted Bennelong's great appetite, 'tis certain he can manage the share of six men with great ease at one meal.' The Judge Advocate, Captain David Collins related the meaning of Bennelong's name, 'Bennelong told me his name was that of a large fish, but one that I never saw taken.'[16] Lieutenant Watkin Tench of the Marines wrote: 'Baneelon we judged to be about 26 years old, of good stature, and stoutly made, with a bold intrepid countenance, which bespoke defiance and revenge',[17] while Captain John Hunter of the *Sirius* found him 'a very good looking young fellow, of a pleasant lively disposition.'[18]

Colbey escaped in the dark at supper time on the evening of 12th December 1789 and Bennelong was only just prevented from going with him. Bradley recorded that following Colbey's departure Bennelong settled down and in 'two or three days he became quite composed and (seemed) reconciled better to his situation than before'. Tench observed that Bennelong 'became at once fond of our viands and would drink the strongest liquors, not simply without reluctance but with eager marks of delight and enjoyment... In his eating, he was alike compliant...' When shown a turtle 'Baneelon... denied it to be a fish, but no common councilman in Europe could do more justice than he did to a very fine one that the *Supply* had brought from Lord Howe Island, and which was served up at the Governor's table on Christmas Day.'

Captain Hunter described Bennelong as 'very good-natured, being seldom angry at any jokes that may be passed upon him, and he readily imitates all the actions and gestures of every person in the governor's family. He sits at table with the Governor, whom he calls "Beanga", or father;[19] and the Governor calls him "Doorow", or son.' Tench's narrative continued,

> His powers of mind were certainly far above mediocrity. He acquired knowledge, both of our manners and language, faster than his predecessor (Arabanoo) had done. He willingly communicated information; sang, danced and capered, told us all the customs of his country and all the details of his family economy. Love and war seemed his favourite pursuits; in both of which he had suffered severely. His head was disfigured by several scars; a spear had passed through his arm and another through his leg; half of one of his thumbs was carried away; and the mark of a wound appeared on the back of his hand.
>
> The cause and attendant circumstances of all these disasters, except one, he related to us. 'But the wound on the back of your hand, Baneelon! how did you get that?' He laughed, and owned that it was received in carrying off a lady of another tribe by force. 'I was dragging her away; she cried aloud, and stuck her teeth in me', – 'And what did you do then?' 'I knocked her down, and beat her till she was insensible, and covered with blood.'
>
> Whenever he recounted his battles, 'poized his lance, and shewed how fields were won', the most violent exclamations of rage and vengeance against his competitors in arms, those of the tribe he called Cam-ee-ra-gal in particular, would burst from him.
>
> And he never failed at such times to solicit the Governor to accompany him with a body of soldiers in order that he might exterminate this hated name.

Hunter mentioned Bennelong's wife, who had apparently died a short time before his capture.

> He sometimes mentions this circumstance and it occasions a momentary gloom but this his natural gaiety soon dissipates... Whenever asked to dance he does it with great readiness; his motions at first are very slow and are regulated by a dismal tune, which grows quicker as the dance advances till at length he throws himself into the most violent posture, shaking his arms and striking the ground with great force, which gives him the appearance of madness. It is very probable that this part of the dance is used as a sort of defiance as all the natives which were seen when we first arrived at Port Jackson joined this sort of dance to their vociferations of 'woroo, woroo' (go away).

In early 1790, food in the settlement was running short and Bennelong, who by this time had been freed of his shackles, was put on a shortened ration along with everyone else. Tench reported, 'Our friend Baneelon during this season of scarcity was as well taken care of as our desperate circumstances would allow. We knew not how to keep him and yet were unwilling to part with him... but the ration of a week was insufficient to have kept him for a day...'. Then one night five months after his capture, Tench recorded, 'About two o'clock in the morning he pretended illness, and awakening the servant who attended him without suspicion of his design, and Baneelon no sooner found himself in a back-yard than he nimbly leaped over a slight paling and bade us adieu'. For four months Bennelong was not seen, then on the 7th of September according to Tench,

Captain Nepean, of the New South Wales Corps, and Mr White, accompanied by little Nanbaree and a party of men went in a boat to Manly Cove, intending to land there and walk on to Broken Bay. On drawing near the shore a dead whale in the most disgusting state of putrefaction was seen lying on the beach, and at least two hundred Indians surrounding it broiling the flesh on different fires and feasting on it with the most extravagant marks of greediness and rapture.

As the boat continued to approach they were observed to fall into confusion and pick up their spears, on which our people lay upon their oars, and Nanbaree stepping forward harangued them for some time, assuring them that we were friends. Mr White now called for Baneelon, who on hearing his name came forth and entered into conversation. He was greatly emaciated and so far disfigured by a long beard that our people, not without difficulty, recognised their old acquaintance. His answering in broken English and inquiring for the Governor, however, soon corrected their doubts. He seemed quite friendly. And soon after Colbee came up, pointing to his leg to shew that he had freed himself from the fetter which was upon him when he had escaped from us.

When Baneelon was told that the Governor was not far off he expressed great joy and declared that he would immediately go in search of him...

The length of his beard seemed to annoy him much and he expressed eager wishes to be shaved, asking repeatedly for a razor. A pair of scissors was given to him and he shewed he had not forgotten how to use such an instrument for he forthwith began to clip his hair with it.

During this time, the women and children to the number of more than fifty stood at a distance...'Which of them is your old favourite, Barangaroo, of whom you used to speak so often?' – 'Oh!' said he, 'she became the wife of Colbee! but I have got Bulla Muree Dee-in (two large women) to compensate for her loss'.

It was observed that he had received two wounds, in addition to his former numerous ones, since he had left us, one of them from a spear which had passed through the fleshy part of his arm and the other displayed itself in a large scar above his left eye. They were both healed and probably were acquired in the conflict wherein he had asserted his pretensions to the two ladies...

When the natives saw that the boat was about to depart they crowded around her and brought down by way of present three or four great hunks of the whale and put them on board of her; the largest of which Baneelon expressly requested might be offered in his name to the Governor...

It happened that his excellency had this day gone to a landmark which was building on the South-head, near the flagstaff, to serve as a direction to ships at sea, and the boat met him on his way... (back) to Sydney. Immediately on receiving the intelligence, he hastened back to the South-head, and having procured all the fire-arms which could be mustered there... set out, attended by Mr Collins and Lieutenant Waterhouse of the navy.

When the boat reached Manly Cove, the natives were found still busily employed around the whale. As they (did not) express... any consternation on seeing us row to the beach, Governor Phillip stepped out unarmed and attended by one seaman only, and called for Baneelon, who appeared but, notwithstanding his former eagerness, would not suffer the other to approach him for several minutes. Gradually, however, he warmed into friendship and frankness, and presently after Colbee came up.

They discoursed for some time, Baneelon expressing pleasure to see his old acquaintance and inquiring by name for every person whom he could recollect at Sydney; and among others for a French cook, one of the governor's servants, whom he had constantly made the butt of his ridicule by mimicking his voice, gait and other pecularities, all of which he again went through with his wonted exactness and drollery.

He asked also particularly for a lady from whom he had once ventured to snatch a kiss, and on being told that she was well, by way of proving that the token was fresh in his remembrance, he kissed Lieutenant Waterhouse and laughed aloud. On his wounds being noticed, he coldly said that he had received them at Botany Bay but went no farther into their history...

Baneelon's love of wine has been mentioned; and the Governor, to try whether it still subsisted, uncorked a bottle and poured out a glass of it, which the other drank off with his former marks of relish and good humour, giving for a toast, as he had been taught, 'the King...'.

Matters had proceeded in this friendly train for more than half an hour, when a native, with a spear in his hand, came forward, and stopped at the distance of between twenty and thirty yards from the place where the Governor, Mr Collins, Lieutenant Waterhouse and a seaman stood. His excellency held out his hand and called to him, advancing towards him at the same time, Mr Collins following close behind. He appeared to be a man of middle age, short of stature, sturdy, and well set, seemingly a stranger and but little acquainted with Beneelon and Colbee.

The nearer the Governor approached, the greater became the terror and agitation of the Indian. To remove fear, Governor Phillip threw down a dirk, which he wore at his side. The other, alarmed at the rattle of the dirk and probably mis-construing the action, instantly fixed his lance in his throwing stick (a stick with a shell at the end used to throw a spear)… the Indian, stepping back with one foot, aimed his lance with such force and dexterity, that striking the Governor's right shoulder just above the collar-bone, the point glancing downward came out at the back, having made a wound of many inches long. The man was observed to keep his eye steadily fixed on the lance until it struck its object when he directly dashed into the woods and was seen no more.

Tench recorded that 'His Excellency described the shock to me as similar to a violent blow, with such energy was the weapon thrown'. According to Hunter

The Governor… attempted to run towards the boat, holding up the spear with both hands to keep it off the ground, but owing to its great length, the end frequently took the ground and stopped him (it was about twelve feet long). Governor Phillip, in this situation, desired Mr Waterhouse to endeavour, if possible, to take the spear out, which he immediately attempted, but observing it to be barbed and the barb quite through, he saw it would be impossible to draw it out. He therefore endeavoured to break it but could not.

While he was making this attempt, another spear was thrown out of the wood and took off the skin between Mr Waterhouse's fore-finger and thumb, which alarmed him a good deal, and he thinks added power to his exertions, for the next attempt he broke it off…

The whole party got down to the boat without any further accident and in two hours (the people in her exerting themselves to the utmost, according to Collins) they arrived at the government house, when the surgeons were sent for. Mr Balmain, who was the first that arrived, after examining the wound, made everybody happy by assuring them he did not apprehend any fatal consequences from it. He extracted the point of the spear and dressed the wound, and in six weeks the Governor was perfectly recovered.

A few days after the accident (wrote Collins) Bennillong… came with his wife and some of his companions to a cove on the north shore not far from the settlement…

At this time the name of the man who had wounded the Governor was first known, Wille-me-ring; and Bennillong made many attempts to fix a belief that he had beaten him severely for the aggression. Bennillong declared that he should wait for some days and hoped that the Governor

18

would be able... to visit him. On the tenth day after he had received the wound, his excellency was so far recovered as to go to the place, accompanied by several officers, all armed, where he saw Bennillong and his companions. Bennillong then repeated his assurances of his having, in conjunction with his friend Cole-be, severely beaten Wille-me-ring; and added that his throwing the spear at the Governor was entirely the effect of his fears and done from the impulse of self-preservation.

On 15th September a party of whites returned to the North Shore with Nanbaree and Abaroo. Tench described the scene as:

> ... a party of us went ashore to them unarmed. Several little presents, which had been purposely brought, were distributed among them; and to Baneelon were given a hatchet and a fish.
>
> A bottle of wine was produced, and Baneelon immediately prepared for the charge. Bread and beef he called loudly for, which were given to him, and he began to eat, offering a part of his fare to his countrymen...
> ... in a few minutes a female appeared not far off and Abaroo was dispatched to her. Baneelong now joined with Abaroo to persuade her to come to us, telling us she was Barangaroo and his wife, notwithstanding he had so lately pretended that she had left him for Colbee.
>
> At length she yielded, and Abaroo, having first put a petticoat on her, brought her to us. But this was the prudery of the wilderness, which her husband joined us to ridicule, and we soon laughed her out of it. The petticoat was dropped with hesitation, and Barangaroo stood
> 'Armed cap-a-pee in nakedness'. At the request of Baneelon we combed and cut her hair and she seemed pleased with the operation.
>
> To heighten the good humour which pervaded both parties we began to play and romp with them. Feats of bodily strength were tried and their inferiority was glaring. One of our party lifted with ease two of them from the ground, in spite of their efforts to prevent him; whereas in return, no one of them could move him; they called him Mur-ree Mul-la (large strong man).

Bennelong arranged another meeting one or two days later at which he offered to return the dirk the Governor had lost at the beach when he was speared. Tench reported how:

> Baneelon inquired with solicitude about the state of the Governor's wound, but he made no offer of restoring the dirk and when he was asked for it he pretended to know nothing of it, changing the conversation with great art and asking for wine which was given to him. At parting we pressed him to appoint a day on which he should come to Sydney, assuring him that he would be well received and kindly treated. Doubtful, however, of being permitted to return, he evaded our request and declared that the Governor must first come and see him, which we promised should be done.

Though Phillip went to meet Bennelong and he invited Bennelong and Barangaroo to dine with him at his house the following day, Bennelong failed to keep the appointment. Tench's narrative continued:

Baneelon still resisted coming among us and matters continued in this fluctuating state until the 8th of October when a fire, which they had agreed to light as a signal for us to visit them, was observed... various parties accordingly set out to meet them, provided with different articles, which we thought would prove acceptable to them. We found assembled Baneelon, Barangaroo and another young woman and six men, all of whom received us with welcome.

On my return I was surprised to see all our boats rowing towards home and with them a canoe, in which sat two Indians paddling. I pulled to them and found that Baneelon and another Indian were in one of the boats and that the whole formed a party going over to visit the Governor.

Not seeing Barangaroo of the party, I asked for her and was informed that she had violently opposed Baneelon's departure. When she found persuasion in vain she had recourse to tears, scolding and threats, stamping the ground and tearing her hair. But Baneelon continuing determined, she snatched up in her rage one of his fish-gigs and dashed it with such fury on the rocks that it broke. To quiet her apprehension on the score of her husband's safety, Mr Johnson, attended by Abaroo, agreed to remain as a hostage until Baneelon should return.

We landed our four friends opposite the hospital and set out for the Governor's house. On hearing of their arrival, such numbers flocked to view them that we were apprehensive the crowd of persons would alarm them; but they had left their fears behind and marched on with boldness and unconcern.

When we reached the Governor's house, Baneelon expressed honest joy to see his old friend and appeared pleased to find that he had recovered of his wound... Some bread and beef were distributed among them, but unluckily no fish was to be procured, which we were sorry for as a promise of it had been one of the leading temptations by which they had been allured over. A hatchet a-piece was, however, given to them, and a couple of petticoats and some fishing tackle sent for Barangaroo and the other woman.

The ceremony of introducing being finished, Baneelon seemed to consider himself quite at home, running from room to room with his companions and introducing them to his old friends, the domestics, in the most familiar manner. Among these last, he particularly distinguished the

Governor's orderly serjeant, whom he kissed with great affection, and a woman who attended in the kitchen; but the gamekeeper, M'Entire, he continued to hold in abhorrence and would not suffer his approach.

Nor was his importance to his countrymen less conspicuous in other respects. He undertook to explain the use and nature of those things which were new to them. Some of his explanations were whimsical enough. Seeing, for instance, a pair of snuffers he told them that they were 'nuffer for candle', which the other not comprehending he opened the snuffers and holding up the fore-finger of his left hand to represent a candle made the motion of snuffing it. Finding that even this sagacious interpretation failed, he threw down the snuffers in a rage and, reproaching their stupidity, walked away.

It was observed that a soft gentle tone of voice, which we had taught him to use, was forgotten and his native vociferation returned in full force. But the tenderness which (like Arabanoo) he had always manifested to children he still retained, as appeared by his behaviour to those who were presented to him.

The first wish they expressed to return was complied with in order to banish all appearance of constraint; the party who had conducted them to Sydney returning with them. When we reached the opposite shore we found Abaroo and the other woman fishing in a canoe and Mr Johnson and Barangaroo sitting at the fire, the latter employed in manufacturing fish-hooks. At a little distance, on an adjoining eminence, sat an Indian with his spear in his hand as if centinel over the hostages for the security of his countrymen's return.

During our absence, Barangaroo had never ceased whining and reproaching her husband. Now that he was returned she met him with unconcern and seemed intent on her work only, but this state of repose did not long continue. Baneelon eyeing the broken fish-gig, cast at her a look of savage fury and began to interrogate her; and it seemed more probable that the remaining part would be demolished about her head had we not interposed to pacify him. Nor would we quit the place until his forgiveness was complete and his good humour restored.

No sooner, however, did she find her husband's rage subsided than her hour of triumph commenced. The alarm and trepidation she had manifested disappeared. Elated at his condescension, and emboldened by our presence and the finery in which we had decked her, she in turn assumed a haughty demeanour, refused to answer his caresses and viewed him with a reproaching eye. Although long absence from female society had somewhat blunted our recollection, the conduct of Barangaroo did not appear quite novel to us; nor was our surprise very violent at finding that it succeeded in subduing Baneelon, who, when we parted, seemed anxious only to please her.

Hunter described how:

> Bannelong appeared very much at his ease and not under the least apprehension of being detained; promising when he went away to bring his wife over, which he did two days afterwards. His sister and two men came like-wise and a third soon followed. Blankets and some cloathing were given them, and each had a belly-full of fish.

And Collins' account described how:

> … at length Bennillong solicited the Governor to build him a hut at the extremity of the eastern point of the cove. This the Governor, who was very desirous of preserving the friendly intercourse which seemed to have taken place, readily promised and gave the necessary directions for its being built.[20]

Tench also related that:

> Farther to please him, a brick house, of 12 square feet, was built for his use and for that of such of his countrymen as might choose to reside in it on a point of land fixed upon by himself. A shield, double cased with tin, to ward off the spears of his enemies was also presented to him by the Governor.

Hunter recorded that after staying to dinner with the Governor, Bennelong 'left the place highly delighted with his shield, which, being made of sole leather and covered with tin, was likely to resist the force of their spears'. Not long afterwards, according to Hunter, at dinner with the Governor 'Bennelong observed that his shield was a good one and said that he had been to fight the man who had some time before wounded him, and that his spear had gone through both the shield and hand of his antagonist'.

Tench described Bennelong's wife, Barangaroo, who 'appeared to be older than himself and had had two children by a former husband, both of which were dead. This probably was the woman he had so often mentioned when at the settlement and whom he had taken as a wife since he left it; she likewise had been twice wounded by spears, one of which had passed through her thigh'. On one occasion Tench saw Barangaroo 'painted in a different manner to which she had been seen before, and it appeared to have been done with a good deal of attention. Her cheeks, nose, and upper lip were rubbed over with red ochre, on which and under the eyes some white clay was laid in spots. The small of her back was likewise rubbed with red ochre, and she seemed to be sensible that she was finer than common'. Hunter told that:

> Governor Phillip did not wrong the natives in supposing that they treated their women with very little tenderness, for Bannelong had beat his wife twice very severely in a short time and for which, as far as could be learnt from the girl, he had very little reason. Still she appeared very fond of him and he professed a great affection for her but laughed when he was told that it was wrong to beat a woman. He now visited the settlement daily, with his wife, several children and half a dozen of his friends, and Colbey was generally one of the party.

A convict stole some fishing tackle from Daringa, Colbey's wife, and Phillip ordered the offender:

> ... should be severely flogged (according to Tench) in the presence of as many natives as could be assembled, to whom the cause of punishment should be explained. Many of them of both sexes, accordingly attended...
>
> There was not one of them that did not testify strong abhorrence of the punishment and equal sympathy with the sufferer. The women were particularly affected. Daringa shed tears, and Barangaroo, kindling into anger, snatched a stick and menaced the executioner. The conduct of these women on this occasion was exactly descriptive of their characters. The former was ever meek and feminine; the latter, fierce and unsubmissive.

Hunter wrote,

> Early in the morning of the 13th of November, sixteen of the natives visited the settlement, and some fish being distributed amongst them, they made a fire in the Governor's yard and sat down to breakfast in great good humour. Those that were strangers appeared highly delighted with the novelties that surrounded them. Amongst the strangers there was a woman whose skin, when free from dirt and smoke, was of a bright copper colour; her features were pleasing and of that kind of turn that had she been in any European settlement, no one would have doubted her being a Mulatto Jewess.
>
> Bannelong, who had been for two days with some of his party at Botany Bay, came along with these people and brought his wife with him. She appeared to be very ill and had a fresh wound on her head, which he gave Governor Phillip to understand she had merited for breaking a fizgig and a throwing stick. The Governor's reasoning with him on this subject had no effect; he said she was bad and therefore he had beat her.
>
> Neither could it be learned what inducement this woman could have to do an act which she must have known would be followed by a severe beating. Bannelong either did not understand the questions put to him or was unwilling to answer them. When these people had finished their

breakfast they all went to the hospital to get the women's heads dressed; for, besides Bennelong's wife, a woman who was a stranger had received a blow on the head which had laid her skull bare.

After this business was over most of them returned and sat down in the yard at the back of Governor Phillip's house, but Bannelong went into the house as usual and, finding the Governor writing, sat down by him. He appeared very much out of humour and frequently said that he was going to beat a woman with a hatchet which he held in his hand. It was impossible to persuade him to say he would not beat her and after some time he got up, saying that he could not dine with the Governor as he was going to beat the woman.

Governor Phillip then insisted on going with him, to which he made no objection, though he was given to understand that he would not be suffered to beat any woman, and they set off for his hut at the point. The Governor took his orderly serjeant along with him and they were joined by the Judge-Advocate.

Though Bannelong had frequently said he would kill the woman, when Governor Phillip was endeavouring to persuade him not to beat her, yet it could not be believed that he had any such intention; nor did they suppose there would be much trouble in preventing his beating her. However, fearing he might strike her a blow with the hatchet which must have been fatal, it was taken from him before they got to the hut, and as he seemed unwilling to part with it, the Governor gave him his cane, but his expressions and his countenance soon made them think even the cane was too much for him to be trusted with and that was taken from him also.

Tench wrote that Bennelong frequently tried the sharpness of the hatchet while talking wildly and incoherently and showing 'extravagant marks of fury and revenge'. He continued:

'When they reached the house they found several natives of both sexes lying promiscuously before the fire and among them a young woman, not more than 16 years old, who at sight of Baneelong started and raised herself half up. He no sooner saw her than snatching a sword of the country (a boomerang) he ran at her and gave her two severe wounds on the head and one on the shoulder before interference on behalf of the poor wretch could be made.

Our people now rushed in and seized him, but the other Indians continued quite spectators of what was passing, either awed by Baneelon's superiority or deeming it a common case, unworthy of notice and interposition. In vain did the Governor by turns soothe and threaten him; in vain did the serjeant point his musquet at him; he seemed dead to every passion but revenge; forgot his affection to his old friends; and instead of complying with the request they made, furiously brandished his sword at the Governor and called aloud for his hatchet to dispatch the unhappy victim of his barbarity. Matters now wore a serious aspect: the other Indians appeared under the control of Baneelon and had begun to arm and prepare their spears, as if determined to support him in his violence.

Farther delay might have been attended with danger. The *Supply* was therefore immediately hailed and an armed boat ordered to be sent on shore. Luckily, those on board the ship had already observed the commotion and a boat was ready, into which Captain Ball, with several of his people stepped, armed with musquets and put off. It was reasonable to believe that so powerful a reinforcement would restore tranquillity but Baneelon stood unintimidated at disparity of numbers and boldly demanded his prisoner, whose life, he told the Governor, he was determined to sacrifice and afterwards to cut off her head.

Every one was eager to know what could be the cause of such inveterate inhumanity. Undaunted, he replied that her father was his enemy from whom he had received the wound in his forehead, and that when he was down in battle and under the lance of his antagonist, this woman had contributed to assail him. 'She is now', added he, 'my property. I have ravished her by force from her tribe, and I will part with her to no person whatever until my vengeance shall be glutted'.

Further remonstrance would have been wasted. His excellency therefore ordered the woman to be taken to the hospital in order that her wound might be dressed. While this was doing one of the natives, a young man, named Bol-a-der-ee, came up and supplicated to be taken into the boat also, saying that he was her husband, which she confirmed, and begged that he might be admitted. He was a fine well grown lad, of 19 or 20 years old, and was one of the persons who had been in the house in the scene just described, which he had in no (way) endeavoured to prevent or to afford assistance to the poor creature who had a right to his protection.

All our people now quitted the place, leaving the exasperated Baneelon and his associates to meditate farther schemes of vengeance. Before they parted he gave them, however, to understand that he would follow the object of his resentment to the hospital and kill her there – a threat which the Governor assured him if he offered to carry into execution he should be immediately shot. Even this menace he treated with disdain.

The affair continued at the Governor's house, as Hunter reported:

When the boat was gone off with the girl our party returned to the Governor's house, several of the native men and boys joining them, as well as Bannelong; and, after some time when his passion began to subside Governor Phillip gave him to understand that he was exceedingly angry with him for attempting to kill a woman, and tried to divert him from his purpose by threats, telling him that if he did kill her, or even beat her any more, he should lose his life; but threats had no greater effect than entreaties, and all his answers shewed that he thought himself greatly injured by having his victim taken from him, saying that she was his and that her father was the man who had wounded him over the eye, and all their tribe were bad and that the Governor should see he would kill her.

When the Judge-Advocate reasoned with him, and told him that if he killed the girl, the Governor would kill him, he marked with his finger those parts of the head, breast, and arms where he said he would wound her before he cut her head off. In this resolution he went away, and the girl was removed in the evening from the *Supply* to Governor Phillip's house.

Bennelong was unrepentant to the end of the affairs, as Tench reported:

> To place the refugees in security, a centinel was ordered to take post at the door of the house in which they were lodged. Nevertheless, they attempted to get away in the night, either from fear that we were not able to protect them or some apprehension of being restrained from future liberty. When questioned where they proposed to find shelter, they said they would go to the Cameragal tribe, with whom they should be safe.
>
> On the following morning Imeerawanyee joined them and expressed strong fears of Baneelon's resentment. Soon after a party of natives known to consist of Baneelon's chosen friends, with a man of the name of Bi-gon at their head, boldly entered the hospital garden and tried to carry off all three by force. They were driven back and threatened to which their leader only replied by contemptuous insolence.

Bennelong's unpredictable behaviour continued. Tench described it:

> Bannelon, finding he could not succeed, withdrew himself for two days. At length he made his appearance, attended only by his wife. Unmindful of what had so recently happened, he marched singly up to the Governor's house and on being refused admittance, though unarmed, attempted to force the centinel. The soldier spared him, but the guard was instantly sent for and drawn up in front of the house; not that their co-operation was necessary, but that their appearance might terrify.
>
> His ardour now cooled and he seemed willing, by submission, to atone for his misconduct. His intrepid disregard of personal risque, nay of life, could not, however but gain admiration; though it led us to predict that this Baneelon... would perish untimely the victim of his own temerity.
>
> To encourage his present disposition of mind, and to try if feelings of compassion towards an enemy could be exerted by an Indian warrior, the Governor ordered him to be taken to the hospital that he might see the victim of his ferocity. He complied in sullen silence. When about to enter the room in which she lay, he appeared to have a momentary struggle with himself, which ended his resentment. He spoke to her with kindness and professed sorrow for what he had done, and promised her future protection.

Hunter reported this event in more detail:

> After an absence of two days, Bannelong returned to the Governor's house, apparently in good humour, and said he would not beat the girl. At the same time he gave them to understand that he had again beat his wife about the head and that he had received a severe blow on the shoulder from a club in return. On this, Governor Phillip proposed their going to the hospital to have his own shoulder and the wife's head drest, but this he refused, saying that White (the Surgeon) would shoot him and that he durst not sleep in the house which had been built for him, as the Surgeon would shoot him in the night.
>
> This story was not told without many threats on his part, and during the recital he twice went out to fetch a spear, which the Governor had made him leave in a back room, in order to shew that he was not afraid and that he would use it if he saw the Surgeon. However, Governor Phillip soon convinced him that he was not to be shot unless he killed the girl or threw spears at the white men.
>
> The moment Bannelong was satisfied that the Surgeon was still his friend, he said he would go to him for a plaister for his shoulder and another for his wife's head; but, as the Governor wished to be present when they first met, he sent for the Surgeon, whom Bannelong received as usual, gave him part of what he was eating and went with him to the hospital; after which he went to the Surgeon's house, and the girl being there to whom he had lately shewn so much animosity he took her by the hand and spoke to her in a friendly manner.
>
> But this attention so exasperated his wife and put her in such a rage that those who were present at the time could not, without some difficulty, prevent her from knocking the girl on the head with a club which she had taken from one of the men for that purpose. Nor did her husband seem inclined to prevent her till he was spoke to, when he gave her a pretty sharp slap on the face. On this, his wife left them, crying with passion, and came over to the Governor's house, where the girl was now brought for greater security, and was followed by several men.
>
> Governor Phillip had ordered the girl to be put into his maid servant's room with which Bannelong seemed pleased, and desired him to let the young man who had remained with her at the Surgeon's stay there likewise. In the meantime, his wife was very noisy and used many threats. She had got her husband's spears, which she sat down upon and would not give them up to a soldier, whom the Governor had ordered to take them from her until force was used...

Later, when the commotion had died down Bennelong stayed to dinner with the Governor behaving, according to Hunter 'with... indifference as if nothing had passed'. Then something quite unexpected happened,

Bol-a-der-ee prepared to leave but his wife, continued Hunter 'cried and forced her way out of the room to go with Bannelong':

> She was brought in again and told if she went away she would be beat, but Bannelong said he would not beat her, neither was his wife angry with her now, and the young man pressed Governor Phillip very much to let her go, saying Barangaroo would not beat the girl, as her passion was over and she was now very good... the Governor was not the least inclined to let the girl go away, but there was no possibility of detaining her unless she was confined, and there appeared so much sincerity in Bannelong's countenance when he said she should not be beat that leave was given, and the moment the girl was without the gate she ran towards Bannelong's hut without waiting for those who were going along with her.
>
> Governor Phillip himself was fully persuaded that Bannelong would keep his word, but the general opinion was that the girl would be sacrificed, and in the evening a considerable number of natives being seen about the hut gave rise to various stories, but the next day Bannelong came to dinner and said he had sent the girl to her father, which was afterwards confirmed by others.
>
> How Bannelong got this girl into his possession could not be learnt, but it appears that she was the same girl whom he went to look (for) when he ran away from the settlement. She appeared to be about fifteen years of age, and when she went away her wounds were in a fair way of doing well. Fortunately for her, the weapon which had first presented itself when Bannelong beat her, was a boy's wooden sword and made of very light wood, but these people pay little attention to wounds and even those which by the faculty are deemed dangerous do not seem to require the common attention of closing the lips of the wound and keeping it clean. This shews that they must be of a most excellent habit of body.

However not long after this altercation took place, the status quo was restored, Hunter reporting the Aborigines became '... very familiar and intimate with every person in the settlement; many of them now took up their rest every night in some of the gentlemen's houses...' Hunter related another story concerning Bennalong and Barangaroo:

> Governor Phillip had recently ordered a small hut to be built for his own accommodation at Rose Hill, and he was going to remain there a few days when several of the natives were desirous of accompanying him, amongst whom were Bannelong and Colebe. The Governor got into his boat with three of them, and Bannelong, going to fetch his cloak, was detained by his wife. However, as they were going out of the cove he appeared on the rocks and got into the boat notwithstanding her threats; but the moment the boat put off she went to her canoe, which was a new one; and after driving the paddles through the bottom, she threw them into the water

and afterwards went off to their hut, probably to do more damage.

The husband had endeavoured to pacify her, and promised several times not to be absent more than one night. As it was likely that he would prefer remaining behind, though he appeared unwilling to ask to be landed, it was proposed to him, and after picking up the paddles which his wife had thrown away he was put on shore.

The Governor then proceeded to Rose Hill with Colebe and two other natives, none of whom ever opened their lips during this altercation. Indeed, none of these people have ever been seen to interfere with what did not immediately concern themselves.

The three natives slept that night at Rose Hill, and though fed very plentifully yet the next morning they were very desirous of returning. On this, Governor Phillip sent the boat down with them, on the return of which he fully expected to hear that mistress Barangaroo's head was under the care of the surgeon; but, to his great surprise, both she and her husband came up in the boat the next morning and Bannelong said he had not beat her; but whether he was deterred by what had so frequently been said to him on the subject or from some other cause could not be known.

However, a reconciliation had taken place, and they both dined with the Governor in great good humour. Every thing this couple wished for was given them and they had both fish and baggaray (red kangaroo) but after dinner was over the lady wanted to return and Bannelong said she would cry if she was not permitted to go; so that late in the afternoon the Governor was obliged to send the boat down with them.

On 28th December 1790, an Aborigine was shot and wounded in Sydney by soldiers after being detected robbing a potato garden. Hunter reported that not long after:

Two colonists who had been in a boat fishing returned with a piece of intelligence very little to the credit of Bannelong, who had robbed them of what fish they had caught; and, as they had no arms, and he had several spears in his canoe, along with his wife and sister, they were deterred from making any resistance.

On the 3rd of January, 1791, several of the natives came to Governor Phillip's house and told him that the native who had been fired at on the 28th of December was wounded and would die... Bannelong and his wife came in soon afterwards and Governor Phillip charged him with taking the fish from the two colonists, which he denied, saying he had been a great way off. But when the two persons were sent for and he found himself known, he entered into a long conversation, the purport of which was an endeavour to justify himself; and this he did with an insolence that explained itself very clearly. He frequently mentioned the man who had been wounded and threatened revenge; but, appearing to recollect himself, he offered the Governor his hand, which not being accepted, he grew violent and seemed inclined to make use of his stick.

One of the centinels was now called in, as it was much feared he would do so some violent act that would oblige Governor Phillip to order him to be put to death; for his behaviour was the height of savage insolence and would have been immediately punished in any other person; but this man had so often made use of the word be-ah-mah that they wished to bring him to reason without proceeding to force, especially as it was suggested by an officer who was in the room that he might not be understood clearly, and the Governor was very unwilling to destroy the confidence Bannelong had for some time placed in him, which the slightest punishment or confinement would have done. He therefore told him to come near, for he was then standing at some distance, but he refused and went away.

Bannelong had not left the Governor with any intention of returning for, in passing the wheelwright's shop, the workmen being at dinner, he stole a hatchet, with which, though pursued, he got clear off.

But some days afterwards he came to the Governor's, who, happening to be in the yard when he came to the gate, ordered him away. He was seen soon afterwards and he appeared very desirous of being received again and disclaimed any knowledge of the hatchet or any intention of revenging the death of the native who had been shot. Governor Phillip appeared to believe him and he was permitted to come into the yard, which was always open to the natives, and some bread and fish were given him; but he was no longer permitted to enter the house. This was putting him on a level with the other natives and he appeared to feel his degradation, but it did not prevent him from repeating his visits very frequently.

Hunter recounted another incident a few months later, by which time Bennelong had been allowed back in the house:

Bannelong and Colebe with their wives dined at the Governor's on the 8th of May (1791) and came in as usual to have a glass of wine and a dish of coffee, after which they left the house to go and sleep at Bannelong's hut on the point. But, in the middle of the night, Governor Phillip was called up by the cries of the young girl whom he had formerly rescued from Bannelong.

She, it seems, had gone to sleep in a shed at the back of the Governor's house, and Bannelong, Colebe and two others got over the paling and were endeavouring to carry her off, which the centinels prevented:... One of these men was seen the next day and, being taxed with attempting to carry off the girl, he denied the charge, as the natives always do when they are not caught in the fact. Bannelong and Colebe were not seen for a week, and the latter appearing first, when accused, said he was asleep at the time and laid the blame on Bannelong, who coming soon after, and not being able to make an excuse or to deny being in the yard, appeared sullen. And when Governor Phillip told him that he was angry and that the soldiers should shoot him if he ever came again to take any woman away, he very cooly replied that then he would spear the soldier. At the same time, he said he was very hungry; and, as no advantage would have followed punishing him, he was ordered something to eat, after the threat had been repeated of his being shot if ever he came again in the night.

Though Tench related

> But if they sometimes injured us, to compensate, they were often of signal benefit to those who needed their assistance... A boat was overset in the harbour; Baneelon, and some other natives, who saw the accident happen, immediately plunged in, and saved all the people. When they had bought them on shore, they undressed them, kindled a fire, and dried their clothes, gave them fish to eat, and conducted them to Sydney... (The natives would take) their leave without asking for any remuneration, or even seeming to expect it.

In 1791 Barangaroo was expecting a baby, and Hunter wrote that: 'Bennelong desired to have a blanket for the child which was given to him... He told Governor Phillip that his wife intended doing him the honour of being brought to bed in his house, but the Governor at length persuaded him that she would be better accommodated at the hospital.'

Barangaroo died not long after the baby was born, and Collins related that Bennelong 'requested Governor Phillip, Mr White and myself to attend him' at the funeral along with Bennelong's sister and some of his friends. A funeral pyre of twigs and branches about a metre high was built and 'when wood enough had been procured,' continued Collins' journal, 'some grass was spread over the pile, and the corpse, covered with an old blanket, was borne to it by the men and placed on it with the head to the northward'. Then, according to Collins:

> A basket with the fishing apparatus and other small furniture of the deceased was placed by her side, and, Ben-nil-long having laid some large logs of wood over the body, the pile was lighted by one of the party. Being constructed of dry wood, it was quickly all in a flame, and Ben-nil-long himself pointed out to us a black smoke which proceeded from the centre of the pile where the body lay and signified that the fire had reached it.

> We left the spot long before the last billet was consumed, and Ben-nil-long appeared during the day more cheerful than we had expected and spoke about finding a nurse from among the white women to suckle his child.

> The following day he invited us to see him rake the ashes of his wife together, and we accompanied him to the spot, unattended by any of his

own people. He preceded us in a sort of solemn silence, speaking to no one until he had paid Ba-rang-a-roo the last duties of a husband. In his hand he had the spear with which he meant to punish the car-rah-dy (karadji, a tribal medicine man) Wil-le-me-ring for non-attendance on his wife when she was ill, with the end of which he raked the calcined bones and ashes together in a heap.

Then, laying the spear upon the ground, he formed with a piece of bark, a tumulus that would have done credit to a well-practised grave-digger, carefully laying the earth round, smoothing every little unevenness and paying a scrupulous attention to the exact proportion of its form. On each side of the tumulus he placed a log of wood, and on top of it deposited the piece of bark with which he had so carefully effected its construction. When all was done he asked us 'if it was good', and appeared pleased when we assured him that it was.

His deportment on this occasion was solemn and manly. An expressive silence marked his conduct throughout the scene; in fact, we attended him as silently and with close observation… When his melancholy work was ended, he stood for a few minutes with his hands folded over his bosom and his eye fixed upon his labours in the attitude of a man in profound thought.

Bennelong's baby died not long after Barangaroo. Collins related: 'The ceremony of sleeping at the grave of the deceased was observed by Bennelong after the death of his little child, Dil-boong, he and two or three other natives passing the night in the Governor's garden, not very far from the spot where it was buried.' Possibly as a result of the death of his wife, Bennelong seemed to settle down, Collins reported that when Phillip embarked for England on board the *Atlantic*,

With the Governor there embarked, voluntarily and cheerfully, two natives of this country, Bennillong and Yem-mer-ra-wan-nie, two men who were much attached to his person; and who withstood at the moment of their departure the united distress of their wives and the dismal lamentations of their friends to accompany him to England, a place they well knew was at a great distance from them.

At the time, according to Tench, Yemmerrawanie 'constantly lived at the Governor's house'.[21]

Collins stayed behind in Sydney and wrote in March 1794, 'We learned that Governor Phillip reached England in the Atlantic on 21st of May last… arriving in the channel without any interruption save what was given by a French privateer which chased her within eight and forty hours sail of land.'

According to a report in the *Dublin Chronicle* 4th June 1793, as well as Yemmerrawanie and Bennelong, '*The Atlantic* has also on board four Kangeroos, lively and healthy, and some other animals peculiar to that country.'

Records are scanty relating to Bennelong and Yemmerrawanie's stay in England, but it is known that Bennelong was received by King George III at St James not long after arriving in London. During their stay in England the two Aborigines apparently lived in London and at the village of Eltham in Kent just outside the city, because there was correspondence between the incumbent Governor, John Hunter, ex-captain of the *Sirius* and the Under-Secretary of the Home Office as to how 'expenses incurred by the natives of New South Wales' of over £63 at lodgings in Eltham and £96 'in town' are 'to be defrayed'. Hunter pointed out 'The bills, you will observe, are made out in my name... a circumstance which I by no means approve... (this) business began with Governor Phillip and should, in my opinion have continued with him...'.

Yemmerrawanie died from a pulmonary illness while at Eltham, and was buried in the village churchyard, the inscription on his tombstone reading 'In Memory of Yemmerrawanyea, a Native of New South Wales, who died the 18th of May, 1794 in the 19th Year of his Age.' On 9th August 1794, Hunter wrote to Secretary Stephens of the Home Department:

> The surviving native man, Benelong, is with me but I think in a precarious state of health. He has for the last twelve months been flattered with the hope of seeing again his native country – a happiness which he has fondly looked forward to, but so long a disappointment has much broken his spirit, and the coldness of the weather here has so frequently laid him up that I am apprehensive his lungs are affected – that was the cause of the other's death. I do all I can to keep him up but still am doubtful of his living.

The *Reliance* finally departed for Australia 2nd February 1795 with Bennelong and Hunter on board, Bennelong recovering his health during the voyage under the care of the ship's doctor, the naval surgeon and explorer George Bass.[22] Bennelong arrived back in Sydney 11th September 1795. Nearly a year later on 29th August 1796, he dictated a letter which was sent to Mr Phillips, Lord Sydney's steward.[23] At the time Bennelong was in England, Lord Sydney lived at Frognal in Kent, a few kilometres from Eltham.

Sir, I am very well. I hope you are very well. I live at the Governor's. I have every day dinner there. I have not my wife; another black man took her away. We have had muzzy (bad) doings; he spear'd me in the back, but I better now... All my friend alive and well. Not me go to England no more. I am at home now... Hope all are well in England. I hope Mrs Phillips very well. You nurse me Madam when I sick. You very good Madam; thank you Madam, and hope you remember me... you give my duty to (Lord) Sydney. ... hope you well, all family very well. Sir, send you please some Handkerchiefs for Pocket. You please sir send me some shoes; two pairs you please Sir. Bannelong.

Bennelong's homecoming was reported by Collins:

About this settlement (the Aborigines) attention had been for some time engrossed by Ben-nil-long, who arrived with the Governor. On his first appearance he conducted himself with a polished familiarity towards his sisters and other relations; but to his acquaintance he was distant and quite the man of consequence. He declared, in a tone with an air that seemed to expect compliance, that he should no longer suffer them to fight and cut each other's throats, as they had done; that he should introduce peace among them and make them love each other.

He expressed his wish that when they visited him at Government House they would contrive to be somewhat more cleanly in their persons and less coarse in their manners; and he seemed absolutely offended at some little indelicacies which he observed in his sister, Car-rang-ar-rang, who came in such haste from Botany Bay, with a little nephew on her back to visit him, that she left all her habiliments behind her.

Ben-nil-long had certainly not been an inattentive observer of the manners of the people among whom he had lived; he conducted himself with the greatest propriety at table, particularly in the observance of those attentions which are chiefly requisite in the presence of women. His dress appeared to be an object of no small concern with him; and every one who knew him before he left the country and who saw him now pronounced without hesitation that Ben-nil-long had not any desire to renounce the habits and comforts of the civilized life which he appeared so readily and so successfully to adopt.

His inquiries were directed immediately on his arrival, after his wife Go-roo-bar-roo-boo-lo; and her he found with Caruey. On producing a very fashionable rose-coloured petticoat and jacket made of a coarse stuff, accompanied with a gypsy bonnet of the same colour, she deserted her lover and followed her former husband. In a few days, however, to the surprise of everyone, we saw the lady walking unincumbered with clothing of any kind, and Ben-nil-long was missing.

Caruey was sought for and we heard that he had been severely beaten by Ben-nil-long at Rose Bay, who retained so much of our customs that he made use of his fists instead of the weapons of his country, to the great annoyance of Caruey, who would have preferred meeting his rival fairly in the field armed with the spear and the club. Caruey being much the younger man, the lady, every inch a woman, followed her inclination and Ben-nil-long was compelled to yield her without any further opposition. He seemed to have been satisfied with the beating he had given Caruey, and hinted, that resting for the present without a wife, he should look about him and at some future period make a better choice.

His absences from the Governor's house now became frequent and little attended to. When he went out he usually left his clothes behind, resuming them carefully on his return before he made his visit to the Governor. ... (Bennelong) went for a few days into the woods with his sisters and other friends (and) sent in word that he had had a contest with his bosom friend Cole-be, in which he had been so much the sufferer that until his wounds were healed he could not with any pleasure to himself appear at the Governor's table. This notification was accompanied with a request that his clothes, which he had left behind him when he went away, might be sent him, together with some victuals, of which he was much in want.

On his coming among us again, he appeared with a wound on his mouth, which had divided the upper lip and broken two of the teeth of that jaw. His features, never very pleasing, now seemed out of all proportion, and his pronunciation was much altered. Finding himself badly received among the females (although improved by his travels in the little attentions that are supposed to have their weight with the sex) and not being able to endure a life of celibacy, which had been his condition from the day of his departure from this country until nearly the present hour, he made an attack upon his friend's favourite, Boo-rre-a, in which he was not only unsuccessful but was punished for his breach of friendship, as above related, by Cole-be, who sarcastically asked him 'if he meant that kind of conduct to be a specimen of English manners?'

By November 1796, Collins reported that Bennelong '... had returned to all the habits of savage life...'. And in May 1797 lamented, 'It was distressing to observe that every endeavour to civilize these people proved fruitless. Although they lived among the inhabitants of the different settlements, were kindly treated, fed and often clothed, yet they were never found to possess the smallest degree of gratitude for such favours. Even Ben-nil-long was as destitute of this quality as the most ignorant of his countrymen.'

In December 1797, Collins related that, 'Coleby and another Aborigine, Ye-ra-ni-bes fought with clubs to settle a difference. Ye-ra-ni-bes' shield fell from his grasp and while he was stooping to pick it up Coleby struck him on the head, inflicting wounds which caused his death six days later'. Colbey fled, but agreed to come forward a few days later to meet Ye-ra-ni-bes' friends. Collins continued:

The rage and violence shewn by the friends of the deceased were indescribable; and Cole-be would certainly have expiated his offence with his life but for several of the military, before whose barrack the affair took place.

Although active and extremely au-fait in the use of the shield, he was overpowered and, falling beneath their spears, would certainly have been killed on the spot, but several soldiers rushed in and prevented their putting him to death where he lay; he himself, from the many severe wounds which he had received, being wholly incapable of making any resistance. His friends, the soldiers, lifted him from the ground and between them bore him into the barracks.

Ben-nil-long, the particular friend and companion of Cole-be was present at this meeting, but, it was supposed, without intending to take any part in it either way. The atrocity of his friend's conduct had been such that he could not openly espouse his quarrel; perhaps, he had no stomach to the fight; and certainly if he could avoid it, he would not, by appearing against him, add to the number of his enemies.

He was armed, however, and unencumbered with clothing of any kind and remained a silent spectator of the tumultuous scene, until the moment when the soldiers rushed in to save the life of Cole-be. His conduct here became inexplicable. On a sudden, he chose to be in a rage at something or other and threw a spear among the soldiers, which dreadfully took effect on one of them, entering at his back and coming out at the belly, close to the navel. For this he would instantly have been killed on the spot, had not Mr Smith, the provost-marshal, interfered and brought him away, boiling with the most savage rage, for he had received a blow on the head with the butt-end of the musquet.

It became necessary to confine him during the night, as well to prevent the mischief with which he threatened the whole people as to save him from the anger of the military, and on the following morning he quitted the town.

This man, instead of making himself useful, or shewing the least gratitude for the attentions which he received from every one, had become a most insolent and troublesome savage. As it was impossible sometimes to avoid censuring him for his conduct, he had been known to walk about armed and heard to declare it was for the express purpose of spearing the Governor whenever he saw him.

A year later in November 1798, Collins reported:

Instead of living peaceably and pleasantly at the Governor's house, as he certainly might always have done, Ben-nil-long preferred the rude and dangerous society of his own countrymen, visiting the settlement only when induced by the recollection of the comforts which he could no where else obtain.

Word was now brought in, of his having been again severely wounded in a contest with some of the natives. This man had lately received and recovered of several wounds, any one of which would have been sufficient to have destroyed a European.

There are very few references to Bennelong during the last 15 years of his life. A letter written by the Reverend W.P. Crook from Parramatta on 5th May 1805, remarked:

> The natives of this country are more and more savage. Though some of them have been quite civilised they prefer wandering stark naked in the bush living on worms, insects, etc. This is the case with Bennelong who was in England. He visits the settlement now and then, is very polite, begs a loaf and departs.

Little is known of Bennelong's life thereafter until the report of his death in the *Sydney Gazette* on 9th January 1813, announcing that the Aborigine had died six days previously on the 3rd at an estimated age of 49 years. Though the article did not mention his cause of death, other sources mention Bennelong died in a 'tribal fight'. The obituary in the *Sydney Gazette* read:

> Bennelong died on Sunday morning last at Kissing Point. Of this veteran champion of the native tribe little favourable can be said. His voyage to and benevolent treatment in Great Britain produced no change whatever in his manners and inclinations, which were naturally barbarous and ferocious.
>
> ... for the last few years he had been but little noticed. His propensity to drunkenness was inordinate; and when in that state he was insolent, menacing and overbearing. In fact, he was a thorough savage, not to be warped from the form and character that nature gave him by all the efforts that mankind could use.

At Kissing Point on the north shore of the harbour ten kilometres west of Sydney, Bennelong lived in a humpy in the grounds of the house of a free settler, James Squire[24]. Squire cultivated barley and hops on land he owned at Kissing Point, was the first successful brewer of beer in Australia and built the Colonial Brewery and a successful hotel called the Malting Shovel at Kissing Point. An article in *The Australian Quarterly Journal,* recorded that 'the garden of the late proprietor of the Colonial Brewery is celebrated for containing the remains of Bennelong. He lies between his wife, and another chief amidst the orange trees of the garden.'

According to P.R. Stephens' *History and Description of Sydney Harbour* published in 1966, 'If any registration of his (Bennelong's) death and burial was made, the documents have apparently been lost. Presumably a headstone was placed on his grave, and remained until the 1860s, and then was removed... In 1927, some of the old inhabitants of Kissing Point located the site of Bennelong's grave, from their boyhood memories, but no note was made of it... and today the exact site is unknown, although the vicinity – in Waterview Street, Ryde, at the back of Halvorsens' boatshed – may be reasonably surmised'. Bennelong Park on the waterfront north of Kissing Point is named after the Aborigine.[25]

The Aborigines held fond memories of Bennelong long after he was gone. In a letter written from Sydney in 1821, the Reverend S. Leigh of the Wesleyan Mission recounted an incident when:

> One day I was conversing with a number of heathen people who were relations of one Ben-nil-long who had visited England some years ago but is since dead. I had a portrait of Ben-nil-long's which I showed his kindred; as soon as they saw it they all wept aloud and observed that was their Brother and friend. The sight was so affecting that Mrs Leigh and Mr Walker were obliged to turn from them, but after all could not help mingling their tears with these sympathising heathens.

Colbey outlived Bennelong for several years although the date of his death is not known. In 1816, Governor Macquarie promised Colbey 30 acres of land at South Creek, near Windsor, 60 kilometres north west of Sydney, as a reward for recent good conduct. Colbey also received a further land grant from the government in 1819 at Bathurst, 130 miles west of Sydney.

CHAPTER 2

FORT MACQUARIE

During the administrations of Governor Hunter and his successor Governor King, a shortage of coinage in the colony had led to rum being bartered as a medium of exchange, with the trade being controlled by the local soldiers, the 46th Regiment of Foot. To counter this unsatisfactory situation the home authorities decided a firm hand was called for and, on the enthusiastic recommendation of Joseph Banks, appointed William Bligh as Governor. Bligh, described by the botanist Mr Caley as 'a man whom nature intended to be the subject of abuse', had already suffered the ignominy of a mutiny on the high seas when his ship the *Bounty* had been seized by the First Mate, Fletcher Christian and Bligh, and 18 companions cast into an open boat.

Bligh fared no better as Governor of New South Wales, and after only 17 months in office the 46th Regiment, or Rum Corps as they were known, rose against him 'for crimes that render you unfit to exercise the Supreme Authority for another moment.' Bligh wrote in a letter to Joseph Banks of how John Macarthur and other malcontents '... checked in the enormous practice of bartering spirits, which had principally been the almost ruin of the colony, became privately discontented; and the arch-fiend John Macarthur, so inflamed their minds as to make them dissatisfied with Government'. Bligh's letter continued how on the 26th January 1808,

> This rebellious act was done so suddenly that in about five minutes from the time we first knew of it, Government House was surrounded with troops, Major Johnstone having brought up in battle array above three hundred men under martial law, loaded with ball, to attack and seize my person and a few friends... that had been at dinner with me... they marched to the tune of the 'British Grenadiers'; and to render the spectacle more terrific to the townspeople, the field artillery... was presented against the house...

Bligh was placed under house arrest. Macarthur wrote to his wife, 'The tyrant is now, no doubt, gnashing his teeth with vexation at his overthrow. May he often have cause to do the like'. Bligh was then released in the hope of the mutineers that he would leave them in peace and return to England, but instead, he travelled to Tasmania.

When news reached London of the overthrow of Bligh, the home authorities procrastinated for a time before appointing Lachlan Macquarie as Governor, a Lieutenant Colonel with the 73rd Foot Regiment, the 2nd Black Watch, who had recently returned to England after service in India.

Viscount Castlereagh, Secretary of State for War and the Colonies, instructed that the 102nd Regiment return to England 'because of the share it has had in the late revolution' and the 73rd Regiment was sent in its place to ensure the peaceful transition to a new government in New South Wales 'to be entirely new modelled and made a military one.' Macquarie's commission invested him with absolute powers, with authority to resist enemies, pirates and rebels, to proclaim martial law, erect castles and towns, punish, reprieve and pardon offenders and to control trade and commerce 'for as long as it pleased the Royal Will.' As a mark of respect to Bligh, Macquarie was instructed to nominally reinstate Bligh as Governor for a day before officially assuming office.

Lachlan Macquarie, born in 1761 on Ulva, an islet off the Isle of Mull off the west coast of Scotland, had started his military career at the age of 15 when he travelled as a volunteer with the 84th Regiment of Highlanders to America following the Declaration of Independence by the American rebels. In 1788, Macquarie sailed from England in the *Dublin* for Bombay as a Lieutenant with the 77th Regiment. On the voyage out they anchored at the Cape of Good Hope where among the vessels that lay in the roads was 'His Majesty's Sloop the *Bounty,* commanded by Lieutenant Bligh', bound for the 'South Sea.' Bligh was invited to dinner on Board the *Dublin* and 'staid on board till very late at night.'[1]

In December 1790, now with the rank of Lieutenant Captain, Macquarie took part with his soldiers in the brief successful siege of Cananore. Later, in Bombay, Macquarie met and married his first wife, Jane Jarvis, born on the island of Antigua in the West Indies where her father had been Chief Justice. She had journeyed to India to accompany her sister who was married to a senior civil servant of the East India Company in Bombay. Jane was the light and joy of Macquarie's life, but suffered in the Indian climate, and Macquarie was weighed down with a great concern for her health when he left on an expedition to take part in the successful siege of the Dutch outpost of Cochin. Macquarie then travelled with a British force in the invasion of the Dutch-held island of Ceylon and the storming of Colombo, '... a most important and valuable capture and acquisition,' Macquarie remarked in his diary in January 1796, 'as it contains the only good harbour for our Navy on this side of India... (and prevents the French) from possessing themselves of this valuable island.' Shortly after, Macquarie personally accepted the surrender of the town and fortress of Point de Galle in Ceylon by the Dutch Governor.

Later that year Macquarie was devastated by the loss of his beloved Jane, who died of fever and was buried in Bombay. Macquarie wore a black crepe arm band for over 4 years, 'the least respect I was bound to pay to her beloved memory' and could not for many years afterwards pass the anniversary of her death without shedding tears. As a diversion to his grief, Macquarie volunteered to march in a punitive sortie against a troublesome Rajah on the Malabar Coast, in the course of which a British sergeant fell dead beside him and a Brigade Major dropped dead, shot through the head while handing out orders and speaking to Macquarie. Macquarie survived the campaign unscathed except for a bruised left foot from a spent ball, but then was struck down with fever, penning in his diary at the time:

> Had I fallen in the jungle it were perhaps the most fortunate circumstance that could have happened me;- but you see I am still reserved for enduring more misery in this life... if you knew what anguish tears and distracts my unhappy heart both night and day, you would hardly – out of pity to my sufferings – wish me to live much longer. But alas ! – live I must as long as God Almighty has ordained that I should do so.

In 1799, yet again in the midst of a bout of fever, Macquarie marched with his troops against Tippoo, the Sultan of Mysore. The British guns pounded to rubble a section of the walls of Tippoo's stronghold of Seringapatam, but Macquarie was too ill to take part in the charge, watching from his sickbed when his regiment stormed through the breach in the blazing heat of noon on 4th May 1799.

In 1800 Macquarie's regiment was posted to Egypt, where he had a chance to explore the 'celebrated and ancient city of Grand Cairo... altogether such an assemblage of grand and beautiful objects of

Nature and Art as I had never seen combined before.' Macquarie then returned briefly to Bombay in 1802 before sailing for England on 6th January 1803. He felt 'extremely low and melancholy' as his ship, the *Sir Edward Hughes,* left the port where he had spent 'by far the happiest period of my whole life' but where 'all that constituted that happiness lies mouldering dust.'

Macquarie was away from India for two years, returning to Bombay as a Lieutenant Colonel in August 1805. With him he carried a lock of hair from his cousin Elizabeth Henrietta Campbell of Airds, who he had met on his return to Scotland and who had promised to be his wife. Macquarie had asked his fiancé to wait until he returned to England to exchange marital vows, as he had promised himself 'never to marry again in India nor to bring a wife to India.'

So it was with a happy heart that Macquarie left Bombay for the last time on 19th March 1807 on board the *Benares,* bound for Basra in present-day Iraq to take the overland route home. On reaching Basra Macquarie received the news that Turkey had declared war on Britain's ally Russia. The Aleppo road and his intended route through the eastern Mediterranean were closed and he would have to journey back through Russia and across the Baltic. Macquarie set off north, stopping fleetingly as he passed through Baghdad at the site of the Garden of Eden to pluck a grain of wheat as a memento. After an adventurous journey across Persia and Russia he set sail across the Baltic in the British ship *Calypso* in September. Approaching Copenhagen:

> We found an immense Fleet of British Men of War and Transports lying here; there being 24 Sail of the Line, besides smaller vessels of War and at least 300 transports; which was a noble and most animating sight to us on board the *Calypso* as we approached Copenhagen Roads from the Eastwood... [2]

A British Fleet had just attacked and captured the Danish Fleet, and occupied Copenhagen, where there were British soldiers billeted outside the city. The *Calypso* sailed north, but the weather was against them and they dropped anchor in the port of Elsinore a short distance up the coast. According to Macquarie's diary, on Tuesday 29th September 1807:

> The Wind being still foul, and a strong current also against us, we are obliged to remain still at anchor in these roads – which is a most cruel mortification and very severe disappointment to me as every day appears

42

now to me as ages as long as I am absent from my dear and beloved friends in England after getting this near to them.

As soon as we had breakfasted this morning Capt. Bradly and myself went on shore at the Sea Port Town of Elsinore in Denmark, which the Danes are still allowed to remain in notwithstanding our Capture of Copenhagen... it was our intention to remain on shore till the Evening, in order to have another long walk and view the environs of Elsinore – We first went to have a good view of the old and gothic castle of Kroningsberg but which we could do so only at some distance, no foreigner being ever admitted inside of the (defence) works that surround it. We then proceeded to Hamlet's Gardens within half a mile of the town and which is a most delightful walk, being very extensive and most beautifully laid out in the finest taste. – We also visited the cave and the tower, named after the same illustrious Danish Prince so famed in story – From the tower there is a most delightful view of the Town of Elsinore and the Castle of Kroningsberg – the Roads and the shipping – and of the opposite Coast of Sweden and indeed of the Baltic all the way up to the City of Copenhagen, which is only 28 miles distant from Elsinore...

Wednesday 30th September 1807:

At length the wind has fortunately changed in our favour... We accordingly weighed anchor at 6 a.m. and made sail immediately with a fine fair wind through the sound at the rate of Eight Knots an hour, and by 9 o'clock were nearly out of sight of Kroningsberg Castle ploughing through the later part before a delightfully fine gale – going Eleven Knots. ... at least a hundred sail of shipping, weighed anchor and sailed at the same time we did from Elsinore Roads...

Macquarie married when he returned to England and would have been quite content to settle down to a quiet life when he heard from the War Office he was to take the 73rd Regiment to New South Wales, 'to restore order and tranquillity in that Colony' with Miles Nightingale as Governor. Initially not enthusiastic about being 'transported' to New South Wales, Macquarie wrote to his friend Charles Forbes in Bombay:

This is not fair, it not being our tour by roster to be sent thither, after having already served 25 years in India – and only two years yet at home. We are, however, now in a great degree reconciled to our banishment... Mrs Macquarie of course goes out with me, and we must endeavour to make ourselves as happy as we can in our exile...

Macquarie's spirits lifted when Nightingale declined his appointment and Macquarie was appointed Governor in his place, with a promise from Lord Castlereagh of a pension if he stayed in New South Wales for eight years. Macquarie sailed out to Australia in the *Dromedary*, whose master, Samuel Pritchard, had been a lieutenant under Nelson at Trafalgar and had relayed the signal 'England expects every man to do his duty.' On board ship were 400 men of the 73rd, and Macquarie was relieved on reaching Sydney in January 1810 that he did not have to fight his way ashore as he expected he might have to but was welcomed by the townspeople. Bligh was still in Tasmania but he arrived not long after, and was furious that Macquarie 'took command without waiting for my return' and declined an invitation to dine with Macquarie in preference to a meal at the table of the Lieutenant Governor. Macquarie later wrote to England of Bligh:

> I must say that I have not been able to discover any act of his which could in any degree form an excuse for or in any way warrant, the violent and mutinous proceedings pursued against him... (but) from my own short experience, I must acknowledge that he is a most unsatisfactory man to transmit business with, from his want of candour and decision, in so much that it is impossible to place the smallest relience on the fulfillment of any engagement he enters into...

Bligh pestered Macquarie to punish Lieutenant Johnstone who had led the revolt against him, but Macquarie would not have any part in it, possibly because Johnstone was an old acquaintance he had met originally in America in 1777. When Bligh eventually left Sydney on 12th May 1810, accompanying him on the same ship was Lieutenant Johnstone, recalled to England to face court-martial for his part in the rebellion. Johnstone was cashiered and eventually returned to Australia where Macquarie offered him an extensive land grant. Johnstone passed his last days in Sydney at the house he named Annandale, built on a land grant donated earlier by Phillip on the shore west of Sydney. The Sydney suburb of Annandale still carries its name.

When Macquarie inherited the government of New South Wales from the mutineers and their heirs, he found the administration of Sydney in a mess, or as Macquarie put it:

> ... I found the colony barely emerging from infantile imbecility and suffering from various privations and disabilities; the country impenetrable beyond 40 miles from Sydney; agriculture in a yet languishing state; commerce in its early dawn; revenue unknown; threatened by famine; distracted by faction; the public buildings in a state of dilapidation and mouldering to decay; the few roads and bridges formerly constructed, rendered almost impassable; the population

depressed by poverty; no public credit nor private confidence; the morals of the great mass of the population in the lowest state of debasement and religious worship almost totally neglected.

With the ever-present support of his wife at his side and carrying his almost dictatorial terms of office, Macquarie energetically set about transforming Sydney from this lamentable state of affairs into a more respectable colony. He set aside land for Sydney's two cathedrals, enclosed the common north of the town and called it Hyde Park, made the first coinage and opened the colony's first bank, the Bank of New South Wales. The number of mainland towns was increased from two to over 12 under his administration, many of them created out of the wilderness including Pitt Town 'in honour of the immortal memory of the late great William Pitt, the Minister who originally planned this colony' and Wilberforce, 'in honour and out of respect to the good and virtuous Wm.Wilberforce, Esq., M.P. – a true patriot and the real friend of mankind!' North on the New South Wales coast the Governor founded Port Macquarie, which he later sailed to visit in the 150 ton brig *Elizabeth Henrietta*, launched at the Government Dockyard in Sydney by Macquarie and named after his wife. In 1813, Macquarie promoted the first crossing of the Blue Mountains and immediately ordered a road to be built to cross them, which as soon as it was finished he travelled on by carriage with a retinue of 37 followers including his wife. The new settlements around Sydney were connected by 500 kilometres of turnpike and carriage road where previously there had been only tracks. No doubt Macquarie drew on his experience of road building in India when he had commanded a detachment building the Poodicherrum Ghaut road up the escarpment east of Bombay so the British army could drag their guns up for the campaigns against Tippoo Sultan. In the Government Domain east of Sydney town, Mrs Macquarie laid out the route of a five kilometre carriage road on which she would journey for relaxation, stopping at the eastern point of the Domain on the harbour, where she would admire the view and sit on a seat that was cut for her in a rock. Macquarie walled off part of the Domain where he ordered Charles Fraser, a soldier with the 46th Regiment, to create a Botanic Gardens. Fraser visited Norfolk Island, New Zealand, Tasmania, Western Australia and Queensland collecting plants and seeds, exchanged seeds with botanists overseas and was later appointed by Macquarie the first 'Superintendant of the Botanic Gardens.'

In Sydney the principal streets had their alignments straightened and levelled and were named: George Street for the monarch; Gloucester, Kent, Clarence and Cumberland Streets for the Royal Dukes, not forgetting York Street, for the Duke of York, Macquarie's friend and senior officer in the army. Harrington Street was named after Macquarie's former commander in London, Argyle Street after his home, Castlereagh Street after his minister for War and the Colonies and Liverpool Street after the Earl of Liverpool, Macquarie's correspondent, the Colonial Secretary and later Prime Minister of England. Phillip, Hunter, King and Bligh Streets were named after former Governors and Bent Street after the Judge Advocate. Spring, Park, Bridge and Market Streets were named after neighbouring public amenities and O'Connell Street after the Lieutenant Governor. Not to be outdone, Elizabeth Street was named after his wife and Macquarie Street after himself.

During the period of Macquarie's rule, the population of Sydney more than trebled, the land under tillage quadrupled, the number of sheep multiplied eleven-fold and that of cattle eight-fold, and Macquarie could boast he had 'inculcated habits of industry and temperance' in the population.

To service the expanded requirements of the colony Macquarie enthusiastically ordered a program of public works, including the construction of Wynyard Barracks, 'the best and most compleat in any of His Majesty's foreign dominions' and an enormous hospital on Macquarie Street with a facade nearly 100 metres long which was one of the largest to be found anywhere in the English-speaking world. To supervise the construction of these buildings Macquarie had promoted Captain John Gill, an engineer and artillery officer with the 46th Regiment, to 'Inspector of Government Public Works.' Macquarie later wrote to Lord Bathurst, 'From the want of a scientific person to plan and superintend the construction of all Government public buildings, most of them have hitherto been very badly planned and still worse executed'. He also wrote to Lord Castlereagh, 'It would be highly necessary and very desirable that a Government Architect should be sent out to this country to plan and superintend the erection of all public buildings.'

At the time Macquarie was requesting the services of a Government Architect from Castlereagh, a west countryman by the name of Francis Greenway was languishing in Newgate Gaol, London. Greenway, born at Mangotsfield outside Bristol, the fourth child of six sons and two daughters born to John and Ann Greenway, was from a family who for generations had been stonemasons and builders. Francis had opened an architectural practice in Bristol in 1805 with his brother Olive, and among the former's designs were the Clifton Civic Centre and The Grand Hotel and Assembly Rooms in Bristol, although because of changed circumstances the last two were completed by others.

In 1809, apparently as a result of being involved in the construction of houses whose developers went broke during the uncertainty caused by the war with France, the Greenway brothers were declared bankrupt and their personal books and belongings, as well as all the stone, materials and statues from their architect's yard, were sold off. Following his bankruptcy, Greenway continued to take architectural work to pay off his creditors, including the design of a house for a Colonel Doolan of the East India Company. The building contract for the house was lost, on which, claimed Greenway, Doolan had agreed to pay £250 over the original contract price for extra work completed. When Doolan refused to pay the extra £250, Greenway advertised a reward of ten guineas for the lost document, which was left anonymously in January 1812 in the vestibule of the *Bristol Mercury* office without the reward being claimed. The resurrected contract included a clause to pay Greenway the extra £250, and was signed by Mr Cooke, Doolan's solicitor. On examination of the document by handwriting experts it was found that Cooke's signature was not only a forgery but that it was also in Greenway's handwriting.

In January 1812, Greenway was escorted to Newgate Gaol, and on 23rd March at Bristol Assizes indicted for 'uttering as true a certain forged instrument, purporting to be an agreement between Colonel Richard Doolan and the said Francis Greenway.' On the advice of his friends that he might receive a lenient sentence, but against the entreaties of his solicitor, Greenway pleaded guilty, only to be sentenced by the judge to 'be hanged by the neck until you are dead.' Greenway's sentence was later commuted to 14 years transportation to New South Wales, and while he waited for a ship to take him to Australia he was incarcerated in the prison hulk *Captivity* on an estuary on the south coast, clutching with him a letter from my 'ever steady friend and patron' Governor Phillip, recommending him to Macquarie as an architect.

It was not until August 1813, that Greenway sailed for Australia in the convict transport *General Hewitt* with 32 other felons from the *Captivity* and 264 other prisoners from London, Gravesend and Portsmouth. Conditions on the *General Hewitt* were atrocious, most of the prisoners were chained in the hold in fetters made for the Guinea slave trade and were not allowed out on deck even while the ship anchored at Madeira for seven days and Rio for ten. No water was provided to the prisoners to wash their linen as the ship sailed through the tropics, and when the *General Hewitt* finally docked in Sydney in February 1814, six months after departing England, seven of the 32 prisoners that had embarked from the *Captivity* had died on the voyage, along with 27 of the other transported convicts. Greenway survived the voyage, arriving in Australia with his fellow convicts as he later wrote '… doomed thus to suffer under the lash of the law, forgotten by their friends at home, despised and insulted here by persons in every way their inferiors in principle, as in knowledge.'

Greenway was granted a ticket of leave by Macquarie shortly after his arrival, which allowed him to work in Sydney but not to return to England during the period of his sentence, and was given the use by Macquarie of the assistant surgeon's house at 84 George Street, where he was joined by his wife Mary and three children who travelled out from England. From the house Greenway advertised in the *Sydney Gazette* in December 1814 he had practised 'for many years as an architect in some of the most extensive concerns in England, private, public and speculative' and offered to design structures in the colony with 'all the advantages Nature has designed they should receive from the art and Labour of Man.' Greenway also offered to provide 'plans, elevations and sections of the building, from the simplest cottage to the most expensive mansion; making out a Bill of Quantities for the workmen to estimate from, and to ascertain the expense of the buildings… all upon terms of five per cent.'

Macquarie's building program to date had proceeded in a haphazard way, the designs of buildings often chosen by Mrs

Macquarie from pictures in her private book collection, and carpenters and masons doing the best they could under the direction of one of the military engineers. Macquarie noted that 'Rear-Admiral Phillip had strongly recommended Mr Greenway to my protection, informing me he was an architect of eminence... feeling a great respect for that excellent man (Phillip), I had pleasure in attending to the first request he ever made to me.' The first time Macquarie approached Greenway for assistance was in the middle of 1814 when he asked Greenway to design a town hall and courthouse based on a drawing in a book. Greenway wrote to Macquarie on 27th July 1814:

> ... I will immediately Copy the Drawing your excellency requested me to do, notwithstanding it is rather painful to my mind as a professional man to Copy a Building that has no Claim to Classical proportion or Character.
>
> I must beg leave to quote the elegant Treatise on Architecture of Sir William Chambers:
>
> 'Let it not... be imagined that building merely considered as heaping stone upon stone can be of great consequence... Materials in Architecture are like words in Phrasiology having separately but little power, and they may be so arranged as to excite, ridicule, disgust or even contempt; yet, when combined with skill expressed with energy, they actuate the mind with unbounded sway... the masterly dispositions of a skilful Artist will dignify the meanest materials; while the weak efforts of the Ignorant render the most costly enrichments despicable...'
>
> ... I will readily exert myself... to carry into effect a building our posterity may have little reason to condemn... (and in) any Public work, I will exert myself in every way to do your Excellency credit as a promoter and, encourager of the most useful Art to Society...

Greenway later wrote that his public buildings should be constructed 'in a style... suited to the... increasing population, trade and wealth' of the colony, displaying the 'necessary qualities of the architectural art... beauty, strength and convenience, to accomplish which requires the greatest consideration and the utmost efforts of the mind.' Never losing sight of 'precision, combined with simplicity, order, character and beauty of form...'

Over the following six or seven years Greenway was fully employed, not only designing Macquarie's public buildings but also houses for the well-to-do of the colony through his private practice. His job was an uphill battle, producing his drawings at night by the light of a lamp or candle without the assistance of a draughtsman and encumbered by an almost total lack of skilled tradesmen. So he arranged for the training of new masons, only to find that those existing masons asked to teach them were reluctant 'to part with their secrets', and the 'Carpenters and Joiners' who did work for him were 'several times in a State of Inebriation early in the Morning.' The workgangs of convicts were frequently urged on by the lash, against the entreaties of Greenway who believed a reward of leisure or a small sum of money was likely to be a far better incentive. Greenway believed that 'the human mind was like a fine instrument of music, and that it required skill and knowledge to harmonise it.'

Greenway was employed on all sorts of projects: a magazine for Fort Phillip on Windmill Hill; buildings for the Government Dockyard;[3] the Macquarie Lighthouse on the cliffs near South Head;[4] St Matthews Church, Windsor; St Lukes Church and a hospital at Liverpool; an obelisk at Macquarie Place in the centre of Sydney from which all road distances in the colony were to be measured;[5] a 'Women's Factory and Barracks' at Parramatta;[6] and a 'very large commodious barrack for the accommodation of 400 convicts' at the top of Macquarie Street, Sydney, with on the opposite side of the road a courthouse[7] and a 'Georgian School.' At the south end of George Street Greenway started on the design of an Anglican cathedral, but most pressing of all for Macquarie was a design for a new Government House, as the structure where he presently lived on Bridge Street was a 'decayed, mean shabby' warren, where the Governor was 'worse accommodated than any private gentleman in the colony' and which Macquarie assured Lord Bathurst was 'so much decayed and rotten as to render it extremely unsafe any longer to live in.' To be built at the same time as the house Macquarie also desired a stables be constructed and a fort nearby on Bennelong Point with seven guns to 'prevent boats leaving... or being cut out of the Cove at night, a frequent occurrence.'

Bennelong Point had been intermittently fortified since the first months of settlement. According to Collins' diary, in July 1788, Lieutenant William Dawes, promoted by Phillip to the post of 'Officer of the Engineers and Artillery in The Settlement,' was instructed to build a small redoubt on the east side of Sydney Cove. By November 1788 this small defence work was finished, two pieces of ordnance from one of the First Fleet ships were in position and a flagstaff erected on which the colours were hoisted on New Year's Day 1789.

On 4th June that year, the two brass six-pounders were discharged for the anniversary of the King's birthday. These guns were later removed to 'Dawes Battery' on the west side of the cove, and in the 1790s a new battery was established at Bennelong Point with guns recovered from the wreck of the *Sirius* on Norfolk Island. A report by Captain Edward Abbott of the New South Wales Corps on harbour defences, dated 1st October 1800 listed 'the Bennelong Point or Eastern Battery' as one of the works.

> At the foot of the cannon were large flat stones on which the blacks baked their fish whole. It was the custom when a convict escaped or when persons were reported to be lost in the bush to discharge the ordnance, to alarm the garrison in one case, and to guide the wanderer in the other.[8]

In 1803 on the declaration of war with France volunteers were called for to train as an artillery militia to man the guns.[9]

Macquarie penned a memorandum to Greenway on 4th July 1817, requesting the architect:

> To draw out a Ground Plan and Elevation of a neat handsome Fort – intended to be erected, as soon as possible, on the lower part of Bennelong's Point with Ten Embrazeurs... The Fort is to be entirely built of the best stone that can be procured near the spot. ... (and a plan) of a court of Offices and Stables... for the use of the Governor's Horses, Carriages and servants... which... are to be built of brick (and thirdly) a ground Plan and Elevation of a Handsome and commodious Castellated House for the residence of the Governor in Chief of the Colony... to be built of stone; – but the form of the House, and disposition of the Apartments are entirely left to Mr Greenway's own taste and judgment.

For Macquarie's 'Handsome and commodious Castellated House', Greenway produced a design based on Thornbury Castle, Gloucestershire, the seat of Sir Algar Howard. Thornbury Castle had mock castellations, and the design Greenway produced for the stables had castellations to be in sympathy with the intended Government House. The stables could also, in times of necessity, be converted into a fort.[10] The Government Domain surrounding the new house and stables could, quipped Greenway, be planted out 'in the manner of the celebrated Brown, the landscape gardener, it having great capability.'

When Macquarie informed Lord Bathurst of his intention to build a new Government House, Bathurst wrote back advising construction of the house be deferred '... till the proper Authority is given for its commencement...' Despite Macquarie's that his intended house was 'by no means on an expensive scale', that he had not intended to draw on the British Treasury for 'a single farthing' and that any expense out of colonial funds would have been 'trifling', permission to build the house was not granted. However, Macquarie was determined to go ahead with his stables and fort, penning in his diary on 16th December 1817

> ... the whole of the stonemason work of Macquarie Tower and Lighthouse (at South Head)... being now completed, Mrs Macquarie and myself made up a party of friends to breakfast this day... to view this noble magnificent ediface... Having breakfasted and remained at Macquarie Tower some time, we returned home by water stopping at Bennelong's Point where the ceremony was performed of laying the foundation stone of the new Fort proposed to be erected on that point and which was this day named Fort Macquarie. At 3 p.m. this same day I also laid the foundation stone of the new stable for Government House... This being altogether a very interesting day – and an auspicious one, I presented Mr Greenway, the Government Architect, his emancipation dated this day, it being delivered to him at Macquarie Tower this morning before breakfast...

It was not until construction of the stables was well under way that Macquarie belatedly informed Bathurst in 1819. 'I had so long suffered such very great inconvenience from the want of Secure Stables for my Horses and decent Sleeping places for my Servants, that I have been under Necessity of building a regular Suit of Offices of this Description...'

Despite Greenway having pointed out to Macquarie 'that the existing Dawes Battery commanded every way that was necessary at present for the protection of the inner harbour which made a fort of any description (at Bennelong Point) unnecessary...'[11] and despite having had no military training or experience in the design of fortifications Greenway dutifully produced a plan for a fort. It was on a square plan with sides 130 feet long, three of the sides washed by the sea at high tide and the fourth separated from the land by a narrow channel with access to the fort from the Point via a drawbridge. Guns were mounted on top of the three seaward-facing ramparts, which were 22 feet above high-water mark, and on top of a small circular bastion or 'barbette' on each angle of the square. The fort had a two-storeyed tower 90 feet in circumference to quarter a garrison of one commissioned officer and 12 men with a magazine in the basement to hold 350 barrels of gunpowder.[12]

Construction of the fort went ahead, using stone from the 'Tarpeian Rock' on the Point, a rocky outcrop not more than 50 feet high which had been named by the early settlers after the Tarpeian Rock in Rome from which traitors were flung to their death. Of the construction Greenway wrote: 'I must confess these fortifications put me in mind of my Uncle Toby and Corporal Trim in the garden, amusing themselves laying out fortifications in miniature, of no manner of service with such ideas.'[13]

Construction of the fort was still underway on 26th September 1819, when Commissioner John Thomas Bigge arrived in Sydney on the convict transport *John Barry* with three servants and a secretary, Thomas Scott, who was Bigge's brother-in-law. Bigge had been sent out by the British Government to report on Macquarie's administration for a Commission of Inquiry into the colony of New South Wales. Macquarie wrote to his brother he was cheered by the arrival of Bigge 'as his report must be favourable to my administration of the Colony and highly honourable to my character.' However, Bigge seemed intent on raking 'together all the dirt and filth, all the scandal calumnies and lies that ever circulated in the colony.'[14] The Commissioner went out of his way to criticise Macquarie; the first question Bigge often asked in gathering information was 'Have you any complaint to make against Governor Macquarie?'

Bigge lamented 'an unfortunate propensity to ornament and architectural effect that has pervaded all the buildings erected by Governor Macquarie since 1810' and wrote to Lord Bathurst of the stables, 'I cannot help expressing my astonishment at the useless magnificence of the plan of this building... in a style... far exceeding the wants or allowance of any Governor of N.S.W...' Why build 'such a palace for horses while people at Parramatta go unhoused?' Bigge also criticised the time spent on construction of the stables, to which Macquarie replied: 'The Commissioner... must be too well aware of Mr Greenway's dilatory habits, to feel any surprize... in regard to the period of time... to complete the building.'

At that time the only other architect in Sydney was Henry Kitchen, who had come out to the colony at Lord Bathurst's suggestion that he might fill the post of Colonial Architect, unaware that Greenway had already been appointed. Kitchen had been haphazardly employed by Greenway, including on the construction of St Matthew's Church at Windsor. Greenway had criticised his performance as a contractor, and Kitchen's subsequent inability to find steady work in his profession had driven him to mortgage his land and sell his cattle. On being asked his opinion of Fort Macquarie by Bigge, Kitchen replied:

> I should presume it to be from the length of time that it has been in progress and the very large number of hands it has almost incessantly employed, the most expensive of any of the public buildings – This building is contemp'bly defective. It has already been the butt and jest of every foreigner who has visited this part of the world... (and) is so badly contrived that from four different directions it is of no defence to itself or to the harbour... The Tower at the entrance port is of itself so weak and ill-calculated for any good object that its only use appears to be that of heroically and disinterestedly affording assistance to the enemy by showering splinters upon the men within the Fort of which it is a part... any (other) plan of defence is certainly superior to the very imbecile and defective one which has been selected.

Fort Macquarie was eventually completed in January 1821, just in time to give a farewell salute to Commissioner Bigge, whose ship, the *Dromedary,* departed the following month and was promptly nearly wrecked on the Sow and Pigs Reef before it left Sydney Harbour.

Before Bigge's arrival in Sydney, Macquarie had already requested permission to resign as Governor, having already been in Sydney for eight years and starting to feel his services were no longer appreciated. He received a conciliatory letter from Lord Bathurst, 'I must express my regret that you should have so far misunderstood the tenor of my communications... (nor) can I see any ground for the inference, which you have drawn...' and persuaded Macquarie to stay on for a year following Bigge's departure. He left with his wife on 12th February 1822, taking with them their favourite cow, Fortune, which was later transported to their farm on the Isle of Mull, five pet kangaroos, five emus, seven black swans and several parrots and white cockatoos. Bigge submitted three reports to Parliament between 1822 and 1823 on his Commission of Enquiry to New South Wales; all were highly critical of Macquarie's administration. On his return Macquarie found himself not being commended on his term of office as he had expected, but having to defend himself before Parliament against

Bigge's tenuous accusations of bad administration. Macquarie's position was not helped when Viscount Robert Castlereagh, who had defended Macquarie in Parliament, committed suicide after Macquarie returned to London only three or four days after conducting him to the King at Carlton House. Macquarie had to battle to obtain a pension, and died a disillusioned man on 1st July 1824, less than two years after arriving in England. When news reached Sydney of his passing, the majority of the inhabitants closed the shutters on their houses, the pages of the *Sydney Gazette* were draped in black and church bells tolled for days on end from dawn to dusk.

A week before Macquarie departed Sydney, Greenway unexpectedly presented him with a bill for architectural services of 20 per cent of the finished cost of his buildings. On his voyage home, Macquarie wrote a letter to his successor as Governor, Sir Thomas Brisbane, regarding Greenway's claim, which was received by Brisbane many months later, 'Concerning a very insolent and disrespectful letter addressed to me by Mr Greenway... You will plainly perceive... that Mr Greenway has not a shadow of a claim upon the Government... (and) you will treat it with the contempt and neglect it so justly merits...' He had given Mr Greenway 'a salary of 3s per Diem' and 'a Government Barrack', as residence for 'Himself and Family' and to make up for the smallness of his salary had granted Greenway 800 acres of land and six cows.

> It is therefore only an impudent and daring attempt to impose and to extort from Government a greater remuneration for his services than they merit; for I had almost daily occasion to reprimand him for his habitual indolence, neglect and inattention to his Duty, as well as for his frequent insolent conduct to the Acting Chief Engineer. His services however were indispensable and therefore I continued him in office from mere necessity.

As a result of Bigge's criticism on expenditure on public works, construction of Greenway's Anglican cathedral on George Street was halted at the foundations, and Greenway was asked to alter the design of his courthouse at the top of Macquarie Street to turn it into a church, called St James. A building behind the church intended to be a school was instead converted to courts. Bigge's brother-in-law and Secretary, Thomas Scott, suddenly took holy orders and on Bigge's recommendation was appointed Archdeacon of Sydney at St James, on a salary equal to Macquarie's.

Bigge mistakenly described Greenway to his superiors as having been transported because he 'concealed his effects in bankruptcy' and in his report to the Commission of Inquiry recommended that in future 'an officer of the Corps of Engineers should be appointed to the Colony of New South Wales, and that he should have the general direction and superintendence of all the works... After the appointment of such an officer shall have taken place, it does not appear to me that it will be necessary to continue that of the Colonial Architect, as there are no buildings... in which it would be requisite or desirable to have reference to his assistance.'

Whether or not the government acted on Bigge's recommendation mattered not, for Greenway had already ensured his own fall from grace. Perplexed at his treatment by his superiors and of the machinations of his colleagues, Greenway, in his own words, 'declined inspecting the progress of public works.' The Colonial Secretary, Major Frederick Goulburn, wrote to Greenway on 15th November 1822, 'By direction of the Governor I am to acquaint you that from the present date your services to the Government will be dispensed with.'

Greenway's plea of remuneration for work done in Macquarie's and Brisbane's time fell on deaf ears. As a result of a writ from an unpaid pawnbroker and moneylender, a notice in the *Sydney Gazette* advised that Mr Greenway's possessions, including chairs, tables, bedding and a pianoforte, would be sold by auction at his dwelling on George Street. Even that dwelling, which Brisbane had written to Greenway in May 1822, 'You will be permitted to live in... which will be kept in tenantable repair at the expense of the Government', Greenway had no legal title to, and on 20th July 1826, he received a letter from the new Colonial Secretary, Alexander McLeay that 'as the House belonging to the Crown in which you reside, will shortly be required for Government, I am directed to inform you that the same is to be vacated by you on or before 1st September next.' Greenway stubbornly held on in residence, and even sold part of the land attached to the George Street house under false pretences for £150 to a local solicitor, Mr Unwin.

Greenway's wife passed on in 1832. Belatedly, on 30th April 1834, Greenway was evicted by the Sheriff accompanied by the new Government Architect, Mortimer Lewis, 'my two daughters alarmed, distressed and driven from the house in consequence and myself... exposed to the insults of a few unfeeling creditors who disposed of every household necessary and comfort in the most unfeeling manner, my credit destroyed and reduced me to the deepest misery...' Though after escorting him out of the gate the Sheriff allowed Greenway to go in again as an honorary bailiff for the Crown and occupy some of the rooms.

A landholders' census of 1828 showed Greenway to be in occupation of an 800-acre property at Tarro near Newcastle; it had 30 acres of cleared land, of which 15 were cultivated and on which he carried 16 head of horned cattle. Greenway died in September 1837, at the age of 60 near East Maitland on the Hunter River; the location of his grave is forgotten and unidentified.

Fort Macquarie was never reckoned to be a practical deterrent as a fort. A typical opinion was one written in 1834 by the editor of the *Sydney Gazette*, 'It is hardly necessary to remark that all military and scientific men have regarded Fort Macquarie as perfectly useless as a fortification...' The main criticism was that the Fort was too low, the guns were on a low battlement that was not enclosed and approaching enemy ships could rake the exposed gunners with grape shot. Provision was made so that if the fort was likely to fall to an enemy the stored powder in the magazine could be blown up to immediately destroy the magazine and fort along with it.

The Fort did, however, mount the largest cannon of all the defence works in Sydney; an 1836 disposition of ordnance listed ten 24 pounder cannons and five six pounders. Additional guns were placed on the Fort during the Crimean War and the Franco-Prussian War of 1871. The guns of the Fort never fired in anger. They were used to salute arriving and departing Governors, dignitaries and foreign warships; they let off a volley on the accession of Queen Victoria and when the news reached Sydney of the fall of Sebastopol during the Crimean War. During a great theatrical occasion in 1886, illustrated by a double-page lithograph published in the *Sydney Gazette*, clouds of smoke shrouded the Fort when a series of blanks were fired during a mock-raid staged on the Fort. For the last 22 years of the Fort's life it was used as an artillery training school for naval volunteers.

At the turn of the century the Fort was demolished; the site was extended with rubble and rock fill and the Fort Macquarie Tram Depot built. The Depot opened on 10th August 1902; it was constructed of sandstone and red brick on a square plan with mock-castellations crowning the circumference of the walls and the water tower.

Greenway's commodious stables, just off Macquarie Street 300 yards from Fort Macquarie, built in a Tudor style with the main walls enclosing a central quadrangle with a fountain, provided accommodation for 26 horses; it had a coach house, a cow shed, harness and saddle rooms and servants' and coachman's quarters. The stables were situated in a prominent position on rising ground above the greenery of the Botanic Gardens, and visitors arriving in Sydney by ship frequently mistook them for a Government House. Indeed Governors following on from Macquarie talked of converting the stables to a Government House as they still occupied cramped quarters on nearby Bridge Street. However, the stables continued to be occupied by horses, and a Tudor-style Government House with crenellations, tall chimneys and small towers was eventually built in 1837-45, designed by the London architect Edward Blore, who was a special architect to William IV and then to Queen Victoria. The house was on a site in the Botanic Gardens overlooking Fort Macquarie with a magnificent view from the front rooms and garden along the length of Sydney Harbour to the Heads.

With the advent of the motor car the stables were no longer required for horses, and in 1913-15 the stables and servants quarters around the insides of the walls were demolished and replaced by rooms for a library, offices, lecture and study rooms and a central auditorium for a Conservatorium of Music. The auditorium roof, rising above Greenway's crenellated walls and designed in a pastiche of Westminster Hall, looked 'like a stable adapted to a bulk store', according to one observer when the building was completed.

According to the committee that established the Conservatorium, it was built to promote 'serious' music over the popular music of vaudeville houses and music halls, enlightening the masses whose morals were sure to improve through an appreciation of 'true music'. Construction of the Conservatorium was justified as having 'nothing at all to do with money… the cultivation of art is regarded in itself as a sufficiently beneficial end.' The 'Minister for Public Instruction' told the press in 1915, that the Conservatorium 'will become as well known in the musical world as any of the great Conservatoriums of Europe.'

The first director of the Conservatorium was Henri Verbruggen, a Belgian-born musician who lived in Scotland. He left in 1922 to take up a post with the Minneapolis Orchestra in Minnesota when a request that his salary be doubled was turned down. A new Liberal/National Party coalition government, which came to power in 1922, seeking to cut wasteful expenditure on education proposed closing the Conservatorium down. The Conservatorium kept going, but the orchestra disbanded when its funding was withdrawn.

CHAPTER 3

THE COMPETITION

Charles Joseph Alfred Moses started his career in the British Army. Born at Atherton Lancashire on 21st January 1900, he was commissioned into the 2nd Border Regiment as a lieutenant in 1918 after passing his officer cadet exams at the Royal Military College Sandhurst. After serving in France, then Germany, his regiment was posted to Ireland, where Moses excelled in seven sports including rugby and soccer, and where he was champion of the Irish command for three years at boxing and shotput. In 1922, irked by an apparent lack of promotion prospects in the British Army, he left the regiment, married, and emigrated to Australia, where the rest of his family had already settled in Victoria. Trying his hand at fruit growing in the Bendigo district, then working for six years as a car salesman, he obtained his first job in radio in 1930 working as a sports and news announcer for radio 3LO in Melbourne. Then in 1932:

> ... I was taken over from the staff of the old Australian Broadcasting Company, which was responsible for what they called the A class stations – the B class were the commercials – we were non-commercial. And we were taken over by the new Commission, lock stock and barrel – everybody except the General Manager.[1]

Working for the new Commission, the Australian Broadcasting Commission or 'ABC.', Moses moved to Sydney where he was made 'sports and talks editor.' Radio in Australia enjoyed a rapid expansion at this time particularly in 1934 'when we started the synthetic broadcast of cricket. It is a fact that the number of licences doubled in that year...'[2] In 1935 Moses was promoted to General Manager of the ABC, but left in 1940 to join the Australian Imperial Force with the rank of Lieutenant Captain. Stationed at Johore in Malaya attached to the 9th Indian Division when Japan entered the war, Moses escaped with Major General Gordon Bennett from Singapore immediately following its fall.[3] He returned to Australia, and was with the Army in New Guinea in February 1943 – by which time he had been promoted to Lieutenant Colonel – when he was recalled to Australia at the express instruction of John Curtin, the Prime Minister, to resume his activities as General Manager of the ABC.[4]

Following the war, a priority for Moses was to increase the size of the small ABC orchestras established by government funding in 1932. Moses remembered that in 1945:

> ... I had negotiated with the City Council and the State Government, or I will put it the other way round, because the State Government were making the major contribution; that they would contribute two, what were then sizeable sums, which would help the ABC to enlarge the orchestra to full symphony size. We had at that time in Sydney the ABC's orchestra which was 45; only 45 musicians, but they did have four horns and all the instruments of a full symphony orchestra, but required extra strings particularly. And if we were going to give public performances; which we did, we had to bring in people from the Conservatorium and some retired musicians – and some who had given up the idea of ever being in an orchestra – and build it up to about 72. But it wasn't a professional orchestra of 72, it was a professional orchestra of 45, and after some negotiations with the State Government – the Minister for Education, Mr Heffron was the man I spoke with – and the Town Clerk of Sydney, I found both of them very receptive. The end result was that we got £20,000 from the State Government and £10,000 from the City Council and this represented, between the two round about 35 to 40% of the cost of the orchestra at that time... we were able to build the orchestra up to a full 72 for its normal strength and for the concert season, which is normally over a period of five months, we could add another twenty with those funds and some extra money which I got out of my own board for this project.[5]

The Sydney Symphony Orchestra (SSO) was the first of the six fully professional permanent State symphony orchestras to be established.[6]

> So it was necessary that we should have a conductor. And somebody of accepted status in the world of music – not merely in Australia, but in the world of music and we were thinking of who we could get. The strong recommendation from both my Director of Music, Mr. W. G. James and the Commission's then advisor, and a close friend of mine, Sir Bernard Heinze, was that Goossens would be just the sort of person. He wasn't what you called a flashy conductor, but he was a very sound musician and had a very high standing in the world of music. So we invited him to come out to Australia to see how we got on with him and he got on with the orchestra.[7]

In 1946, when he was invited to Australia, Goossens had already enjoyed a reputation for 20 years as one of the world's finest conductors, ranked with contemporaries such as Aaron Copland and William Walton. He was descended from a long line of talented musicians:

When the famous Carl Rosa Opera Company performed at London's Covent Garden in 1921 a rising young conductor named Eugene Goossens was invited to conduct Wagner's Ring Cycle. Some 50 years earlier his grandfather, who bore the same name, had been the company's principal conductor. In due course this first Eugene Goossens was succeeded in the position by his son Eugene Goossens II. Now the third conductor of that name was on the podium and in a performance of Rheingold he had a slight difference of opinion with an elderly cello player. The old man shook his head resignedly. 'I've played under three generations of Goossens', he murmured, 'and I've cursed them all.'

... As well as his two notable conducting predecessors Eugene Goossens III had a brother Leon, regarded as possibly the world's finest oboist and twin sisters Sidonie and Marie, who are renowned harpists. His Belgian grandfather went to England in 1873 (as) the pioneer conductor of the Carl Rosa Opera Company in London. His father, also Belgian-born, took over direction of the Carl Rosa Opera Company when the grandfather retired to Liverpool to teach music. His mother, Annie Cook, a well-known singer, was a daughter of Aynsley Cook an operatic basso who was a direct descendant of Australia's discoverer Captain Cook. At one time in London his grandfather was conducting an opera, his father was playing the violin in the orchestra and his future mother and her father were singing in the company. 'My father should have been looking at his notes', Eugene Goossens III used to tell the story, 'But instead he was looking at my mother on the stage. They were married – and here I am.'

In fact Eugene Goossens was born in a boarding house in London's Camden Town on May 26 1893 next door to the house where Crippen murdered his wife in 1903. His brothers, Leon and Adolphe and sisters Marie and Sidonie were born over the next six years-born; brother Leon once said 'into an atmosphere in which the worship of God and music was the sole motivation for life.' There was no doubt about the future occupation of any of the Goossens children. The father decided to make his eldest son, Eugene, a conductor and set him learning the violin and piano at five. He showed such promise with the violin that at eight he was packed off to the Bruges Conservatory for two years of school and special violin study. In his holidays young Eugene would tour England with his father and the Opera company, attending rehearsals and 'letting the atmosphere seep into me.' At 10 he returned to continue his education at the Liverpool College of Music. The Goossens family lived in Liverpool while their father was away touring with the Carl Rosa Company. Already his younger brothers were practised musicians. Leon with the oboe and Adolphe with the French horn. All three played regularly in a Liverpool amateur orchestra.

THE COMPETITION

At 13 Eugene Goossens began a four year scholarship at the Royal College of Music and before long was made leader of the second violins in the college orchestra. One day the famous French composer Saint-Saens was invited to conduct a rehearsal of his Third Symphony by the orchestra. All went well until the finale when the second violins bungled a lead. Saint-Saens turned to Goossens' section with a withering look of scorn and ordered them to play it again by themselves. They did but not to the composer's satisfaction. Exasperatedly he looked at young Goossens and ordered: 'You show the others how it should go.' He tried and the tremulous and ineffective playing brought a long concentrated glance from the conductor-composer. Then he removed his pince-nez and muttered in French 'Nice try, but what an awful violinist.' Everyone including Goossens understood what he had said. Apparently Saint-Saens did not realise this for he pointed to Goossens and before proceeding said: 'Vairy nervose.'

... Eugene Goossens graduated at 17 and despite Saint-Saens's opinion of his playing went straight to a violinist's chair with Sir Henry Wood's Queen's Hall Orchestra. He stayed there for another four years during which time he began composing and also conducting at times at Queen's Hall and the Drury Lane and Aldwych Theatres. His conducting ability was obvious and when he was 21 it attracted Sir Thomas Beecham's attention who offered him a job as assistant conductor to himself with the Beecham Opera Company. After that Goossens packed away his violin for good and remained a conductor with Beecham until 1923. The experience was invaluable and hectic for Beecham often called upon him to conduct at perilously short notice. He conducted 60 or 70 different operas for Beecham and at least 40 of them without orchestra rehearsal. 'You can dispense with the orchestral rehearsal only if you have a good knowledge of the "score" and a "strong nerve" ' Goossens reminisced years later. 'Fortunately I had both.'

Goossens got all the experience a young conductor could wish. About a year after he started with the opera company he received an urgent call to see Beecham. The conductor was waiting with a bundle of scores. He said 'My father died this morning. Catch the 8.30 from Euston to Liverpool and rehearse the Philharmonic for a concert tonight.' Goossens took the scores and rushed for the train. That night after only three hours rehearsal he conducted Beecham's concert brilliantly...

Goossens was with Beecham all through World War I. Three times he tried to enlist but was rejected on medical grounds. His younger brothers both enlisted and one, Adolphe, was killed one day in 1916. He was rehearsing in Glasgow with the Scottish Orchestra when outside down the street marched a line of kilted soldiers. Adolphe walked out of the rehearsal and fell in behind the soldiers. He joined the Artists' Rifles and was killed three months after reaching the front in France. That made Eugene Goossens keener than ever to enlist but it was no good. Finally he went to France as conductor of the Canadian Massed Bands. As an honorary lieutenant he toured France with 275 musicians including 70 clarinets, 40 trumpets, 25 trombones and with such a success that later he conducted a concert of the whole British Army Massed Bands.

In 1923 came an offer to head a new symphony orchestra and music school set up by Kodak millionaire George Eastman at Rochester in New York State. Goossens accepted and thereafter worked seven months each year at Rochester and the remaining five as guest conductor with English and European orchestras. In 1931 he became permanent conductor of the Cincinnati Symphony Orchestra.[8]

Goosens appeared as a guest conductor with the SSO when he came to Sydney. Moses recalled:

Whilst he was here I found that he was interested in the country – he liked the country – he liked the orchestra, and he would be interested in becoming its resident conductor. But of course it was a question of how we were able to get him away from Cincinnati where he had a sizeable salary by U.S. standards and by our standards. It was something not within our reach. By a certain amount of – I won't say skulduggery, but cunning – I was able to make the position attractive enough to persuade him to come. This was done by giving him a salary as the principal conductor of the orchestra and an entertainment allowance which was non-taxable. Then it was suggested that it would be possible to get him to act as Director of the Conservatorium. Well, this of course made the thing more possible, because we were then able to give him a salary as Director of the Conservatorium – even though they wanted his name more than his time – and he also got a small entertainment allowance from the Conservatorium. And then to make the whole thing possible, I arranged that if he conducted any of our orchestras in other states, then he got a special fee for that, and I had a verbal guarantee that he would have no less than twelve such interstate concerts. So with the fees from conducting other Australian orchestras, his own salary as conductor plus allowance and his salary as Director of the Conservatorium plus allowances, we were able to add up to make nearly $2000 more than he was getting in Cincinnati. And I might say, my own Board never knew how it was; the only other person that knew was my controller of finance.[9]

When Goossens was in Sydney, he had been surprised to find that he would be conducting the SSO not in a proper concert hall but at the Sydney Town Hall, which he was also further surprised to learn was their regular concert venue and that a concert hall as such did not exist in Sydney. Furthermore, there were no theatres whatsoever in Sydney large enough to stage even medium-sized operas let alone grand opera. However, Goossens accepted Moses' generous offer of a job,[10] and returned to Sydney on 2nd July 1947. Reporters were waiting to meet him when he arrived, and the following morning an article appeared in the *Sydney Morning Herald* entitled, 'Planning for the Top'.

> Mr Eugene Goossens's plans for Sydney's musical future include a symphony orchestra among the six best in the world, and a conservatorium that will rank with the greatest in Europe. Mr Goossens explained these plans in a Press interview last night. He returned to Australia by Tasman flying-boat yesterday afternoon.
>
> Mr Goossens also explained why he had left the Cincinnati Symphony Orchestra, whose conductor he had been for 16 years, to come to Sydney as resident conductor of the Sydney Symphony Orchestra and Director of the N.S.W. Conservatorium. He said he felt that in remaining in Cincinnati he would be perpetuating a great musical tradition, but that in Sydney and Australia there was a challenging situation from which something fine could be created for music, and for the people.
>
> Asked how he proposed to build up the orchestra to the desired high quality, Mr Goossens said it would be largely a matter of teaching it to acquire the 'grand manner.' In technique, the orchestra was already excellent, but he proposed to work at it until it achieved perfection of style.
>
> Mr Goossens said his ambitions include a fine concert hall for the orchestra, with perfect acoustics and seating accommodation for 3,500 people, a home for an opera company, and a smaller hall for chamber music. He said he saw no reason why a city the size of Sydney, with such keen music interest, should not have these.[11]

Goossens was joined in Sydney by his considerably younger third wife, Marjorie, a talented American pianist, (as a couple they were known as Eugene Goossens the third and the third Mrs Eugene Goossens), and the two youngest of his five daughters, Sidonie and Renée, the children of his second marriage. Under his guidance, Sidonie, at the age of 17, became the SSO's principal harpist.

When he had stepped off the plane in 1947, Goossens had vowed not only to make the SSO one of the six best orchestras in the world, but also to make its musicians as well-known as the players in Australia's test cricket team. Although his musicians found he had a certain 'Godalmightiness' about him, and he had a tendency to 'talk down to the colonials', they flourished under his tutorship, the SSO's concert master, the Australian violinist Ernest Llewellyn remembering how Goossens 'allowed the musicians to play, rather than demanding a strict attention to beat, which would have reduced their dynamic drive.'

By his own choice, Goossens introduced his Sydney audiences to concerts often composed by less well-known composers, such as Mahler and Bruckner, but even so, the SSO concert season at the Town Hall was quickly oversubscribed and it became impossible to get tickets, subscription holders leaving their annual right to season tickets to relatives in their wills. Those lucky enough to get into Goossens' concerts were expected to pay full attention to the proceedings, the master once laying down his baton during a concert at the Town Hall 'to glare two whispering women in the organ gallery into silent submission.'[12]

> Apart from music, his interests and considerable knowledge extended from... philosophy (to) classical and modern literature, poetry, painting and languages. He was an excellent painter of water colours and an expert in various aspects of architecture and archeology, a talented photographer, an authority on contemporary ships... (during his transatlantic career) crossing the Atlantic by ship 38 times in 34 different vessels.[13]

Moses recalled that:

> ... he (also) liked his garden, but the real interest he had was an extraordinary one, (chuckle), locomotives. He loved railway trains – railway engines. In fact I remember when the orchestra went to Newcastle on one occasion, he got permission to take the wheel, as he had done in England on many an occasion, and drove the engine from Sydney to Newcastle. Certainly the Union had that the engine driver and stoker had to be there as well, but he actually drove the engine and got great pleasure from it. It wasn't the first time he'd done this type of thing... The fact was this, that he genuinely did like railway engines and (would)... get onto the plate of the engine at any time if he had an opportunity.[14]

Goossens' daughters, Sidonie and Renée could 'recall their father at home, playing recordings of trains rattling along the tracks...'[15]

When Goosens had talked of a new concert hall and a home for opera on his return to Australia in 1947, it was not the first time a new centre for the performing arts had been mentioned for Sydney. On 2nd August 1928, an article in the *Daily Guardian* under the heading 'Grand Opera for us permanently'[16] outlined a proposal for a 'National grand opera house' by Sir Benjamin Fuller. Fuller hoped Madame Melba would also get behind the project 'financially and in other respects. What could be a better monument to her fame and name than a national grand opera house?' Construction of the centre should be essentially a 'citizens' venture, designed for the advancement of music and the allied arts.' Sir Ben suggested an ideal site for the theatre 'to seat at least 3,000' would be that currently occupied by the Supreme Court, and outside the opera season 'the building would be available for individual concert artists (and) orchestral performances.' However, the suggestion was as far as the project got and when Walter Burley Griffin, the architect of Canberra, produced a design for a university in Allahabad, India in 1940 he jestingly entitled the design 'An Opera House for Sydney.'

Also in the year of 1940 an organisation called the National Theatre Movement of Australia, following protracted debate, 'unanimously adopted the recommendation made by Mr Stuart-Layner... (the movement's secretary) of Bennelong Point as the prospective site for (a) "National Theatre".'[17] On 30th March 1944, a meeting took place between a 'Public Buildings Advisory Committee' and the Sydney Municipal Council to consider 'post-war reconstruction projects in certain areas of the city' including an area bounded by Martin Place, Macquarie Street and Phillip Street. The Labor Premier, Mr McKell[18] had already broached the possibility to the City Council the previous year of setting aside this area if it was required for 'post-war planning.' The Advisory Committee and the City Council prepared an ambitious scheme that included a new Parliament House and Law Courts, recommending also 'the erection of either a Civic or State Opera House on the King Street end of Macquarie Street.' Their plans were shown to the Premier, who instructed the Government Architect, Cobden Parkes, 'to prepare a rough sketch' of a revised scheme, placing the opera house on the east side of Macquarie Street 'between the Mitchell Library and the Registrar General's Office.'[19]

The idea of an opera house or 'National Theatre' stayed on the Labor government agenda, though nothing concrete was done about it. Meanwhile, Goossens had got wind of their proposals and had been introduced to a prospective site:

> Mr Eugene Goossens... said yesterday that he agreed with a plan to build Sydney's opera house on the site of the present tram sheds at Fort Macquarie.
>
> The idea originally arose in a conversation with the consultant planner of the Cumberland County Council, Dr K. Langer, who had included it in his proposals for architectural additions to Sydney's cultural life.[20]

'Whether it finally appeared on the plan recently presented by the council to the Minister for Local Government, Mr J. J. Cahill, and whether – or how soon – the site may be made available for this purpose, I cannot say as yet', Mr Goossens said.

'Many considerations are entailed besides the important one of alternative accommodation for Sydney's trams, but I am confident of winning the interest and sympathetic co-operation of the Government in this regard. Only the prize-winning architectural design of an international competition (which I hope an Australian wins) will be worthy of such a site. Like the San Francisco War Memorial Opera House, it must furnish a permanent home for our symphony orchestra, opera, ballet, and choral festivals. The auditorium must accommodate audiences of from 3,500 to 4,000 – no fewer. Given a sufficient area, Sir Laurence Olivier's smaller playhouse might be included under the same roof... An opera house we can be proud of will focus the international spotlight of culture forever on Sydney. Without it we'll stagnate in outer darkness. But we must get started, or else it'll be too late.'[21]

The following day the then Minister for Local Government, Mr J.J. (Joe) Cahill... said the master plan for Sydney made no provision for an opera house on Bennelong Point but that it did provide for cultural centres to be built. The then acting Premier, Mr J. M. Baddeley, said he was interested in Goossens' proposal. The Transport Minister of the day added that he favoured the building of an opera house for Sydney but he did not want to lose the tram sheds on Bennelong Point. A few days later Goossens was at it again: on 20th October , 1948 he was predicting that Sydney would have an opera house on Bennelong Point.

'We must have the opera house within five years', he said. 'Sydney orchestra is taking its place among the world's major symphonic groups. A fine hall is essential if the public is to hear the orchestra at its best. If my plan succeeds Sydney will have, with the co-operation of those in authority, a great opera house. There is substantial support for the site and we intend to follow it up.' [22]

At the University Club at the University of Sydney, Goossens met George Molnar, a Professor of Architecture at the Faculty of Architecture. Molnar was born on 25th April 1910[23] at Nagyvarad, Transylvania, in the former Austro-Hungarian Empire. It was the oldest town in Hungary, known in the past as St Laszlo, 'a little town of about sixty to seventy thousand inhabitants... (which) had a marvellous theatre by Helmer and Ferner who built about 70 theatres all over the Austro-Hungarian Empire.' Here Molnar's mother and father took him to watch plays and opera from the time he was five years old. 'After the First World War, which ended in 1918... there were revolutions and there was a communist revolution in Hungary... (and) the Rumanians came in and put (it) down and... went right up through Hungary. And then they took that part which was given to them in the peace treaties, all Transylvania, that was in 1919, and after that you were brought up, you had to go to school and everything was in Rumanian. And my father who was a professor, had to teach in Rumanian and all these sort of things...'[24]

Molnar studied architecture at the Royal Joseph Technical University of the University of Budapest, graduating in 1931. He had a compulsory spell in the Rumanian Army in the cavalry, where, as a university graduate he went in automatically as a lieutenant, then he settled down in Nagyvarad, which had now been renamed Oradea by the Rumanians, working as an architect for an architectural company which also financed and built projects and was the biggest company of its type in the county. Then, 'around '38 or '39, when it was a question of what is going to happen in Europe, and that was everybody knew there will be a war, and I was an oppressed minority, being a Hungarian in Rumania... In any case I wanted to get away and wrote to the Institute of Architects in London and asked where is the best place to go. And they said well there is a place called Australia. South Africa or Australia where things are going well. And I didn't like something being south of something, I didn't know anything about any of these places and wrote to the Institute of Architects in Australia and Professor Hook, who was then president of the Institute wrote back very nicely and after that we corresponded...'[25]

Encouraged by Hook to come out to Australia, Molnar travelled 200 kilometres to cross the border into Yugoslavia near Timisoara in the west of Rumania. He avoided the border crossing into Hungary, just 10 kilometres north of Oradea, as the border guards knew him and he was worried that at any time he could be called up into the Rumanian Army and prevented from leaving the country. Having stopped for a holiday at Monte Carlo, Molnar embarked on a ship at Marseilles bound for Australia. He was met in Sydney on his arrival by Hook and a Hungarian architect who had emigrated to Australia earlier and who knew Molnar and could recognise him. After staying one night with Hook in Sydney, Molnar travelled on to Canberra where Hook 'already had a job for me... for £5 0s 0d a week, which was a lot of money at that time, since I had my lodging and everything... for £3 0s 0d'[26]

During the war, Molnar worked for the Ministry of Munitions on 'the great Australian tank' in Melbourne, a Mark IV version of a British tank...'all we'd done was converted the dimensions from decimals of an inch to fractions and made some changes for local requirements', and had come up to Sydney for a firing test 'which was a disaster.' However, during the testing he was talking to some people who wanted to build hospital ships but did not have the people to do the work; Molnar said 'Well I can do it' and was set to work at the requisitioned David Jones' Mens store on Elizabeth Street, Sydney. He later designed another ship intended for General Blamey's floating command headquarters, but events moved ahead of themselves; the war ended, the floating hospital ships and headquarters were completed but never used, and even the 'great Australian Tank' never got further than the first prototypes.

Bernard Hesling was working at David Jones '... and he was doing cartoons for the Daily Telegraph and whenever he didn't have any ideas or whether he couldn't draw something he asked me to help, and being such a sweet, nice fellow, he kept on telling Brian Penton (the editor), "what a marvellous man, there is George Molnar running the department and look you should get him as a cartoonist", and later I saw Brian Penton and I didn't like him, I didn't want to be a cartoonist... but I liked Cyril Pearl, who was doing the Saturday Telegraph, and then I started to do cartoons for him. And at the same time Professor Hook asked me would I come and teach at the University because we will have this influx of returned soldiers, (it would be) "... just for a little while"; I said "no, I don't want it... ", "just for a term when we get these people" (pressed Hook). And so I went for a term and originally I was supposed to have the first year, but then Professor Wilkinson who was head of the school, after I talked to him he said "Oh no, you'll be in charge of the final year", and, a delightful man, he took me and introduced me to the students and he said, "now here is Mr Molnar and he has completely different ideas about everything and it is very good for you to have two opinions".'[27]

As a Professor of Architecture, Molnar found 'I was doing all sorts of very marvellous projects. Because I had these students you see, I had so many students and they were like draughtsmen to me. And other architects in practise couldn't get down to anything after the War, just little three bedroom houses or hospitals. But nothing else went on and there I have 15 to 30 draughtsmen and I can think of anything we wanted to do and at one time we had the architectural problems of Sydney (solved)...' 'In any case, Goossens asked me why should I not try to give my students a project of solving the Opera House. Now here was a man who, by that time, was composing operas, he was one of the great conductors of the world, he travelled very widely in America... where there were many multi-purpose halls... And he knew the problem of having a hall that can be used as an opera house and a concert hall. All the techniques he used, he performed there, he knew whatever was required to make a change of reverberation time which is necessary and so on. In any case, he wanted this double purpose hall, mainly opera. And so we designed a beautiful opera house for him... My students designed the first Opera House (at Bennelong Point). That was the first design of the Opera House according to Goossens' requirements at the right site... And (the students) had to solve it you know. (There)... was no question about (it) being not solved, without everything working, everything worked'[28]

Molnar's students worked on the opera house and various other architectural projects for a term, '... and we solved them all with beautiful models...' which were put on public display on the exhibition floor of David Jones from 13th to 24th August 1951. A booklet was available of the exhibition, entitled, 'Some architectural problems of Sydney, presented by the Faculty of Architecture Sydney.'[29]

Goossens' Opera House at Bennelong Point became a problem that was set by other architecture professors at the university for their students, but an opera house in reality was proving elusive. So much so that in March 1954 Goossens was calling the opera house 'purely my dream child – nothing more.'[30] Although the Minister for Transport had insisted that the Fort Macquarie site was not available, Goossens continued to press for it: if you arrived in Sydney by ship, 'First you will see the Opera House, then you will see the Bridge.'[31] He would prevail on Phyllis Williams, his secretary at the Conservatorium, to walk with him through the Botanic Gardens at lunchtime to the park at the north end of Bennelong Point, where he would stand and inform her in no uncertain terms, 'This is where it must be.' Frustrated by government inaction on the Opera House, Goossens started to attack members of the government in the press, 'didn't they know that no city was a city without an Opera House', and what were these 'Philistines doing in government anyway.' He would ring Charles Moses at the ABC on an 'urgent' matter, and Moses would leave a meeting to take the call and be told 'I should do something about getting a new Opera House built.' 'He used to get quite heated', Moses recalled.[32]

> ... there was always some glee if you can get somebody to criticise an establishment body like a Government or a City Council or the Australian Broadcasting Commission – remembered Moses – the result was that when one or two remarks like this had appeared – because he didn't let it go, he had another go a few months later – I felt impelled to get him to come and see me. I called him in and I said, 'Gene, look, what you are doing is very embarrassing to the Government. They're employing you, really in a dual capacity, partly with the orchestra and as a Director of the Conservatorium. And even the City Council is partly your employer, they are on the Advisory Committee for the orchestra and it is certainly very embarrassing for us as partners of the Government and the council that you should be critical of our partners in this way.' 'Frankly', I said, 'I don't think you can continue making remarks like this.' He said, 'Something ought to be done', and I said, 'Yes, well, something ought to be done. I don't think this is the proper way to do it, to do it publicly in the press.' I said: 'I think the best thing to do is for us to go and have a talk to with the Premier.' He said he'd be delighted to and could I arrange it. Of course he didn't know the Premier. So I rang the Premier's office... (and though) I wouldn't have been surprised if the reply had come back that the Premier wasn't interested in meeting Mr Goossens... he could have been quite sensitive about it... (Mr Cahill's reaction (was) 'I would be delighted to see you.'... So the two of us went down to see him (and) he showed a real interest... He was most co-operative and before the end of the interview he said: 'Well, I tell you, we've got to get on and do something. I'll call a public meeting.' Which he did – in fact, within a few days he called for a public meeting which was held in the... Public Library and it was attended by some hundreds of people.[33]

John Joseph 'Joe' Cahill (pronounced 'Carl') was 63 years of age when he met Goossens. He was born in the working class Sydney suburb of Redfern. From an Irish Catholic background, he had started work at the age of 15 as an apprentice fitter and turner. He went to night school and obtained a degree in law, got involved in the union movement and was elected to State Parliament in 1925. He had his first Cabinet post in 1941 when he was made Minister of Works. Even when he became Premier in 1952, he continued to live in the small brick home in Marrickville where he had brought up his family. Although Cahill played the pianola at home, Moses could never recall having seen him at one of the ABC symphony concerts; Cahill preferred a day at the races.[34]

For the meeting at the library, Cahill arranged to have invitations sent out to a wide cross-section of those involved in the arts in Sydney, from Eugene Goossens and Charles Moses to those involved in opera, the theatre, cinema, drama, ballet, music and dance. They included Pierre Stuart-Layner, secretary of the National Theatre Movement, but also many personalities not involved so directly in the arts: Frank Packer of Consolidated Press, Dennis Winston, Professor of Town and Country Planning at Sydney University and Cobden Parkes, the Government Architect; also diverse interests from the President of the Employers' Federation of New South Wales and the Director of the New South Wales Chamber of Manufacturers to the Chairman of Directors of the Royal Prince Alfred Hospital.

At the meeting, on 30th November 1954, 'concerning the question of the establishment of an opera house in Sydney',[35] Cahill was the first to speak:

> As you are aware, the Government has decided that an Opera House shall be established in Sydney and that it will be worthy of this city... The people who have gathered here this morning are interested in opera and other forms of art to which perhaps many in the community might not give a second thought. Experience has proved that it is always the few who have to pioneer the way, and the Government has decided to go ahead with this project...
>
> ... The purpose of this conference is not to decide the form the building will take or the site on which it will be erected...
>
> ... This meeting has been called to enable the government to hear the views of as many interested groups as possible, and draw on the experience of people who are interested in opera, drama and ballet, and may possibly have investigated or been associated with opera both here and overseas... The Government has no preconceived ideas as to site or design, but we hope that from this conference will emerge a broad

pattern which will be of assistance to the small working committee whose job it will be to examine such matters in detail on the Government's behalf and submit recommendations.

I do not propose to ask this meeting to nominate a committee because it must be small but if any party feels that the proposed committee is not sufficiently representative or should be enlarged by Government it is willing to consider any suggestions. The Government proposed that the committee should consist of Mr Eugene Goossens, Professor Ashworth, Professor of Architecture at the University of Sydney,[36] Mr Charles Moses, General Manager of the Australian Broadcasting Commission, the Town Clerk of Sydney, Mr Hendy[37] and Mr Haviland, Under Secretary, Department of Local Government[38] – all of whom I am happy to welcome here this morning.[39] Necessarily, to be effective, the committee must be small, but it represents those broad aspects which are most obviously associated with the establishment of an Opera House. The committee will have power to co-opt or consult with any body or person able and willing to give advice. No interest will be overlooked, and when the committee is functioning I am sure that it will be pleased to examine any views which may be expressed both at and subsequent to this conference. I invite you to give your utmost co-operation and help to the committee.[40]

Some will say that the time is not opportune to build an Opera House in Sydney and that we could apply our resources to better advantage. I have been in public life for thirty years and there was never a time when a similar criticism would not have been offered against any great national venture of this nature. If such a criticism were valid one wonders how London ever got its Covent Garden, Paris, New York and Vienna their fine opera houses and Milan its La Scala, which was destroyed during the war and has since been rebuilt. This State cannot go on without proper facilities for the expression of talent and the staging of the highest forms of artistic entertainment which add grace and charm to living and which help to develop and mould a better, more enlightened community. The Opera House should not be regarded as the special preserve of Sydney people. It should be regarded as something which belongs to the people of New South Wales as a whole – or, for that matter to the people of Australia.

… Surely it is proper in establishing an opera house that it should not be a 'shandy gaff' place but an edifice that will be a credit to the State not only to-day but also for hundreds of years. … If we in our lifetime did nothing more than express our love of the arts by providing a building worthy of them, even when names are forgotten, the building will always remain as a testimony to what was done in the year 1954 by a group of citizens for the encouragement of talent and culture.

In 1941 a gentleman was leader of the party that I now have the honour to lead and he had a comprehensive scheme prepared for a new

THE COMPETITION

Macquarie Street. The Government Architect, who is here this morning, will probably remember it. According to that plan Martin Place was to be extended through to the Domain, there was to be an opera house on the corner of Martin Place and Macquarie Street and another great building – I think the Law Courts – and a new Parliament House were to be built in the vicinity. Some people seemed to have the idea that all those proposals would be accomplished overnight. That plan was made fourteen years ago but nothing seems to have been done about it.

Various suggestions have been made as to the location of the proposed Opera House. We may have a personal point of view as to the location of the building but I hope that a decision that it shall be built elsewhere will not dampen your ardour, and that the utmost co-operation will be given by all parties. The government will have to decide whether this proposal shall be taken over entirely by the government or whether private citizens or the community generally shall be responsible for it. Unquestionably the major portion of the cost will have to be borne by the government.

Mr Eugene Goossens, Director of the Conservatorium of Music, then stood up to speak.

I have asked permission to speak first because my services are required at the Conservatorium in connection with a diploma test. I should like it to be understood that I have no order of precedence; it is purely a matter of exigency. First, Mr Premier, I thank you and congratulate you and your Government on the splendid decision to build an opera house, which represents the realisation of the hopes that we have held for so long. When I came here permanently in 1947 I was invited by the Australian Broadcasting Commission to speak as a guest of honour, and I submitted then that Sydney must have an all-purposes building to house its different cultural activities, similar to opera houses in Europe and in the United States of America. For instance, the San Francisco Opera House provides for orchestra, opera, ballet and choral festival and is an all-purpose building. At that time I mentioned a particular spot, Bennelong Point – the tram-shed at Fort Macquarie. The person who first suggested that site to me was the architect of the Cumberland County Council. He said, 'How would you like to have an opera house there?' Having seen it I was tremendously impressed, and I still regard it as the ideal location. I have crystalised my views and I shall present them as rapidly as possible in the hope that they might form a basis for discussion. The building that I envisage, is primarily a home for orchestra. The Town Hall was built in 1888 for a city of about 300,000 inhabitants. To-day the population is 1,750,000. When I first came to Sydney the subscription audience for symphony concerts was 4,500. To-day there are 10,000 subscribers, a world record. A further 6,000 youth subscribers make the total of 16,000 people who pay annually for the privilege of hearing the orchestra. These figures cannot be equalled in any other part of the world. New York and London cannot come anywhere near it. Playing to this enormous audience involves a number of repeat concerts. This is adroitly done by dividing the concerts into red, white and blue series so that as many people as possible may hear a varied program. These concerts involve no fewer than thirty-six repeat performances. A great deal of time could be saved if a larger hall were available, because the repeat concerts could be substantially reduced in number. The orchestra would then be free to undertake work in connection with the presentation of opera, a most important point. Those responsible for the presentation of opera – and some of them are here this morning – agree that the orchestra is one of the major items of expenditure. Further, there are not sufficient reserves of players of the right calibre to provide both a permanent symphonic orchestra and an orchestra for opera, even if the funds were available. This is a lamentable fact. A casually-recruited orchestra for intermittent seasons of opera would not be of the same quality as a group of players practising and playing together uninterruptedly throughout the year.

Ballet is increasing in its appeal and Mr Borovansky is with us this morning. Ballet can be produced effectively in a theatre with a larger seating accommodation of 4,500. It is generally conceded that dramatic productions demand a more intimate association between players and listeners. It is apparent that there are four types of organisation concerned and the question is whether their apparently different requirements can be met in the one building. I say that they can, even though it may be difficult. At orchestra and choral concerts, 3,500 to 4,000 can listen adequately and comfortably. Grand opera is best presented to audiences of 1,800 to 2,500, though theatres in Milan and elsewhere have larger audiences. In my own former town of Cincinnati, operatic performances are given in buildings accommodating 3,800 patrons. The effective presentation of drama involves much smaller audiences – 1,500 to 1,800. The Architectural profession overseas has succeeded in designing buildings to meet the varying needs.

For instance, the War Memorial Opera House in San Francisco with accommodation for 3,200 is used for symphony concerts, grand opera, ballet and drama, and is considered entirely suitable for all these purposes. The Academy of Music in Philadelphia and the music hall at Cincinnati with a capacity of 4,000 are excellent examples of the all-purpose auditorium needed here. The Opera House at Malmo, Sweden, a city of 130,000 inhabitants, has a capacity of 1,800. By the use of travelling walls it can be converted to a theatre with accommodation for 1,200 or a hall suitable for recitals before an audience of 800. Attached to the Malmo Opera House is a small hall to provide for 220 patrons for chamber music and intimate recitals. With this device Malmo has equipped itself with auditoriums of varying sizes to suit all needs, but all in the one unit. Some compromise will have to be achieved if the proposed building for Sydney is to meet all needs. It must always be remembered that an orchestra is the basic need for opera, ballet and large choral performances and its existence is the means by which orchestral concerts become possible. Obviously the principal use of this theatre will be as a home for orchestral concerts, and it will be constantly in use for that purpose. In San Francisco orchestral concerts and opera run concurrently and the auditorium could be so designed as to make it simple to adapt for opera. There is no question of conflict, it is merely a matter of arranging dates. The right approach would be to envisage an auditorium large enough to seat from 3,500 to 4,000 people and to make that auditorium adaptable, by simple mechanism, for opera, for drama and other uses, for which a smaller auditorium is desirable.

The location of the proposed opera house has evoked diverse views, which is not surprising in the absence of knowledge of the type of building proposed and a definition of its objective. A functioning building is the first requirement. If at the same time it can be made monumental, so much the better. Much will depend on the nature of the selected site in determining whether the building can be both functional and monumental as the latter demands a site of much larger dimensions than does the former. The site should be of adequate proportions and should be centrally situated. It should have easy access to transport, and parking space, with frontages to at least two streets, and its surroundings should be appropriate to its cultural objectives... (Goossens mentioned a possible proposed site for the Opera House at Wynyard Park, over the ramp approach to Wynyard Station and another at the corner of College and Liverpool Streets, but...) Bennelong Point, where there is a famous tram shed which may or may not develop into a bus depot, is the ideal place. Imagine visitors on a liner coming up Sydney Harbour, seeing this magnificent building and being told 'That is Sydney's Opera House.' Bennelong Point lends itself to the erection of a monumental building. We might have to remove the tramway shed, but that is a matter that can be left to the experts.

The opera house that I envisage will contain a good restaurant and all the services that would make a visit to the opera house a pleasant event, quite apart from the cultural fare it offers. I suggest that a proposed committee of experts should be required to report on the purposes to which the building is to be devoted. This is important, because if we are not clear in mind about it we shall find ourselves in endless confusion. It should recommend the size and nature of the building required to meet those purposes. Its size and nature will very much affect its appearance and proportions. The recommendation of a site considered to be most suitable to meet all of these requirements will offer the committee the greatest subject of debate.

I hope that some if not all of the points that I have raised will give food for profitable discussion and eventual decision. I speak only as a musician; my function in this city is not administrative. I do my best, and hope that it meets with approval, to contribute to the city's musical culture. The practical details of the provision of an opera house are matters for discussion by the experts. This is the only State of its size in the world that has not an adequate hall to accommodate the activities that I have specified. In the performance of my *Apocalypse* [41] a couple of hundred of seats had to be taken from the public to house the large choirs in the galleries. That would not happen in the new opera house. Thank you for giving me this opportunity to speak. I am most delighted to offer my experience and to do anything I can to assist in bringing the proposal to fruition.

Following Goossens' address, Dr H.C. Coombes of the Elizabethan Theatre Trust spoke:[42]

... The address of the Premier is a magnificent inspiration. He has opened our eyes to a splendid vision of a Sydney with the first and the most magnificent Opera House in Australia to serve the arts of music, drama and the dance... He can count on any assistance of a technical or other character that I and the organisation I represent are able to give. Mr Premier, I promise you the most enthusiastic response from us.

After Coombes, Mr Lindley Evans of the Musical Association of New South Wales:

... I hope a great many people will support Mr Goossens' view on the suitability of the Bennelong Point site. When this site was mentioned I had the same thought as he expressed this morning. What a wonderful thing it would be for all the thousands of people who come to Sydney Harbour to see a magnificent building on that point and to be told with pride by Sydney people, 'There stands our Opera House!' I hope, Mr Premier, that you will share my views and Mr Goossens' views and the views of thousands of others on the excellence of this site and will do all in your power to get it for an Opera House. I am certain that if you succeed your name will live for the next 400 years as the head of the government that put the Opera House there.

Two representatives spoke on ballet, including Mrs Vera Lacey of the British Ballet Organisation:

'... musical students are in a much more fortunate position than students of the ballet. Music has the Conservatorium as its teaching ground, but students of the ballet and ballet teachers have nothing whatever... There is pressing need for a place in which the ballet can be taught here...'

THE COMPETITION

Mr O.D. Bissett on drama:

> I feel sure that I can speak with confidence for all the people interested in drama in Sydney when I say that we are honoured indeed that it is proposed to provide a building for opera, music, ballet and drama. I do not wish to be controversial but I am certain that in Sydney the people interested in drama far exceed in numbers those who are interested in opera. Therefore, I hope that the claims for a suitable theatre will be kept well to the front when considering the planning of the building. It is a little disturbing to note that on the suggested committee there is no-one truly representative of drama. We who are interested in drama welcome this discussion to-day but it has been rather on the lines of music and opera and ballet. I hope that drama will be kept in mind.

Later followed Mr Hal Lashwood:

> I represent Actors' Equity, the organisation of the people who are most vitally concerned in this matter, because they earn their livings as dancers, actors and singers. Musicians belong to a different organisation... (I) feel that Mr Goossens laid a little too much stress on music... It is very nice to imagine overseas visitors entering the harbour and saying 'Isn't that a magnificent theatre', but we must consider first the convenience of our citizens. They will come in both cars and public transport, so accessibility is of primary importance... It is most necessary for a theatre or even two theatres to be built for the purpose of drama... the second to seat about 1,100, which Sir Laurence Olivier has told me is the best size for drama...
>
> Mr Goossens suggested that the prime purpose of the theatre would be as a home for symphony concerts. Of course my organisation could not agree with that... My organisation feels that there should be a number of sub-committees. First there could be a finance sub-committee, consisting of bankers, underwriters, and business and insurance executives; a public committee of newspaper, advertising agency and publishing representatives; a building sub-committee of architects, master builders, and designers; an education sub-committee of leading educationists; a parliamentary committee with representatives from all parties to provide a vital link with the legislature, and a legal sub-committee. I feel that the committee suggested is a little too small and would like to see represented upon it the fields of ballet and drama.

Cahill interjected:

> I do not wish to curtail discussion, but we must be careful not to spend all our time discussing details before we have got a building. We have talked about the subject for years and we must now make a decision on how to get the building of an Opera House under way. Should we make an appeal to citizens to join in a combined effort?... (We) should now say, 'The Opera House will cost £1,000,000 or £1,500,000. Who shall we

interest in it? If we merely leave these matters to the Government they do not always go as well as they should... We are all anxious to make a start. Can someone tell us how we can get going quickly in the matter?

Following ideas from various individuals on finance, Goossens said:

Before I reluctantly depart, may I say that I am convinced that every one of our 16,000 subscribers will come up to scratch in this matter. I am now touching on the concert side, and not including the enormous public support for opera. However, I do not think people will help until they are told exactly where the Opera House will be. That, I think, is the prime consideration.

Warwick Fairfax of the *Sydney Morning Herald* had some ideas on finance:

... We wish to pull together in the matter and do what we can to help building it as quickly as we can. You have mentioned the very ticklish question of finance and the fact that it might cost £1,000,000 or £1,500,000. I do not doubt that it will. You mentioned, also, the possibility of its gaining public support. While no doubt there will be great public support for it, you might have trouble getting that much money... I think that if you expect to get hundreds of thousands of pounds (for) it from the public, you will have an uphill fight. Of course I might be wrong...

Then there followed a lengthy exchange of words between Mr W.L. Hume of the Parks and Playground Movement and Cahill. The Domain, east of Sydney Hospital, had been mentioned as a prospective site for the Opera House, but Hume said:

... I shall preface my remarks with the movement's slogan, 'Hands off the parks'. ... A site of at least five acres would be needed. It is quite impossible to get a vacant area of that size in Sydney, which is not built out. Only the parks will provide it. Are we to use our parks piecemeal for public buildings? In the past eyes have been cast towards the parks as a source from which building sites could be obtained without cost and no one of any account would be dispossessed or inconvenienced. It is simple to take the line of least resistance and filch five acres from a park...

Cahill interjected: 'I do not wish to interrupt, but I think you are getting a little beyond the scope of the meeting.'

Hume replied: .'If you are not willing to hear my submission I must seek the privilege of being represented on the committee...' Cahill retorted: 'I cannot accept that at the moment.' 'Then there will be no chance of representing our views? You have refused me permission to give them here...' came back Hume's frustrated response.

Cahill assured Hume the committee would hear his views '... but we must do things in an orderly way. At past meetings someone has always objected to this, that or the other and the meetings have got nowhere. We are going on with this scheme, and for that reason we must try to avoid dissension...' Then Mr Gale, of the Workers' Educational Association said:

> I congratulate the Premier and his government on this important decision. To make the venture politically possible one must avoid antagonising the country, and I believe it is essential to enlist the support of the country people... The Committee should consider how best to interest country dwellers... It should be made clear that this will not be a place for highbrows, but a place where people may enjoy themselves. It should certainly be licensed. Then with the introduction of 10 o'clock closing, opera patrons would be able to enjoy a drink at interval, in the continental manner... At present, one cannot attend a concert in the Sydney Town Hall unless one is a subscriber, and one cannot become a subscriber until a ticket holder dies... The committee might consider the possibility of setting aside blocks of seats at the Opera House for use by casual country visitors...

Following some further suggestions including some ideas of raising finance, Cahill closed the meeting: 'I thank everyone present for the interest shown in this matter. Many persons present are most important in their own vocations, and although they have not spoken, by their presence this morning they have shown their enthusiasm in this matter, and the Government is most appreciative. I am sure that this humble beginning today will result in something of real cultural value for our grand city.'

Moses remembered; 'The place was packed with music lovers and there was such enthusiasm.' When Cahill named the Committee, 'He hadn't discussed it with me, or my membership of it.'[43] 'I wasn't asked beforehand – I don't think anybody was. The Premier had obviously made up his mind.'[44] However, recalled Ashworth, 'there we were, just five men with no money allocated, no plans and nobody with any idea where the funds were to come from. All we had was just an instruction to build an Opera House.'[45] Haviland received a letter from the Under Secretary of the Premier's Department, '... The Premier is most anxious that the Committee should meet immediately and commence its functions at an early date, and I should be glad if you would kindly arrange accordingly.'[46] The Committee assembled for meetings once every few weeks at a convenient location such as the Under Secretary's Ante Room at the Department of Local Government or a room at Sydney University to discuss the Opera House. The immediate pressing problem was to find a site. Professor Ashworth invited his colleague at the University, George Molnar, to assist at the Opera House Committee meetings. Earlier that year, the City Council had been examining sites for an Opera House. Molnar recalled:

> They produced all sorts of silly sites. And the last, which was agreed on, was to be at the corner of Hyde Park and Oxford Street. Well it was an unbelievable site because they thought (the Opera House) should be in the centre of the city. But that site, it was agreed, and I went and talked to Dennis Winston[47] who was the first Professor of Town and Country Planning (at the university) and said look; 'that is an impossible site', and then he said, 'but if they think it is a good site, it's a good site.'[48] And I talked to the President of the Institute (of Architects), 'That is not the site, you can't have a site like that'. 'But it's all right', they used to tell us. And then I had an article. At that time John Pringle was editor of the Herald, and a good friend, and I used to have my articles on the second page of the Herald on the leader page.[49]

In the article, entitled 'Opera House Site is Too Small For a Worthy Building',[50] Molnar included a sketch which superimposed the Paris Opera and La Scala Milan on the proposed site, 'and not only was the site not suitable but the buildings themselves were much bigger than the site. It was an idiotic thing.'[51]

In the article, Molnar argued his case:

> The public buildings of Sydney are not very distinguished. Especially their settings are mean. (This does not apply to tram sheds, overhead railways and lavatories.) Unless a building happens to face by good fortune a park; it is most of the time only an accidental element in a streetscape instead of dominating its surroundings. Our opera house should not suffer from the same defect. The site of an opera house should be generous, to give scope to imaginative design. It should be a commanding site. It should take advantage of the natural beauty of its surroundings. It should be freely accessible, with plenty of parking space around it; but not on a street that carries heavy traffic all the time. The building built on it should represent the spiritual essence of the community that created it; or at least an ideal to be aimed at. The site at Liverpool Street is lacking all this.
>
> What does make an opera? Not just an auditorium to seat so many people. Not just a stage house to harbour all the mechanism of stage production. You go to the opera, dressed up, to dissociate yourself from

your everyday self; to live in a world of magic. This world of magic should be around you, as you enter the place; between intervals; and it should still surround you after the show. Expressed in terms of space it means foyers where you can wander around without feeling that you are just part of a mob; it means bars and coffee stands, where you can meet friends in comfort; it means restaurants, where you can dine leisurely before and after the performance. It means all the paraphernalia of gracious living. It means space. More than that, it means spaciousness.

The site at Liverpool Street is sufficient only for a picture theatre where you go because you've alighted from the Bondi tram by mistake, have two hours to spend and nowhere to go. But we must not let an opera house degenerate into a place where three dimensional talking pictures are faked by live actors. If we want to build an opera house let's have something that is first rate. Something that can stand comparison with anything built anywhere. Our opera house will be the newest in the world. With proper care in the choice of site and design it could be a prototype we can be proud of; and which will be studied all over the world.

By the choice of the site at Liverpool Street by our gracious civic fathers and experts we are condemned to have a second-rate picture theatre instead. The people of Sydney should not allow this to happen.[52]

Moses recalled that:

... various sites had been mentioned... Goossens said he thought the best site was Bennelong Point, and Stan Haviland, the Chairman, said: 'Well, that's a bus depot. The Department of Transport, they've got that. And apart from that', he said, 'the Harbour Board Trust have taken that side of the Quay for the overseas shipping terminal'... and... I think the Sydney Harbour Board Trust had already drawn up specifications for the terminal to be on that side. My own feeling was that this was an impossibility, that it was too far gone, that it was too late for us to be looking at a site like this, because if here you have got a Government Department in residence and another very important authority, the shipping authority already has its site for the overseas terminal there, so that it seemed to me to be that it was impracticable. But when we went down to see the Premier – I might say that he saw us quite frequently – it wouldn't be more than two or three months between visits. He would be saying: Now look, come down here, I want to talk to you and see how you're getting on – you know, what's holding you up – where are you? When we told him about this site, Mr Havilland pointed out of course the bus depot was there and they don't want to move. Mr Cahill said 'Oh, I can't see any reason why they shouldn't – we can move them over the other side of Pyrmont where the railway goods yard is... They can move there' he says, 'that's all right.' No hesitation – he was going to move them there! Then there was this question of the overseas terminal. 'Oh well, they can go on the other side of the Quay' – just like that. He was a man who, once he got his mind made up, right here was a site he could visualise. Here was some exciting place. We felt so keenly about it, but here were these impossible obstacles to be overcome, but to him they weren't obstacles, these are things – 'right, we'll fix that', and he did. The thing is, the Harbour Board Trust, they had to start planning for the shipping terminal to be on the other side of Circular Quay.

So, he was very determined, very forceful. There was no arrogance about him – I've got to say this he was not – when I say he was forceful – but he was determined in his quiet way, and the things we saw as obstacles, he saw that those were something that he could get rid of. And so he went ahead, and with his support we got the site we wanted. No one else gave us any support at all – it was the Premier. He had to argue with his own Minister for Transport and the Harbour Board Trust. These were bodies that came under the Premier himself – he had to convince them – they've got to change their minds. [53]

On 17th May 1955 the New South Wales Cabinet announced Bennelong Point would be the site for the Opera House. Out of the 21 sites considered the committee was looking for one that had a 'setting offering full rein to architectural expression; and at a location where it would not dominate or be dominated by other buildings… consideration of these factors led the committee to the unanimous conclusion that Bennelong Point is the outstanding suitable site. With the removal of the tram depot, sufficient area will be available for the building, its approach roads, surrounding garden area and parking space for about 200 cars… Above all the site being on a predominant headland of Sydney's magnificent waterway will provide a setting unique in the world for a building of such monumental character as an opera house.'[54] In the opinion of a *Herald* reporter the next morning:

By its choice of Bennelong Point as the site for Sydney's Opera House State Cabinet performed an act of rare imagination. No finer site for a great theatre exists in the world. Mr Cahill deserves credit for his energy in a matter where he may think that there are few votes to be gained and possibly some to be lost; but Sydney-siders will remember him with gratitude if in a few years time they can share with the citizens of Stockholm and Venice the civilized pleasure of hearing great music in a perfect setting, beside the waters of their own harbour.

A second early important decision was whether the architectural competition for the Opera House should be national or international.

At the Opera House Committee meeting on 21st December 1954, 'The Committee of the N.S.W. Chapter of the Royal Australian Institute of Architects suggested the competition should be national rather than international.'[55]

Molnar recalled '... and it was Bunning, miserable Bunning,[56] who was all for just to have an Australian competition. That was already a step down because he thought it should be given to Bunning, not to anybody else. And then again I wrote articles saying well if Australians think they're getting the best Opera House in the world, because they're just as good as anybody else overseas, then what's wrong with asking them (the overseas architects) to compete.'[57] Molnar's article, which covered half a page, appeared in the *Sydney Morning Herald*:

> The site of Sydney's opera house has been decided on. It is one of the most beautiful sites in the world. The next step is to find out what we want to put on it, and how to get it.
>
> A competition has three main elements: The program (that is, the requirements); the assessors, and the competitors. To get a good result all three have to be of the best possible quality. It does not matter how good the competitors are if the program is too vague or too precise, or if the assessors lack courage and imagination...
>
> The architect, of course, gives the three-dimensional interpretation of the director's and public's wants. Through his knowledge of materials and construction, he provides the producer with smooth mechanism for staging shows and good acoustics for the hearing of music. Through his understanding of forms, proportions, colours and textures, he will create the right emotional climate for the public. And, if he can achieve these two things, no controversy between modern and traditional architecture will arise. He will be creating good architecture which is timeless.
>
> So a committee will have to be set up, representing the musical director, the producer, the public and the architect, to work out the program for the competition. It will be a hard task. We have not had many past competitions compared with Switzerland, where there is one nearly every week. We have not developed the right technique. There has been something wrong with every big competition held recently...
>
> The Olympic Stadium program[58] set the axis of the stadium running the wrong way and, by insisting on the observance of existing building regulations (later amended), faced the competitors with the problem that the total length of exits prescribed was greater than the perimeter of the stadium. The Olympic Swimming Pool competition called for an indoor 10-metre diving tower (left out in the final design), and by doing so

increased unnecessarily the height of the hall to nearly 60 feet.

Apart from obvious mistakes caused by lack of information or time, most of the harm is done by careless wording. New ideas are always on the brink of disqualification. The most common offence in phrasing the program is to give a solution instead of the intention or aim to be achieved. Aims should be clearly stated, but ways of achieving them should be left to the competitor.

So much for the program. Now for the assessors. Every competition is as good as its jury. In our case, and that applies to the competitors, too, we have a great disadvantage. No theatres have been built in Australia for a long time, and the existing ones are not sufficiently distinguished to be worthy of study. So we lack people who have first-hand experience and can talk authoritatively on theatre-design. We have to have somebody from overseas to help up. It was suggested that Professor R.H. Martin, designer of the Festival Hall in London, should be approached. He certainly would be a very good choice, even if some people do not agree with his facades. Failing him, there are other prominent architects with a background of theatre design, whom we could ask. But ask we must...

Before discussing the competitors, let us state our aim: We want for Sydney the best Opera House that can be built. This must mean an international competition. Apart from getting the best brains to ponder our problems, the world-wide interest centre on the Opera House of Sydney will be a good advertisement for Australia...

There is a strong feeling among some of our architects that the competition should be restricted to Australian architects only. They feel that the standard of the profession is sufficiently high to be able to do the job. But that is not the same as getting the best the world can offer. If we feel that we can compete on equal terms with the best architects from overseas, surely that is no reason to exclude them from the competition. And how much greater the glory if an Australian architect wins. We have some definite advantages over our overseas colleagues. We know the site, our building conditions, our ways of living better than they do. We have at least two months more time to prepare our design. On the other hand architects from overseas understand more about the atmosphere and requirements of the theatre. For many of them, designing and building theatres is part of their everyday practice...

A competition can be public or by invitation. A public competition means more entries, more ideas, a chance for unknown young architects to be discovered. On the other hand, it means more work for the assessors, and a chance that not everybody you would like will take part in it. A competition by invitation, on the other hand, invites only those architects whom you expect to have the best answer to your problem... The number of competitors is small – 10 at most – and of course everybody has to be paid a fee. The winner usually gets the job. Certainly if, for a total fee of £10,000 we could get the services of, say Aalto, Saarinnen, Martin, Breuer, Nervi, Gropius,[59] and a corresponding number of Australian architects, we could be sure of a good result. Yet the magnificent, lonely ideas may still escape. And of course there will be the difficulty of whom to choose, especially in Australia...

In this article I have used the term 'Opera House' to mean the complex edifice which is to be used as a concert hall and a theatre as well as an opera house... The fact is that the building, in reality, will be a centre of all musical and dramatic arts. We have to find a new name before the Opera House will take root. Has anybody got a suggestion?

Meanwhile, the Opera House Committee were fleshing out the competition guidelines. At their second meeting, on 21st December 1954, attended by Haviland, Ashworth, Hendy, Goossens and Thomson, they agreed after general discussion that 'The building should include two halls, one to seat 3,500 persons, the other to seat 1,200...'[60] Tabled at the meeting was a report by the Committee of the NSW Chapter of the RAIA suggesting provision be made for the following activities:

1. Symphony Concerts
2. Choral Festivals
3. Operatic Performance
4. Ballet
5. Drama
6. Small orchestral concerts, i.e.chamber music,etc.

The (architectural) committee would like to point out the great difficulty in creating a satisfactory auditorium for more than one purpose: this will have to be done in the present case, but it would be impossible, however, to combine an appropriately intimate theatre for serious drama with the large auditorium necessary for symphony concerts.

This means, therefore, that there should be two major halls; one a large hall to seat approximately 3,000 persons and a smaller one to seat not more than twelve hundred persons. Although we appreciate that it would be possible to envisage a larger hall than the above for symphony concerts alone, we consider this would be undesirable in view of the other usages to which the hall is to be put.[61]

Meanwhile at the seventh meeting of the Opera House Committee held on 26th July 1955,

... The Chairman extended to Sir Eugene Goossens on behalf of the Committee congratulations upon the honour recently conferred upon him by Her Majesty the Queen.[62]

Method of deciding design:

... Mr Hendy favoured an open competition and suggested that the length of time before possession was obtained of the site at Benelong Point might be an important time factor.

Sir Eugene Goossens... expressed the view that the competition should preferably be international.

Colonel Moses said that he was in favour of an international competition. This would attract world-wide attention.[63]

Time required for deciding design and commencing work:

Colonel Moses suggested that it should not take more than three months to decide the conditions governing a competition and the winning design might be decided in approximately twelve months...

Professor Ashworth said that it would take about two months for the assessors to examine the plans submitted. He anticipated perhaps 150 competitors.

... Sir Eugene Goossens considered that the prizes for the winning designs should be such as to attract world-wide attention, and suggested a first prize of £5,000; a second prize of £2,000; and a third prize of £1,000.

Assessors to select winning designs:

Professor Ashworth expressed the view that there should not be more than five assessors, preferably three. The three assessors should be one from Australia and two from overseas. A majority of overseas assessors would inspire confidence in competitors from overseas.[64]

The Chairman asked members if they had any ideas respecting the proposed Australian assessor and, in reply to a suggestion by members, Professor Ashworth indicated that he would be prepared to act in that capacity.

Colonel Moses suggested that the assessors co-opt Sir Eugene Goossens for advice respecting the functional aspects of the Opera Auditorium and Mr Hugh Hunt... in respect of the other auditorium. The assessors from overseas should be one of a modern outlook and one of a conservative outlook.

At the Opera House Committee's next meeting, on 4th August 1955, regarding the number of assessors.

Mr Hendy questioned the wisdom of appointing two assessors from overseas and one only from Australia... He considered that there might be a possibility of the overseas assessors over-riding the local assessors.

The Committee agreed that there should be four assessors, two from Australia and two from overseas, and, in the event of the assessors being equally divided in the choice of a winning design, that the chairman of assessors should have a casting vote... The Committee agreed on Cobden

Parkes as the second Australian assessor...

The RAIA had submitted a list of overseas architects who, in the opinion of the association 'would be suitable for appointment as the assessors from overseas'.

> ... The (Opera House) Committee agreed that the following two gentlemen should be invited... From the United Kingdom, Dr J. L. Martin, M.A., P.H.D., F.R.I.B.A., Chief Architect to the London County Council.[65] And from the U.S.A. Eero Saarinen, M.A.I.A...
>
> In the event of either of these gentlemen being unavailable for appointment the following two gentlemen should be invited respectively: They were Basil Spence from the U.K. and Pietro Belluschi from the U.S.A.

To assist in the drafting of the conditions, the RAIA nominated two of their members, Kelvin Robertson and W.R. (Bill) Laurie, to be paid, concurred the (O.H.) Committee, 'a consulting fee of 50 guineas each in lieu of an hourly rate'. To cover assessors' fees,[66] prizes and costs, the Committee asked the government for £14,500,[67] which, after duly receiving ministerial approval, was advanced by the Treasury, from their 'Advance Account for competition to determine design of the proposed Opera House.'[68]

Saarinen,[69] Martin and Parkes accepted their invitations to judge the Opera House Competition, clearing the way for the production of the official 'Conditions of Competition' a 25-page softback booklet measuring 8 inches high by 11 inches wide with a beige cover, which included ten uninspiring pictures of the site,[70] two from the air, five from the ground and three from the water.

The 'Promoters', the government of New South Wales, invited architects 'in any country in the world' to submit designs for 'a proposed National Opera House, to be erected on Bennelong Point.' Intending competitors needed to register their name and address with the secretary of the Opera House Committee not later than 15th March 1956. This register was kept confidential until after the judging was completed in early 1957. By paying a £10.00 deposit architects received a copy of the conditions and if they entered a bona fide design this was refunded. Intending competitors who required any further information than was outlined in the competition conditions were asked to forward questions anonymously before 15th May, and a copy of all the questions received and the answers would be airmailed to all registered competitors by 1st June.

The assessors were named in the conditions,[71] and the prizes stipulated; 1st £5,000; 2nd £2,000 and 3rd £1,000. The drawings required included one to show 'principles which would be followed in obtaining satisfactory acoustics in the auditorium', one to include sight lines, and a perspective, all of which should have a title placed at the bottom 'National Opera House, Sydney, Australia'. Regarding cost '... the Assessors feel that the cost of the building cannot be limited to a specific amount... although... funds are obviously not unlimited... extravagance cannot be entertained.' Drawings had to be airmailed to the Secretary on or before the 3rd December 1956, unsigned, but with an opaque envelope marked 'Identification' containing the name and address of the competitor and a tracing of part of the ground plan for identification, 'attached to the external face of the inner package, so that it may be detached as soon as the outside wrapping... is taken away and before the inner package is passed to the Assessors. ... The Secretary will receive the packages and each package will be numbered and the same number will be placed on each drawing... and the envelope containing the identification...' The envelope '... will be kept in safe custody under the personal control of the Secretary and will not be opened until after the Assessors have made their award.'

'The designs, except the design placed first, will be posted to competitors... within four weeks after the closing date of the competition.

The design placed first and any copyright thereto will become the sole property of the Promoters. The Promoters reserve the right to illustrate or publish any of the designs submitted... The author of the design placed first shall be employed as Architect of the work, unless the Assessors shall be satisfied that there is some reasonable objection to such employment, in which case the author of the design placed first shall be required to enter into an agreement with some other Architect selected by him, and approved by the Assessors, for the joint design and supervision of the work... Should the author of the work placed first, fail to enter into such agreement within a reasonable time to be determined by the Assessors, he shall forgo all right of employment as Architect for the work, and the Promoters shall be at liberty to make other arrangements for the carrying out of his design... the winning Architect(s) if necessary... will be required to submit to the Assessors proof of the adequacy of his... qualifications to organise and carry out the commission.

If, before any further drawings are made, and within two years of the publication of the award, the Promoters shall not proceed with the building, (the winner will receive)... the sum sufficient to increase the first premium to 1 per cent of the cost of executing the building as estimated by the Assessors.

... In the event of any dispute arising... then the Promoters will seek the advice and assistance of the Union Internationale des Architectes in the settling of such dispute.'

The conditions included a description of the site, Sydney's average annual rainfall, '46.93 inches' and daily hours of sunshine, 'between 7.6 in November and 5.3 in June', maximum and minimum recorded temperatures 'Lowest... 35.7°F... maximum reading 113.6°F.' '... Snow and frost conditions may be disregarded' and the highest wind gust ever recorded was '95 m.p.h.'.

The 'Building Requirements' were prefaced with a notation that 'competitors should appreciate that it is unlikely that the winning scheme would be erected without variation and that in consequence the Promoters seek a sound basic scheme by a competent Architect.' Besides 'separate bars for theatre patrons within the building,... a restaurant to seat approximately 250 people', a broadcasting room, rehearsal rooms and 'a large organ for use in the main hall', '... mandatory requirements are limited and are listed below in Items 1 and 2 in order of their importance.'

1. There shall be two halls – one large hall and one small hall. The large hall should seat between 3,000 – 3,500 persons. The small hall should seat approximately 1,200 persons.

  The large hall to be designed for use for the following purposes:-
  (a) Symphony Concerts (including organ music and soloists).
  (b) Large-scale Opera.
  (c) Ballet and Dance.
  (d) Choral.
  (e) Pageants and Mass Meetings.

2. The small hall to be designed for use for the following purposes:-
  (a) Dramatic Presentations.
  (b) Intimate Opera.
  (c) Chamber Music.
  (d) Concerts and Recitals.
  (e) Lectures.

The requirements under 1 and 2 above, have been listed in order of priority with respect to the attention which should be given to their specialised building needs.

It is expected that ideal conditions will be provided as far as possible acoustically, visually and in connection with stage and orchestral facilities. Compromises which will prejudice the entirely satisfactory performance of a function with a higher priority in the above list should not be made.[72]

The competition, recalled Moses: 'was advertised in every suitable paper in all the major cities of Europe and North America, the U.K. and also, I am quite sure, we included South America and Africa and Asia.[73] In London the RAIA organised an exhibition in April 1956 and devoted a panel to the Opera House project.[74] Receipts were issued for the £10 deposits as the requests for a set of competition conditions came in. The first receipts, issued in December 1955, went to architects with addresses in Sydney.[75]

At this time, Goossens' name had dropped off the attendance list on the minutes of the Opera House Committee meetings.

At the end of 1955 he had left Sydney to make his customary appearances as a guest conductor with orchestras in Europe, and to prepare a report on the Hamburg and Vienna State Opera Houses for the NSW government which was later forwarded by the Opera House Committee to the competition assessors. He was due back in Sydney in March, and Moses remembered:

… I had a phone call from somebody I don't know – a man – who rang me up to say: 'Look, If I were you, send a cable to Goossens, and tell him to be careful what he brings back in his luggage.' Now I ignored it – this was just, I suppose, a few days before he left to come back. I ignored it, because, I thought he meant in a sense, that he was going to smuggle something in. Now, this to my mind – the idea of Goossens trying to smuggle something in that was illegal, was something that I couldn't believe. It's like stealing – you know that the man's incapable of doing it. To me it would have been an insult for me to ring him up and say, 'Now look, somebody warned me that you want to be careful what you bring in the luggage', and I have a feeling he would have been furious with me for even suggesting it. I did nothing about it .

Goossens landed in Sydney by Qantas Constellation at 8 o'clock on the morning of 9th March and had his baggage searched by customs officers on arrival, and according to the next day's *Sydney Morning Herald*:

Vice squad detectives yesterday interviewed the conductor of the Sydney Symphony Orchestra, Sir Eugene Goossens, for more than six hours, on his arrival in Sydney from London. Detectives and customs officials examined Sir Eugene's luggage.

Police said later that they had taken possession of between 1,000 and 1,100 photographs and several rubber masks... Detectives went to the overseas terminal at Mascot airport when Sir Eugene arrived... The detectives met... (him) as he entered the Customs Office. When he had passed through Customs he went with them to a nearby room... [76]

The police brought a case against Goossens which went to trial on 22nd March. Goossens was found guilty in his absence of importing 1,100 'indecent items' and fined £100, the maximum penalty. Moses' reaction was:

One of complete disbelief. You see, I knew him very well, and to me, he was a highly sensitive, very thoughtful, a very – let me use a word which one can use truthfully about him – he was a gentleman. I gave evidence in court, and I think I was the only one that did, for him; gave evidence that we had become friends, and that at any time when I was away, that if he had asked my wife to go out for lunch or dinner, I would have been quite happy, because he was a man for whom I had the greatest respect and real affection, and I found this impossible to believe, that this could be true. [77]

Goossens decided to leave Australia. His daughter, Renée and wife Marjorie were in Switzerland where Renée had just entered a convent. His daughter Sidonie had recently married a local musician John Young, and at the time the scandal broke the couple were performing in a production of *Kismet* in Melbourne. Between performances they 'dashed to and from Sydney... to help Sir Eugene with the sad business of packing up.' [78] John Young drove Goossens to Sydney airport on 26th May 1956 to catch a KLM flight for Rome. Though his baggage, tickets and papers were all marked in his own name, KLM had entered his name as 'Mr E. Gray' on the passenger list 'to try to keep away one or two sections of the press.' [79] He left Australia saying, 'I will continue my life work for music elsewhere.' [80]

Two days after he left, Goossens' solicitor, Mervyn Finlay issued a statement on his behalf to the *Daily Telegraph*.

... I regretfully bid farewell to Australia, where I have spent so many years in making my modest contribution to its musical development... It is my misfortune that I allowed myself to be used to bring prohibited matter into this country as a result of persistent menaces I could not ignore, involving others. [81]

The competition proceeded without any further input from Goossens, his name did not appear again on the attendance roll of the minutes of Opera House Committee meetings, and no explanation appeared in the minutes regarding his absence.

Nine hundred and thirty-three architects or groups of architects registered for the competition and 721 paid £10 to receive a copy of the conditions. Seventy-nine intending competitors of those 721 asked 470 questions about the terms of the competition, and a copy of the questions with the 470 answers were airmailed in June 1956 to architects who had paid their deposits.[82] Two hundred and seventeen designs were entered. From the £5,000 provided in funds from forfeited deposits, Stan Haviland said that '… there will be no saving… when all the administrative expenses of the competition have been met. Almost £3,000 has been spent on postage alone.'[83] Entries came in from 27 countries, including 61 from Australia, 53 from the UK, 24 from the USA, 8 from South Africa and two from Denmark; Czechoslovakia, French Morocco, Israel and Cyprus sent one entry each.[84]

The entries, stacked in a room at the Department of Local Government, in packages ranging in size from a foot square to a 'mammoth construction in hardboard 8 ft long by 4 ft wide and several inches thick and a steel drum 2 ft in diameter and 3 feet long', took up so much space that if the worst came to the worst '… they could just about build the Opera House out of the packing cases.'[85] Although the State government had insured each set of plans for £400, members of the Committee thought that some of them, containing up to 30 detailed sheets of drawings, represented four months work and were worth £1,500.[86]

Stan Haviland and Professor Ashworth met Martin when he arrived in Sydney from San Francisco on board a Qantas jet on 7th January 1957.[87] Ashworth, Parkes and Martin started the judging that day, without Saarinen, who was late, and discarded '… at least 100 of the 250 designs in one day…'[88] The assessing took place in a gallery at the Art Gallery of NSW, which had been especially cleared of paintings to allow room to display plans on the walls.[89]

On 9th January an article by Walter Bunning on Saarinen was published in the *Sydney Morning Herald*:

(Saarinen is)… known for his concern with the local environment in his buildings, his design for the U.S. Embassy in London reflected the appearance of the nearby Georgian Town houses. He likes to suit each building to its setting and surroundings in a way which denies any dogmatic rules of design... He is the one leading architect who is always likely to surprise with his unique solution to a problem.

Bunning had recently visited the Massachusetts Institute of Technology, located on the bank of the Charles River, facing the Boston skyline, where the old school buildings '... classical edifices crowned with domes' were complemented by Saarinen's new Kresge Auditorium at the Institute, in which '... the most up-to-date thin shell concrete structure was used with the weight of the whole dome supported from the ground on three slender pin-points. The dome has been slashed to a triangular plan shape, presenting a graceful arch filled with glass to each of the three sides.' [90]

Saarinen arrived in Sydney halfway through the second day of judging on 11th January. [91] On his arrival, Parkes took him to lunch at the kiosk in the park across the road from the Art Gallery, then walked with him the half mile or so through the Domain to Mrs Macquarie's Chair, where there was a view across Farm Cove to Fort Macquarie and the Harbour Bridge. Parkes recalled; 'as we strolled along I tried to point out Government House and a few other landmarks, but Saarinen said: "No, never mind that! Let's not think about anything but the Opera House site – where is it?"' When it was pointed out, Saarinen delved into one of his pockets, pulled out an old envelope and made a sketch on it with a pencil of Bennelong Point with a vague outline of a building standing on it.'[92] Saarinen later said to the press that Bennelong Point was '... perhaps one of the best sites for the purpose in the world... absolutely marvellous. One of its great merits is the absence of surrounding buildings leaving the architect free to break all the traditions of previous buildings in Sydney if he wished to.'[93] 'Sydney will undoubtedly have an Opera House which will be known throughout the world.'[94]

On the evening of the 16th, at a Civic Reception held for the judges, Saarinen said, 'The Harbour Bridge would play an important part in the choosing of the winning design. The bridge provided a backdrop and the Opera House would have to be chosen with this in mind.'[95] And Martin said 'There will of course be controversy over our selection – in aesthetic matters like this, everybody has his own ideas of what he likes... I think there is bound to be criticism. It is very important there should be. I hope a vigorous piece of modern architecture will be produced to please, not only those of our generation, but those of the future.'[96] On 19th January, the *Sydney Morning Herald* ran a story entitled 'Judges Choose Design – But It's Hush-hush.'

Someone among the 220 architects from all over the world who submitted designs for Sydney's National Opera House yesterday became richer by £5,000 and a reputation for having created what will be a world-class opera building. Until Tuesday, January 29, however, when the Premier, Mr Cahill, will name him, neither the man nor the public will know what design has been selected.

The four judges handed their report and their selection yesterday to Mr S. Havilland, Chairman of the Opera House Committee, in a sealed envelope, at an informal ceremony in the Lands Department Building. Two of the four, Mr Eero Saarinen, a leading American architect, and Professor Leslie Martin, Professor of Architecture at Cambridge University, both of whom came to Sydney to participate in the judging, are returning to their homes this weekend. They took the opportunity yesterday, with their fellow adjudicators, Mr Cobden Parkes, the N.S.W. Government Architect, and Professor H. Ashworth, Dean of the Faculty of Architecture at Sydney University, of discussing the judges' choice. The discussion was in general terms, of course. The winning design is top secret, and the winner could not yet be identified even by clues.

'The prototype of most Opera Houses in the world to-day was built 70 or 80 years ago'. said Mr Saarinen. 'The one we've selected won't look anything like these.' Rapidly he drew a pencil sketch of a building which looked like a Town Hall-cum-Cathedral. Professor Martin added: 'Predominantly, most of the competitors tried to solve the problem in to-day's techniques. 'We looked for a monumental work. After all, you don't go to the opera very often. It is a bit of an occasion, and it's nice to go to a magnificent building. That's why we kept in mind that the Opera House design had to be an imaginative thing!' 'There'll be criticism, of course', Mr Saarinen warned. 'But you can't do a good piece of work without criticism.'

The designs submitted were numbered and the key to their authors has been in the possession of the Opera Committee's chairman. It was not known to the judges until they were told yesterday – in camera – to whom they had awarded first, second and third prizes.

In all, the judges took 10 days to make their choice. 'Short in days, perhaps, but we made up for it in hours', said Mr Cobden Parkes. 'It was almost a night and day job except a Sunday morning we took off to go to Palm Beach', Mr Saarinen said. 'But a most pleasant job to work on. The judging has been most cordial. And you can say that our choices were unanimous. Absolutely unanimous.'

The modus operandi of the judging, explained Professor Martin, was that each of the entries was looked at very carefully. At each viewing session, a number of entries were eliminated. Some of the 'possibles' were put on one side, and then reviewed again a day or two later. Towards the end, about 50 entries were still 'in the running.' 'We dissected the final 50 entries very carefully', Professor Martin said. ' We looked over all the detailed areas, for instance, to see whether some were wasteful. This was really a most searching analysis.' Mr Saarinen said: 'Usually an international contest of this kind can be judged in three or four days. The requirements of your Opera House competition called for such detail that it has taken a lot longer to judge.'[97]

'Was there anything the judges could say about the new winning design. Just a little appetiser, as it were, for the official announcement?'

'The architect has made use of quite new materials, I think we can say' Professor Martin said. 'it is a building which will have to stand for a number of years. And it is the sort of design which will be appreciated in the future. I'm afraid that's all I, can say', he added apologetically. 'Besides his prize money, the successful architect will supervise the building of the Opera House at Australian professional fees. The greatest reward for the winning architect will be to build a significant building', said Mr Saarinen. 'The prize money is not large, and in dollars and cents the reward for designing your Opera House is no different to any other building. But an architect will be very happy to get this job. It is the significance which counts.'

Finally it was the big day; and the press were tipping a win for Walter Bunning.

Perhaps it is just as well that... (the winner) was at home... while his success in the National Opera House contest was being announced at the Art Gallery yesterday afternoon. At least he avoided the suspense which many Sydney entrants endured for 30 long minutes before the final announcement was made.

'One of the great charms of an architectural competition', said the chairman of the Art Gallery, Mr B.J. Waterhouse, as he opened the ceremony at 3 p.m. 'is that one never knows at all what the result will be. I remember another architectural competition, many years ago, when all the Gothicist dons of England competed for the Liverpool Cathedral. All and sundry were sure that a certain prominent don who had done a great deal of important work would win. But it proved to be Sir Giles Gibert Scott, then aged 21. So we never know. We might find some young man here who has produced something of real architectural value. Hence the excitement.'

There was certainly excitement. The audience, seated in front of the official dais or standing behind the rope enclosure, began whispering as

Mr Waterhouse resumed his seat. Did he have any advance information? Was he hinting that a local architect had won? It seemed unlikely, since not even the assessors knew the names of the architects who had submitted the 217 numbered designs. But you never know.

Reporters, seated at a table below a florid Italian painting of 'The Five Senses', were listening with half an ear and scanning the assessors' report which had already been released. The report was not much help, though it described the winning design ('The white sail-like forms of the shell vaults relate as naturally to the harbour as the sails of its yachts...'), but it mentioned no names. 'There are two French words on the plan', said a photographer who had been photographing the winning design, 'if that means anything.' One of the words was 'nord' instead of 'north.' Was the winner a Frenchman? Well at least a Continental?

The chairman of the Opera House Committee, Mr S. Havilland, began describing how the four assessors had worked their way through the 2,000 drawings which had been examined. At 3.15 p.m., he handed to the Premier, Mr Cahill, two drawings of the winning design which had been prepared by one of the assessors, Mr Eero Saarinen.[98] He had not presented them earlier, he explained, because they each bore the winner's name. A movie camera started purring behind a battery of arc lights, and a Press photographer hurried across the floor. Mr Havilland handed the Premier an envelope containing the winner's name and said: 'It is interesting to know that at all stages of the adjudication, the assessors amused themselves by trying to guess the nationality of the winner – and they were all wrong!'

Well, who did win? But the Premier was in no hurry to open the envelope. He stressed the national importance of an opera house and expressed his confidence that everyone once having seen the winning design, would think the prize money well spent. At 3.22 p.m., the Premier paused significantly, and a whisper ran through the audience. But not yet. 'Before announcing the name of the person who submitted the winning design', said Mr Cahill, 'I shall run the risk of trying your patience by making one or two general remarks...' At 3.27 p.m, he paused again. 'Now, ladies and gentlemen', said the Premier. Another whisper stirred the crowd. 'Before I announce the prize... If I can just for a moment take your minds back to a meeting two years ago in the Library building when it was decided that this project should be put in hand...'

By 3.29 p.m., there was no delaying it any further. Mr Cahill opened his envelope and announced: 'The design awarded the first premium is Scheme Number 218; the design awarded second premium is Scheme Number 28; and the design awarded third premium is Scheme Number 62.' Mr Cahill hesitated. 'Those are the numbers.' he said. 'I'm afraid I haven't the names. Whether somebody will tell us...' The audience was seething. Mr Havilland stepped forward quickly and found another document in Mr Cahill's envelope. 'Design awarded first premium' read Mr Cahill, 'is Scheme Number 218,[99] submitted by Jorn Utzon – the correct pronunciation is Yawn Ootson – of Hellesbalk, Denmark, 38 years of age.'[100]

CHAPTER 4

ENTER UTZON

After the competition winner was announced, newspaper reporters made an immediate frantic search for Utzon's phone number in Denmark. It was early in the morning on 29th January local time when the first reporter got through to Utzon's home. Utzon's ten-year-old daughter Lin picked up the phone and said her father was out. He was on his morning walk in the forest. Lin raced after him on her bicycle, told him that he had won the competition for the Sydney Opera House, then threw her old bicycle in the ditch and told her father that now he did not have any excuse for not giving her the white horse she wanted.[1] Later, after Utzon returned home, the *Sydney Morning Herald* spoke to him personally:

> Mr Joern Utzon, the Dane who won the Sydney Opera House competition, is overjoyed by his success. He told 'The Sydney Morning Herald' in a radio telephone interview last night that he hopes to settle in Sydney before the construction of the Opera House begins... Mr Utzon, who spoke from his home in Hellebaek, Denmark, said:-
>
> 'So far the Opera House committee has not contacted me, but I am expecting a cable at any moment. It depends on what they can advise me how soon I migrate.' But I shouldn't think I would have a great deal of trouble getting a good position in Australia now, do you? It must be a wonderful country with plenty of what we have not been getting lately-sunshine.'
>
> Who is He?
>
> Mr Utzon is 38, and has been a member of the Danish Institute of Architects since 1942. He is in partnership with two brothers.
>
> 'We have three children', he said, 'a boy aged 12, a girl aged 10, and our baby son, who was born on New Year's Day this year. This news from Australia is almost as good as the news of his arrival.
>
> My wife is just as thrilled about the win as I am. I have won 20 prizes for architectural design before, in Denmark and Sweden, including six first prizes. But this is far and away the most important.'
>
> How Long Did He Spend on the Design?
>
> 'I spent about six months from May to December 1956, whenever I could get time off from my other work.
>
> I studied hundreds of pictures, photographs, and maps of the site. It is a very lovely position for an Opera House and most inspiring to any

architect. But from this distance it naturally took a great feat of the imagination to "see" it in its setting.'[2]

The *Daily Telegraph* reporter Emery Barcs got through the same evening:

Jorn Utzon, Danish winner of the Opera House competition, was celebrating with champagne when I spoke to him by radio-telephone last night. Through the phone I could hear the excited chatter of his wife, three children and friends. Utzon is evidently a great Viking of a fellow – 6 ft 9 in tall, with a tremendous laugh.

'Oh, I'm a big, very big fellow', he said.

He was speaking from his home in Hellebaek, a Danish seaside resort. It is near Elsinore Castle, the scene of Shakespeare's 'Hamlet.'

'How do you feel about your success?' I asked him.

'I'm terribly happy', he said in fluent English but with a rather heavy accent.

'You sound as if you were celebrating.' I said.

'Naturally', he shouted. 'We are celebrating. There is plenty of champagne.'

'What inspired your design?'

'The beautiful pictures I have received of Sydney Harbour – all sorts of pictures, not only of Bennelong Point, but also of the whole Harbour. It must be one of the most beautiful spots in the world. I have dreamt of it so much. Then came the idea with that roof. Do they like it in Sydney?'

I assured him that Sydney had been terribly excited about his design.

'Where did you study?' I asked.

'In Copenhagen.'

'What have you mainly built so far?'

'I have built everything – small houses, big houses, factories. But this is my first opera house.'

I asked what he would do with the prizemoney... A great boom of laughter came 12,000 miles through the phone.

'Of course I need all that money to come to Australia, and I'll bring the whole family. It's a long way and it will cost a lot of money. But I hope the fare won't take the lot of it. What do you think?'

I assured him that he would have some pocket-money left out of his £5,000.

I asked whether he would like to come to Sydney for good.

'Not sure, depends...' he said. 'At least, I mean I want to go for a long time. I mean it depends whether they want me permanently. An opera house is not built in a day, you know – not even in Australia. Au revoir', Mr Utzon shouted into the phone.

'Thanks for ringing me. It was a nice thing to do. We are very, very happy... Au revoir... in Sydney...' And he laughed again.[3]

Utzon was the son of an English-educated Danish naval architect, who later became a well-known yacht designer with many successful racing yachts to his credit. Born in Copenhagen, where he also later graduated in architecture, Utzon was brought up in Elsinore (local spelling Helsingor), where his father was at the time manager of the local shipyard.[4] On his twenty-second birthday on 9th April 1940 Denmark was invaded by Germany. Utzon stayed on at university to complete his degree in 1942, then crossed to Sweden for a time to join 'Danforce' the Danish brigade, a resistance group to the German occupation, and to work as an architect in Stockholm. During the following years Utzon was frequently on the move, advancing his studies in architecture in Copenhagen, working for the great Finnish architect Alvar Aalto in Helsinki, living for a time in Morocco, and travelling to Paris and meeting Le Corbusier and the French sculptor Henri Laurens who he credited with teaching him how to express forms in space and to express suspension and ascension. In 1949 Utzon won a travelling scholarship to Mexico and the USA where he met Mies van der Rohe and attended lectures by Frank Lloyd Wright. At the time of the Opera House Competition he was settled with his family at Hellebaek,[5] a village on the coast three miles north west of Helsingor, 'in a house he had designed himself in a grove of fir trees... a long flat-roofed home of brick and glass, open-planned with three fibreglass domed skylights in the roof and a heated cement floor.' Since 1952 he had been working in partnership on various projects with Erik and Henry Andersson, Swedish brothers who worked from an office at Helsingborg in Sweden. Besides individual houses and contributions to large projects, apparently the only job that Utzon had seen through from conception to completion was an estate of 63 town houses on the outskirts of Helsingor completed in 1956.[6] His reputation in architectural circles was of 'A young architectural thinker, dabbling in numerous competitions and concerned not so much about meeting practical terms and conditions as with solving aesthetic problems.'[7]

Along with a flair for design, Utzon had a quite remarkable ability to visualise ideas, not only in his own mind, but by the application of his personality, charm, and choice of words, in the minds of other people also. A technical draftswoman, Jytte Beauman, recalled:

One of the great qualities about him is as a friend he would tell you at times what you should do with certain things in your life. I remember him once telling me standing up at Church Point that I should buy a yacht, and a big one at that, and I said 'that's ridiculous, I haven't got the money.' He said 'Money; where does money come into it. Can't you imagine yourself...' and within ten minutes he had me imagining myself, sailing away to the South islands, and beautiful things. And he could do this with people. He could create moods for them. And it wasn't until half an hour after he'd left you you suddenly came back to earth and realized that it was just his marvellous way of creating that even came out just as a person.[8]

Arup engineer Bob Kelman recalled that during construction of the Opera House podium:

at that stage, you know, the co-operation between himself and us was absolutely marvellous – he was terrific. And we had a sort of joke that he would suggest the most outrageous things, and one of us would go over to Denmark to try and... argue him out of it and we'd all come back saying "No, it's right. He's got the right idea". It was a case of being brainwashed when you went over there... I can remember Ronald Jenkins going over and myself going over and other people going over to talk to him and all coming back with this conviction that we had to try and do what he wanted to do. He was a very persuasive man... [9]

A reporter, interviewing Utzon, found that his approach to his profession was that:

He sees architecture as art – a belief he demonstrates with memorable simplicity. 'Kahn described art like this.' He takes my pen and draws a line on a note pad. 'On one side of the line is truth – engineering, facts, mathematics, anything like that. On the other are human aspirations, dreams and feelings. Art is the meeting on the line of truth and human aspirations. In art, the one is meaningless without the other.'[10]

And Utzon was to say on his own philosophy to life:

I live very up-to-date. I don't live in two worlds like many people of our time live with refrigerators and aeroplanes and then live in the Victorian Age with their furniture and their dress. I like people who live in our age... and I like to be on the edge of the possible.[11]

Utzon saw the competition advertised in a Swedish architectural magazine,[12] registered for it and sent in a £10 deposit for a set of conditions. Receipts were issued for the £10 deposits as the requests for a set of competition conditions came in and Utzon's receipt was posted from Sydney on 4th April 1956.[13] On receiving the conditions Utzon later recalled in an interview with Professor Rasmussen:

The strange thing was that it was an ideal project for an architect. First, because there was a beautiful site with a good view, and second, there was no detailed program... In short it had not at all been specified what was wanted. It was left to the competitors, so that they were not handicapped in exploiting the site in a natural way. If there had been too many details and fixed rooms it would have made it quite difficult.

Rasmussen: What did you know about Sydney... when you worked out your project? Was there so much information that you could see in your mind's eye the whole situation?

Utzon: There was quite a lot of information, but as it so often goes with programs and rules like these they had been made by people who knew everything about the questions, and they could not know what the competitors as architects specially wanted to know. They could not know the importance of the colour of the sea or about the shades of light. These were things one had to find out for oneself. I studied very carefully everything I could lay my hands on in the way of Australian literature. It was very sparse.

A film of Sydney was shown to me (at the Australian Consulate in Copenhagen). It did not tell me very much. I got much more from some charts of the sea I obtained from Copenhagen. From these I could measure distances and form a judgement of heights (Utzon also met some Australian girls while he was working on the design in 1956 who were on their way to the Olympic equestrian events in Stockholm, who enthusiastically described Sydney Harbour to him.[14]) By these means I got the first feeling of the landscape and the nature of Sydney.[15]... The opera site was near the centre of the city... almost a stage in the Harbour... an open space in the centre of the city seen all round from great areas, in a way as significant to the city as the Acropolis in Athens, which can be seen from all round.[16]

If you go for a walk in the woods or stroll along the beach you look on things with new eyes in relation to your project... I stood looking at clouds over a low coast-line, and I had a look at Kronberg castle at Elsinore and at Gothic churches. There you have forms against a horizontal line like the sea or the clouds without a single vertical line, nothing constituted a weight, and with forms that are different from all angles.[17]

... Sydney is a dark Harbour. The colours of the waterfront are dull and homes red brick. There is no white to take the sun and make it dazzle the eyes. Not like the Mediterranean or South America and other sunlit countries. So I had white in my mind when I designed the Opera House. And the roof, like sails, white in the strong day, the whole thing slowly coming to life as the sun shone from the east and lifted overhead. In the hot sun of the day it will be a beautiful, white, shimmering thing – as alive to the eyes as architecture can make anything, set in the blue-green waters of the Harbour. And at night the floodlit shells will be equally vibrant – but in a softer, more majestic way.[18]

Rasmussen: Did you believe your project stood a chance? Did you believe in it? I mean, it was so different from all the other projects.

Utzon: I am not going to say I believed in it, because you do not know that while you are taking part in such a competition. You are so absorbed by the work that the question of actually winning the competition recedes.[19]

Utzon was still working on his design as the deadline for the competition approached.

The ground plan was completed in considerable detail but some of the other drawings were little more than sketches on small sheets of paper. Utzon had them photographed and blown up to the size specified in the competition conditions, rolled them into a tube, and posted them to Sydney. If a strict interpretation of the competition conditions had been adhered to, and if the Opera House Committee's answers to architects' questions intending to compete in the competition had been considered as binding, Utzon's design would have been disqualified immediately it was inspected on arrival. The boundaries of the site and its dimensions were indicated on a site plan that was included for all competitors in the competition conditions. The 'Site Requirements' in the conditions stated that 'The building may be located anywhere upon the site, but should not be placed right on the boundary of the site, either on the east or on the west. Location of the building and landscaping of the remaining site are entirely to the discretion of the competitors.'[20] There were many questions from architects intending to compete in relation to extending the site over the boundary marked in the conditions, and to each question, the answer was emphatically NO, the building must not extend over the site boundary. Typical of the questions asked were:

239. Q. Is there any possibility of an extension of the site in a western direction
    A. No.
243. Q. Why is a limitation placed on building on the east and west boundaries.
    A. Irrelevant.[21]

The conditions stated that 'A design shall be disqualified if... It exceeds the limit of the site as outlined on the site plan.' Utzon's design was outside the limit of the site on the west side.

The conditions also stated a design shall be disqualified '… If it is not drawn and submitted substantially in the manner prescribed in the Conditions…'. The 'drawings required' in the conditions included a 'Perspective drawing of such elevation as the competitor may select as his main elevation and/or approach to the building.' Utzon's drawings did not include a perspective.[22]

However, Utzon's design was accepted as bona fide and was examined along with all the other entries by the competition assessors. John Yeomans talked to Ashworth and Parkes following the judging and established that '… when Saarinen arrived, Utzon's drawings had already been earmarked by Professor Martin as an entry which must be on the short list. Saarinen certainly could not see beyond Utzon's entry, although the other judges had many reservations about it. But as fast as the other judges advanced objections, Saarinen advanced solutions.'[23] Lacking a proper perspective, Saarinen sketched two pictures of Utzon's design, one from the east, and one facing the entrance stairs, because to visualize how the building would look from Utzon's sketches was very difficult.[24] Parkes recalled that: '… there was quite a problem' selecting the best design from all the entries.

> We spent the first day agreeing on what we felt were the basic issues. We were looking for a building in our own day and age. It had to be an outstanding looking piece of architecture. Also, whatever building went there had to look well from all sides. I mean it's not like a building on King Street, where no one would ever see the top… The whole thing looked so disarmingly easy. That worried us for quite a while.[25] My only reservation about Utzon's drawings was: Could it be built?… My colleagues, particularly Saarinen… were convinced that it could.[26]

The judges had Utzon's report to refer to that explained the features of his design.

> The architecture emphasises the character of Bennelong Point and takes the greatest advantage of the view.
> The approach of the audience is easy and as distinctly pronounced as in Grecian theatres by uncomplicated staircase constructions…
> The requirements of the fire regulations have been met by exiting directly on to terraces from any room in any storey of the Opera House. Dead space for fire escapes has been avoided completely.
> The audience is assembled from cars, trains and ferries and led like a festive procession into the respective halls thanks to the pure staircase solution…

Light, suspended concrete shells accentuate the plateau effect and the character of the staircase constructions...

This construction implies the possibility of a complete opening of halls, foyers and public areas towards the open-air during intermission whenever weather permits and presents to the audience the full sensation of the suspended shells while moving through the foyers, which command beautiful views of the Harbour...

The whole exterior radiates lightness and festivity and is standing as a clear contrast to the square harbour buildings of Sydney.[27]

When the competition winner was announced, the assessors released their own report on Utzon's design.

The drawings submitted for this scheme are simple to the point of being diagrammatic. Nevertheless, as we have returned again and again to the study of these drawings, we are convinced that they present a concept of an Opera House which is capable of becoming one of the great buildings of the world. We consider this scheme to be the most original and creative submission. Because of its very originality, it is clearly a controversial design. We are, however, absolutely convinced about its merits...

The white sail-like forms of the shell vaults relate as naturally to the Harbour as the sails of its yachts. It is difficult to think of a better silhouette for this peninsular. The dynamic form of this vaulted shape contrasts with the buildings which form its background and gives a special significance to the project in the total landscape of the Harbour.

Saarinen had left a taped message to play at the ceremony announcing the competition winner. Because he had a pronounced stutter, an ABC technician had cut and respliced the tape so that the message broadcast smoothly. Saarinen said that Utzon's design was 'simple' and an 'outstanding piece of art.' And 'while all Gothic cathedrals had used the interlocking shell vault system, they had used stone, this was the same concept in concrete.'[28]

The competition conditions had not asked for a cost estimate.

There was a Quantity Surveyor standing by, Mr Major of Rider Hunt & Partners, to give help to the jury if they needed it. He was shown the Utzon drawings. He could guess at the foundation structure, roughly measure up the seating and minor walls and so on, but when it came to the great sails, which were the walls and roof in one, he was stumped. Shell concrete was in its infancy, or rather its precocious adolescence, at the time, and there were as yet no examples of it in Australia. He asked Saarinen for guidance; 'How do I estimate this?' Saarinen said: 'There's nothing in it. These shells might be about three inches thick at the top, and say twelve inches thick at the base.' No doubt he was thinking of the Kresge auditorium at M.I.T. which was only about half as thick as that (though it sagged, you'll remember, and had to be propped up with steel). Probably he had that deflection in mind when he doubled the figures. The Quantity Surveyor was doubtful, but he doubled Saarinen's figures again, to be on the safe side, when he calculated the concrete in the shells. With reservations, he was able to advise the jury to estimate the cost of the Utzon entry at £3,600,000.[29]

The assessors announced in their report:

> ... It is perhaps not unimportant to mention that we have had approximate estimates made for all the schemes which have been given places and several others in addition. The scheme which we now recommend for the first premium is, in fact, the most economical scheme on the basis of our estimates.[30]

Besides the second prize-winning design submitted by a group of seven Philadelphia architects and the third by a British company, Boissevain and Osmond, the judges chose 14 designs as being worthy of mention.[31] A design by Kollar and Korab was commended by the judges as 'very skilful planning.' Peter Kollar, aged 30, of Cremorne in Sydney had emigrated to Australia from Hungary six years previously. Korab, a friend of Kollars in Budapest, emigrated to the United States but flew to Australia for six weeks to participate with Kollar on his design. Kollar recounted:

> We were deep in the middle of it when the revolution broke out in Hungary. For a long time we debated whether we should abandon everything and go to Budapest and join forces with the fighters there. Then we decided we could perhaps assist more by keeping our flag flying here, and we went on with the design.[32]

The day after the competition winner was announced, the Art Gallery was due to open for a public exhibition of the competition drawings. Utzon's designs were very sketchy, 'nothing more than a magnificent doodle' art critic Robert Hughes was to say, while the *Herald* called Utzon's entry the least 'finished design in the competition.'[33] It was considered the general public would find it very hard to visualise how the Opera House may look. At the request of the judging panel the NSW government commissioned an artist, A.N. Baldwinson, a lecturer in architecture at Sydney University, to produce a coloured rendition of the Opera House to display at the Art Gallery with Utzon's competition sketches. Baldwinson had already spent two or three days working on his colour picture to have it ready. He recalled how he worked 'very carefully from Utzon's elevations so that my representation of the roof would be as accurate as possible.'[34] As soon as the designs went on display:

> More than 8,000 people... visited the Art Gallery to see the National Opera House designs...
>
> People crowded about 12 deep around Jorn Utzon's prizewinning design for the Opera House at Bennelong Point. Scores of people who went to the gallery especially to look at the design had to leave without seeing it. Nineteen out of twenty people interviewed after seeing the design said they liked it. The odd-man out was Mr W.Schotanus of Kings Cross. He said 'The design is completely European. I should have liked to have seen something more typically Australian.'[35]

On 30th January the *Sydney Morning Herald's* front page headline was 'DANE'S CONTROVERSIAL DESIGN WINS OPERA HOUSE CONTEST.' The *Daily Telegraph* on the same day carried a picture of the Opera House drawn by its own artist and asked readers 'What do you think of the winning design. Send your view to the Daily Telegraph.' They needn't have asked; all the Sydney newspapers received a torrent of mail on the Opera House which continued for weeks after. On 1st February every single letter published in the *Sydney Morning Herald* concerned the Opera House, and the letters page included a note by the editor, 'Correspondents are reminded of the need to be brief and to the point so that as many readers' letters as possible may be published in the space available. Professor Dennis Winston wrote of the design:

> It gives the impression of a wonderful piece of sculpture, deliberately placed to be seen from all points of view.[36]

P. Hennesey from Little Hartley in rural New South Wales thought:

> The Opera House design reminds me of a haystack covered by several tarpaulins which are being lifted by a strong wind.[37]

Mrs Margaret Reeves from Maroubra wrote:

> I am a housewife. The beauty of the new Opera House design caught my breath. It gives a bright ray of hope that some day whole cities may be places of beauty, uplifting to walk in. I can't see how anyone could oppose this design. It is so obviously right for its setting.[38]

S. M. Grafton-Williams from Banksia believed:

> Judging of the Opera House designs must have been in the hands of a mentally retarded group. I have never seen such a monstrosity as the winner, except in children's space comics. An Opera House, of all places should be a delight to the eye as well as to the ear. The contraption

resembles a sink with plates stacked in readiness for washing. Imagine a visitor in a liner on the Harbour being confronted with this monster... [39]

Mrs Gladys Doggett of Milsons Point considered:

... It is the most stimulating thing I have looked at for a long time. I believe it to be the most beautiful and inspiring design of our time, so in keeping with our fast-moving era! I'd like to give the architect a big hug. [40]

Margaret Thompson of Darlinghurst was convinced:

It looks very much like the Loch Ness Monster. If that is supposed to be art I realize how fortunate I am to belong to that happy band to whom the following may be applied: 'Where ignorance is bliss 'tis folly to be wise.' [41]

Bruce Loder of Bankstown wrote:

Sir, – At last! A clean, refreshing breeze has found its way into the musty corridors of Australian architectural thought... [42]

Alan Robson of Chatswood had the impression:

... The prize-winning design is suggestive of some large and lovely ship of the imagination, sailing on the winds of inspiration, that has come to rest in the Harbour.

It is a lofty and uplifting design for a house where 'new arts shall bloom of loftier mould, and mightier music fill the skies...' [43]

W. H. Peters had his own particular opinion:

Faced with the nightmare illustrated in your columns today, some twenty-fifth century Bluebeard's lair, its ominous vanes pointed skywards apparently only for the purpose of discharging guided missiles or some latter-day nuclear Evil Eye. Words fail.

... it is well to remember that the people who have to pay for it will also have to live with it, and if at some suitably remote period, our descendants regain any sense of taste or proportion, they will be forced to foot the bill for removing it and putting up something less repellant.

Let us therefore cut our losses now, pay the Scandinavian gentleman his prize, and pigeonhole the plans. Better the worst of the Department of Public Works and the Government architects than this armadillo in concrete!... [44]

Anne Regan wrote from Tamworth:

I must express my great joy in the music that flows from the true poetry of Mr Utzon's vision.

Remarkable magnificence, beauty and grace are born in this sail-like structure where the rhythms of its vaults link with those of the wind-lashed sails on the water.

This is a building which has the power to speak, and still more to sing in the melodies of its forms, which, so beautifully gradated, echo so much the perfection of an exquisite musical phrase.

Surely through its simplicity there is born not poverty, but a richness, nobility, and wonder that wakes the heart to the joy of new horizons.[45]

G. R. Guymer of Crown Street Sydney was not so inspired:

When I saw the winning Opera House design I thought I was having a hang-over. Or is it another plane crash?... [46]

Colin Roderick of Homebush voiced his concern:

... Why build an Opera House on a spot where damp, salt, fog, noise and wind will create costly problems for the staff and discomfort for the audience?

... Future generations of Australians, whether they live in Sydney or only visit it, will derive more pleasure from a native park on the site than from the dream-stones of "Goossens Folly."[47]

Lynd Nathan of Killara wrote:

Sir, – We could, of course, scrape off the soaring concrete vanes altogether and keep the lower half of the building as it is. In the middle, where the stage machinery has to go, we could erect a tower to look like a modern silo. In this way the top of the building would be familiar enough to satisfy unnumbered tastes, and the lower half as satisfactorily dull as the thousand and one buildings that rise today here, in London and elsewhere...[48]

W. Watson Sharp of Sydney held the view:

Sir, – Several surprises have come out of the Opera House competition. One was that four assessors with so widely divergent views, experience and qualifications, should be unanimous in their choice of winner. But the most amazing of all is the spate of ill-informed criticism from people who, apparently have not yet seen the plans, but have rushed into print on the strength of one perspective sketch that was not even prepared by the designer.[49]

One lady writing to the *Herald* on 30th January likened the Opera House to 'a piece of Danish pastry' and another, Mrs Mason of Pennant Hills, writing to the *Herald* on 21st February thought it was 'like a flock of white gulls alighting on our Harbour.' P.P. Chulow of Peakhurst was quite adamant:

I am shocked at the winning design for the Sydney Opera House. It will be a blot on the Harbour.

Oh no, Sydney! Don't let them do this to us! This design is like a hideous parachute which we cannot fold up and put away.[50]

Though G. Delmar of Darlinghurst wrote: 'For unfair critics comfortable facilities could be provided nearby to jump in the lake.'[51] While Herbert Johnstone of Cremorne was relieved that: 'Sir, – There is one consolation. Although it looks like a disintegrating circus tent in a gale the building is estimated to cost up to £4,000,000; and that consideration alone will almost certainly ensure that it will not be erected for some considerable time to come, if at all.'[52]

R. Maxwell of Newtown, lamented:

> ... the defects of leaving decisions in matters of public importance to experts, and non-resident experts at that. Outside their own particular province, the judgement of experts is no better than that of the educated layman, and, in fact, it is usually worse, because of their specialised, and therefore narrow, outlook. And being non-resident they lack a restraining sense of responsibility to the local community, which will have to live with the result of their decision.[53]

And as the non-resident assessors had departed, it was Ashworth who leapt to the defence of the Opera House. [54]

> It is easy for people to say the winning design is like a collapsed circus tent. But their criticism does not count unless they argue objectively... The four judges spent many days trying to fault the plan on any major issue. But we could not. Its simplicity and magnificence staggered us.
>
> People looking at the design must look on it as if looking at a beautiful woman; not as to whether she's a good cook.[55]
>
> ... An architect can only be as good as his client allows him to be... [56] The design is so strikingly simple and straightforward that it offers a perfect solution to the requirements we set.[57]
>
> I was surprised there were not more schemes of a more advanced character in terms of architectural thinking. I imagined we'd be spoilt for choice with half a dozen outstanding designs; instead there was only one.[58]

Meanwhile criticism came in from around the world on the Sydney Opera House, which was duly reported in the Sydney press. *Time* magazine on 25th February 1957 considered, 'so many opera houses look like boots. There is the high proscenium arch, then the lower part which is the audience. Utzon has solved the problem.'[59] The *Architects Journal* in London reported on 14th February, 'the design will always be of interest, however the theorists may argue, and will be worth travelling many a mile to see, admire and wonder at.' Also in London *The Observer* reported three days later on the 17th:

The whole conception is one which cynics may ridicule for no better reason than that it is unorthodox; it will lend itself to parody, it may change in the course of building, but it will remain in its essentials as an example of grace, exciting and as functional as need be. It has an ever rarer quality; it is poetic.

And Basil Spence in London was quoted as saying 'I am certain it will be one of the great buildings.' Meanwhile in the United States:

Frank Lloyd Wright took one look at a picture of Sydney's proposed opera house and cried, 'God help us all!'

Then he hurried to his desk and wrote an exclusive comment for The Sun on the prizewinning entry... Wright made his comment from his winter retreat in Arizona. He refuses to install a telephone – mail and cable are the only ways to communicate with him.

Last week I sent him a picture of Jorn Utzon's winning entry, newspaper clippings and a letter asking his opinion on the judges' choice. Two days later he sent this telegram:

'Candid expression of opinion in air mail today. God help us all. Frank Lloyd Wright.'

Wright, considered the greatest and most imaginative living architect, did not find one word of praise for Utzon's design. His full comment arrived today...

'I suppose this reckless design was chosen by official authority because it exhibits neither rhyme nor reason for its purpose. This circus tent is not architecture.

In a free country, a disrupted circus tent – even one like this, manifestly blown open and apart by the wind – might be used to shelter opera. But why? Why does non-constructive, inorganic fantasy appeal to these novices in our greatest art?

As I take it, architecture should still be significant, permanent building – that is, excellent construction. To me the absurd effloresence of this opus again shows the folly of these now too-popular competitions. I venture to affirm that not yet has one truly great or even good building issued from a competition – one either past or present or will in future.'[60]

On 28th February, Ashworth wrote to Saarinen, enclosing with the letter the article from *The Sun* about Lloyd Wright:

... As we anticipated, the design created tremendous controversy here and was indeed headline news for some 10 days in the local press – which was quite extraordinary. There is, in my opinion, no serious opposition to the scheme, which seems to have caught the public imagination (except)... that public money should be expended in schools, houses, hospitals, etc. (Regarding Lloyd Wright's opinion)... I do feel -
a. It is a poor criticism.

b. It is a little unfortunate that a young man producing a fine imaginative scheme in an international competition should receive such scant support from such a big figure.

c. That the very design itself would appear to meet, at least, to be almost based upon earlier teachings of Wright himself.

Saarinen replied on 11th March.

> ... I could have told you that Wright would have said just about that. He has always hated competitions and has very little good to say about anything but work he has done himself, but in spite of that I think he is the greatest living architect.
>
> Both Time Magazine and Newsweek published the Opera House, which is really the best kind of press you can get... [61]

Although much criticism against the Opera House scheme was published in Sydney newspapers; comments such as it's like 'a flailing scarecrow falling into the sea'[62] was typical of many, the overwhelming opinion in Sydney was one of support for the project. One architect, Guy Tasman Lovell, wrote:

> Sir, – Perhaps an unsuccessful competitor in the Opera House competition may be permitted to express unqualified satisfaction with the assessors' award.
>
> Epithets like 'Danish pastry, armadillo and disintegrating circus tent' spring easily to the lips of adverse lay critics, but names cannot detract from the essential merit of this design.
>
> This merit consists in the astonishing simplicity of Joern Utzon's solution of a complex problem. How complex was the problem can, I suggest, be best judged by those who set it, those who tried to solve it perfectly and those who made the award.
>
> The N.S.W. Government trawling oceans of architectural thought the world over, cast its nets wide and wisely and had its catch expertly appraised.
>
> That a work of the utmost architectural significance should be thus stimulated, discovered and suitably recognised reflects nothing but credit on all concerned.
>
> How depressing, not to say humiliating, it will be if a project of world-wide interest is blocked or mutilated by any adulteration of the imagination and foresight displayed to date.[63]

Another, Harry Seidler, wrote:

> Sir. – Architecture is a language and architects speak it. Most of them just barely manage to speak – very few ever speak eloquent prose, but it happens rarely indeed that any of them create poetry with just a few words.
>
> Our proposed Opera House is just such poetry, spoken with exquisite

economy of words. But then how many of us appreciate or even understand poetry when we have only ever heard crude language.[64]

The architect, J.P. Tate, who was on the Committee which had chosen the site, thought the design 'has captured the possibilities of the site and the whole spirit of what an Opera House should be.'[65]

However, there were detractors among Sydney architects. The NSW Town Planning Association President, the architect Bertram Ford, said the design was 'insane, farcical, and would completely disfigure the foreshores.' Overseas architects have 'gone mad over contemporary and futuristic designs.'[66]

Walter Bunning, on inspecting Utzon's design on display at the Art Gallery, thought it looked like 'an insect with a shell on its back which has crawled out from under a log',[67] and strenuously opposed the acceptance of the design. Seidler and Bunning debated the pros and cons of the design at a gathering of architects at a judge's house.[68]

As soon as he saw the design, Charles Moses had said, 'Wherever artists and architects meet they'll discuss this wonderful structure.'[69] But later, recalled

> ... it was a shock to me when I saw (Utzon's design)... because I thought 'Look, the Government will never accept this. This is so unorthodox'... I thought well, this was so different from any other Opera House in the world, and so – I would have expected the Premier and his Government,... to have been more enthusiastic about a more orthodox design. But he wasn't. As a matter of fact, he accepted the judgement of these distinguished people who formed the panel of judges and got in behind them at once and supported it wholeheartedly, (he) never once questioned the matter of whether this was a suitable building. And he had the job of trying to persuade his Cabinet Ministers, the Caucus, and finally Parliament, to support it... [70]

Cahill did not offer any criticism of the winning design, 'It is not my intention to enter the lists on that score at any time', and had said '... there has been and doubtless will be, some criticism of the project itself, of the site which the government has chosen, of the wisdom of building an Opera House at all, and of the community's ability to shoulder the expense of maintaining a National Opera House. Those are the things that crop up from day to day and are something that the Government and I will have to face.'[71] Talking at a lunch for the competition assessors at the NSW Royal Australian Institute of Architects on 17th January, Cahill recounted, 'Although we are burdened with financial troubles, we must be courageous enough to bring this scheme to a successful conclusion.'

However, though the cost of the Opera House and a way to finance it became of immediate pressing concern, so did the question of a suitable name for the project. An architect intending to compete in the competition had asked:

375. Q. 'The large hall to be designed for use for the following purposes;
(a) Symphony Concerts... (b) Large-scale Opera.' Is this intentional or a mistake? If the primary purpose of the building is Symphony Orchestra and not Opera, why call it 'Opera House'? Why not 'Concert Hall'?

A. Appendix 5/1 clearly indicates the uses for which the large hall is to be designed. The question would appear to be a mistake.[72]

David Griffin of Sydney, in a letter published in the *Herald* on 1st February wrote:

Dead plans for dead buildings can be filed away and forgotten: not so Operasaurus Melba, the New South Whale or Moby Joe (whichever you wish). It will need more than ordinary courage to grapple with it in a life and death struggle at the portals of the pigeonhole. This creature, strange and beautiful, having chosen Sydney for its home, cannot be denied. Whatever happens it must be built – not left to die and rot upon the shore.

At the Opera House Committee meeting on 12th February, under item six on the agenda, 'Question of a name'

During discussions, members expressed the view that the name 'Opera House' may prejudice the view of the public regarding the use of the building in light of the launching of an appeal for funds, and that a press statement should be issued to draw attention to the fact that the building would only be used for opera two months of the year.

The Herald asked its readers on their ideas for a name for the Opera House and their replies came in in an absolute avalanche. 'What about "Macquarie Hall" after our first Governor and because it was at the bottom of Macquarie Street';[73] 'Why not name the new Opera House after the biggest benefactor? People would scramble for the honour';[74] '"Aurora Musicalis" would suit the modern conception of music and our southern geographical position';[75] or '"Cahill Hall" after the man who's courage and love of culture will finally make the scheme possible.'[76] Joyce Carter of Sydney wrote:

Sir, – I personally am quite satisfied with the title 'Opera House', but can understand that many others are not. The Harbour and the Harbour

Bridge are perhaps the only two features of the city of which residents are unanimously proud; why not add the Harbour Hall to the list?

While Paul Butz of Strathfield considered:

> Sir, – Why not call it simply Bennelong Hall, a name that would inevitably be abbreviated to Ben Hall[77] and would thus be in keeping with the bushranger prices that will no doubt be charged for admission.
>
> The problem of distinguishing the large auditorium from the smaller could then be resolved by referring to them as Big Ben and Little Ben.

Finally Sheila Howard of Mosman thought:

> Sir, – Why, indeed, even think up another name? The Opera House is concise as well as dignified; and whatever it is finally named the bulk of the population will no doubt continue to call it the Opera House.[78]

But on the question of financing the Opera House, there were many in the community who felt the money could be better spent elsewhere:

> Sir, – This is a disgraceful state of affairs, when so much money can be spent on the frivolous things of life, of benefit only to a few. Let's find money for the living, give little children a home and education, and build cottages for the aged. Let's float loans to build homes for the widows and deserted wives and children.[79]

The NSW government had planned to seek financial help from the City Council, the ABC and from federal sources for funding. Indeed this had been one of the reasons why the scheme had been referred to as a 'National' Opera House in the first place.[80] From the NSW government's coffers, preliminary appropriation of funds for construction was expected to be included in the next budget, and the Opera House would be on the list of NSW Loans Works put to the annual meeting of the Loan Council later in the year. However, Alderman Jensen, the Lord Mayor, speaking for the City Council, said he was reluctant to agree that such a project should be given priority over essential needs such as housing. The ABC could not afford the funds; they were financed by the City Council and government anyway, and attempts to obtain federal funding from the Commonwealth Government proved to be a dead letter from the start.[81] The question of finance for the Opera House was on the agenda for discussion in the NSW Parliament by Labor MPs:

> The plan to proceed with the building of the £3½-million opera house at Bennelong Point looks like blowing up into a furore in fortissimo at

Wednesday's Parliamentary Labor Caucus meeting. Several members will protest strongly on the projected spending of millions on what they call 'a luxury' at the cost of urgent and essential works.

The Premier (Mr Cahill) is expected to come in for his share of criticism for Opera House sponsorship at what could be the stormiest Caucus meeting for years. Several members are believed to have been directed by their Labor Leagues to oppose the Opera House to the limit...

Several Labor M.L.A's said yesterday the State Government could not afford to build an Opera House, which would have to be heavily subsidised and be a recurring charge against the taxpayer.

Diversion of a substantial amount of loan money for the purpose could not be justified, they said.

One member said 'The state is living from hand to mouth on Commonwealth handouts... Towards the end of last year the State had to obtain near £10 million from the Commonwealth Government in short-term Treasury bills to see it through immediate difficulties. How can we afford millions for an Opera House?' Some Caucus members on Wednesday intend to point out:

• That the education system is failing because of lack of money; that children all over the State are being herded into inadequate temporary classrooms; that of 170 school building projects listed as urgent, only 20 will be completed by June...

• That N.S.W. is short of 150,000 homes and that more than 260,000 men, women and children are living in huts, sheds and sharing inadequate housing.

They intend to emphasise too, that the estimate of £3½-million for the Opera House could increase alarmingly in the next few years.

(In 1955, when the Opera House was first mentioned the cost was put down at £1 million).

'Whatever the Opera House outcome' one Labor M.L.A. said yesterday, 'There'll be no sweet music at this Caucus meeting, it looks like discord all the way.'[82]

Professor Ashworth talked on funding the Opera House at a Sydney Rotary Club lunch:

Spread over five years the Opera House would cost £600,000 a year to build. If this money were spent on housing it would build only 200 homes – a drop in the ocean when compared with the number needed. Spent on a hospital £600,000 would build only one 80 bed hospital... [83]

Ashworth though, was optimistic on the question of finance, on 12th February in a letter to Ralph Goddard of Rider Hunter and Partners in London he had written:

We now face the problem of the raising of the necessary funds and finance in the teeth of the usual political gale in which shortages of houses, hospitals, schools, etc. are all hurled against the proposal. I, myself, find that very frequently things that appear man-sized mountains on first view become rather like molehills when we really get close to them.[84]

The *Sydney Morning Herald* on 7th March quoted John Mansfield, an architect who had assisted the Committee drafting up the competition conditions, as saying, 'Why not build homes as well as the Opera House.' However, the *Telegraph* carried an article on the same day with the title, 'Opera House building still in doubt', and related an exchange from question time in Parliament:

Mr Askin (Liberal Collaroy) asked, 'Is the present the right time to push ahead with this desirable but lavish venture? And how does the Government propose to finance it?'

Cahill replied: 'Building the Opera House will involve the expenditure of a good deal of money. We will have to make up our minds whether we are prepared to do it. In a young country like this we ought to be courageous. We should pledge the future if need be.'

Ashworth in a letter to Professor Martin wrote:

... The Government is moving a little slowly at the moment due to various political upheavals which have occurred. There is a particularly raucous row going on at the moment over the housing problem and I think possibly the Premier is wise in not deeming this an appropriate moment to throw another controversial item into the ring.[85]

On 27th April, the headline in the *Daily Mirror* was 'CAHILL COLD ON OPERA PROJECT':

State Premier (Mr Cahill) today forecast that the proposed Opera House at Bennelong Point might not be built. Mr Cahill said he believed homes should come before opera houses.

Mr Cahill was addressing the annual conference of the Women's A.L.P. Organising Committee.

'I had no idea it would cost so much when the project was approved' he said.

'If it is still possible to build it, we will. We are anxious to build this Opera House if we can. We have to be prudent, keep our balance, and have regard to the views of the people.'

Mr Cahill added: 'We cannot disregard the more immediate wants of the people, and I refer particularly to housing.'

Mr Cahill said to an enthusiastic audience that building homes was just as important as fighting a war.

The organising committee's conference, which ended last year in a riot, today got away to a quiet start, after Mr Cahill and A.L.P. President, Mr Campbell had given the 350 delegates a 'pep talk' about last years debacle.

Then a headline in the *Telegraph* on the 29th was 'Premier 'hopeful' on Opera House.'

... Mr Cahill said last night Cabinet had 'every hope' that a way would be found to build the Opera House at Bennelong Point. He hoped to be able to release soon the Opera House Committee's report suggesting ways to raise money. He denied that remarks he made to the Women's A.L.P. Organising Committee meant the Opera House would not be built.

The Deputy Leader of the State Opposition (Mr Askin) said last night: 'Mr Cahill should make up his mind on the future of the Opera House. Where is the huge amount of money needed going to come from?'

Mr Askin said the cost probably would go beyond the present estimate of £3½ million. He said he had asked Mr Cahill in Parliament last session how the Government would find the money, considering the claim that insufficient money was available for homes. 'The Premier brushed the matter aside', Mr Askin said.

In the same newspaper, another story ran; under the heading 'Funds bid urged by women':

The A.L.P. Labor Women's Central Organising Committee conference yesterday decided to ask the Premier (Mr Cahill) to launch an immediate appeal for building the National Opera House.

Conference unanimously carried a motion urging the Government to carry on with building the Opera House as well as with providing homes.

Moving the motion, Miss M. Walker (Concord) said homes were important but it was also important that culture-loving Australians should have their own Opera House.

Mrs W. E. Dickson, wife of Mr Dickson, M.L.C. said the State Government should launch an appeal immediately for finance to begin building the Opera House. 'Some time ago we asked for a National Theatre' she added. 'We got that largely because of an energetic Englishwoman called Elsie Beyer, who would not let up until we had started our Elizabethan Theatre. I think I am safe in saying that we lost no houses because that appeal was made to the public.'

On 1st May Cahill announced his proposal to finance the Opera House partly through special lotteries, and on the 8th he put his proposals on finance for the Opera House to the Caucus:

State Labor Caucus yesterday authorised the Premier (Mr Cahill) to launch a public appeal to finance early building of the Opera House. Caucus made the authorisation by a majority of 24 to 17. But Mr Seiffert, M.L.A. for Monaro, immediately gave notice of a motion to rescind this decision. Caucus will deal with this at its next meeting on the first Wednesday in June. Members said later they did not think Mr Cahill could go ahead with the appeal for funds in the meantime. They said that although Caucus by a majority had backed Mr Cahill's scheme, Mr Cahill was visibly shocked by the size of the vote against it.

Mr Cahill's scheme is to

- Organise an appeal for funds with the Government contributing £100,000.
- Run special quarterly lotteries, with a first prize of £50,000 and tickets at 30/- each.
- Ask the City Council and the A.B.C. (through the Federal Government) to contribute...

Government supporters said they believed Mr Seiffert's rescission motion would fail.

One of the Government's supporters, Mr Mallam of Dulwich Hill, told Caucus he gave his support with the proviso that he was against lotteries or any other form of gambling to raise the necessary money. He said 'The Government should be courageous enough to tell the people the Opera House is needed and go ahead and build it, but should not resort to gambling.'

Main argument of those opposed to the Government's scheme was that the time was not opportune and money was required for housing, hospitals, and urgent public works. Mr Maher (North Sydney) said people used the same argument against building the Sydney Harbour Bridge. He accused some who criticised the Opera House proposal of having a 'horse and buggy philosophy.'

Mr Wyatt (Lakemba) said he accepted the Premier's assurance that the money raised for the Opera House would not interfere with the housing problem. Mr Seiffert interjected: 'What about using this money to house the people of Herne Bay?' Mr Wyatt retorted that the people of 'Herne Bay, which is in his electorate, were all right and that Mr Seiffert should get back to his 'cockies and squatters.' (Mr Seiffert's electorate of Monaro includes grazing lands).[86]

Following the meeting, Cahill said, 'Nobody is more anxious than I am to see that when a determination is made it is carried through.'[87] But Cahill put off the launch of the plan, deciding to let the decision go before the vote of all Labor members at the State ALP Conference in June. In answer to criticism that he was postponing the Opera House proposal, Cahill replied:

But I think you will find in the long run that it was the best decision. We can't undertake a project like this which will cost a lot of money, with a substantial section of the community opposed to it. It is best to wait and get this important section in agreement with the proposal.

Although he conceded, 'The thing I am worried about is the cost of the project. Some of the methods we have to adopt to raise finance are a bit difficult.'[88] Though, as Cahill was to say in June, 'If we are not prepared to take a bit of a risk, we are not worth our salt.'[89]

On 17th June, the day following the ALP State Conference, the headline in the *Sydney Morning Herald* was 'Opera House Project is Approved.'

> The annual State Conference of the Labor Party yesterday approved the Government's plan to build an Opera House in Sydney. A big majority of the 730 delegates approved the Opera House plan. A recommendation that the Government launch an appeal for funds for the Opera House was carried on the voices. The decision is regarded by observers as a major victory for the Premier, Mr Cahill, who made a strong plea to the conference on Saturday for the Opera House.
>
> Mr Cahill had the backing of Mr Campbell and other members of the executive, and the Lord Mayor, Alderman H. F. Jensen. The conference made its decision by adopting a recommendation by the Labor Women's Organising Committee conference last April. The recommendation read: 'Homes as well as an Opera House – We appeal to the N.S.W. Government to immediately launch an appeal for funds to commence the building of the Opera House.'
>
> The conference defeated by a surprisingly large margin a proposal by Mr J. W. Thompson (Leichhardt) that the section of the women's report dealing with the Opera House be deleted. Mr Thompson declared amid interjections that the Opera House proposal was included in the women's report as a 'subterfuge' to get it through the conference...'The Premier, if he comes down to earth, can take it that the ordinary people are more concerned with homes than Opera Houses... Hoity-toity people who like this sort of thing have plenty of dramatic societies and other organisations in which they can put their efforts. It will be something for the people with minks and diamonds, and not what ordinary people want. If this motion is carried it is an indication that we agreed to the Opera House.'
>
> Miss M. Napper (Clothing Trades):
>
> 'Many working women these days have furs, although they may not have diamonds. Are we going to bring up our children in an atmosphere of rock and roll, or of better things?' (Applause)
>
> Mrs K Anderson, secretary of the Women's Organising Committee and wife of the Mayor of Bondi, said the intention was to have a public appeal for funds: 'It would give those who cry out for an Opera House the opportunity to subscribe.' she said.
>
> Opposition to the Opera House, which was extremely vocal and apparently strong at the outset, waned noticeably as the debate proceeded.

Mr E Pedersen of Glebe, a former City Council alderman, began the debate by moving that the words 'homes for aged persons' be substituted for 'Opera House' in the women's report. He said it was hardly the time to be talking about Opera Houses when the party was running raffles to build homes for aged people.

The president ruled the amendment out of order.

Mr E. C. Bennett, a member of the State executive, said if the conference supported the Opera House project it would 'give the lie direct to the dirty innuendo of the so-called intelligentsia that Labor people are just a bunch of hillbillies without any artistic taste or aspirations.'

The chairman of the Friends of the Opera House Society, Sir Bernard Heinze, commenting on the conference's decision, said: This is exciting news. It surely means we are going to get our Opera House. The way should now be cleared to channel public enthusiasm into a determined drive for funds and to begin work on the building without delay.[90]

On the 19th, there was an article in the *Herald* entitled 'OPERA HOUSE FUNDS TALKS EXPECTED TO OPEN THIS WEEK.'

The State Opera House Committee is expected to begin discussions this week with the Premier, Mr Cahill, on plans to finance construction of the Opera House. The Committee chairman, Mr S. Havilland, said yesterday he hoped to see Mr Cahill on the matter 'in the next few days...'

Following the State A.L.P. Conference's endorsement of the Opera House proposal at the weekend, Mr Cahill, is understood to be anxious to make arrangements for a start on construction as soon as possible.

Although he will attempt at once to determine a method of financing the scheme, he will take no firm action until after next month's meeting of the Parliamentary Labor Caucus. He has promised Caucus that he will refer the issue back to it for concurrence. Mr Cahill gave the promise after a strong, militant section of Caucus last month attacked the Opera House proposal, but was defeated in a move to postpone it by 24 votes to 17.[91]

Finally, the headline in the *Herald* on 4th July was 'A.L.P. CAUCUS VOTES SOLIDLY FOR OPERA HOUSE.'

The State Parliamentary Labor Caucus yesterday voted overwhelmingly in favour of building Sydney's Opera House. The Premier, Mr Cahill, gave Caucus an assurance that he would not use State loan funds to help finance the construction, which will cost £3,500,000. Mr Cahill said he hoped the project would not need 'one penny' more of Consolidated Revenue that the initial £100,000 grant promised. The Lord Mayor, Alderman H.F.Jensen, would be invited to open a public appeal for funds at the end of this month.

Mr Cahill said no decision had been made yet about launching lotteries to help finance the scheme. This would be considered after the public appeal opened. Mr J. W. Seiffert, M.L.A. for Monaro, bitterly attacked the proposal. He moved an amendment for the Government to limit its contribution to £1,750,000 but this was defeated...'The most the Premier can hope to get from public donations is £250,000', Mr Seiffert said.[92]

After the State ALP Conference endorsed the Opera House project in June, Ashworth wrote to Cahill on 18th June:

> ... I was delighted to hear the news on the wireless over the weekend. I must... compliment you on your masterly tactical handling of a most difficult situation... it would have been, to say the least of it, most disappointing if the scheme had been shelved at this stage and would, in fact, I feel have been a great slur on Australia... [93]

On 8th July, following the Labor Caucus' approval of the Opera House, Ashworth wrote to Martin:

> ... The political battle has now been won and the Government has decided to proceed with the project. The Opera House Committee... has now been renamed the Opera House Executive Committee... (and expanded to include):
>   Mr E.W. Adams (Town Clerk of Sydney)
>   Dr Nicolai Malko (Conductor, Sydney Symphony Orchestra)
>   Sir Bernard Heinze (Director, N.S.W. Conservatorium of Music)
>   Mr Hugh Hunt (Executive Director, Elizabethan Theatre Trust)
>   I have persuaded the Committee to appoint two advisory panels: 1. A Music and Drama Panel which will deal primarily with all basic requirements for the different users of the halls. 2. A Technical Panel responsible to me, and to advise the Executive should the necessity arise.
>   This arrangement precludes Utzon, as the Architect, being badgered in any way directly by advisory panels... [94]

Three weeks after Utzon won the competition, Ashworth announced on 22nd February that he had received a letter from Utzon who would be coming out to Australia in March, bringing with him a model of the design; 'Mr Utzon doesn't seem to be wasting any time' said Ashworth. This story appeared in the *Sydney Morning Herald* on 23rd February, with a picture of Utzon's wife, Lis, sitting in a chair at her home in Denmark, reading a copy of the 30th of January issue of the *Herald* with the story on the front page about her husband winning the competition.[95]

However, with no clear indication that the government had established a way to finance the project, or even approved of it, Ashworth said in April that though Utzon had finished his scale model '... he won't come to Australia until the appeal is due to go on, and you can't blame him.'[96]

Photographs of Utzon's model of the Opera House appeared in Sydney's newspapers on 19th June. Utzon had sent the photographs to Cahill with a note, 'With all my best compliments on your fine fight for the new Opera House and for a richer life for your people, and with kindest regards.'[97]

Stan Haviland sent a cable to Utzon straight after Caucus had voted on a scheme to finance the project, saying that the State government had decided to proceed immediately with plans to build the Opera House.[98] The *Daily Telegraph* on 16th July announced, 'OPERA HOUSE ARCHITECT HERE JULY 29.'

> The Danish architect who designed the proposed State Opera House will arrive in Sydney on July 29. The architect, J Utzon, advised the Opera House Committee of his plans. The chairman of the Committee (Mr Haviland) said Mr Utzon had received a cable clinching the contract and authorising him to go ahead with the job.
>
> Mr Haviland said: 'Mr Utzon is entitled now to prepare plans and specifications. We don't know whether he will want to work in Sydney or Denmark on the detailed planning of the building.'

Utzon's arrival was announced in the Sydney papers on the 30th:

> A man who looked like Sir Edmund Hillary,[99] the conqueror of Everest, stepped out of a plane at Mascot last night. He is Mr Joern Utzon, the 38-year-old, six-foot four-and-a-half inch Danish designer of the Sydney Opera House. Neatly dressed in a grey suit, with grey suede shoes and black and white striped tie, Mr Utzon passed almost unnoticed through the crowd at the airport.
>
> Although he was tired after his long flight from Copenhagen, and had been off-loaded for a few days at Nandi (Fiji) with an affected sinus, Mr Utzon looked very fit. He spent a few minutes in the Customs shed looking for his scale model of the Opera House, which had been sent ahead of him. Finally Customs men assured him that the model had arrived safely and would be released to him later.
>
> Officials of the Opera House Committee met Mr Utzon and his partner. They included the chairman (Mr S. Haviland), Professor Ashworth,... Mr Hugh Hunt, and Mr R. J. Thomson. A party of 25 Sydney Danes also welcomed Mr Utzon and his partner. The Danish Consul-General in Sydney (Mr F. Henning Hergel) waved the red and white Danish flag as Mr Utzon walked across the tarmac. Later Mr Hergel said two Sydney men had already asked Mr Utzon to design homes in Sydney.

(after passing through customs)... Mr Utzon had to satisfy reporters that he wasn't the six feet nine inches that the cables had said. Standing back to back with the Danish Consul-General,... who admitted to a height of six feet two inches, Mr Utzon was measured by his Swedish partner, Mr Erik Andersson (five feet five inches), who had to stand on a chair to do the job.

Speaking quietly in perfect English, Mr Utzon told a gathering of pressmen and radio interviewers that he had come to Australia to realise his greatest dream – to bring into existence a magnificent Opera House. He said he had spent six months thinking and working on the design and had used up most of the money he had won in another architectural competition keeping his family while he worked on the Bennelong Point project. He also revealed that his partner, Mr Andersson... had a big hand in the design. He gave Mr Andersson credit for much of the work on the design, but Mr Andersson said; 'Joern did most of the work, and it is our practice for the one who does most of the work to sign the plan, so he signed it.'

Mr Utzon said: 'We are really a Danish-Swedish partnership, because Erik is Swedish, and lives and works in the Swedish town of Helsingbord, which is only three miles across the water from Elsinore. We had no trouble visualising Bennelong Point, because we had colour pictures and many diagrams. In addition, at Elsinore, we have the castle on a point of land just like your tram depot at Fort Macquarie. We could look at Kronborg and just visualise the Opera House. We drew many plans and rejected them before we hit on the design which we finally submitted. We studied many theatres and places like railway stations, and drew ideas from them. Steps and platforms make good places for meeting people.

The Opera House roof will be of concrete, several inches thick, and will be covered with ceramic tiles, almost white. This is a very economic method of roofing, and is used quite a lot overseas. In Berlin recently, I saw a congress hall with such a roof spanning about 240 feet, and it was only three inches thick.' He said the unusual roof design had been chosen because the site seemed to require this type of sculptured effect.

'Your Opera House (continued Utzon)... is the talk of Europe. After I had won the competition I travelled the Continent looking at other opera houses. Everywhere I went architects and music lovers were wildly enthusiastic about the fact that Sydney was going to have an opera house of such an unusual design. Many marvelled at the fact that it would be the same size as the new Metropolitan Opera House in New York.'

Utzon said final plans for the Opera House would take about 18 months to complete. 'Using a lot of men the Opera House could then be built in two years', he said.[100]

Utzon and Andersson had arrived in Sydney on a Monday night, and the following morning they walked along the Tarpeian Way[101] with

Professor Ashworth, Charles Moses and Stan Haviland to see the Opera House site for the first time. Utzon and Andersson 'stood there in a snarling north-westerly under a grey sky.' The fronds of 'the date palms that grew in a circle behind the tram shed' were flailing in the wind, 'and beyond a low sandstone wall, the harbour was flecked with foam.' They looked at the tongue of land on which they will build Sydney's Opera House. "It's right!" Utzon said in his lilting Danish accent, his hair and gaberdine coat blown as wildly as Bennelong's palm trees, "It's O.K.! This is the way they placed the temples in the old days!... It's absolutely breath-taking. There's no Opera House site in the world to compare with it... This site is even more beautiful than in the photographs from which I worked."[102] Half an hour later, out of the wind in the lounge of the Australian Club... Utzon said, talking on architecture:

After all this pure functionalism, we need a little human smile. You must belong to your surroundings. When we design for Copenhagen, we are Danes, when we made this scheme for the Opera House we camped on Bennelong Point. We were Bennelong Pointers.

'We made it to fit this spot, and no other spot', said Andersson.

'We don't want Ford cars all over the world', said Andersson. 'Do you understand that? We don't like standardisation... The bricks in America are the same colour from east to west, but in Denmark and Holland they treat bricks like fine old stone!'

To his own embarrassment, Utzon has been likened to both Sir Edmund Hillary and the Duke of Edinburgh. He has steady blue-grey eyes, a high sun-tanned forehead, and an easy smile. Andersson, no mountaineer or polo player, is as sharp and alert as his profile; his personality is based on a fiery, impulsive enthusiasm...

Andersson, who studied architecture at Gottenborg, formed a partnership with his younger brother, Henry Andersson, and Utzon in 1952. Their firm now employs 18 architects and has its headquarters in Helsingborg.

Erik Andersson lives with his wife and two children near Helsingborg, which is only 30 minutes by ferry from the Danish town of Elsinore. Utzon lives with his wife and three children at the village of Hellebaek, just outside Elsinore and only about 30 miles from Copenhagen. 'Both of us have rich family lives', said Utzon 'and that is good.'

Their firm designs an average of 800 flats a year, and at the present time has in hand some 50 separate projects, including houses, flats, health centres, social institutions and a large school at the iron mining town of Kiruna, just inside the Arctic Circle. 'This school is going to be wonderful place for kids', said Andersson. 'Snow three metres high there, but we are having Finnish baths and artificial sunlight.'

'We didn't dream of winning it', said Utzon this week. 'We were inspired to do it. A certain amount of your time you want to devote to clean architecture – without clients or anything like that. That's one of the symptoms of architecture. That's when the architect is closest to the pure artist.'

Utzon and Andersson are organic architects. Like Aalto and the American Frank Lloyd Wright, they feel that architecture should derive from nature, that a building should seem to have grown from the earth rather than to have been built upon the earth. Unlike Gropius or Mies van der Rohe, they do not consider function to be sufficient of itself. Describing his first conception of the vaulting concrete shells which will surmount 'the House', Utzon says: 'I looked at flowers and insects, at organic forms. I wanted something that was growing out.'

Yet Frank Lloyd Wright has bitterly attacked Utzon's Sydney design. 'Sensationalism!' said the old man last March. 'Nothing but sensationalism! This design is not characteristic of Australia, or opera. It's just picture architecture... A whim, that's all it is, a whim!'

Utzon is not sure why Wright takes this view. 'But he would not bother attacking it if he were not interested in it', he said.

Almost as unexpected as Wright's criticism was the praise offered by a celebrated but unsuccessful entrant in the Sydney competition, Richard Neutra, of Los Angeles. Neutra's allegiance lies with Gropius or Mies rather than the romantics and the organic architects. But when Utzon and Andersson visited him in Los Angeles on their way to Sydney, he told them that he had been much impressed by the design and hoped that it would be built. 'Don't let me be a self-praiser', said Utzon after mentioning this. 'Self praise stinks in Denmark.'

In becoming Bennelong Pointers in spirit, Utzon and Andersson were helped by many photographs and colour slides of the point and the Harbour. They were helped, too, by Kronborg Castle – Hamlet's castle at Elsinore – which stands on a point in the Sound not unlike Bennelong Point.

'It was not really the same', said Utzon this week. 'At Kronborg, part of the horizon is open; here, the site is more intimate because the other side of the Harbour is so close. Kronborg Castle is a big, heavy structure with high towers, and as the ferry runs out around it, the towers seem to move. "The House" will have several shells behind each other so that when you move past, they seem to move too.'

Utzon opened his brief case and extracted a folder of photographs of the Opera House model. 'Here!' he said, 'It's a most important thing, in a way. It's what they call sculptural effect. In sculpture, you work with shadow and new lines, new silhouettes. That is how it will be at

Bennelong Point. But in a purely functional building you have just a side and then another side. No new sensation!'

Utzon and Andersson are now busy surveying their site from all possible aspects. 'We will do the best we can', said Utzon, 'because it is our only interest. I can't say anything to people who say 'Modern foolishness.' That doesn't interest me.

'We ride in automobiles and fire rockets. Why should we build in Victorian style today?'

Utzon tapped one of the gleaming, shell-white photographs on his lap. 'This is Our Time style', he said. 'It is our own.'[103]

On the afternoon of the 30th, Utzon and Andersson '... spent an hour with the Premier in his office, talking about their plans. They said they were confident they could cope with the detailed preparation of designs without the help of other architects... Mr Cahill asked (Utzon)... if he could have his plans ready within 18 months. ... Mr Utzon told Mr Cahill, 'All right, we will do it.'

Mr Cahill said later: 'Mr Utzon is like a breath of fresh air. He seems to bring a new outlook to the whole scheme. His carefree way of being able to answer "yes" and "no" straightforwardly to all questions impressed me greatly.'

Cahill went on to say, 'The State Government will have the tramway sheds at Bennelong Point demolished and the Opera House site ready within 18 months, (and) the foundation-stone would be laid before the next State elections – due after March, 1959.'[104]

At the end of that week, on Friday, 2nd August, Utzon and Andersson went on a tour of Sydney Harbour at Cahill's invitation, in the Premier's official launch 'to get a full perspective of the site.'[105] In the evening, Utzon appeared on Channel 9 in Robert Kennedy's 'TV Town Talk' session. He nominated Christmas Eve, 1960, as a possible opening date of the Opera House. Mr Utzon said: 'It depends on the speed of Australian workers – we'll be fast with the drawings.' Mr Utzon said that inspection of the Bennelong Point site had not caused him to alter his ideas on the design of the building.[106]

Utzon's model of the Opera House had been cleared through customs, and was set up in the vestibule of the Town Hall in a glass case, to be viewed following the opening of the Opera House Appeal at the Town Hall on the 7th. Meanwhile, donations were already coming in for the appeal. Cahill received a cheque 'for two guineas from Mr Seiffert, Labor M.L.A. for Monaro who led the opposition in the State Parliamentary Caucus to the Opera House project earlier this year.' Mr Cahill said...'he appreciated Mr Seiffert's gesture in sending the cheque with wishes for the success of the Opera House appeal.' Cahill himself, put in a cheque for £50. The Opera House Committee was ready to hand to the appeal when it opened £180 which it had received already. It included an American dollar bill from an amateur radio 'ham' who had picked up an ABC broadcast. The broadcast had led him to believe there would be a shortage of funds for the Opera House.[107]

A Melbourne resident made one of the first interstate contributions to the appeal with a donation of five guineas. The contributor, who signed himself 'Legis Filius', wrote, 'Mr Cahill's statement about the Sydney Opera House should be an inspiration to all Australians. Here is an opportunity for us to repay Sydney for their generous attitude towards our Olympic Games effort. Let us make a gesture of goodwill to show them that our interstate jealousies don't really count in matters of this sort.'[108]

On the 7th the doors of the Town Hall were due to open at 2.30 pm, ready for the official start of proceedings an hour later. As a tribute to Utzon, from 3 pm to 3.30 pm an organist would play a work by the Danish composer, Diderik Buxtehude.[109] The meeting would open with speeches by Jensen, Utzon and Chairman of the ABC Sir Richard Boyer, followed by performances by celebrity artists, American violinist Ruggiero Ricci, Italian pianist Carlo Bussotti, Australian soprano Joan Hammond[110] and flautist Miss Elaine Shaffer. Cahill would then open the appeal. In the evening Jensen would lay on a reception for the visiting artists and other guests at the Town Hall. According to the next day's papers:

> The Sydney Opera House appeal, which was launched at the Town Hall yesterday, raised £235,500 within an hour for the £3,500,000 project. The Premier, Mr Cahill who opened the appeal with a £100,000 cheque from the State Government, said it was hoped that the foundation stone of the Opera House would be laid within 18 months.
>
> A wildly enthusiastic crowd of 2,500, packing the Town Hall, stamped their feet, clapped, and cheered as the Lord Mayor, Alderman H.F. Jensen, read a list of the initial contributions. He announced that the City Council would contribute £100,000 over a five-year period to the appeal. Gasps followed by cheers and applause interrupted Alderman Jensen several times as he read the list. City Council officials said the audience

was the most emotional they had ever seen in the Town Hall at a public meeting. Hundreds of people waving banknotes swarmed around clerks taking donations, while other subscribers formed queues to borrow pens to write cheques.

At the start of the meeting Alderman Jensen led the official party on to the stage amid cheering, exploding flashbulbs and the whirring of newsreel and television cameras.

Seated under an array of Swedish, Danish and Australian flags were the designers of the Opera House, Messrs. J. Utzon and E. Andersson; the chairman of the Opera House committee, Mr S. Haviland; the chairman of the A.B.C., Sir Richard Boyer; Mr Cahill, Alderman Jensen, the Leader of the State Opposition, Mr. P. H. Morton, and the Vice-Chancellor of Sydney University, Professor S. H. Roberts.

The Lord Mayor, opening the meeting, said: 'The Opera House will be a symbol of our appreciation of the great cultural efforts of those who have gone before and of our faith in this great city. It will be more than a building, in fact a shrine, a memorial to the great artists of the past and the present. We must always be on guard to see that purely material needs do not supersede and usurp humanity, the cultural needs, the things for the improvement of our minds.'

Alderman Jensen said the Elizabethan Theatre Trust would donate the profits from the gala performance of the Opera Tosca on September 13th. Miss Joan Hammond, who will star in the opera, was among the artists who gave performances at yesterday's meeting. The audience cheered Miss Hammond's performance of the aria 'One Fine Day', from the opera 'Madame Butterfly.'

The chairman of the A.B.C. (Sir Richard Boyer) moved the motion inaugurating the Opera House Appeal Fund. Sir Richard said: 'In launching the appeal we should remember that a great deal of its early inspiration came from one who did much to develop our musical life in this city and state. I refer to Sir Eugene Goossens. I hope that not only will the committee secure money from industrial firms but that every citizen of the state including the children will have some part in ownership of the Opera House.'

Mr Cahill was almost overcome with emotion as he told the applauding crowd: 'We are determined that this building shall be finished. We need only a continuance of this present mood to ensure that in the not too distant future a mighty Opera House will stand on Bennelong Point.' Mr Cahill said the building would be the most outstanding of its type in the world. 'However, the name Opera House has given rise to a misconception that it will be used only for grand opera, which would interest only a fragment of the community.' he said. 'The facts are that the two halls which will be included in this project will be used for opera performances for a maximum of only two months a year. The use of the title Opera House has become so widespread and general in recent months that we thought it best to preserve that name. I hope that it eventually will become known as the Royal Sydney Opera House. Representations will be made to Her Majesty for permission to use the prefix 'Royal' and it is our hope that she will approve.

The ordinary working man and his family will be able to go there just as well as those in more favoured circumstances. There will be nothing savouring even remotely of a class-conscious barrier and this project will stand as a monument of democratic nationhood in its truest sense.'

Mr Utzon, whose speech was also frequently interrupted by applause, said:

'My partner and I have difficulty in expressing how welcome we feel here. I hope we have answered all the letters we have received from the day we got the message telling us we had won the competition; those letters showed us how much you wanted this Opera House deep in your hearts.[111] The committee has done a lot of great work and I want particularly to congratulate the Premier. We, together with the hundreds of other architects who entered this competition, have done a lot of hard work too.' The audience cheered when Mr Utzon laughingly added: 'It is up to you to pay for it – that's the easy part.'[112]

When the meeting ended, men and women filed out into the foyer to look at the model of the Opera House. 'Superb!' said Miss Doris Fitton before she bustled back to the Independent Theatre to add the finishing touches to the first-night performance of *Macbeth*. 'I've always admired it very much' said artist Elaine Haxton, peering through the plate glass at the snow-white plastic petal-like structure. Actress Ursula Jeans spent longer than most inspecting every angle of the model, and said, 'I think it's a 21st cultural birthday present to the people of Australia.'[113]

Then that night, an impromptu kissing party in the Lord Mayors' reception room at the Town Hall raised nearly £300 towards the Opera House appeal.

Selling their kisses were Australian soprano, Joan Hammond; her manager, Miss Lolita Marriott; flautist, Miss Elaine Shaffer; and Mrs Ruggeriero Ricci, wife of the celebrated violinist. The party was held after the public meeting in the Town Hall, when the Lord Mayor, Ald. H.F. Jensen, entertained the Premier, Mr Cahill, the artists and distinguished guests.

Mr Erik Andersson, co-designer of the Opera House started it all by offering £50 for the appeal if he were allowed to kiss Miss Hammond.

Amid applause and laughter he and Miss Hammond kissed each other delicately on the cheek and Mr Andersson hastily wiped off the lipstick mark. His architect partner, Mr Joern Utzon, then topped this effort by paying £50 each to kiss Miss Shaffer and Mrs Ricci. As 6 ft $4\frac{1}{2}$ in tall Mr Utzon bent down to kiss Mrs Ricci she quipped: 'I am reducing the fee. The normal price is £100.' Miss Shaffer, herself, donated £10 to the appeal for the kiss she had received from Mr Utzon, and Miss Hammond followed by giving £50 in appreciation of Mr Andersson's kiss.

Mr Hugh Hunt, director of the Elizabethan Theatre Trust, gave £10 for permission to kiss Miss Marriott. Ald. Jensen then announced that the Leader of the State Opposition, Mr P.H. Morton, had given 15 guineas to kiss him.[114] 'I'll see you later about that, Pat', said Ald. Jensen. 'Very much later', Mr Morton said above the laughter.

Mrs Ricci said she would kiss the general manager of the ABC (Mr Charles Moses) and would give £10 if her husband would pay. Mr Ricci muttered something about pistols at dawn, but cheerfully paid up. Mr Moses said he had appreciated the kiss so much he would give £50.[115]

Mr Cahill, faced with the task of finding £3,500,000 to build the Opera House, beamed. The kissing proceeds at the end of the party amounted to £295 15s 0d.[116]

On the 18th, Utzon spoke as Guest of Honour on an ABC broadcast.

Mr Utzon said he had never met with such enthusiasm from people as he had experienced during his stay in Sydney... (And though)... people argued that Australia's housing shortage should be overcome before we built the Opera House, 'In Germany you see quite new buildings for opera and concerts in the middle of ruins. '[117]

He said that on its 'wonderful Harbour site' the Opera House, as planned, would be 'the finest of its sort in the world... This house of music is a house for various sorts of entertainments. It will be a house holding your Symphony Orchestra, you can listen to opera, you can have light music there. But especially it will be the home for the Sydney Symphony Orchestra – and you have got a wonderful symphony orchestra here. I have heard it once and it was a great experience. ... I really hope and I couldn't be happier if this Opera House would help Australia to have a new musical culture of its own and have its own face of art, together with its wonderful pioneer spirit.'

He said it would be necessary to train and encourage good Australian artists such as we trained our tennis players.

'If you don't build theatres and houses where audiences and artists meet, and buy only expensive stars from abroad, you will kill your own culture of music', he added.[118]

Shortly before leaving, Utzon was interviewed again by the *Herald*.

The interview was reported in an article headed 'Private Lives', 'In which a celebrity speaks his mind on a topic of his own choice.'

> In Europe there is little chance in big towns of getting a large space of clear land. Here your Government has a wonderful piece of land. It will place the Opera House on the "centre stage"'of Sydney. The pioneer period and the spirit of Sydney have shown themselves in the way this world-wide competition was conducted, with the architects themselves given the chance to assess the merit of the designs.
>
> In Europe it is always difficult to overcome old prejudices, and compromises are made. Here there has been no compromise. The Premier of New South Wales has himself been the first to back this 'no compromise' attitude. Before the last war the older, wealthier people supported the arts with large donations and patronage of individual artists. This was followed, in Germany, by the National Socialist Party domination of all things cultural. This resurgence of youthful enthusiasm is becoming world-wide, and culture is no longer restricted to the very wealthy.
>
> Even one building may make a difference to a city. In 1920 the city of Stockholm commissioned an architect to design a new City Hall. From the day that building was finished the face of the city began to change. For the architect had seen the soul of Stockholm, and turned the people's minds to the beauty of the waterfront and the possibility for improvement.
>
> When architects work they try to express the climate, and the personalities of the people who will live and use a house. The architect must be inspired...
>
> Before I left Denmark I had already received more than 800 letters from Australia. Both my partner, Erik Andersson, and I were very touched by the kindness and tremendous interest. I am sure the people of Sydney will understand when I say how deeply I feel my responsibility, and how much I am inspired by it.
>
> The setting of Sydney bears a close resemblance to Stockholm, and I know when I return home I shall continue to go to Stockholm to think out any problems concerning the Opera House.
>
> At a Youth Concert in the Town Hall recently I felt it a great privilege to be able to thank the leader of the orchestra personally, because until now I've always been sitting down in the audience. One thing I remember each time is my own love for music, and that in life every second spent in appreciation of feeling, is the most worthwhile thing a man can do.
>
> Naturally, both of us are looking forward to returning home. And, of course, we shall be taking koala bears back to our children.'[119]

On 21st August, before their departure later that day, Utzon said:

'We will be back next February with a set of large drawings of the Opera House. We will discuss these drawings with the Opera House Technical Committee in Australia and return to Denmark to complete our detailed working drawings. These will take us another 12 months. We will be ready for the foundation stone to be laid in 18 months from now.'

Mr Utzon said that while in Australia he and his partner had been approached to design numerous other buildings, including homes. 'We rejected the other work to devote our entire energies to the Opera House project', he said. 'We will not take on any other work until we have completed the Opera House.'

Mr Utzon said that their present office staff of 20 would be increased substantially to produce the plans in the time at their disposal. He said that the whole of his present staff were experts in their respective fields, would be concerned with the Opera House plans, and new staff would be taken on to complete other work his firm had in hand.

Mr Andersson said he and Mr Utzon were returning home via Japan and the U.S. in order to have discussions with experts on the shell-vault type of construction they had selected for the roof of the Opera House. And then the two architects left as they had come here – tourist class. 'It saves money and gets you there just the same', they explained.[120]

CHAPTER 5

ENTER ARUP

On 14th October 1955, at the time the Committee were formulating the Opera House competition guidelines, Pier Luigi Nervi presented a paper and was giving a speech to a learned body of engineers in Euston Road, London. Nervi had done much path-finding work in reinforced concrete since the 1930s in the construction of domes and vaults in buildings from aircraft hangars and sports stadiums to exhibition halls. Nervi designed these works and was a director of the firm which built them and believed:

> Constructional complications, or designs that require structural acrobatics are always a sign of a false structural conception – even to the untrained eye of the non-technical observer... I am absolutely certain that the prime condition of architectural expression in a structure is the correctness, and I might say, the inevitability of its structural design... form must be the necessary result, and not the initial basis, of structure... the contribution of technical constructional knowledge is only effective if it is brought into collaboration with the architect from the inception of the scheme; as with living creatures, it is very difficult to eliminate in the development stage any initial deficiency or malformation...[1]

Ove Arup opened the discussion following Nervi's speech:

> ... Professor Nervi was absolutely right in saying that the best results are obtained when the designer and the constructor are the same person, or when they at least collaborate intimately, share in the responsibility and experience over a number of years. If new ground had to be opened up, then this close collaboration was absolutely essential...
>
> Professor Nervi had mentioned that a designing contractor may suggest daring solutions which might have seemed impossible to the professional designer. Mr Arup agreed, but suggested that it might also be the other way round, that the professional designer may have unorthodox ideas which seemed impossible to the contractor and which he therefore could not get carried out... [2]

On 3rd February 1957, Ove Arup wrote to Jorn Utzon after reading about the competition winner and seeing a sketch of his design in the London *Times* newspaper.

> Congratulations on the first prize! I am very glad that it was a Dane that

won and after seeing a sketch of your project, I am even happier – and not a little surprised – that such a fanciful but unusual project has been chosen instead of just being praised as is usually the case.

It will be very interesting to follow its development. I cannot believe other than doubts and protests will be raised and those who dislike the unusual will no doubt say that it is impractical and impossible to build. But I know that this time the pessimists will not succeed and it will be built...

So far as I can see, it would not be easy to calculate and detail your plans so as to give justice to your ideas with full clarity and still make them economically possible. Nor do I believe that you can count on Australian workmen and Australian technical resources being on the level of the Danish. But after what I have seen of your work and after what I have heard about you from other Danish architects, I think you will overcome all difficulties and will manage to do justice to the architecture.

If my firm can be of assistance to you in any way, it would give me great pleasure. I have of course over 30 years experience in co-operating with English architects and institutions and my partner Mr Jenkins is probably the leading authority in the structural field. Most importantly, you have your own engineering colleagues but maybe we could give them a bit of advice here and there. I would in any event welcome the opportunity to meet you. Are you coming through London on your way to Australia?...

Anyway the best of luck.

P.S. If you don't know who the hell I am you may think it very odd that I write to you. You may be right![3]

Ove Arup, 62 at the time of the Opera House Competition, was, 'one of those rare and elusive broad-gauge characters -... a mixture of philosopher, engineer, humanitarian, architect, scientist and perhaps other things as well – who rise seemingly without effort to the top of their chosen professions...'[4].

With a mental and physical energy that belied his age, Arup was described at about this time as 'a tall slim man, he walks purposively into his office always bent slightly forward as though in a hurry and always seemingly deep in thought. He's a man of enormous charm whom everybody must like. He'll talk for hours about almost anything preferably in terms of the abstract rather than the concrete. His accent betrays his Scandinavian origins. He never finishes a sentence. He paints pictures with his words to which he gives dimension with a pair of flashing hands...'[5].

Sir Hugh Casson recalled Arup as a man '... who was never one to let facts become the enemies of imagination. His amiable appearance, that kindly stooping stance, that wide gentle smile, his immediate and generous interest in everything and everybody disarmed all those who met or worked with him."[6]

Long-serving members of staff in his engineering business were tolerant of his minor idiosyncrasies, including his absent-mindedness, for they would occasionally be sent out on search parties at lunchtime because he had forgotten where he had parked his car.

During a speech on the founding of Arups at a Partners' Meeting at which Ove Arup was also present, senior partner Peter Dunican mentioned some of the jobs they had worked on over the years and the partners and staff who had carried these jobs through:

I hope that I haven't overlooked anyone. If I have, I am very sorry.

But the main source of our strength was Ove Arup. His ideas which may to-day seem commonplace and self-evident, were an inspiration to all of us. Simply, he believed in the integration of structure with architecture; that the structure had not only to be statically sound but that it should be constructionally viable and aesthetically acceptable. Simplicity with elegance – this was the lesson he taught us…

Coming as I did from an old-established and perhaps old-fashioned firm of consulting engineers in Victoria Street, I naturally found the Arup office a bit peculiar – to say the least of it. I had been accustomed to working with architects – but not quite the sort of architects we had to work with…

(One) architect who made a great impression of me was Michael Scott, for whom we worked on the Bus Station in Dublin. The Bus Station, like some other jobs, was mis-named. It was not only a Bus Station it was intended to be the headquarters offices of "Coras Iompair Eireann" – the Irish Transport Commission. This job had a rather chequered career, but it was the foundation of our Dublin office.

I remember the day Michael Scott came to talk to Ove Arup about the job. He'd made an appointment for 10 a.m. At 10.30 we had a telephone message to say that he couldn't quite make it, but that he'd be along within the hour. Well, this performance went on all day and he arrived at 7.15, apologising profusely. But there it was, he had arrived eventually and we could get down to business. That evening we left the office at about 9.30 p.m. having agreed that we would undertake the work – which of course implied setting up the Dublin office… [7]

Ove Arup, born on 16th April 1895 at Newcastle, England while his Norwegian mother and Danish father – who was the Danish Consul – were staying in the U.K., was the founder and senior partner of Ove Arup and Company Consulting Engineers. Going to school in Hamburg where his parents moved when he was seven, then studying philosophy and mathematics at Copenhagen University, Arup determined from these studies, 'that we don't know anything'[8], that 'introspection has a bad effect on you'[9] and that he would possibly rather be an 'artist' or a 'musician' but decided in the end that he would like to create buildings. 'Unsure of his artistic ability but sure of his mathematics, he chose to study structural engineering rather than architecture. In 1922, Arup graduated from Copenhagen's Royal Technical College with a masters degree in civil engineering, specialising in the theory of structures.'[10]

Arup's first job was in Hamburg with Christiani and Nielsen, a Danish company specialising at that time in marine projects. He then worked for the same company in London as their chief designer. In 1933 he joined J.L.Kier and Co., a company doing pioneering work in reinforced concrete construction, then in 1938 formed with his cousin, Arne Arup, a firm of engineers, Arup and Arup Ltd.

On the outbreak of the Second World War Arup turned his attention to the design of air raid shelters, aiming for the greatest protection as economically as possible, and wrote two books on the subject. Later in the war he designed underground concrete fuel tanks for the Air Ministry, and a big jetty at Heysham in north western England, which employed for the first time the principle of weight-lifting fenders, a technique later used successfully in the floating concrete Mulberry Harbour for the Normandy landings which Arup also worked on.

From the time he set up his partnership in 1946, Arup devoted his energies to structural consulting work for architects. 'I try to help him to express himself',[11] Arup would say of architects. Sir Basil Spence, who was working with Arup on Coventry Cathedral at the time of the Opera House competition, said he enjoyed working with Arup because 'working with him has always been an adventure. Always out of every meeting we ever had, something positive has come out...'[12] Another architect, Denys Lasdun, said of Arup 'His contribution has been not so much a propping up of architect's ideas – this any routine engineer can do – (but)... He always enters into the exercise of architecture itself.'[13]

Peter Dunican thought that working with Arup meant an attitude of mind, 'It's the building that matters... structure is only important insofar as it is part of a building.'[14] But as well as that 'It is a very simple lesson which Ove has taught us, to care about what we are doing and the way in which we do it.'[15]

On 12th February, Professor Martin wrote to Ashworth in Sydney:

I am writing to let you know that Utzon flew over to England on Wednesday last and that Eero Saarinen and I saw him and discussed with him the way in which the Opera House project would be carried out.

I am now sending you this letter with Eero Saarinen's agreement. In the first place we would like to say that we feel that Utzon is a charming person. We are sure that he will be both enthusiastic and helpful in developing the project with the Committee. He apparently has an office in Denmark and is carrying out a housing scheme in Sweden, but all the drawings for this work are finished and Utzon states that it can now be carried on by his staff. He is, therefore, ready to start at once on the Sydney scheme.

We have considered with him various possibilities of collaboration. We are, however, completely satisfied that he ought to take the personal responsibility of working with the Committee in developing the program, and that he is admirably equipped to deal with all matters of design. The support which he needs is, in fact, connected particularly with the technical problem of calculating and later building the very complicated shell vault system. We therefore feel that the best type of collaboration would be with an engineering firm of outstanding reputation from the start. I should perhaps add that this suggestion has Utzon's complete agreement. We have in mind that he should work with a firm of the standing of Ove Arup and Partners in London or Christiani and Nielson of Copenhagen. We feel that this collaboration would give Utzon any support which he might need on the managerial and financial side of the work. We think that this type of collaboration would be the most effective way of using his capabilities to the full and of ensuring that the best advice is available on the structural aspects of the work... [16]

Ashworth in turn wrote to Stan Haviland on the 28th to confirm that the assessors believed Utzon should '... undertake the task of building the Opera House without the necessity of having to associate himself with any other firm of architects... (and)... that Ove Arup and Partners of London should definitely be the engineer for the work and I am certain that Mr Utzon would have no objection to this...'.[17]

George Molnar, who had taken part in the first Opera House Committee meeting and played an active role in contributing data for the competition conditions, then withdrew from any further meetings. 'I wanted to win the competition.'[18] He entered with one of Australia's biggest architectural companies, Stephenson and

Turner, 'They were to supply the draftsmen, I the concept.'[19] Molnar recalled his design and the events that followed:

> It was exactly the opposite of Utzon's. He was inspired by white sails and blue water, I by the lights of the Manly ferry scurrying across the water. The halls were back to back, wrapped in blazing foyers. In the centre, like a giant smokestack, stood the stagetower, exaggerated in height by the two-storeyed restaurant on top of it, a floating island of light. It was not a good design.
>
> The fateful day of announcing the results at the Art Gallery came. Steam gave way to sail. Rightly I thought, and went back to the *Herald* to do my cartoon... [20]
>
> The editor was Colin Bingham: 'What is Utzon's design like?'
>
> 'Marvellous.'
>
> 'Explain it to me.'
>
> So I explained, and Colin wrote a leader coming in strongly with all the authority of the *Herald* behind the winning entry.[21]

Molnar had a Carnegie grant, and the day following the judging of the competition he left the country on sabbatical leave. In Mexico he looked up Felix Candela, a Spanish immigrant producing 'fabulous' concrete shell constructions of his own invention based on parabolas. 'He took me to one of his latest structures. Huge concrete shells, two inches thick, soared from the ground, intersecting each other, supporting each other, leaning, curling, spreading, like the spray from a frozen fountain. It was a church.'[22]

Candela built his structures with his own construction company, without using engineers because 'They always tried to prove that what I want cannot be done.'[23] The architect of the church Candela showed Molnar had been told by engineers it could not be designed like that: 'They wanted heavy arches to support heavy beams and vaults. The architect came to me at the end. I said "Yes, why not? Well here it is".'[24]

Molnar showed Candela the *Herald* clipping of Utzon's winning design, who said '... Yes, it can be built. Some of the shapes have to be altered. I would like to see the drawings. We should have no one way curvatures. But it can be built. And the shapes can be even more beautiful.'[25] Molnar wrote an article on his visit to Candela which was published in the *Herald* on 23rd March. But what Molnar *had not* written in the *Herald* was that on seeing Utzon's design, Candela 'looked at it; photographed it, then said, "but these shells are not self-supporting".'[26]

On 18th June, once it was clear that construction of the Opera House would proceed, Ashworth wrote to Ove Arup to inform him unofficially that the assessors had recommended his company as consulting engineers for the project, adding:

> ... There is some opinion locally even amongst engineers, that these forms cannot be constructed either economically or safely, but the Assessors of the competition do not subscribe to this opinion. I am quite sure that there will be numerous difficulties to overcome, but equally sure that you are the person to overcome them... [27]

Ove Arup thought that the assessors had shown 'great courage' to back the Opera House plan, which showed almost no details or had any evidence of its structural feasibility. Indeed Utzon had 'conceived the scheme which he submitted for the competition apparently unaided by structural engineering advice... All surfaces were free shapes without geometric definition and their structural viability had to be proved... Strictly speaking, Utzon's intuitive technical assessment turned out to be erroneous. He had visualized the roof as thin shells. This was not possible since the very shape of the roof introduced high bending moments regardless of any structural system.'[28]

Arup though thought the Opera House was 'one of the most exciting buildings ever designed from the point of view of architects and engineers... I don't know how you could do anything to cheapen it without spoiling the idea. You just can't compromise. It's the most marvellous thing that has been built this century... (and) could become the world's foremost contemporary masterpiece if Utzon is given his head... What we want is to do our utmost to make Utzon's dream come true, at whatever cost to ourselves, as long as we can bear it...'[29]

Ove Arup had his first meeting with Utzon before Utzon went to Australia for the first time. Arup later said of Utzon: 'He is a brilliant designer – one of the best, and probably the best of any I have come across in my long experience of working with architects – and he has a remarkable grasp of or ability quickly to understand the essence of other technical disciplines as they impinge on his architectural conception...' He found Utzon '... always prepared to consider anything... very refreshing... without prejudice and preconceived ideas.' And his personality 'very strong, ascetic and controlled...'[30]

Ove found to be in the presence of Utzon 'Working with this young architect, it actually excites me. I feel that being in his company, and talking over plans with somebody so exciting as Utzon gives me great excitement and great pleasure.'[31]

Although Utzon was 'very disappointed when I told him at our first interview that the shape (of the shells) was not very suitable structurally... It soon became clear that any alteration to the cross-section... would completely destroy the architectural character... So in the end Utzon and I decided that the scheme had to go ahead as designed by Utzon, more or less...'[32]

Arup replied to Ashworth on 24th June:

> ... We should certainly be very interested in collaborating with Mr Utzon on his extremely imaginative project.
>
> I have seen Mr Utzon, and I have seen other work he has done, and I have formed the highest opinion of his ability as an Architect. I am quite sure that he will make a success of the scheme if it goes forward, and I also think that we can deal with the shells in the spirit in which they have been conceived. As you may know, my Partner, Mr R. S. Jenkins, is a world authority on the design of shells, and has just been perfecting methods of dealing with shells of such unusual shapes. ... I am quite sure that we shall be able to work very happily with Mr Utzon if the project matures... [33]

On 5th July R.J. Thomson, Secretary and Executive Officer of the Committee, wrote officially to Ove Arup letting him know they planned to appoint him as structural engineer. In his reply on 15th July, Ove Arup promised to

> spare no effort to make (the Opera House) a success... Obviously the calculation of the shells will be a very intricate business which will call for the development of new techniques both for the calculation, testing and construction. The shells are of a shape which has never been constructed before, and are on a large scale; moreover the shells are different in shape, so that there is no repetition as is normal in reinforced concrete work.
>
> Although the shape of the shells is structurally very sound, and indicates that the Architect has a true feeling for structural shapes, the actual calculation by theoretical analysis will be extremely complicated, and will require the use of electronic digital computers...
>
> We will of course also have to pay very careful attention to the method of constructing these shells. We have already some ideas on the subject, but it will be most important to go very carefully into this in order to reduce the cost of the shells which could be considerable unless tackled rationally.

As I have mentioned before, we do not anticipate any difficulties which we cannot overcome, but it will require considerable effort, and close collaboration with the Architect to achieve the right result... [34]

On 31st July 1957, the Sydney *Daily Telegraph*, quoting an 'official', reported that '... the Government would engage an English firm, Ove Arup and Partners, as consulting engineers to work with Mr Utzon on the Opera House... In a letter to the Committee, the firm said the shapes of the shells in the Opera House design were structurally sound.'[35]

CHAPTER 6

THE APPEAL AND LOTTERY

It did not matter whether or not the Opera House had the approval to go ahead, what it was called[1] or if the shells would stand up if the funds were not available to build it. Cahill was determined at the outset the Opera House would be paid for as it was built, free of debt, so that its cost would not become a financial burden on the community. It was a crucial factor in gaining a vote of confidence in the Opera House from the State Labor Caucus and the annual meeting of the State Labor Party conference that Cahill was able to assure those organisations the Opera House could be funded by a public appeal and special lotteries.

The appeal had got off to a flying start with the meeting at the Town Hall, and there followed an enthusiastic rush of ideas for raising funds. Utzon, on his way to appear on Channel 9's 'TV Town Talk' program during his first visit to Sydney:

> With his partner Erik Andersson, he stopped for a coffee – and got talking about raising money.
>
> Utzon went up to the coffee shop proprietor and asked for a small box. The bloke, looking oddly at this Great (6 feet 4½ inch) Dane, found one.
>
> Utzon cut a slit in the lid, wrote 'For the Opera House' on the top, put it on the counter and popped two bob in it.
>
> 'If you can, so can I', said the proprietor. And he put in two bob. By the time they left, another 6d. had found its way in... [2]

One member of the public suggested making advance sales of seats to raise finance for the project. Sydney housewives gave Opera House luncheons to raise money. While the appeal organising committee asked the Chief Secretary if special meetings of horse races could be held in aid of the Opera House fund.

One reader of the *Herald*, Palmer Kent suggested the Post Office could issue a special 'Opera' stamp at a higher price than the standard letter stamp rate, the extra money going towards the building, but the public could still buy stamps at the usual 'face' value if they wanted to.[3]

Agnes Jackson of Ryde wrote that it would be the women of the

State who would be the driving force behind raising funds for the Opera House, because at any display of the arts, from art exhibitions to theatre going, 'women far outnumbered men, and of those men present, the majority wear an expression of resigned compulsion.'[4]

Sir Bernard Heinze suggested that Australia could follow Italy's example, where an opera tax is imposed on theatre tickets, race tickets and tobacco, and the revenue from the tax subsidises Italian opera.[5] The president of the Taxpayers' Association said the association was opposed to any new tax to help build the Opera House.[6]

To drum up publicity for the project, three models of the Opera House were made, the largest of which was displayed at the Museum of Modern Art in New York. The Federal Treasurer, Sir Arthur Fadden, sent a telegram to Cahill informing him donations to the Sydney Opera House appeal would be allowable as an income tax deduction. This meant if the full amount of £1 million that was expected to be raised by the appeal was received, it would mean an indirect Commonwealth 'subsidy' of at least £100,000.

The Lord Mayor announced that all names of people who subscribe to the Appeal Fund would be recorded in a book to be displayed in the Opera House. The book would be of special parchment which would last permanently and would be placed in a specially designed part of the Opera House. Names of all subscribers would be inscribed in the book in alphabetical order and the book would be opened at a different page every day. [7]

To woo prospective donors a special appeal booklet entitled *A time for Action* was produced. The booklet included pictures of the 12 divisional chairmen of the Sydney Opera House Appeal Campaign and appealed for 'dedicated men: men of goodwill and purpose who will bring the glorious vision of the Sydney Opera House to triumphal realisation. Australia needs the drive and enterprise of leaders in business and the professions who will see that the project does not lag for need of money'. For those with £1,000 to spare 'The name of each donor of £1,000 or more will be recorded on an engraved brass plate on a chair, in one of the auditoria of the Opera House'[8] while donors of £100 or more would receive a personal '"Donor's Certificate", printed on antique parchment paper, suitable for framing.' As all donations were tax deductible a table gave a net cost to donors for a gift of £100 depending on which tax bracket they fell into.

THE APPEAL AND LOTTERY

On 29th September 1957, the appointment was announced of Mr Alan Palmer, a former Adelaide journalist and public relations officer as publicity and liaison officer for the Opera House Appeal on a salary of £2,500 a year. Major General Ivan Dougherty, Director of Civil Defence and Director of State Emergency Services was chosen as fund organiser for the appeal. 'Quite appropriate' it was suggested by one reader of the *Herald* because his 'job is to prepare to meet national disasters.'[9]

In the newspapers over the following months donations to the Fund were listed and tallied, sometimes daily, from individual donations of five shillings to a gift of £15,000 from The Rural Bank. Donations poured in from the meek and the mighty. Australian Consolidated Press gave £10,000 to be paid in three equal yearly instalments, Hoyts Theatres and Ampol Petroleum both gave £1,000. The Wine and Spirit Merchants' Association of NSW gave 100 guineas, the Sydney University Women's Group £69 10s 0d and 'Three Canberra legal officers', £8 10s 0d.

An American shipping company, the Matson Lines, donated £500 and ten US dollars was received by international postal order from Mr Warwick L.Smith of Los Angeles. From the Brewers Association of NSW came £2,500, the Elizabethan Theatre Trust gave £717, the proceeds of a gala first-night performance of *Tosca*. Woolworths gave £1,000. At the Australian premiere of *Around the World in Eighty Days*, for which patrons paid from £50 to £5 a seat, over half the proceeds of £3,802 went to the Appeal Fund, the remainder going to other charities. Schools held collections and the NSW Headmistresses Association gave £21. One gift of two guineas was listed 'anonymous'. The Federated Storemen and Packers Union gave £10 and 'proceeds of wine tasting party organised by Miss Margaret Gillespie £100', while the 'proceeds of dinner and musicale at the home of Mrs MacKenzie-Forbes' raised £35 10s 6d. George Sutherland from Wau in New Guinea, sent £50, 'in memory of soldiers killed in the New Guinea campaign in World War II who appreciated good music.' General Motors Holden gave £5,000.[10]

Following the first flush of enthusiasm during the months after the launch of the Appeal, Fund organisers found it an uphill battle to maintain the momentum of donations, until money coming into the Fund nearly dried up completely. In May 1958, the Opera House

Appeal Fund administration costs were 60 per cent of the months' collections, with gifts for the month of £1,164 11s 10d and expenses totalling £691 19s 7d. At the meeting of the Appeal Fund Committee on 19th June 1958, one member expressed concern that at this rate Cahill would be 'laying the Opera House foundation stone on a vacant lot.'[11] There were 102 members of the Appeal Fund at the time it was established, but in September 1958, 13 months later, the Chairman of the Fund, the Lord Mayor, Mr Jensen, announced that only eight or nine of the original Fund members continued to attend meetings. Since the 17th of July salaries and stationery had cost £728 but only £480 had been received in donations for the same period.[12]

On 17th July 1958 when the Appeal Fund stood at £218,147 the Fund Committee dismissed two secretaries and Mr Palmer took a salary cut from £2,500 to £2,000 'on the understanding that he would take on other part-time work.' Appeal Fund staff were moved from Caltex House to free office accommodation in the Australian Electrical Industries building offered by the Chairman of AEI who was one of the Appeal Committee members.[13]

On 18th September 1958, Mr Jensen accepted the resignation 'with regret of the publicity officer of the fund, Mr. Palmer and henceforth City Council staff would be employed part-time on appeal fund work.'[14] Palmer's resignation took effect on 3rd October. On 18th October Palmer said the Appeal was being damaged by ineptitude, political grandstanding and social climbing. Being associated with the Fund fiasco had damaged his professional reputation and 'every constructive idea ever put forward was knocked on the head.' Palmer said he had been in PR a long time, but this was his first connection with any government project and 'If I had know the way they go on I'd never have touched it.'[15]

Doing his best to keep donations to the Fund rolling in was the Appeal Fund Chairman, the Labor Lord Mayor of Sydney Harry Jensen. Jensen was from a Danish background – his grandfather had migrated from Copenhagen in 1870 – and in April 1958 he left on a nine-week world tour to 'sell' Australia wherever he went, in the hope of attracting as much capital as possible to Australia. Optimistic of collecting large sums for the Appeal from the 'home of his ancestors',

He said Danish industrialists in Copenhagen had stated they would make major contributions to the Opera House Appeal if Sydney's 'Danish'

Lord Mayor would collect it from them on the steps of the Copenhagen Town Hall.

'So you can be sure that while I am visiting the Lord Mayor of Copenhagen I will also make sure I have time to meet these Danish industrialists.'[16]

Initially Jensen had belonged to the school of thought that funds should be found for houses before Opera Houses, but had since been caught up in the general enthusiasm for the project and had asked the Sydney County Council to give £10,000 a year for five years to the Sydney Opera House Appeal Fund. But there followed a wrangle with the aldermen of Council about a section of the Local Government Act the Sydney Council under which they were authorised to donate such large sums. The general manager of the Council, Mr Ranger, referred to Section 504 of the Act, under which the council was permitted to make gifts of only £100. 'Alderman E.C. O'Dea (ALP): It looks like there is nothing else we can do but give only £100; Alderman F. Joyce, (ALP): The law is there and we must abide by it.'[17]

Jensen claimed it was not Section 504 of the Act he was referring to, but Section 358 which stated a council may subsidise various institutions including those providing for the 'cultural welfare of the people.' 'If the Sydney County Council had the will to contribute to the Opera House under this section of the Act it could do so.' Jensen was voted down and the Council made a donation of £100 to the fund.[18]

Instead of taking on another publicity officer, on 20th November 1958, the Appeal Fund Committee announced it would approach a company of fund-raising consultants, J. Raymond, Stocker and Co., as it was anticipated their fees would be less than employing a full-time organising staff.[19] The director of the company, Mr. J. R. Stocker would recruit workers, some of them voluntary, to carry out initiatives from door-knocking campaigns to direct appeals to large industrial and commercial interests. The Appeal Committee remained confident of raising the £1,000,000 towards the cost of the Opera House and it was anticipated Stocker would charge 3 per cent or £20,000 to raise the extra £700,000 to make up the balance needed.[20] This proposal was rejected by the Appeal Fund Committee because Stocker would charge £20,000 if his company raised the money or not, and the Committee decided to launch its own fund-raising effort along the lines outlined by Stocker. 'It is necessary to revitalise the appeal' said Jensen. 'The original target which would mean raising another £700,000 was an arbitrary figure and not necessarily a realistic one... we should adopt a more realistic target and make greater efforts to raise it.'[21]

In September 1959 Jensen launched a new drive to raise £250,000 for the Opera House. Headed by eight business and community leaders, the six-week campaign with 500 voluntary committeemen would approach 5,000 firms and large organisations for gifts each year for three years of as many pounds as they had employees.[22] At a dinner at the Trocadero on 10th November, the Appeal Fund Committee announced the special drive had raised £53,660 for the Opera House.[23] Harry Ashworth showed slides at the dinner of Utzon's Opera House model and afterwards business leaders reported the funds collected from various divisions of the business community. They included food and clothing industries, £20,460, commerce industries £1,200, building and construction industries £6,190, light industries £12,210, general finance industries £960, heavy industries £4,500, service industries £5,000, transport industries £3,000, trade unions £140.[24]

Significant as the funds raised by the Opera House Appeal were, they paled in comparison to the funds rolling in from another method of financing construction.

When early schemes were floated of methods to finance the Opera House, one reporter proposed doubling the licensing fee on poker machines (one armed bandits) to raise capital:

> ... why not let poker machines build it? After all clubs are alleged to be sponsors of culture.
>
> The Government is culture minded. Hence the acceptance of an Opera House design that looks like Capetown's Table Top mountain in eruption.
>
> And of course when the Opera House is built, somewhere high above the roof could stand a huge illuminated poker machine, symbol of culture in this state.
>
> (While to complement the bars)... what better can be provided than a battery of poker machines in the foyer.[25]

Using poker machines to raise finance was not quite as ludicrous as this proposal seemed. Just one club with 20 poker machines made a clear profit on them of £28,000 in 1958.[26]

But the government already had its eye on an alternative method of gambling to finance the Opera House. On the suggestion of the Committee,[27] the government was examining whether lotteries could be a viable source of revenue. Since 1932 the State government had been raising money for hospitals, schools and public works through lotteries, and on 10th February 1957 a small article appeared in the newspaper saying the Opera House Committee would consider a suggestion of lotteries to finance the building of the Opera House at its next meeting.

> A Government official said yesterday that big lotteries with first prizes of £100,000 or more would capture the imagination (and cash) of people of New South Wales who send large amounts to Tasmania and Victoria for tickets in mammoth lotteries.
>
> 'The people of N.S.W. would know when they bought a ticket that they were investing in the future development of culture in their own State as well as having the knowledge they could win some money', he added.[28]

Following the vote of the Labor Caucus on 8th May in support of an early start to construction and the launch of a public appeal and running of special lotteries to finance the project, Cahill had conceded 'The thing I am worried about is the cost of the project. Some of the methods we have to adopt to raise finance are a bit difficult.'[29]

The initial proposal for an Opera House lottery had been with tickets of £1 10s 0d each and a first prize of £50,000, with four lotteries a year, but following concerns this may not raise the necessary cash to cover construction costs, the Labor Caucus approved a plan for up to three lotteries a year with a first prize of £100,000 with tickets at £5 each. Second prize was £50,000, third £25,000 and there were 2,645 prizes of from £25 to £1,000. The first prize was the highest ever offered in a NSW State lottery, the odds of 1 in 38 the shortest on winning a prize and the cost of the tickets the most expensive ever in NSW. Five pounds was not a small amount of money at the time, and amounted to a week's wage for many low paid employees. Receipts in each lottery from the sale of 100,000 tickets would be £500,000, total value of the 2,648 prizes would be £330,000, with a balance of revenue of £170,000 less costs going to finance construction of the Opera House.

Following Utzon's visit to Australia and the launch of the appeal, the announcement of the £100,000 lotteries was officially made on 29th

September 1957, the day State Labor Caucus gave approval to their formation. It was intended to hold the first lottery before Christmas. 'The Premier said that if the estimate of £3½ million needed for the building were correct, at least two-thirds of the funds required would be in hand by the time the Opera House was finished. The lotteries would continue until the Government had all the money required.'[30]

The Opera House was not to be a project like the pyramids, built on the sweat of the brow of a pharaoh's army of slaves, but on the sweat of the brow of the NSW working public who were slaves to the dollar. If they must throw their money away they could throw it away on something constructive like the Opera House. It was to be the ultimate gamble. Utzon had taken a gamble with his design. Any architect who enters an architectural competition is taking a gamble; he is hoping, against long odds, that his scheme will be the winner. The assessors had taken a gamble choosing it – it was so unusual. Arup had taken a gamble taking the project on as an engineer, he could not immediately see a solution to the shells but he was certain given time he would find one. And now the Australian public were gambling to finance it.[31] But this method of raising finance did not meet with universal approval. 'Gambling and culture are antitheses' wrote W. G. Hanson from Parramatta.

> We cannot mix the two to form a healthy concoction; they are as fire and water, for gambling destroys culture. If Jack Lang[32] could build the Sydney Harbour Bridge with clean money why cannot Mr Cahill and his Government produce a home of culture, the Opera House, clean and free from the taint of gambling?[33]

Dr Malcolm Mackey, the Minister of Scots Church in Sydney, stated that if the government financed the Opera House through lotteries it would be 'erecting a perpetual memorial to the cultural and moral poverty of Sydney. Future visitors to Sydney will look eagerly for Cahill's casino on Bennelong Point.'

While the Coadjutor Bishop of Sydney, the Right Reverend W. G. Hilliard said, 'The whole thing is deplorable. It is regrettable that a Government should be financing cultural movement by the encouragement of a social vice.'[34] Though a spokesman for the Catholic Church, the Reverend Dr. L. Rumble went on record as saying 'The method proposed does not violate any principle of our church.'[35]

Most people approved of State lotteries, a Gallup Poll indicating only 11 per cent were opposed to them and 4 per cent were uncertain. The State lotteries were big business in NSW, employed 450 people directly and augmented the income of countless ticket-buying agents. In the financial year 1956-57 N.S.W. had 350 State lotteries with ticket sales amounting to £12,800,000. Nine out of ten people bought lottery tickets, though not always on a regular basis.[36] A staff correspondent on the *Herald* wrote:

> It may be asked whether simple judgments of the 'good or bad' variety, such as have already been made about this new lottery, have any relevance in the face of a social phenomenon so well entrenched. A history stretching back to ancient Rome suggests that lotteries, far from being a disease of the times, express something inherent in human nature. And sociologists have long treated them as such.
>
> William McDougall, discussing the acquisitive instinct, wrote in his 'Introduction to Social Psychology':
>
> 'Like other instincts, it ripens naturally and comes into play independently of all training...'
>
> And the actual trend of lotteries strongly supports the idea that people indulge in them impulsively, instinctively, without too much resort to reason.[37]

On the opening day of the lottery, 25th November 1957, NSW lottery offices sold 1,250 tickets 'well up to my expectations' said Mr C. T. Tallentire, the director of State lotteries.[38]

At the York Street lottery ticket office in Sydney, a jewel-encrusted dowager examined her £5 lottery ticket through a pair of lorgnettes before tucking it away. 'In 15 years of selling lottery tickets, I've never seen that before', said Miss Patricia Hinchey at the counter. Traditional syndicate names like 'Avago' and 'Free Beer' were giving way to 'Mozart', 'Beethoven' and 'Grand Opera.' Mr Cecil Johnson, in charge of the York Street office said, 'I have seen lots of new types fill in application forms but I'll wager the music they want to hear is of winning that £100,000.' Utzon wrote in with a payment for a ticket, 'I seem to be a very lucky fellow, I am sure I have a good chance of winning the lottery.'[39]

The first Opera House Lottery was filled in five weeks and one day, and tickets immediately went on sale for a second. In the first televised draw of a NSW lottery, in January 1958, the first three prizes of £100,000, £50,000 and £25,000 were drawn by Stan Haviland at 8.45 one morning in the auditorium of the Lotteries Department in Barrack Street, Sydney. Tickets had been sold as far afield as the UK, US, Canada, South Africa, Fiji and New Zealand, but the first prize-winner was Oswald Sellers, who owned a sheep station, a chocolate factory and an advertising agency among other business interests and lived in a Point Piper mansion in Sydney with his housekeeper, chauffeur and gardener.

One of the criticisms raised against the lotteries at the outset was that money going to the Opera House lottery would be at the expense of other lotteries, which raised money for schools and other public works. On the announcement of the intention to hold Opera House lotteries, Liberal MP Robert Askin had asked Cahill in Parliament '... does the Premier agree that inevitably these special lotteries will result in less support for the ordinary lotteries and consequently less finance for our hospitals?' To which Cahill had replied '... It is believed that the proceeds from the ordinary lotteries will not be affected to any extent'[40] and that NSW money which had previously gone to interstate lotteries with large first prizes would now stay in NSW. In the event Cahill was proved right, the Opera House lotteries only had a minimal effect on revenue from other lotteries. Comparing revenues from sales of ordinary lottery tickets during an eight-month period before and after the start of the Opera House lotteries, Tallentire announced figures of £8,448,793 and £8,484,200 for the respective periods, 'The deficiency is £35,417... This is slight when set against the whole balance sheet.'[41]

Revenue from the Opera House lotteries quickly surpassed funds raised by the Appeal. When the first Opera House lottery opened on 25th November 1957, money actually received by the Appeal was £174,080. By the close of the second Opera House lottery the lotteries had raised over £300,000. But the Opera House lotteries were taking longer and longer to fill. The first in 1957 was filled in 28 days, the sixth in 1959 took four months. To revive interest, in 1960 the government introduced new 'windfall lotteries', still with a first prize of £100,000 but with many smaller prizes, short odds of just one chance in fourteen of winning a prize and tickets at £3 each.[42] These lotteries were an immediate success, the first sold out in 13 days and the second was selling just as quickly.

One of the first winners of the new windfall lotteries drawn on 1st

June 1960 was Basil Thorne, a travelling salesman. He had been at Tamworth when the lottery was drawn and at first had thought the travellers at the hotel where he had spent the night were trying to pull his leg:

> He said he realised it was no joke when the newspaper reporter told him the number of the ticket and the name of the syndicate. 'I suddenly went cold all over. I felt flutters in my stomach and I could not talk. I could not even write and someone nearby finished the orders I was making out.' He refused to get excited over his win and said the money would not be spent recklessly or given away. 'I believe in the saying charity begins at home and intend to make this my policy', he added. Mr Thorne said that apart from buying a house he would make no other immediate decisions about how the money would be spent (and) said he did not know yet whether he would give up his job since his father had to be considered. 'If I left the road it would be leaving him in the lurch' he said.[43]

Then on 8th July 1960, there was a headline on the front page of the *Herald*, '£25,000 DEMAND FOR BOY, STATEWIDE HUNT FOR KIDNAPPER':

> The whole of N.S.W. was alerted last night in the search for the kidnapper of Graeme Thorne, 8½-year-old son of a recent £100,000 lottery winner. The kidnapper, speaking with a foreign accent, telephoned the boy's home yesterday morning and demanded £25,000 for his safe return. While the search went on relentlessly, the father, Basil Thorne, made a heart-broken appeal: 'For God's sake send him back in one piece.' The distraught mother, now under sedation by the family doctor, said: 'Even if we have to pay out the £100,000, we shall do so to get back our boy.'

Graeme Thorne had left his home in Bondi on the morning of the 7th to go to Scots College and on his way was bundled into a car by Stephen Bradley, a Hungarian-born former male nurse and one-time confidence trickster, who worked in a poker machine factory on £18 a week. Bradley had at one stage called at the Thorne's house posing as a private detective to gather information on Graeme's movements and later when he had rung the Thorne's with his ransom demand he had threatened 'feeding him to the sharks' if it was not paid.

The crime shocked the nation. It was the first kidnapping in the history of Australia. The Premier, Mr Heffron, describing this 'appalling happening' said 'Somehow, we have never thought that kidnapping a child and holding him to ransom could occur in this country.'[44] There followed a massive manhunt by the police, which intensified when Graeme Thorne's body was found in a car boot at vacant land at Seaforth on Sydney's North Shore on 16th August. Bradley escaped from Sydney aboard the P & O liner *Himalaya*, but was arrested and deported to Australia when he went ashore at Colombo.

Bradley was found guilty at his trial of murder, and sentenced on 29th March 1961 to 'penal servitude for life.' When the jury passed their verdict the crowd in the courtroom had greeted it with clapping, whistles and catcalls, while one woman screamed 'Feed him to the sharks.' In another part of the court Graeme Thorne's mother was weeping, consoled by her husband who had his hand around her shoulders.[45]

Bradley was later to die in gaol. Until the Thorne's kidnapping, the names and addresses of Opera House lottery winners were published in the papers. Afterwards names of lottery winners were only published at the discretion of the winner.

But tragic as it was, the Thorne kidnapping did not put a blight on the Opera House lotteries. A sound basis had been established for financing the building and throughout its construction and for many years afterwards money poured into the Opera House account from the proceeds of the lotteries like manna from heaven. It was wonderful, like picking pound notes from a money tree, as if no one was having to pay for it.

CHAPTER 7

THE PODIUM

One reader of the *Herald* suggested a verse for the Opera House:

– Upon the walls of the soaring Opera House let there be graven the lines of Oliver Wendall Holmes, so much more applicable to our Opera House than to the chambered nautilus; –
'This is the ship of pearl, which, poets feign,
Sails the unshadowed main,
The venturous bark that flings
On the sweet summer wind its purpled wings
In gulfs enchanted, where the Siren signs;
And coral reefs lie bare,
Where the cold sea-maids rise to sun their streaming hair,
Build thee more noble mansions,
O my soul,
As the swift seasons roll!
Leave thy low-vaulted past!
Let each new temple, nobler than the last,
Lift thee to heaven with a dome more vast,
Till thou at length art free
Leaving thine outgrown shell by life's unresting sea!'[1]

Though Utzon believed the Opera House did not need to be identified. He called the new buildings on the harbour front near Circular Quay 'boxes'. 'If the Opera House was designed like a box it would have to be labelled "This is the Sydney Opera House." Cathedrals do not have to be labelled. In the same way an Opera House should be distinctive and not like a box.'[2]

When Utzon received the competition conditions and was able to study the Opera House site from the photos in the competition booklet, he could see that the site would be looked down on from the Harbour Bridge, the buildings of the city and from the apartments in Kirribilli on the opposite side of the Harbour. The site was 'almost a stage in the Harbour'[3] and quite small, so 'I made the whole peninsula to be the building.'[4] Utzon's inspiration for the base or 'podium' of the building came from the Mayan temples of Yucatan in south east Mexico, which Utzon had visited with Lis some years earlier. 'The platform as an architectural element is a fascinating feature. I first fell in love with it in Mexico on a study trip in 1949, where I found many variations... A great strength radiates from them.'

> Yucatan is a flat lowland covered with an inaccessible jungle, which grows up to a certain uniform defined height. In this jungle the Mayans lived in their villages with small pieces of land cleared for cultivation, and their surrounding picture, background as well as roof, was the hot, damp, green jungle. No large views, no up and down movements.
>
> By introducing the platform with a level at the same height as the jungle top, these people had suddenly obtained a new dimension in life... On these high situated platforms – many of them as long as 100 meters – they built their temples. They had from here the sky, the clouds and the breeze, and suddenly the jungle roof had been converted into a great open plain. By this architectural trick they had completely changed the landscape and supplied their visual life with a greatness corresponding to the greatness of their Gods.[5]

'It's a tremendous experience to see how an architectural idea must have evolved in order to create contact with their Gods... I wondered who thought of it. It's such a brilliant idea...'.[6] Standing on the platform would be like standing on the cliffs of the Sydney Heads[7] 'the feeling under your feet... is the same as the firmness you experience when standing on a large rock.'[8] For theatre-goers approaching the building, 'rather than a long, dreary walk, this will mean for many people a new experience to rest their eyes on such an expanse of straight lines and massive structure – a change from the tense and ragged skyline of the buildings surrounding the harbour.'[9] 'When you see a hill before you, you want to climb up it, and so I put the wide steps in front of people leading into the foyer.'[10] 'People who come to the building will automatically move upwards towards the entrances in a calm way with no confusion. This means that the building takes them in and brings them in in the right mood for the fantasy world they are going to experience inside. It separates them completely from their daily life.'[11] And of the relationship between the podium and the theatres, Utzon said 'The idea has been to let the platform cut through like a knife, and separate primary and secondary function completely. On top of the platform the spectators receive the completed work of art and beneath the platform every preparation for it takes place.'

The podium, ' a troglodyte's haven of rooms and corridors... embedded in the base of the building',[12] when completed would be the largest – in terms of the area it covered – concrete building in the southern hemisphere.[13] In technical terms the podium was described as a 'monolithic structure', because the walls, floors and staircases of reinforced concrete, although to be constructed in stages, when completed would form one structure containing 125,000 tons of concrete and 6,000 tons of steel.

The dimensions of the podium would be 312 feet wide by 600 feet north-south and up to 83 feet above sea-level at the top seating terrace of the Major Hall, surrounded by the 'broadwalk', a harbourside promenade on three sides. Inside would be the general clutter of rooms found in any theatre complex, over 900 of them in this case, including offices, set storage areas, workshops, plant rooms, toilets, cloakrooms, lounges and exhibition and reception halls. There were also 40 suites of dressing rooms, rehearsal rooms, wardrobe and 'wig' rooms for performers, bars, canteens and restaurants with pantries and cool rooms, all connected by a maze of passages and corridors that Utzon called 'the rivers of the building, carrying people, pipes and ducts.'[14]

Utzon returned to Australia in March 1958 with Ove Arup to present to Cahill his *Red Book* scheme, a more advanced collection of plans than his competition drawings, produced in collaboration with his consultants.[15] With them they brought models, including one that was 30 feet wide and 12 feet high, built to test the Opera House acoustics.[16] Utzon said his competition-winning design 'looked very sketchy, but it was purified, without all the details.' With his *Red Book* in front of him in his Bondi hotel room, Utzon told an interviewer:

> I have been doing nothing but eat, sleep and work on the house with a lot of people at the office and now we know how it will be built... When you enter you get a feeling you don't get in any other house. The roof and the walls are one thing; you can't say where the one starts and the other ends. When I was in London, Mr Jenkins, who is Mr Arup's partner took me to a blackboard in his office. It was covered with mathematical formulas describing the shells of the house. Can't you see the beauty of it.

So that work could get started on site before the next election which was due early the following year, and as plans for the shells and interior were at an embryonic stage, Ove Arup suggested the work be split into two stages, Stage 1, the podium or base of the building and Stage 2 the remainder of the work.[17]

The Arup engineer most closely associated with getting the drawings completed for the podium was Bob Kelman. Kelman was an Australian who had been working for the Australian civil engineering company, MacDonald, Wagner and Priddle in Sydney, who had gone to London privately, got an introduction at Arups, was offered a job and found himself in a position as Job Engineer on the sub-structure of the Opera House. The work involved co-ordinating with Utzon – who he found 'absolutely delightful' – and organising three groups of engineers at Arups who were producing the working drawings for the podium structure of the Minor Hall, the Major Hall and the 'central passage', a loading area for scenery and so on between the two stage wells. Not least among Kelman's problems among the 30 or so engineers in his charge was keeping an Israeli and Arab engineer on the team in a harmonious working relationship.

The battle at the start was to extract out of the ether the information required to get the drawings underway. Utzon had received no brief other than the competition conditions, and information about what the Committee required inside the Opera House only came in in dribs and drabs. An early change by the Committee was the position of the dressing rooms, which in the competition design were 'in a rather poor position in the basement.'[18] In June 1958, the Committee made changes to the administration area, workshops and dining rooms, and on 2nd July, Stan Haviland announced the Opera House would now include an 'Experimental Theatre' with 400 seats.[19] Two days later, on 4th July, Charles Moses requested through the Committee that television broadcasting facilities be included. In a letter to Utzon on 15th September 1958, Ashworth expressed his concern that costs should be kept down, and in the same letter requested that the orchestra pit in one of the theatres be enlarged to accommodate 120 instead of 105 musicians. Kelman wrote to Utzon on 26th September, 'I notice that the clients want to make alterations and enlarge the orchestra pit. I think it is time that you made a stand and told them to stop this because all their good ideas tend to make the scheme more expensive.'[20] The *Herald* had interviewed Ove Arup in London the previous month:

'It is an extremely difficult job, and we want to make the finest job in the world out of it.' There was a lot of hard work involved, and they really needed 'almost a year's peace to get the thing properly dovetailed.'

As each floor is different, everything is curved, uniquely created, three-dimensional and without the repetition there is in most constructional jobs, there's as much work in the Sydney Opera House as on another building 10 times its size.

The complexity of the design means that any alteration affects every section. 'You cannot change anything without altering everywhere else... The stage machinery has been the most trouble. Inside details are constantly being changed. Enormous patience is required... We are doing our damndest to get the building started.'[21]

Utzon himself, who liked to oversee every detail of the scheme, was sometimes hard to get hold of. His letterhead did not list his address or phone number, and Arup engineer Poul Ahm wrote to Utzon on 14th February 1958 requesting details of podium beams, 'We would be grateful if you would let us have your telephone number at the office, and perhaps also at what times it is most likely to get hold of you there.'[22] Following his trip out to Sydney in March-April 1958 to present his *Red Book* scheme, Utzon had stopped off in the East. Ove Arup, anxious to get on with work on the podium vehicle concourse wrote to Lautrup Larsen of Utzon's office on 1st May 1958 requesting two books of drawings of the sketch scheme which Utzon had told him had been sent to London but Arups had not received. Utzon announced his return to Denmark to Arups at the end of May. 'It was nice to hear from you' – wrote Ove – 'I really thought you had been lost in the wilds of Asia.'[23] Utzon had visited Kyoto in Japan among other places, and reached the conclusion that the differences in Chinese and Japanese architecture were due in part to the differences in taking measurements. In Japan measurements are made with a flexible cord, in China, with a stiff rod. Utzon had also gone to Peking, not an easy place to obtain permission to visit at that time, where he had met Professor Liang. Liang had made a collection of ancient Chinese building laws dating from before 800AD and had translated them into modern Chinese. Among other things, the laws described in great detail pre-fabricated building systems used in ancient China. Liang gave a copy of the laws to Utzon, who kept them as a treasured possession.

With the design in a state of flux, there was nowhere near the information required to produce a bill of quantities so that contractors could quote on the cost of podium construction at the end of 1958. The quantity surveyors did produce a bill based on incomplete drawings and information, so that at least all firms intending to tender could quote on the same incomplete information.

Utzon returned to Australia on 3rd November 1958 with Varming of Steensen and Varming, the mechanical engineers, and Balslev for the electrical work with updated information for prospective tenderers. They were followed a few days later by Ron Jenkins of Arups who had come out in particular to interview the tenderers.

Though Utzon was the architect for the Opera House, responsible for the design and choice of finishes, the government had made a separate agreement with Ove Arup and Partners for the engineering work. This agreement between Arups and the government of New South Wales read in part:

> Whereas the Client proposes to proceed with the construction of the Sydney Opera House and has appointed... Jorn Utzon to be his architect and has requested the Consulting Engineers to prepare a scheme in their London office for all the Structural Engineering and Engineering Services for the proposed Sydney Opera House... [24]

Arup did not have an office in Australia at that time, and appointed MacDonald, Wagner and Priddle as their representatives in Australia, at a fee of $1\frac{1}{4}$ per cent of the contract cost, for local technical advice, representation at site meetings, setting out on site, general supervision and liaison with local authorities.[25] Jenkins was sure MacDonald, Wagner and Priddle '... would give more care and attention than we normally would for a job in England.'[26] MacDonald, Wagner and Priddle's man on the spot looking after the day-to-day details on the Opera House site would be Malcolm Nicklin.

MacDonald, Wagner and Priddle produced a list of who they felt were the five top building contractors in New South Wales able to tender on the construction of the Opera House podium. One company they had not mentioned was Civil & Civic, but Ove Arup himself added them to the list after one of their representatives came to see him.[27]

When the Committee wrote to Arups in October proposing to place an ad in Sydney newspapers inviting other contractors to offer to tender, Arups cabled immediately back 'STRONGLY ADVISE

ONLY SELECTED CONTRACTORS TO BE ASKED TO TENDER' and sent a covering letter:

> We feel strongly that we should only invite those firms who we feel confident could carry out this rather unusual and intricate job. It could be fatal if the contract was secured by a builder who was not very familiar with Civil Engineering contracts and who therefore underestimated his costs. As you know, this particular contract is rather out of the ordinary, involving very long spans in pre-stressed concrete and other unusual features... [28]

The Committee sent out a letter to the six suggested contractors on 22nd October 1958:

> The construction by the New South Wales Government of an Opera House at Bennelong Point, Sydney, will be carried out in two stages, the first stage being the carcase of the building up to podium level.
>
> Commencement of the first stage construction is expected to take place early next year and to be completed within 12 months (a tentative timing program drawn up last April envisaged commencement in January, 1959 and completion by December, 1959, whereupon the second stage construction would commence and the project as a whole would be completed by June, 1962; it is desired to adhere to this timetable as nearly as possible).
>
> The Engineers for the project, Messrs. Ove Arup and Partners of 8 Fitzroy Street, London, will shortly be forwarding to you some preliminary information as to what is involved in the first stage construction.
>
> The purpose of this letter is to inquire whether your firm would be prepared to tender for the stage one contract and, in view of the limited time available, your early reply will be appreciated. [29]

However, it was practically impossible to prevent other companies expressing an interest in tendering for such a prestigious project, with the result that Jenkins interviewed representatives from 25 companies interested in tendering, out of which he selected six to which tender documents would be sent! Stan Haviland announced that Jenkins was '... greatly impressed by the standard of the nominated firms. He said they were equal to any in his experience.'[30] Tender forms would be sent out to the selected firms in December and tenders would close on January 19th.[31]

One architect wrote to the *Herald* of the interest he had experienced in the Opera House on a recent overseas tour:

> – Having just returned from a round-the-world tour, I would like to report my pleasant surprise at the keen and enthusiastic interest being

shown in the Opera House, particularly among people who are normally uninformed on Australia. Utzon's conception seems to have captured universal admiration.

Reproductions of the design were to be seen frequently in the drawing offices of architects in England and the U.S.A., and there was evident pleasure at my generalisation that 'it was out to tender at present.' Expressions of goodwill ranged from congratulations to the civic authorities for their enlightened courage (from an Oxford don) to predictions for a record increase in air traffic to Australia when the building was finished (from Mrs Walter Gropius).

I received the strong impression that this one building will make a major contribution to Australia's international prestige, particularly in the older nations with a long established cultural history.[32]

Tenders closed on January 19th as planned. The lowest, from Civil and Civic, was £1,397,929.[33] When the tender prices were published J. C. Dunningham of Sydney wrote:

The vast variation between the published tenders for the Opera House foundation work indicates that the project was either badly presented, or the tenderers failed to appreciate the requirements of the contract. The lowest tender (£1,397,929) is £211,778 below the second lowest and £829,852 below the highest tender...

The calling of tenders in this manner; ie., one tender for the foundations, and one or more for the superstructure, is not the most economical or efficient method, and it is apparent that the scheme has not yet been thoroughly planned. For some obscure reason the State Government is determined to make an unnecessarily hurried start on this project.

It should be borne in mind that once a tender is accepted for the work, the tenderer is entitled to full compensation for loss of profit in the event of the contract being cancelled, and this could easily happen should we have a change of Government.[34]

Which received the reply: 'Sir, I think I could enlighten your correspondent, J.C. Dunningham in connection with the new Opera House... Mr Cahill thought it prudent not to call for the whole scheme, as the figure for completion of the job would be too much of a shock to everybody...'[35]

Civil and Civic's tender was accepted at £1,397,878, a reduction of £51 after 'a technical and arithmetical check by quantity surveyors'[36] and the contract signed amid great fanfare to build Stage I of Sydney Opera House on 5th February.

'This is a great day for New South Wales and Australia', said Cahill at the signing ceremony, 'Sydney deserves the best and it's getting the best.' After signing the contract Cahill walked around the site with Haviland, and Dusseldorp of Civil and Civic; Dusseldorp and Haviland holding Cahill by the hand as he climbed over the rubble of the site.

Civil and Civic was run by a Dutch engineer, Gerardus Dusseldorp, chairman of directors. Their general manager was Mr Leavey, and Mr Dennis Holland would be the project manager on the Opera House site. Following his signing of the contract:

> Mr G. J. Dusseldorp said last night that in tendering to construct the first part of Sydney Opera House his firm had taken a risk on the problems it would meet below sea level... He was speaking on the 'Meet the Press' session on Channel 9 TCN. A member of the panel had asked him how his firm's tender could be £800,000 below the highest tender.
>
> Mr Dusseldorp pointed out that his firm's tender was £200,000 below the next highest tender and £100,000 below the official estimate. He said that much of the work on the first section of the Opera House would be below sea level. He added: 'That is always a risk factor. It depends on what risk one allows for. That could vary several hundreds of per cent between the assumption of one person and another. One does not know until one actually digs.' Mr Dusseldorp said the possibility existed of a loss on that part of the work. He added: 'I would hate to be in a business where I took no risks.' Mr Dusseldorp, a Dutchman, said that working below sea level was 'an old Dutch custom.' He said: 'Holland is the only country in the world not created by God, but made by a Dutchman...'.
>
> Mr Dusseldorp said that in 1950 a fact-finding mission from Holland visited Australia to investigate the Australian potential for expansion. In some other countries his organisation went from project to project, then left the country.
>
> He added: 'But we are here to stay. This is a permanent establishment, because of the great potential in Australia and the rapidly increasing population.'[37]

Work had started at the Opera House site at the beginning of June 1958. The Maritime Services Board began drilling bores to collect core samples of the bedrock beneath Bennelong Point for MacDonald, Wagner and Priddle, who would analyse them, and send the data to Ove Arup in London to determine the foundations required for the Opera House. Some bores were sunk into the seabed using a drilling rig set up on a wharf on the eastern side of the site because part of the Opera House podium was going to extend over the water.[38] The first 12 test bores found rock between five and 20 feet below the top of the soil.[39]

Fort Macquarie had been used as a bus station from 1956-58 after trams were phased out in Sydney and then been leased to the City Council as a car park for a short time until demolition started on 18th August 1958.[40] Following the clearing of the roof and interior of the sheds, all that remained on 4th December 1958 were the high surrounding crenellated walls of the exterior. A story in the *Telegraph* on 5th December had a picture of a section of the wall coming tumbling down with a story headed 'Long Siege on Old Landmark.' The tramshed had stubbornly resisted and a section of the wall did not want to budge. A demolition team started work at 5.30 am; but the first part of the wall did not come down until 3.30 pm. Cables were attached to the top of the wall, but they snapped several times, and a U-bolt straightened under the load. A mobile crane was then used to winch the cables, but its driving chain snapped. Finally, after mending the chain, part of the wall came tumbling down.[41]

The ceremony to start construction was set down for 2nd March 1959, before the State elections due later that month. The Liberal/Country Party coalition in opposition had not up to that time announced their support for the Opera House, and Cahill had a real fear they might scrap the building if they won government unless it was contractually impossible for them to do so. On 22nd October 1958 in State Parliament, 'E.A.Willis (Liberal) asked the Premier whether in view of the advent of television causing a big drop in the number of people attending film theatres… would the Government consider the possibility of purchasing a large city theatre for the temporary use of the State Opera House.' "No", replied Cahill.'[42] There was still considerable opposition to the Opera House in the community, notably from Actors' Equity, which on 12th January 1959 issued a statement asking Cahill to abandon the Opera House plans and write off the money already spent rather than continue with the building. No more than £1 million should be spent on an Opera House they argued, and the remainder should be spent on financing the arts in other ways, pointing out that £5 million could support opera, ballet and theatre companies for many years. Ashworth was prepared to write off the Cahill government, writing to Jenkins that '… on this occasion the present Government might lose out, although I think it will be rather a close thing either way', though Ashworth conceded '… if there were a change of Government, I feel the project would have to be accepted – perhaps grudgingly in the post-election period, but probably quite enthusiastically when the roof begins to soar.'[43]

Finally the great day was at hand, and according to the papers the following day:

> After more than four years' planning, work began yesterday on the first stage of the building of the Sydney Opera House at Bennelong Point. More than 400 people watched the Premier, Mr Cahill, lay a plaque to commemorate the start of construction. Drizzling rain fell from a low bank of dark clouds and several times threatened to interrupt the hour-long ceremony.[44]

Sharing the platform with Cahill were Robert Askin, Deputy Leader of the Liberal Party and Mr Cutler, Deputy Leader of the Country Party whose Leader, Davis Hughes, had been unable to attend due to illness. Askin read a message from the opposition leader P.H. Morton, then closed with a few of his own words '... when this Opera House project was first mooted there was a great deal of controversy. I am firmly of the opinion now that the decision has been made that the time for controversy is finished. It now remains only for us to work together in a spirit of goodwill to raise the necessary finance to bring this magnificent concept of an Opera House into being...' Cahill made the closing speech, '... I am glad to say that there is one matter which is purely non-political, and I venture to predict that no Party will attempt to make an issue of it at the coming election... which means that in cultural matters we are all for the advancement of this country of ours and the little things that could divide us at a time like this, the things – the petty things, the small things – will have no place when this magnificent institution begins to be erected...'. Cahill added 'We are not, as some people overseas unfortunately still seem to think, a nation of rough and ready pioneers devoted solely to the needs of self-preservation. Surely we are grown up in the sense that we can turn some portion of our attention to the finer things of life and demonstrate that we are not savages but civilised human beings, capable of contributing our share to world culture and appreciation of the arts...'.

After his speech, Mr Cahill moved from the official dais to a large sandstone table to lay the plaque. He appeared confused about the procedure until the designer of the Opera House, Mr Joern Utzon – who flew from Denmark for the occasion – took a large metal bolt from a container. He and Mr Cahill screwed this bolt into the centre of the plaque. Intersecting grooves on the bolt mark the point from which all measurements for the construction will be taken. Mr Utzon then showed Mr Cahill how to tap a pin into the bolt to prevent it from turning.

After completing this ceremony, Mr Cahill raised his hand and a siren on a nearby police car sounded. Immediately, six workmen with pneumatic drills and a large bulldozer went into action preparing the site.[45]

The official guests then moved to a marquee on an adjoining lawn and had afternoon tea against the background clatter of machinery and the music of the Police Band.[46]

'Who', remarked another reporter in Column 8 of the *Herald* '... achieved the distinction of being the first musicians to play there.' They opened with, 'With a little bit o' luck' from 'My Fair Lady' and one of their later items was – 'Oh, What a Beautiful Morning, Oh What a Wonderful Day.'

The papers carried pictures of Premier Cahill and Stan Haviland chatting with the soprano Gladys Moncrieff, who was a guest at the ceremony, and of Utzon and his wife, who had travelled out with him. Lis was wearing a wide-brimmed straw hat, picked up for under a dollar in Honolulu, and one reporter asked her '"Honolulu suntan?" as her husband came up. "No" she laughed, "Bondi sunburn. We both got burnt noses on the beach yesterday".'[47] Lis was the most comfortable woman at the ceremony, reckoned a reporter from the *Herald*:

> She was stockingless and wore rubber-soled flat-heeled yellow sandals with a cool white cotton dress...
>
> Other women shot her envious glances as their high-heels sank into sand on the site, and grit worked its way into their shoes.
>
> As cameras clicked Mrs Utzon clutched a bouquet of white carnations and scarlet nectarine flowers – Denmark's colours – that the Vice-Consul for Denmark... gave her. Mrs F. Henning Hergal, wife of the Consul-General had a more unusual present for Mr Utzon – an aboriginal didgeridoo.[48]

Though the reporter of Column 8 in the *Herald* felt:

> There was only one blemish – and that was a very sad one.
>
> Mr Joern Utzon, architect of the whole business, was on the dais – and that's all.
>
> Nobody mentioned him and they failed to introduce him to the audience – even failed to mention the charming plaque he had designed for the occasion.[49]
>
> But his reward was the stream of unstinted praise which dominated the messages received from the world's leading architects.[50]

Before leaving Sydney by BOAC airliner with his wife on the night of 13th March, Utzon told reporters that all details of construction of the Opera House had now been worked out. 'Problems such as the size of the rooms and the halls of the building have been overcome; there will be no more alterations.'[51]

All those involved in the project and every person in Sydney who was enthusiastic about it going ahead, breathed a collective sigh of relief when the Labor government was voted back in at the elections, even if it was by a majority of only five seats.

After signing the building contract for Stage I on 5th February, Cahill had said as part of his speech, 'I've watched brick by brick being taken from the old tram shed that was here, and I'm going to watch brick by brick of the Opera House go up.'[52] But in October 1959, with work still going on on the Opera House foundations, Cahill was attending a Caucus meeting in State Parliament when he was suddenly afflicted with severe stomach pains from a gastric ulcer. He was taken to Sydney Hospital next door, but died two days later at 11.55 am after suffering his third coronary occlusion in three days. 'There were emotional scenes in Parliament House when the news was announced and Parliament adjourned. Several Cabinet Ministers, including the Chief Secretary (Mr Kelly), one of Mr Cahill's closest friends, wept openly.'[53] Cahill, who was 68, was given a State funeral the following Saturday, and was buried in the Roman Catholic Cemetery at Rookwood. The Deputy Premier, Mr R.J. Heffron, was sworn in as the new Premier.

On Cahill's death, Charles Moses said, 'without the determination and drive of the late Premier the Opera House would not yet have reached the drawing board.'[54] There were suggestions the Opera House be named after Cahill, but Alderman Jensen said that the Opera House Committee had submitted to Mr Cahill a list of about 12 names for the Opera House but Cahill did not choose any of these. Instead he suggested the name 'Sydney Opera House.' Jensen said, '… it was probably best that this name be used because it was Mr Cahill's wish.'[55] Moses recalled that there were 12 members of the first Sydney Opera House trust '… I doubt… whether there would have been one Labor voter amongst us. We decided unanimously the Major Hall would be called the "Cahill Auditorium".'[56]

Ove Arup wrote that Cahill was 'the driving force behind the project' and Utzon called him 'a man ahead of his time.' When Utzon visited Sydney the next time in February 1960 to inspect work on site for stage machinery areas, he said at the airport before flying on to San Francisco, 'Mr Cahill was a great inspiration in the Opera House project, I missed him a great deal on this visit.'[57]

In September 1959, with the Opera House site still looking like nothing more than piles of rubble with rough tracks winding between them, work in progress was described by Gavin Souter under the heading 'Spring comes to Bennelong Point.'

The last time I had been to Bennelong Point was the bleak winter's day two years ago when Joern Utzon first inspected the site for his opera house, 'It's right!' Utzon had said, measuring his idea against the grey windswept Harbour. 'It's O.K.!'. It was warmer when I went back yesterday. A yellow butterfly jittered around piles of broken sandstone; a little patch of clover left by the bulldozers was in bloom; and all over Bennelong Point, like grown buds ready to flower, steel piers were sprouting from the rock. Spring has come to the bare bones of Utzon's idea.

But the idea is still not easy to grasp. 'People don't realise how it's going to be', said Mr Dennis Holland, site manager for Civil and Civic Contractors Pty Ltd. He pointed up to the Harbour Bridge and said: 'The top will be 20 feet higher than the deck of the Bridge. It will be 230 feet high – about as high as the top of that flagpole on the Unilever building.'

The salt-glaze tiles of the Opera House's sails will not reach the flagpole until 1962 at the earliest. But the £4,800,000 job is now well under way. Civil and Civic Contractors have already been at work for 13 weeks of the 21 months in which they have contracted to complete the first stage of the building at a cost of £1,397,878.00. They must move 37,000 cubic yards of excavation, including 11,000 cubic yards of rock; sink two miles of three feet diameter steel-encased piers (500 separate piers in all); and pour 120,000 cubic yards of concrete foundations (about ten times as much concrete as contained in the average city building of 12 storeys).

So far, the 80 men working on the site have moved 22,000 cubic yards of excavation, and put down 1,000 linear feet of steel casing for concrete piers. (Most of the piers at present extend only a few inches above the ground). They have relocated the high tension cable which crosses the Harbour from Bennelong Point, and are now doing the same to a six feet diameter stormwater tunnel which would protrude through the stage machinery floor of the main hall of the Opera House if left in its present position. Next week, the Civil and Civic men will begin pouring concrete with a pneumatic conveyor which can force concrete into position at the rate of one and half tons every two minutes.

They were hard at it yesterday morning. Two percussion drills pounded away, driving holes down below sea level; a skid shovel was gouging out sandstone for the machinery basement.

Mr Holland stopped beside a pile of rubble at the city end of the point. 'This is the start of the steps', he said, 'and the concourse comes right across there at a height of 18 feet. It will be a folded slab of seven-inch concrete suspended for 150 feet. Cars will be able to drive underneath it and turn around.'

We passed three pier casings, steel burrows ready to receive the Opera House's concrete roots, and paused beside a huge timber frame. 'This will be the foundation for one of the sails', said Mr Holland. 'The supporting column for the corner of the sail here will be 80 feet high – 30 feet down and 50 feet up! Some of the larger columns will take 2,000 cubic yards of concrete… The more you see of this Opera House, the more you realise it's got a touch of the sea about it. It's not just the sails, either. You won't be able to see Bennelong Point at all; there'll be about five and a half acres of building, and it will extend over the Harbour on both sides of the Point. It will look as if it's floating in the Harbour.'

We picked our way across the site towards Farm Cove, 'It will overhang the Harbour for about 50 feet on this side', said Mr Holland. About 50 feet out, three seagulls were riding in the spring sunshine. Their folded wings might almost have been made of salt-glaze tiles.[58]

Another story in December 1959 described the work for the columns to support the shells and the steel processing plant on site.

The reinforced concrete columns which support the shells are 70 feet long, with bases of varying diameters ranging from 7 ft to 15 ft. The columns will each have about 28 ft of their length below ground level with an average of 42 ft above ground level. They will be stepped gradually to the point where they meet the base of the shells. Square twist steel, made by Civil and Civic on the site will be used as reinforcement in the columns.

The problem of seepage from the Harbour was combated in the shell column excavations by the use of cofferdams. These are made of sheets of steel piling which are sunk to rock level, forming an 18ft square having an average depth of 25 ft. Excavations begin once the cofferdams are placed in position. Wooden frames, with a space in the middle to allow the excavation gear to operate are lowered into the hole to support the steel cofferdams as the earth is removed. The wooden frames are made so that the formwork can be lowered inside them for the concrete pouring…

All steel being used in the project is processed in a self-contained steel plant costing £12,000. The plant, which is 200 ft long, treats the raw steel delivered from the mills and has a weekly output of 100 tons. Layout of the plant is in the form of a continuous production line with the 30 ft lengths of raw steel entering at one end on an overhead monorail which runs the length of the plant. The square steel is conveyed to the twisting section, where it is treated in special twisting machines imported from England. Round steel misses this section. By way of the monorail, the steel is then bent, cut and finally tagged. According to Civil and Civic it is the first square twisting plant specially erected on a project site in Australia.[59]

Then four months later in April 1960:

> Down on Bennelong Point you can now see the first recognisable fragment of Sydney's future Opera House... in the last week or so, after 10 months of underground development, it has begun to emerge into the open air. Down the centre of the site runs a rough-finished, unglamorous concrete slab which a little imagination can transform into the spacious ground-floor passageway that will divide the two main auditoriums. When I saw it last week it was already half-hidden in a forest of steel form-work which was ready to receive the concrete floor of the second-level passage...
>
> The subterranean progress of the job does not seem so slow when one grasps the scale and the difficulty of the operations. It involves removing 40,000 cubic yards of rock and rubble, of which 37,000 have already been extracted. It involves constructing a complicated maze of underground passages, store-rooms, and machinery-rooms – an area that the public will never visit, but which is just the place for a Phantom of the Opera.
>
> ... The contractors had to relocate a century-old stormwater channel (the old tunnel can still be seen like an enormous rat-hole in the side of the excavations) and shift the power lines to the north side of the Harbour without interrupting the supply. Near the point they uncovered the foundations of the old vehicular ferry wharf which operated before the Harbour Bridge was opened. They were so solidly built that they had to be blasted out.
>
> At the moment there are 200 workers on the site. ('You can't see many of them', the site manager, Mr Dennis Holland, explained. 'A lot of them are underground.') If one stands on the patch of high ground still remaining at the point one begins to see the scale and diversity of the operations. One begins to realise, too, how big the building is going to be – a thing that is hard to grasp from figures. The Opera House will more than cover the whole of the present site... It will cover nearly six acres, or the area of 20 average city buildings. Three rugbyfields could be laid side by side on the site... [60]

A year later, a reporter from the *Daily Mirror* thought that 'At present the building looks more like an uncompleted dam (complete with slipways) than any part of an Opera House.'[61] Meanwhile the Americans were wondering if Australians were really ready for grand opera. Homer Bigart of the *New York Times*, calling Sydney a 'Seaport in Australia, where Strip Tease is much admired' wrote,

> Mr Utzon's design has been widely praised but doubt persists about whether Sydney's residents are really ready to take grand opera to their busoms.
>
> This frisky seaport seems to prefer strip tease. Four night clubs in Kings Cross, the local Greenwich Village, feature stripteasers, some imported from the United States. The Lord Mayor of Sydney Henry

Frederick Jensen, insists, however, that Australians are marching towards cultural maturity. Thanks to the influx of Southern European immigrants (visitors) are no longer confronted with a steady diet of overdone steak and rubbery chips.[62]

Roger Covell, music critic of the *Herald,* wrote of the state of work at Bennelong Point:

> For the first time... it is possible to discern the major outlines and proportions of Sydney's Opera House as it takes shape. Where the Point juts furthest into the Harbour, two curved concrete walls are rising, rather like the ramparts of some medieval fortification. Behind the present height of these ramparts it is already possible to see the concrete catacombs where Opera House administrators will rule and mediate on the empire of four auditoriums in their care. ... Just behind the larger of the two ramparts there is now a sprouting of steel rods, like rifles crossed for a ceremonial volley.[63]

But the public were blissfully unaware of the Herculean efforts going on behind the scenes to keep that work going through. Ove Arup recalled that when construction got underway on the podium:

> ... We had to start the work... before we had any idea of what we had to build. We had to start in (March) 1959 and the sketch scheme had been presented in May 1958 and been drastically altered by the technical panel... then they wanted full tender documents by February of 1959. It was utterly impossible and I told them that when I went with Utzon to present the sketch scheme. (Cahill) said it was absolutely essential that that should be done for various political reasons otherwise the whole thing may fall through. What we had to do in the end was... well just put foundations according to (Utzon's) preliminary sketch scheme which was just... a pencil line (drawn) free hand on a bit of paper which had been blown up to the required size for the competition.[64]... as a result we had to start the job without a single correct drawing.[65]

While Utzon's office produced the architectural details in Hellebaek, Kelman's team in London produced from them the structural working drawings, which were snapped up by Civil & Civic on site as soon as they received them to build the Opera House on the ground. But often the site drawings were not the final word, Utzon's office imposing the well-established architectural principle that design is a continuous process; and never finishes. 'We don't intend to make more alterations to the basement', wrote Utzon to Kelman on 11th June 1959. 'We are sorry that you had so much trouble with us... I will force Mr Mathieson, Steensen and Varming, to make up his mind immediately for the holes in the basement walls, etc.'[66]

Meanwhile the Committee were still making up their mind about what they wanted: '... we have switched all our strength to the concourse' wrote Kelman to Utzon's office on 28th October 1959, 'in an effort to make the Committee's dithering over the Stage Area the ultimate cause of delay so that we are not as far advanced with the ground to 1st Floor wall elevations as planned.'[67]

'Apart from the design difficulties with the concourse' – wrote Kelman to Utzon again on 17th November 1959 – 'the worst feature of the job is the trouble the contractors are having in keeping track of the flood of minor amendments we have to send off to Sydney... Our Resident Engineer has written to us in very strong terms about the dissatisfaction on site over the number of changes received after they have had our reinforcement details... (having) discussed the major hall stage area at length... It became obvious that no one can afford to wait until the Committee formally approves your latest plans... When your scheme is fully worked out you should send it to Professor Ashworth... stressing that he must give immediate authority to go ahead.'[68]

As if life on site was not exciting enough, on 1st December 1959 a 50-foot section of sea wall around the north end of the site collapsed into the Harbour after wet mud excavated from the Experimental Theatre basement was piled on top of it '... and the Maritime Services Board are not pleased.'[69]

At this time Kelman sent a confidential letter to Eric Wagner of MacDonald, Wagner and Priddle, '... It seems to me that the present difficulties on Stage I have largely been brought about through our loyalty to the very optimistic Mr Utzon.' The letter finished 'P.S. I would find it very helpful if you could let me know the real feeling in Sydney about completion date of the Opera House.'[70]

Yet still the stage area was not finalised, Kelman writing to Jenkins who was then in Sydney on 21st January 1960 '... Although I was given to believe before I left Hellebaek that the two stage techniques were settled and Prof. Unruh (the consultant on stage technique) had approved except for the elimination of the batten lift in the Minor Hall, almost as soon as I returned to the office the main proscenium wall of the stage was moved South two feet... Sorry to sound such a Jeremiah... but we have suffered too much in this respect already. If we lose this opportunity of forcing Utzon to face reality, we won't get another opportunity.'[71]

Yet two weeks later, on 15th February 1960 after Utzon had said the only changes were to the batten lifts, Kelman wrote to Harvig-Petersen of Utzon's office '... Since then, a week after (the drawing) was to have gone to London, the Minor Hall slab was issued and there were in fact a lot of minor changes – extra holes, ducts and moved lift positions. So there is at least one week's work involved in changing it, with all the attendant risks of error.'[72]

Later it was found '... the electrical load requirements for stage machinery are about ten times the MAN estimate. The electrical specialist finds this means increasing the number of transformers in the central passage from two to five. To accommodate these extra transformers we are now working out a scheme to cut out part of the central passage wall and introduce alternative means of carrying the load coming down on this section. This will be a major structural modification...'[73]

On 11th March 1960 Utzon's office sent a hand-written letter to Arups listing – among other things – the numbers of 30 drawings sent under separate cover – which finished: 'They are up to date, but must not be considered as final.'[74] And on 3rd August 1960 Kelman wrote to Knud Larssen of Utzon's office in summary of the previous day's telephone calls. 'We would appreciate your drawings you have done on the galleries as soon as possible as we are doing detailed calculations on this now and although we have not done more drawings, minor changes can affect dozens of pages of calculations. This would not make us happy!!'[75]

Kelman received one drawing from Utzon's office and he did not have a clue what it was, but pinned it up on the noticeboard with a note 'Does anybody know what this is?' and offered a prize for the first correct answer. No one else knew either. Then one day Utzon visited the London office and saw the drawing before Kelman could take it down. 'But he took it very well.'[76] It turned out to be a detail for one of the stages. Though it was not only Arup's office who were sometimes puzzled, Utzon's office wrote to Kelman on 5th January 1961, '... In the heaps of drawings which we have received in recent times there are some points we would like to mention... We are curious to know what actually will happen in the triangular space between E.33 and E.36 south of the stair leading down to the basement. As far as we can see it is inaccessible. What about an opening from the stair-well? No workers were missing!'[77]

Then there were problems of interpretation of the drawings on site. Alan Levy, an Arup engineer on site in Sydney, wrote to London asking what the four lines were across a drawing of restaurant columns. London replied, 'The four lines running across the left hand side of 5254 indicate this portion has been cancelled!! This part of the drawing was originally done when we hadn't intended building columns 22 and 25 into the structure...' And as always, Utzon was in command of every decision, a passage in the same letter pointing out '... the tie will be left exposed on the soffit, shouldn't matter too much as it is in a toilet. Utzon knows about it.'

And two and a half years on from when all the drawing details were supposed to have been finalised to prepare the original tender documents, and a year on from when the Committee originally expected the podium construction to have been finished, Kelman was finding himself writing to Utzon's office on 27th April 1961:

> In conclusion, we would like to point out that the position is rapidly approaching when we shall not be able to accede to this steady stream of small amendments to drawings which have already been issued to the site. Approximately half our staff is kept busy trying to keep drawings up to date while we have strict committments to the site. Our site staff have recently stressed to us the vital importance, both politically and structurally, of avoiding any delays due to late issue of drawings.[78]

To which the reply followed from Knud Lautrup of Utzon's office, which was marked on the letter with three exclamation marks by someone at Arups:

> Everyone here expects this stream to calm down very soon. The ability of the firm of Ove Arup & Partners to absorb amendments has always impressed everyone in this office and is deeply appreciated.
>
> Every single amendment from this office is solely inspired by the sincere wish to make the most perfect building. We trust that you feel the same way.[79]

A few months later, during the (northern) summer of 1961, the design of the Opera House shells was completely changed. The earlier design of the shells had the stage machinery hanging off them, the later design had the stage machinery supported on a stage tower built on the podium. This meant a further revision to drawings to support the new stage structure. Bob Kelman later reckoned '... there were something like 1,500 items in the original provisional bill (of quantities for the podium). I think about 500 of those were not used and about 500 new ones were generated during the course of the job. And Utzon's standards were exceptional for anything previously experienced in (Australia).'[80]

On 14th March 1962 with the construction work on the podium three quarters completed, Civil & Civic wrote to MacDonald, Wagner and Priddle:

... In reviewing this contract it has been a long history of changes, frustrations, inability to logically plan the work due to the lack of information and detail, starting and stopping parts of the work and prevention of orderly execution of the work as a whole due to information not being available in logical sequence, and drastic increases of complexity which could not be envisaged from the original documents.

Civil & Civic claimed that among other things, after the whole original contract time of 21 months had elapsed they had only received 55 per cent of the final drawings.

This situation has been further aggravated by the vast number of changes which have been made. Some 700 drawings have been issued over the course of 3 years, and there have been some 695 amendments to these issues.

Throughout the job work has commenced on various sections, has been stopped awaiting further information – altered because of last minute design changes – restarted when further information came to hand and, in some cases stopped and restarted again through lack of further follow-up information.[81]

Shouldering the burden of making amendments to drawings issued to site was Arup's engineer, Ian MacKenzie. MacKenzie had studied engineering at Canterbury College in New Zealand, and after qualifying went on a trip to London and called in on Arups – where one of the partners was married to a New Zealand girl – and eventually ended up with a job. One evening MacKenzie was having a drink at the Carpenters Arms in London for one of the Arup's people that was leaving, when Bob Hobbs, one of the partners, asked 'Would you like to go to Australia?' MacKenzie was at that time thinking about going back to New Zealand, but did not have the money 'so that the prospect of a trip out to Australia, paid... by someone else, was well worthwhile, and would give me a simple step on to New Zealand.'[82] On 18th March 1959, Ron Jenkins wrote to the Committee:

... we have in this office a young Engineer from New Zealand who now wishes to work in some other part of the world.

His name is Ian MacKenzie, aged 26... He joined us in November 1956, and his outside experience mainly consists of frequent supervisory visits to the extension of University College, London, which is situated quite close to our office.

Although he has not previously been a full-time Engineer, we consider he is a very good type of young man whom we could recommend for the post of Resident Engineer on Sydney Opera House... [83]

MacKenzie departed for Sydney on the understanding that if he left the company before the end of the Stage 1 contract he would repay his airfare,[84] and arrived at the Opera House in May 1959, a week after Civil & Civic had moved on site.[85] MacKenzie wrote to London on 29th May:

My first impression of Civil & Civic is that they know their stuff. Their organisation on the site seems to be good. There is no doubt that the consistent production of quality, controlled concrete is going to be a major concern. Civil & Civic are well aware of this and already have their site laboratory (for testing concrete samples) functioning. So far, so good.[86]

As the work got underway 'There were an awful lot of changes being made' – recalled MacKenzie – 'In those days... there was no telex. There was a telephone that was a bit hairy to get through on – there was a telegraph (so) you could send telegrams, but all of these things took time.'[87] Meanwhile, MacKenzie had Civil & Civic with their workforce on site clamouring for the drawings and saying '... unless I have that detail tomorrow... I will be delayed and... claiming an extension of time.'[88] MacKenzie was the only Arup employee on site at that stage, so he took the obvious route which was to do the drawings himself. It meant working extraordinarily long hours '... it was turn up at seven, (and) leave at midnight. I was doing that six days a week and then down here most of Sunday as well.'[89] MacKenzie was living at Cremorne across the harbour and coming into work by ferry, and when he missed the last ferry back, which left at 1 o'clock in the morning, he would sleep the night at the office on site on a rack underneath the big drawing layout tables.

Eric Wagner of MacDonald Wagner & Priddle reported to the Technical Advisory Panel on the long hours MacKenzie was working and 'The Panel felt that appreciation should be expressed to Mr MacKenzie for the great interest he is showing in the work and also the hours he is working beyond normal requirements.'[90] This sentiment was duly passed on to Jenkins, who wrote back, not thinking it '... right in principle, to disturb MacKenzie's salary.'[91] Though MacKenzie did receive a not very hefty bonus.

The job had started with a three month 'pre-planning period' devoted to re-routing the high tension cables beneath the site, excavating to re-locate the stormwater channel which ran through the centre of the site and starting work on sinking bores for the concrete piers for the Opera House foundations. In the centre of the site where the basement levels lay directly on the bedrock, which in some cases had to be excavated first, concrete footings were poured directly onto the rock. Outside the centre of the site and where the Opera House extended over the Harbour on the east and west sides the foundations would stand on concrete piers standing on solid bedrock. The work of building these piers was expected to be completed in 1959, but in fact finished on 16th November 1961. Some areas of the ground beneath the old tram depot consisted of rough fill, old stone, reinforced concrete and timber walls and jetties and other debris which had to be drilled through before hitting rock. Once the borehole had penetrated rock, a $1\frac{1}{2}$ inch diameter hole was drilled at the bottom and 'a man then descends, and with a kind of one prong rake, scrapes the sides of the drilling to measure the size and frequency of the faults. Local experience has evolved formulae which relate these to bearing capacity.'[92] To stop the water pouring into the hole it was sealed with a steel cylinder, but the rock was very poor quality in most areas and heavily fissured with clay seams. 'In many cases it was necessary to break the seal and continue (boring) the hole up to six times, the deepest pier hole being 68 feet.'[93]

Altogether, 460 piers were drilled on the land and 160 drilled and constructed over the water around the Harbour foreshore of Bennelong Point. A well-boring company, Godfrey Bros. Ltd., was employed to sink the piers. Percussion and Caldwell-type drills were used in boring the holes for the piers because normal rotary type drills could not cope with sandstone rubble. 'These drilling rigs pounded up the sandstone with a huge star-shaped bit that weighed about a ton and a half...' – recalled MacKenzie – '(they)... proceeded very slowly, about one foot an hour was good progress, and that was just pounding away the sandstone... The drillers were a very rough lot... often they'd been out in the country drilling... water bores for the farmers... and they were used to sort of sitting out there, camping out in the bush beside a drilling rig that drilled 24 hours a day. And, quite a number of them had caravans on the site and just lived on the site... some of them would be on the day shift and they'd spend all their nights celebrating or drinking... I recall one driller who accidentally dropped a bolt down his own hole, and he could see major problems in getting out that bolt (in order to continue drilling which was on piecework) and so he just stripped off and dived head-first down that 900mm diameter hole into 4 or 5 meters of water, picked up the bolt, turned round and came up head first.'[94] MacKenzie thought that was taking things a bit far, his own job being lowered down '... through this steel casing and out into the rock below, complete with raincoats and gumboots, because there would be water pouring in through faults in the rock, (to) scrape a small test hole in the bottom of the pile and hope that all the water didn't come in and drown you before you got out' was quite bad enough.

The completion of the bored piers became a matter of urgency because in those areas where they were needed, no work could take place on the sub-structure of the Opera House until they were completed. Godfreys first worked one shift, then two, until finally they were working 24 hours a day, six days a week. MacKenzie had to be on site to inspect the bores and initially extended his hours with the drillers, but when they were working a 24-hour shift this was too much even for MacKenzie, and Arups employed a 22-year-old engineering student from Malaya, Mr Hon Phang, to assist.

> At that stage the site was a mud bath... these drilling rigs... pounded up the sandstone into effectively sand, and in order to (pump) it out, they used to put in a mud fill... which would take the sand up into suspension... (this would be pumped out) and it just got dumped on the ground alongside the place where they were drilling the hole. So with a dozen drilling rigs around the place the site just got covered 6 inches deep in this sea of mud. And this Malaysian student was walking across the site one day to go and check a pylon and he just suddenly disappeared, because there was a hole there. The (steel) casing had been cut off at ground level, the... complete hole had filled up with this mud and he just disappeared down it. And he went down, and came popping up – and – I've seen a white Malaysian... his colour changed – he just came up – and we never saw him again. He just left the site and that was it.[95]

In November 1960 Olaf Skipper Nielsen (known as 'Skipper' to his friends) left Denmark for Sydney to represent Utzon's office on site.

By now it was apparent to Civil & Civic that their competitive quote on the job was going to translate into a small profit – if any – and this combined with the difficulty of planning work due to the haphazard supply of drawings had led to a fall in morale among the supervisors and workers with the result that the quality of work was starting to suffer.

'... I feel that the general lack of interest and poor workmanship' wrote Nielsen to Utzon on the 1st of October 1961, '(means) we may be forced to either accept inferior work or reject in some cases work which in practice conforms with the specifications... but are nevertheless not up to a proper workmanlike standard...' On the 10th Nielsen wrote to Utzon again, '... two curved walls of class "C" formwork in the Major Hall with faults were condemned and pulled down... the Resident Engineer and the Construction Supervisor are putting in a great effort to produce a good job... It has surprised us all, that (Civil & Civic) apparently does not realise that his present attitude necessarily will increase his losses on this work.' Nielsen also wrote that Civil & Civic '... has also been instructed to remove the foreman responsible for this section (the Major Hall) and to substitute him with a man of a capacity equal to that of the foreman for the other two sections of the job.'[96]

But disagreements with Civil & Civic over the quality of work on the main sub-structure of the Opera House were nothing compared with a battle that was already underway to produce an exceptional off-form concrete finish on the vehicle concourse.

CHAPTER 8

A CASE FOR ARBITRATION
– THE FOLDED SLAB

The vehicle concourse of the Opera House at the south (landward) end of the site was designed by the architect as a stairs and landing, but as a monumental stairs and landing, with the treads of the stairs 300 feet long, rising to a height of 20 feet above the roadway to a landing which was a plateau the same width of the stairs and 250 feet deep with an area of 75,000 square feet. Cars pulled up beneath the shelter of the flat landing or top of the concourse to drop off passengers who ascended enclosed staircases to the Opera House foyer, while the cars did a 'U' turn and drove beneath the podium in the opposite direction to find a car-parking space.[1] Theatre patrons arriving on foot were treated to the spectacle of the soaring white Opera House shells as they walked across a courtyard to the base of the monumental stairs, walking up the stairs then crossing the plateau to an entrance door leading directly into the Opera House foyer. With this simple concept of a mere staircase and landing Utzon had separated the avenues of approach of pedestrians and those arriving by vehicle, for both groups to assemble together in the foyer in anticipation of enjoying the other world of the theatre. During inclement weather pedestrians could approach the Opera House from Circular Quay beneath a covered walkway that ended close to the vehicle entry beneath the monumental stairs.

The concourse or 'folded slab' as it became known could be simply described in the following way. If a desk or table is placed against a wall, place your elbow against the wall with your arm and hand at right angles to the wall parallel to the table top and six inches above it. Keeping your arm parallel to the table top and your fingers straight, bend the hand down at the wrist until the tip of a finger touches the table top. If it is imagined all four fingers were the same length, your hand and arm become two pairs of beams in the folded slab. Ove Arup recalled that:

> ... The structure has a somewhat unusual shape, which was determined more by architectural than by structural considerations... Certainly,

functional and structural reasons alone would not have produced it, although they had a considerable influence on it.

... the architect had originally shown the Concourse (on the competition drawings) supported on a number of columns at midspan. However, when this structure was first discussed between the Architect and Engineers, the Architect asked whether it would not be possible to do without these columns. A typical question, which received the typical answer, that of course it was possible, but it would cost a lot of money, and as the columns did not obstruct anything this expenditure might not be justified. The Architect then explained that his concept demanded that the architecture should be expressed through the structure, in fact the structure in this case was the architecture; it should be bold, simple, on an impressive scale and on a form which combined sculptural quality with a clear expression of the forces acting on it. This achieved, finishes could be simple; 'the concrete itself would speak. The area covered by the Concourse was the place where people would arrive by car to the Opera House, and the impact of this vast unsupported roof would be spoilt by centre columns, even if they did not hinder the traffic.' He felt justified in achieving the desired architectural effect by spending the money on a bolder structure rather than on expensive finishes.

Utzon had demanded the top surface of the plateau be as flat as a billiard table, which meant there was no fall to drain off water. To overcome this, the paving laid on top of the concourse would have open joints to allow the water to pass through, which could then be channelled towards the north and south side of the concourse by the shape of the top of the concourse structure. Utzon also demanded the 'total depth of structure should be uniform over the full length of the span, and this depth should be as small as possible.'[2] The challenge for Arups was to design a series of beams 'which in a dramatic or sculptural way would reflect the variation in the external forces along the span and indicate how they were resisted at each point.'

This aspiration to have the structure "truthfully displayed", to achieve "structural honesty", is of course very familiar to students of architectural theory. It is a declared architectural ideal of long standing, and rightly so. But it must not be taken too literally. Geoffrey Scott showed fifty years ago that this requirement was psychological rather than factual. It has nothing to do with choosing the most efficient structure.

The spectator does not in fact understand the subtleties of a modern concrete structure, whose strength in any case may be hidden from the eye in the form of reinforcement or cables. It is not so much a question of how the structure really acts, but rather of how the spectator thinks it acts, or whether he can relate it to some simple structural facts which lie within his experience. Thus he may be able to appreciate the strength of an arch springing from solid abutments, a cantilever which is strong at its root, a simply supported "fish-belly" beam or a fixed beam with haunches producing an arching effect, and this may give him an impression of structural "rightness". More subtle effects would be lost on him; they would not form part of his architectural experience.

In this particular case the most economical answer would probably have been a series of box-sections of I-beams spaced 6 ft apart, uniform over the whole length, with prestressing cables catering for the variations in the moment. But this would obviously not have met the Architect's request at all. It seemed natural to the Engineers, therefore, to seek the solution by exploiting a typical and by now very familiar reinforced concrete form, the T-beam. This can be said to be the best shape to take positive moments in reinforced concrete. And the same shape, only upside down, is the best shape for negative moments. So that the desired expression of the variation in the external moments could be obtained by varying the shape from a series of inverted T-beams at the supports (effectively a bucket shaped cross-section) to T-beams at midspan... [3]

This suggestion by the engineers, which could be achieved using straight and twisted plywood boards for the formwork, was accepted by Utzon, '... and was the one incorporated in the preliminary design submitted to the Client by the Architect and Engineers in April 1958, and approved. The architect had however introduced a further modification in the design, which the Engineers were not too happy about.'[4] This was that the visible corners of the beam when seen from below should be rounded off at the base of the T at centre-span through to the corners of the buckets at each end, and inside the right angle formed beneath each arm of the T. Utzon:

> ... explained that this was very necessary in order to bring out the sculptural quality of the design. The Engineers did not dispute this, but were worried about how to produce these rounded corners, and thought it would be very difficult and expensive. It had been their idea that the forms should be made of straight narrow boards forming the twisted surfaces, which would therefore show the familiar boardmarkings characteristic of structural concrete. However, the Architect demonstrated on a small model that these board marks and the sharp corners would be out of scale, and that the desired effect could only be achieved by smooth rounded surfaces.

A joint visit paid by the Architect and the Engineers to the Sydney plywood factory of Messrs Symonds, who were masters in the manipulation of plywood, confirmed that the Architect's ideas would be difficult to realize, and on the return journey from Sydney the designer therefore considered other and more practical ways of effecting the transition (from a T to a U shaped cross section)...

A solution now proposed by the engineers was 'to rotate the side B-C round point B... and simultaneously to rotate part of the beam soffit D-C round D, in such a way that the point of intersection C between the two lines moved on a straight line from C to its ultimate destination, point F (Fig.14). The resulting shape of the beam, assuming that the sinusoidal variation of cross-sections was maintained, proved to be very interesting and to possess that roundness or voluptuousness which the architect was looking for,[5] in spite of the fact there were no rounded corners... After considering this new proposal and making models to judge its effect,[6] the Architect wholeheartedly approved of it, adopted it, and had it passed by the Technical Panel.'[7]

Two changes caused unexpected complications to the design. Utzon, at the request of the Technical Advisory Panel, increased the tread to riser ratio to give a gentler rake to the stairs, and the sandstone at the southern edge of the site was found to dip down and be heavily faulted at the base of the stairs, so would not provide a suitable buttress for the base of the stairs at that point. The first change meant new calculations and drawings by the engineers, the second meant adding a tie-beam to the design which extended from the base of the concourse steps back beneath the concourse below the level of the roadway to the Opera House sub-structure.[8]

All these changes naturally delayed the completion of the detailed drawings which were urgently needed on site, and further aggravated the almost impossible situation which was created by the Client's insistence that work should begin on site early in 1959, long before the brief – let alone any finished and dimensioned drawings – had been completed. The situation was not improved by the Contractor's insistence that his program demanded an early start on exactly this particular part of the job. Add to this the difficult nature of the job, complicated or unusual formwork, narrow sections packed with steel, etc. and the Contractor's unfamiliarity with prestressed concrete, and it is no wonder that the atmosphere on the job deteriorated and the workmanship suffered.

... it may be of interest to mention another complication which was happily avoided, because it concerns the design, and it throws some light on the somewhat different points of view of Architect and Engineers.

It arose from the fact that a part of the Concourse slab (the part under the restaurant) was raised a few steps over the rest. It was part of the

Architect's philosophy – to use a now popular phrase – that the structure, i.e. the shape of the slab as seen from below, should register this fact; one should be aware of what happened above, just as one should be aware of the forces acting on the slab.[9]

The effect would have been similar to that in the bedrooms of some houses, where there is a slope between the top of the wall and the ceiling to follow the line of the roof. Utzon's intention was that:

... the beams under the higher portion are lifted up and there is a gradual transition to the normal level, more or less following the steps above. It was difficult to argue that this could not be done, although it posed tremendous problems, because the five special beams were unsymmetrical in cross section and the prestressing would create torsional movements which would have to be absorbed by the adjoining, already fully stressed, beams. This would require structural additions and might even prove to be almost impossible – apart from the fact that it would upset the whole arrangement of stressing two adjoining beams at a time, and would require five sets of special and more complicated forms, thereby invalidating the excuse of repetitive formwork.

The Engineers' view was that even if the Architect was correct in preferring his solution from an aesthetic point of view – which they did not dispute – the very considerable cost, and the disturbance it would cause in an already critical situation, would be too high a price to pay for something which after all would not be missed by anybody. However, the Architect was insistent and the Engineers were bracing themselves to attempt a solution to the problem when the Heating Engineers intervened with a demand for space over the slab in which they could accommodate their pipes and other services. This clinched the matter: by keeping the beams at the same level... (as the others) the desired space would automatically be created and everybody was satisfied![10]

The folded slab beams, each of which were six feet wide and comprised the beam itself and a sloping section at the south end to support the stairs, were cast as pairs 12 feet wide. A two inch gap was left between each pair of beams so that stressing operations could take place on a pair of beams without affecting the adjoining units. The most remarkable feature of the concourse both visually and from an engineering point of view is the extremely flat angle of only $19\frac{1}{2}°$ at the bend in the knee where the flat concourse dipped down for the gently sloping stairs. This quirk in the structure meant that any up and down movement in each pair of beams due to concrete movements, time, temperature and load tended to be exaggerated, and the elastic properties in the concrete could lead to vertical movements between pairs of beams. The result could have been that the line of the beams looking along the length of the concourse from west to east could, instead of presenting a straight edge, have been uneven like the white keys on a piano if they were not all at the same level. An arrangement using two 200-ton ship's jacks and steel wedges with plates or 'shims' was included in the design at the base of each pair of concrete beams at the bottom of the steps, between the tie-beam cross head and the concourse beam foundation. The jacks were used on each pair of beams not only to compensate for changes in thrust due to creep and shrinkage in the concrete, but also to maintain the $19\frac{1}{2}°$ angle at the knee and to compensate for any movement when the paving slabs were laid.[11] As a temporary measure, when the concourse construction was completed it was intended to stack bricks on top to simulate the load on the structure with the paving slabs in place. When the paving slabs were ready, expected to be in 18 months from the finish of concourse construction,[12] the bricks could be removed. It was intended to lay the paving slabs in lines east-west on top of the concourse to restrict to a minimum any possible vertical movements in the pairs of concourse beams.[13]

When a particularly delicate and difficult piece of construction happens to come into a project – wrote Ron Jenkins to Professor Ashworth in a confidential letter on 19th April 1960, – and this chiefly occurs with some prestressing operations, it is quite normal to provide additional supervision on such an item by sending from the office the man who is most intimately acquainted with the design and detailing of it. We have such a case in the Stage 1 contract in Jorn's Concourse conception.

Because of the very flat angle of the stepped section this Concourse is particularly sensitive to shrinkage, creep and temperature variations. For this reason it has been necessary to employ hydraulic jacks to interpose predetermined thrusts between the ties and the foot of the stepped section. These jacks have to be operated during the process of prestressing and also brought back several times to make good creep losses before the jacking gap is finally grouted up in approximately one year from the concreting of each particular pair of folded slabs. The jacks are to be equipped with special dynamometers or load cells so that the thrust can be read accurately...

The design of the Concourse has been a very lengthy and intricate matter in our office... MacDonald, Wagner & Priddle... have already made the point that the Resident Engineer (McKenzie) has required assistance and will be increasingly in need of this as the tempo of the work speeds up... We therefore recommend that Mr A.M. Levy be sent from this office to supervise the construction of the Concourse... In this way the proper continuity from the design office to construction would be ensured.[14]

Alan Levy's impending arrival was greeted with relief by Ian McKenzie, who had just come back from an unexpected trip to New Zealand after the death of his father. 'His detailed knowledge of the design will be invaluable here', wrote McKenzie to Jenkins 'I had been visualising some awkward questions on the folded slab so I am happy that there will be someone here to answer them.'[15]

Alan Levy arrived in Sydney by liner in August 1960 with his wife Jeanette and one child. 'Alan is settling in this week' – wrote McKenzie on the 30th – 'and already his detailed knowledge is showing up to advantage. I am not sure whether this is all for the good as I sometimes think blissful ignorance is our best approach!'[16]

'There does not seem so much to discuss this week;' wrote Arup engineer Peter Skead to Levy from London on 4th October 'we must at last be starting to tie up all the loose ends which arose while you were on the water. The nightmare days of the Concourse (in finalising the structural analysis, completing the drawings and reinforcement details) seem to be slowly passing by and a feeling of elation coming instead. Still, until they have cast and stressed a few folded slabs, I don't suppose we can afford to be too cocky... Your... slides (arrived) yesterday morning... They were in fact just in time for a slide show which we had at lunch time yesterday. The pictures of the shuttering for the "J" Type beams on a big screen really did look most impressive and it seems a shame to have to put plywood inside. The forest of pillaster steel looked pretty frightening!'[17]

'In general everything is under control' wrote Alan Levy to Jenkins on 10th October. 'It does appear though that the Contractor has not yet grasped the full appreciation of the difference in workmanship required between prestressed and reinforced concrete. This has inevitably led to several clashes. ... their original time estimate of 12 months for the complete concourse construction has, as I think we always felt in London, been rather under-estimated by at least 3 months. Consequently the Contractor and myself are striving for opposite ends: he to complete the structure, at almost any cost within the next 12 months; and myself to guide the construction and prestressing (at least in the initial stages) gradually. It's a question of "hasten slowly" I think.

My own feelings are that once the first few beams have been prestressed, the efficiency and general morale will have quite an uplift.'[18]

'You are quite right to insist that there must be no relaxation on high standards of workmanship for the concourse' wrote Jenkins to Levy on 16th November. 'Time is a secondary consideration and anyway the Contractors seem to be able to get a few months extension whenever they see that the job is going to take longer than they thought... I derive a lot of comfort from the knowledge that you, who know the design and detailing of the concourse so well, are out there to look after the construction... I hope life and climate is agreeable to both you and your wife.'

A short time later it was time to pour the first concrete, which Civil and Civic insisted on doing on the concourse itself instead of on a trial beam to test the shuttering and concrete compaction. On 6th December 1960 Alan Levy wrote to Peter Skead in London.

> The most important event was the first folded slab pour viz. beams J6 and J7. It was a most difficult piece of construction. Two mixers were used, one starting from the south end and one working south from the north end. Particularly in the early part of the north end pour, it was evident that the concrete was too stiff and also the design of the upper forms was such as to preclude the efficient compaction of the concrete in the horizontal soffit portion... As things turned out, the concrete was not getting right down the vertical 7 in sides into the soffit section. The pour did improve progressively, but it was disorganised at this stage (Ian and I were even on the vibrators). The one inch air vibrators proved useless, and the only effective compaction was obtained using the two inch electric vibrators. The pour took place on Monday 28th November and on Tuesday they began the removal of the upper forms. Our worst fears were realised. There was a gaping 3 ft square hole in the soffit at section 46; a smaller one at 44; also inadequate concrete beneath dead anchorage B1.
>
> The central portion is fine. Then there are empty pockets on anchorages 01 and G1. The worst is a huge 4 ft x 3 ft hole against dead anchor P1, at section 7, J6 west. Personally I feel the beam is not over safe in its present condition and while I feel disinclined to demand Civil & Civic pull it down, I think it would be prudent to state that, at this stage, we cannot accept the responsibility for the prestressing of beams J6 and J7. We will nevertheless naturally do our best to assist in corrective measures. We will do this by gunniting the "hollows" and building up, the section beyond, in some cases, more than its original geometrical boundary. We will also weld extra steel in. All in all mind you, I think we have a pretty good chance of getting away

with it.[19] I shall feel much happier when that pair of beams is finally stressed – and standing! I have since requested that the first stressing operation take place on Beams J4 and J5 which they plan to pour before Christmas. This won't delay them any, as there is a 12 day break over Christmas, and they can probably commence stressing at the beginning of the new year. This is a reasonable move I think, as we would prefer to stress a sound pair of beams in the beginning.

As to correcting errors in the previous pour, there have been some meetings already and both sides are getting together tomorrow. One of the points I have introduced is to thicken the walls from 7 in to 9 in between sections 6 and 7. There is a fantastic amount of steel there and rather than try and calculate how to cut this down, I have increased the section slightly.

Ironically mind you, after this pour and subsequent discussions I feel quite confident that future beams will be well up to the standards required.

Jorn is here this week and was most impressed with progress of work on the site. He was particularly amazed at the formwork for the folded slab – and was bubbling over with joy. He had not at that stage seen the 1st beams stripped. When he did, he was very sympathetic though.[20]

'Things have not started off as well in 1961 as we might have hoped for' wrote Levy to Skead on 11th January. 'On Friday J4 and J5 were poured. Despite their mixing plant breaking down (there have been 8 similar breakdowns in the last few working weeks) and the pour dragging on for 12 hours, it appeared reasonably successful. The upper forms are in the process of being removed and it seems that we have still got (hollow) areas in front of and/or below the 12 inch by 6 inch by 7 inch dead anchor boxes... Despite my having warned them several times before the pour of exactly a similar occurrence on J6 and J7, they still neglected to tackle the problem on section 20... If you could say J6 and J7 were 50 per cent (100 per cent being a perfect beam) I would say J4 and J5 were 75 per cent. This is a step in the right direction of course. But I am disappointed as I expected (and been promised) 90 per cent...'[21]

Skipper Nielsen wrote an official letter to Utzon on 21st January outlining some of the defects on the beams:

Beam No. J6

A bulge in the eastern wall face, about 2 in by 5 – 6 ft long. It was explained already during your visit, that the formwork had moved during the pour.

The dummy joint between J7 and J6 shows a slight curve, maybe $\frac{1}{2}$ in. Two bulges show in the plywood – "ceiling", depth about $\frac{1}{2}$ in.

Beam No. J5
The open joint between J6 and J5. shows a curve as indicated, deviations on the raked part being 1 in - 1$\frac{1}{4}$ and possibly more on the horizontal part.
  Beam-sides at the "knee" are out of plumb, about 2 in.
  The plywood buckles in one place, – as for J6.
  … I should be glad to have your instructions by cable whether to go on or not, and your further comments by letter as soon as possible.[22]

And wrote a personal letter to Utzon on the same day.

  … It is true that there is an improvement in respect of the faults disclosed on the first two (beams), and the new defects no doubt were just as much a surprise to Civil & Civic as to us…
  … The question of a 100% perfect slab was put forward to find out, whether the question of costs had any influence. According to Mr Holland this is not the case – he maintains that they are losing money, but they would not have used any other method of constructing even if they were to start from scratch again…
  I think myself that they can do it, and that they will do it. I think that this has made them stop and think again, before they start on the next two ones.
  Ian has mentioned, that the most efficient way of dealing with Civil & Civic is to appeal to their prestige rather than trying to kick them – I think that you have mentioned something on those lines too.[23]

'It is quite clear that this work has been too difficult for these contractors' wrote Jenkins to Utzon on 27th January. 'I think that with the help of Nicklin and our people in Sydney the Contractors will get the shuttering right before very long… I am therefore instructing the site not to pre-stress any of the earlier faulty Concourse castings and it will have to be left to you to decide whether you will accept them or not. If you find these earlier sections are unacceptable they will have to be broken down and rebuilt. This sort of thing happens even in London from time to time… I think that a matter of this seriousness would require you to visit Sydney to make the decision… I have (sent) the following cable:

DO NOT START STRESSING FAULTY CONCOURSE BEAMS
STOP
ARCHITECT MAY DECIDE THEY ARE UNACCEPTABLE.[24]

To which Utzon replied on the 30th, with an apology for his bad English:

  … I do not feel… that I should be the one to inform the contractor as the highest authority, that the beams are unacceptable because of their unaccuracy in form. I think I should only be concerned with the surface and

191

the sharpness of the edges… it is Ove Arup & Partners' structural design. The architectural side of it has been made by your firm. You have described it, designed it, designed the outline drawings for the formwork… I think it is unwise and wrong that I am going to be involved with this… I think it is obvious that we must paint the beams on some sort of surface treatment. Any repair on the beams can be done, even on the edges, because that will be covered completely up by the painting and treatment…[25]

Jenkins replied on 1st February: '… I agree that the whole idea for the Concourse beams was evolved by us and we made drawings and models. You said you liked it and that you would have it. Well, so far you haven't got it… If you think the errors in the shapes of these four beams are going to spoil the whole effect it is up to you to say so…'[26]

Ron Jenkins travelled to Sydney in March 1961, and a decision was made that if the faulty beams could be stressed successfully they would be left. Levy had prepared a 16-point checklist for Civil & Civic before the stressing of any cables was to take place, including item 9 'Ensure that all personnel are not in unnecessarily dangerous positions, e.g. directly behind prestressing jack.' Levy reported progress to Peter Skead on 4th April:

Well its up and standing! I have, along with several others I expect, a marvellous elated feeling. The stressing of J4 J5 with relatively little incident has been no less than a tremendous achievement – an achievement I feel that belongs to quite a few people.

That week of stressing – and then depropping, I shall remember all my days. It makes all the troubles, all the sweat seem so worthwhile. Its a structure to be mightly proud of.

Down to the details now. We had a team of 4 stationed as follows: One at tower on G.L.12N. observing horizontal movement of folded slab; and also nipping across to observe horizontal movement of the tie; one under the structure observing vertical deflections at the South knee and centrespan, and horizontal deflection at the E.W.girder (Prof. Roderick of Sydney University had insisted on latter). This chap also took some strain readings in the soffit at centrespan. A third member was located on top of the beam, taking the bulk of the strain measurements (over 100 of them) and also keeping a careful eye on setting up of wedges, barrels, jacks, etc. etc. I myself was set up in a little hut or "nerve centre" and was in direct and continual communication with the three lads. I thus had a grip over the complete operation. As results came through I was able to decide, in a calm atmosphere, how we were going. Particularly around the bad anchorages, this procedure was important. Any cracks were immediately reported. The latter were few – and mainly hair cracks. They did in fact occur around the gunnited anchorages – but were not severe.

... There were two very bad scares – both at anchorages – in the upturned beam area. The first was on J5, cable B1 east, where an imminent shear failure nearly took place. This was almost certainly precipitated by a heavy ramset nail (a nail driven with a charge) driven coincidentally with the point of maximum stress. A large crack started developing at the full load – and we quickly wedged home.

The second took place on J4, north end of cable G2 west, while we were attempting to shim. At a load of about 50 (tons), a large shear crack began to show – whereupon the load was immediately released... The beams, now depropped and completely self supporting look magnificent. It would be a great pity to have to treat them in any way, as part of the grandeur (of the) appearance is derived from the rough concrete texture. I also feel that... several minor faults that appeared serious at the time (eg. the westward movement of the south knee) are quite lost in the overall picture...

Mr Jenkins' visit proved very stimulating and re-assuring... Just before Mr Jenkins arrived we were stressing one of the tie beam cables. At a load of 46 tons one of the wires of the strand failed in tension. At the dead-end, the wedges were unable to grip the remaining wires, and the cable unleashed its energy to the extent of completely turning over the prestressing jack, hanging 2 dynamometers on the embankment behind (we were calibrating one) and pulling out some 50 ft of cable. No one was injured. Just badly shocked.

I have decided to throw a beer party for all those involved in the construction of the concourse, in celebration of J4 and J5: to take place Tuesday night. I think it's a good idea to express our appreciation.[27]

Levy asked Skead in the same letter that if the stressing of J6 and J7 proved unsuccessful '... having stressed several cables and then one failing, how does one release the stress in the others, before demolition?' To which Skead replied, offering several suggestions, including '... drill away the concrete from somewhere near the midpoint of the cable... direct a medium size flame on the duct and cable and stand clear. (Heavily sandbag the anchorages, of course).'[28] Kelman too wrote to Levy '... I hope the beer party went off well. That is one activity at which Australians are notoriously successful.'[29]

Concerning J6 and J7 Levy wrote to Jenkins on 17th April

... In preparing for the gunniting, labourers toured the beams with chisels and mallets and exposed many more holes than had previously been noticed. There are two or three anchorages which have only a very remote chance of surviving the high stresses set up. There is no assurance that other as yet unexposed holes do not exist... J6 and J7 would not be stressed for at least 9 months. This would enable Civil & Civic to gain more experience on folded slab construction. If in addition it appeared that J6 J7 were far inferior to the other beams, there would be no loss of morale when they were demolished.[30]

'J1 was poured on Saturday 22.4.61,' wrote Levy to Skead on 28th April, 'They are taking the upper boxes out at the moment. It has really been a masterly executed pour. It looks a powerful, beautiful beam. No holes (as yet) and no apparent formwork movement at all.'[31] Levy struck an interesting problem with the wedges.

> Have had a slight scare with the re-shipjacking on J2J3 and J4J5. The normal procedure is to grease the faces of the wedge and any plates inserted. Applying a 10 pound hammer on the wedges does not extrude this grease. Only when the shipjacks are removed, and the complete load (about 160 tons a time) transferred to the wedges, is this grease forced out. The result is that we are losing two to four hundredths of an inch closures in the gap – approximately 7 to 14 tons loss in thrust, I figure. The idea is now to coat the wedge surfaces with an oil, rather than a grease.[32]

'News is good news,' wrote Levy to Bob Kelman on 3rd November. 'C6 C7 successfully prestressed this morning at 9.15am. The beam took a full week to complete instead of 2 or 3 days... As predicted cable B2 north end, the most critical on all the prestressed work, cracked in several places – not to an unhealthy degree though. The Cement Fondu stood up terrifically. We got 7600 p.s.i. cubes in 3 days – and field cured! Progress on the prestressed work is really gaining in momentum... In my opinion the general standard of workmanship is well to the fore.'[33]

Arups had been light on site supervisory staff earlier that year, with Malcolm Nicklin going down with hepatitis. 'He will be confined to bed for at least 3 weeks' wrote McKenzie to Kelman, 'and there may then be a rather lengthy convalescing period before he is fit for duty again. Perhaps the most regrettable aspect of this particular form of infection is that no beverage based on hops may pass one's lips for 12 months!'[34]

Work on site seemed to be settling down to an extent when Levy wrote to Jack Zunz in London on the 26th July of 1962 to report

> The last pair of folded beams stripped on the western side, D1-D2 are the "best ever". Ironically these are the last pair allowed with the old forms, but we do feel that if they were patched again the result would be worse than J6-J7! The only reason for the D1-D2 result is the care, attention, determination and craftsman knowledge of the Roberts/Prosser (Clerk

of Works) combination, but this situation could not continue really, hence our instruction. Civil & Civic seem now to be taking the whole thing seriously and the new formwork for the lower beams is really first-class – a proper start to the job of obtaining a good result at last.[35]

On 18th May Skipper Nielsen had sent Jack Zunz some recent photos taken under the folded slab, with a note 'The upper span beams above the wide staircase have now been stripped, and the feeling of movement through the total expanse of lower and upper span beams is quite an experience, although difficult to capture on a photograph.'[36]

But the apparent calm on site was deceptive. There was a row brewing with Civil & Civic, who were claiming the cost of constructing Stage I of the Opera House was more than they were getting paid to build it. The source of the disagreement could be traced right back to the tender documents for Stage I and Civil & Civic's winning quote for the job.

When Rider Hunt & Partners had examined Civil & Civic's tender for the Stage I contract, they had not only uncovered an arithmetic error of £51 but some apparent discrepancies in the rates charged for sections of the work: 'We consider that the rates for basement excavation' pointed out Rider Hunt's letter to Ove Arup on 29th January 1959 'are very low indeed and probably uneconomical from the Contractor's point of view... We... believe that he has gambled on there being little or no rock excavation when the basement is dug... In effect, the Contractor has made a large part of the anticipated saving on the basement, in his tender... which has allowed him to go in on a price perhaps £30,000 lower than less astute tenderers... We noticed that the prices for certain types of pier hole excavation are low and are inconsistent with other similar items... We feel... that it would be unwise to pursue this matter with the Contractor, since it appears that he has taken a gamble which will probably operate to the Client's advantage.'[37]

In drilling the bored piers Civil & Civic not only had to bore through all sorts of rubble, but the piers had to go down much deeper than anticipated, and where the piers went down anywhere close to the Harbour shore they kept filling up with water. As Arups pointed out in a confidential report to the Committee:

(This) mainly result(s) from poorer quality rock underlying Bennelong

Point than was anticipated. At our request 12 bore holes were put down on the site in June, 1958. These revealed sound rock over the whole area falling gently to the north and steeply away to the east and west. Only one bore hole showed a clay seam. This was deceptive; had no seam been shown at all suspicions might have been aroused. In fact the boring techniques did not reveal clay seams and it was not until excavations were begun that the exceptionally jointed nature of the rock was revealed. Foundations had to be deepened... [38]

As work got underway 'Boring of piers has commenced both inside the sea wall in the Major Hall area and in the sea' wrote McKenzie. 'There have been teething troubles with both sets of rigs, particularly on the inner bored piers where ground water and the rubble fill combine to make conditions very difficult... Financial matters relating to the inner bored piers have also been raised by the contractors. I get the impression that Civil & Civic are pretty shrewd on this aspect of contracting and there may well be quite a bit of wrangling in store for the future... There appears to be a marked difference between English and Australian practice in the approach to disagreements over interpretation of a bill of quantities. Disagreements here seem to be accepted as inevitable and even common place.'[39]

MacDonald Wagner and Priddle wrote to Jenkins regarding the piers inside the sea wall:

We do not think for a minute that Civil & Civic can carry out this work for the prices offered in the Bill, nor do we consider their claim is an unreasonable payment for what they are actually doing. However, we are of the opinion that, at the time of tendering, the information available to the Contractor was sufficient for him to foresee the difficulties now being encountered. This is borne out by the rates given to us by two sub-contractors before tenders closed and by the rates quoted by the other tenderers.

Because of this, we feel that Civil & Civic have gambled on these foundations and we are inclined to think they have tendered "dishonestly". For this reason alone, we are recommending that the latter be considered by an independent arbitrator. If the decision is with the Contractor, the Principal will not in any way be penalised as value will have been gained for the money expended. Civil & Civic are carrying out the work very satisfactorily. If the decision goes against Civil & Civic, they will have been taught a lesson and we shall have kept faith with, among others, the other firms invited to tender.[40]

So in response to three letters written by Civil & Civic requesting extra payment for piers inside the sea wall, MacDonald, Wagner and Priddle replied '… Careful consideration has been given by Messrs Ove Arup & Partners and ourselves to the various points raised… with the conclusion that we are unable to see fit to accept your claim.'[41] Civil & Civic replied they were referring the matter to arbitration.

A description of work on site in December 1959 referred to '… The machinery basement, which is below the main part of the building… has been excavated to a depth of 20 ft below ground level and 10 ft below sea level. Seepage of harbour water through fissures in the rock strata has been bothersome in this excavation, and, in fact, in most of the excavations. The solution to this problem was found in filling the fissures with concrete plugs and a battery of pumps kept the diggings dry.'[42] The orchestra pit in the experimental theatre, close to the sea on the west side of the site was even deeper, 15 feet below sea level, while the general level of the sandstone bedrock on the Opera House site was three or four feet below sea level. The result was that Civil & Civic put in a claim for de-watering (extra work for pumping out water), among many others. In the event, the arbitration claim for the bored piers turned out in their favour.

'There seems to be a spate of claims from the Contractor at the moment, and many… seem pretty dubious' wrote Kelman to MacDonald Wager and Priddle. '… the Contractor feels he has us all on the run and is naturally following up strongly… we do feel the time has come to get a little bit tough. We have a lot of sympathy for anyone trying to build the Concourse (and supervise the building of it!) and recognise that it may require extra time. We do not appreciate a steady dribble of claims over every small extra or addition… Incidently, his claims now seem to be based on minute and exact costing of the Bill items, whereas the Bill itself was notably reticent. Dewatering is an item in question. To argue that variations from the Tender drawings have almost tripled the dewatering problem is utter nonsense… the Contractor grossly underestimated the problem and is using the variation from the Tender drawings to make up what would have been a loss. This is a technique which he is making the maximum possible use of, and he must not get away with it.'[43]

'I have received particulars of the Contractor's claim for an extra of £47,878 for dewatering' wrote Jenkins to Malcolm Nicklin.

> In my opinion we are not interested in how the Contractor arrived at the lump sum he put in the Bill. He would have to show that the scheme was substantially different from that upon which he tendered to justify the extra. In my opinion the foundations have been subjected only to normal minor modifications.
>
> The modifications have in fact been in the Contractor's favour. In the tender the Minor Hall basement was at level plus 1 (below high water) and it was later changed to plus 4 (above high water)...
>
> My own feeling is that we are in a stronger position in resisting this claim than we were on the bored piles.[44]

Jenkins summarised the general position to the Committee:

> ... It will be appreciated that the scheme which formed the basis of the contract was really only a sketch scheme, and the contract although in the form of a lump sum contract was at the time thought of as a Schedule of Rates in which we and the Quantity Surveyors endeavoured to include all items that were likely to be required with approximate quantities so that there could be a fair comparison between the tenders received. We appreciated the reasons for starting work on the site when we did but we are bound to point out that when Mr Arup was in Sydney in April 1958, he told the Committee it would be reasonable to start the first contract early in 1959 provided the Architect's final details were completed by June, 1958. In fact, the detailed architectural design has been running concurrently with work on the site all through. This has made life difficult for us. There have been many changes after detailed drawings had been completed. These drawings went into our "superceded" files and one, two or three new sets had to be made before finality. On the other hand; we found it impossible to halt that state of things because we appreciated the Architect and what he was doing. He has the whole time refused to be satisfied with any solution if he could see a better one. We could see that that was the way to work to make the design in keeping with the importance of the building and the amount it is going to cost. In our opinion Mr Utzon has a very fine team of assistant architects numbering the maximum it would be possible for him to direct. He has kept himself free from all other commitments in order to give his whole attention to the Opera House. This is what we all want. Had he had several other projects going at the same time we are sure that this very complicated Opera House would have been the sufferer.
>
> As you know, the contractor was not getting information sufficiently ahead of his work to plan the job properly. In fact, he had to go back and alter completed work on many occasions and the crisis was reached in

October, 1959, when a standstill of contract time had to be agreed for us to get ahead again with our detailed drawings. At the same time a considerable modification to the Major Hall stage basement was called for by the Client.

The Contractor.

I want to make it quite clear in this report that the Client is doing very well on Stage I largely at the Contractor's expense. Consider the tenders for Stage I. We had from Civil and Civic what we regarded as a freak low price because of lack of time to consider the tender properly or some motive we do not know. Their tender figure was £1,398,000. We had two tenders very close together from John Holland and Hornibrook, McKenzie and Clark averaging about £1,610,000. We regard these two figures as realistic costs of what was covered and described in the Bill of Quantities provided the work went smoothly and final drawings had been issued sufficiently far in advance of the work to allow efficient site and organisation planning. These two tenders included for casing internal bored piers and had a much higher rate for excavation than Civil and Civic.

The fact that the result of the arbitration about the bored piers made Civil and Civic £143,000 better off cannot be regarded as a loss to the Client. In fact, the amount of bored piers in the Bill for which Civil and Civic had had no extra represents a considerable loss to them because it is quite clear they did not include for steel casing for any of these internal piers. The negotiated figure of approximately £48,300 for increase of overheads due to the standstill of contract time would be sure to have applied to any of the other tenderers because they would have been faced with exactly the same position. The dewatering claim has not yet been settled but we anticipate that that will be at the order of £50,000. This would have applied to any contractor. Two typical reasons are the Major Hall stage pit measuring 36 feet by 64 feet had to go down to -8 below low water level whereas the whole of the Major Hall stage area on the contract drawings was at +3 above high water level, and the very large increase in the size of the Experimental Theatre Orchestra Pit which goes into water logged ground...

So we can see that there is no doubt Civil and Civic face and have known for some time that they face a heavy loss on this contract. In those circumstances, it is to be expected that the contractor will try to reduce the loss by minimising labour costs resulting in an inferior quality. In my opinion it is to the great credit of the supervisory staff that, at their insistence, any sacrifice of quality has not been allowed to happen. I know the Contractor has felt they have been very hard on him but from our point of view this is right. I am sure also that in settling the various claims for the sums mentioned above the Quantity Surveyors and Messrs MacDonald, Wagner and Priddle have been very strict indeed and have only agreed on strict net costs leaving the Contractor no margin in which to set against his losses.

So we see that the only effective way Civil and Civic could have minimised the loss consequent on their tender would have been by intensive preplanning and efficient organisation. We do not know of course how good they would be at this but we believe their organisation is capable to some extent. It is, however, a hypothetical point because as already explained the progress in design has for most of the time resulted in the issue of information just as they reached the section where it was required and any kind of planning ahead was quite impossible. We have reason to believe that Civil and Civic are giving considerable thought to framing some claim for compensation due to loss of efficient contract organisation but their experience of the strictness of our representatives and the Quantity Surveyors makes it difficult for them to put this forward in a form that will carry the day. It may well be the question will never arise.

I was surprised to find that Civil and Civic, apparently, have no experience of prestressing. They knew nothing about the necessity of smooth cable profiles and accurate anchor setting. Our Resident Engineer on this section has been patiently teaching them their job and they are getting quite good at it. They could have had an experienced man sent from Holland. Not to have done so is, I presume, another example of a foolhardy saving on a losing job. Without our man the result could well have been disastrous... [45]

Though Arups and MacDonald Wagner and Priddle resisted many claims by Civil & Civic, there were also many others that were accepted without demur. For example a claim for £336 for alteration to formwork in the Major Hall Stage Area was accepted.[46] Also, '... beams with tilted soffits (on the central passage steps) are not described in the Bill nor shown on the tender drawings... You should therefore negotiate directly with Mr Young of Rider Hunt & Partners in order to establish fair and reasonable rates for this section of the work.'[47] But one item Arups were not prepared to negotiate on was the class 'C' formwork, specified by Utzon 'to be finished formwork of a very high standard, lined with plywood or other smooth surfacing material, and able to give a true and smooth finish to concrete exposed in the most important sections of the building.'[48] The concourse beams were class 'C' formwork, and when the first beams had been stripped of formwork revealing a number of defects, a conference had occurred between Holland for Civil & Civic and Nielsen, MacKenzie and Nicklin to look at ways of improving subsequent beams. 'Mr Holland... stated, that he thought that the present method of construction was correct for the result asked for in the specification, but if a perfect beam – meaning no tolerances and a cabinet-maker's finish – was required, regardless of time and cost, a different set-up would be necessary – and at a different price.'[49]

'... it should have been quite obvious to the Contractors that the tolerance mentioned in the specification for ordinary beam and slab work could not apply to the Concourse'- wrote Ron Jenkins to Malcolm Nicklin – 'and further than that, Utzon had Dusseldorp's assurance that the Concourse would be done exactly in accordance with the drawings... If the remedial measures are not successful on the next casting the work will have to be stopped and we shall have to choose between new shuttering and a new contractor... I think many Contractors would prefer to demolish and rebuild new rather than leave this monument to their inefficiency...'[50]

Utzon was in Sydney in April 1961, among other things to inspect the ceiling in the Central Passage. Though his guidance to Nielsen on acceptable concrete quality was open to interpretation, Utzon said to Nielsen:

> I have accepted the ceiling in the Central Passage as good enough and the rest of the ceiling must be of the same type (the joints as in the folded slabs). I hate the modern tendency in Japanese concrete architecture with all the lists and joints being formed so that they make continuously cast concrete houses look like element houses. I can see all the difficulties from the contractors' point of view by meeting the plywood forms in the joints, but I accept their accuracy and I will later on make up my mind on treatment and repair. As a matter of fact, I do not think I will repair anything. The big house can take this freshness, but an important thing, of course, is that the joints are neatly done and the plywood panels sizes and forms are orderly made.

The question of the Central Passage being 'good enough' was later subject to some discussion between Utzon and Nielsen. Some misunderstandings were clarified, and the net result was that the standard should be defined as 'at least as good as the folded slab.'[51]

Besides the Concourse, the most extensive areas of class 'C' formwork in the Opera House podium were the bar areas facing the Harbour at the north end of the Major and Minor Halls. In this case Civil & Civic agreed to produce a mock-up. Nielsen wrote to Utzon:

> ... The second pour of the mock-up has now been stripped... the standard of workmanship is far from satisfactory and does not indicate a serious attempt to produce the finish required... it is in one way an advantage as

we are enabled to point out, clearly the faults that cannot be accepted...
I feel we may have to condemn the sample... and to ask for some form of
assurance that the contractor intends to and is capable of doing a proper
job. It has taken them seven folded beams to reach a satisfactory standard
in the concourse, and I see no reason for a repetition of this procedure...[52]

Followed by another letter four days later reporting on the last site
meeting:

... It was stressed to Mr Holland that an improvement of the quality of
work was most important as regard to the bar-areas (class "C") and to this
Mr Holland remarked, that they were not interested at all in this type of
work and that they would in fact rather see it done by somebody else. We
answered that it was of the greatest importance to us to get a
workmanlike and first class job and that we would make every effort to
see that this was done. Mr Holland said that he could see our point, but
as the firm was facing a severe financial loss for this type of work... he felt
that it would be inevitable that this attitude (worded: "we have not our
hearts in it") would be reflected all the way down to the man on the job
and therefore the standard we would get would not be as good as if the
rates had been adequate. An increase of 100% was quoted as the correct
rate. He also mentioned that no special instructions had been given to the
men working on the mock-up as to the quality required...

After this it looks to me that unless some action is taken we will face
the situation on the folded beams over again, but this time with the
difference that we will be dealing not with men who are anxious to make
the best of a difficult job but with an attitude of no interest from
supervisors and workmen as well...

... I think that the mock-up will have to be condemned on completion
as being unsatisfactory and the Contractor asked for a statement on his
intentions but whether this will produce any reaction I do not know... I
should be glad to learn your opinion at your early convenience as to what
should be done and who should do it... I feel that this is of such major
importance that any movement should be planned very carefully and in
co-operation with Arups and yourself.[53]

MacKenzie wrote to Jenkins regarding the meeting with Holland,
relating how Holland had also pointed out '... the area (of class "C"
formwork) involved in the upper levels has increased roughly 5 times,
resulting in a substantial financial loss. This does not mean that Civil
& Civic deserve any sympathy', had continued MacKenzie 'for while
the area in the upper bar areas has increased, the elimination of
"C" class areas measured in the Bill below 2nd floor level means that
the total area is likely to be much the same as measured.'[54]

Utzon wrote to Dusseldorp on 12th September:

> ... I am glad to hear that the folded beams, J6 and 7 have been successfully stressed... we agreed that I should contact you directly when I wanted to express dissatisfaction of any kind. From reports received from our site staff in Sydney, I have had many complaints about bad craftsmanship...
>
> I think it is deeply important that you, personally, inspire your staff and take any step necessary to overcome future deviations so that we can be absolutely sure of the finishes and tolerances specified in the Bill...
>
> We are just about to start one of the most important parts, namely the Bar Area, where we have exposed concrete of the highest standard. In this area the public will be in close contact to the walls and beams...
>
> You and your firm have proved that you can live up to an acceptable standard. It is just a matter now for your firm to carry this through in spite of any difficulties you may have.
>
> I expect that you personally will study these problems and take any necessary precautions in order to accomplish this great job.
>
> The architecture of this building is its structural expression.[55]

That same day, Ian MacKenzie wrote from Sydney:

> ... to return to class C formwork. The main point is that while Civil and Civic may say officially that they will fulfil all their contractual obligations, in practice they are unlikely to satisfy our requirements. In doing the work to our satisfaction they would incur a substantial loss. Their only possibility of reducing this is to skimp in material and workmanship. This of course applies to all work on the job but, in particular C class formwork areas are bound to suffer as a result.[56]

In March-April 1962, Utzon came out to Australia with Jack Zunz of Arups, who had inherited overall responsibility for the Opera House from Ron Jenkins. On Thursday 15th March, the day after arriving in Sydney, at 2.30 in the afternoon Jack Zunz and Utzon with Jones and Young of Rider Hunt & Partners had a meeting on site with Civil & Civic staff. 'Mr Jones confirmed, that the contractor in his opinion would have no right to walk off the site, as he has threatened.'[57] The following Monday an offer of £15,000 to cover the extra cost of the work involved was made but '... There was no indication that the contractor would accept.'[58] On 26th March at another site meeting Utzon '... stressed that the quality obtained on the small section of ribbed slab already poured must be maintained at all costs... and that any portion falling short... must be demolished.'[59] On 4th April

Jack Zunz and Malcolm Nicklin met Mr Dusseldorp. All work on class "C" north of radius 196 ft 0 in (is) to be left out of this contract. Reinforcement already up (is) to be taken out, but formwork to remain. Civil & Civic (is) to complete what is structurally necessary up to plus 66.00 south of this boundary and otherwise (is) to complete (the) Concourse and remaining stage areas.[60]

To the relief of all concerned, Civil & Civic would not build the bar areas which would be left for the contractor that would build the shells. Civil & Civic had employed a photographer to take monthly photos of progress on site from the Harbour Bridge, and when he asked why the workers were taking down reinforcing at the north end of the building, they explained that Utzon had had a last-minute change of mind on the architecture. But that still left the folded slab. According to the minutes of meetings of that same Utzon/Zunz visit in 1962:

Jorn Utzon referred to Holland's undertaking some days ago, that he was confident that he could maintain the standard of work on the ribbed slab, although only a minor part of it had been built. Mr Dusseldorp disagreed with the project manager on this and said, that to be 100 per cent sure of a first class job, he would reconsider the procedure of works, and spend much more time by fewer men in setting-out, that this would take about three months longer than estimated, and asked the architect's reaction to this. Jorn Utzon objected strongly to this and said that he could not foresee the consequences at the moment.[61]

On 4th April, before they left Sydney, Zunz and Utzon conducted the Lord Mayors of Sydney, Melbourne and Brisbane on a tour of the site. The Lord Mayor of Sydney later brought up at an Executive Committee meeting a passage in *Engineers Report No.2* that referred to Arup's dissatisfaction of the site supervision of the Stage I contractor 'and asked whether in fact inferior work had gone into the job. The chairman and Professor Ashworth assured him, that this was not so.'[62]

On 29th May 1962 at a site meeting to discuss which portions of forms for the folded slab were suitable for re-use, MacKenzie, Nielsen and Roberts, the Clerk of Works had disagreed with Civil & Civic about which forms could be re-used, said 'there was no point in continuing... broke off the discussion...' and walked out.[63] Ian MacKenzie then rang Jack Zunz in London asking him to terminate Civil & Civic's contract. Zunz replied:

Having spent some time with you we had a taste of the day to day difficulties arising from the bad feeling existing on the site. We know that you and the other fellows on the site are bearing the brunt of it and while we will do anything we can to help there are certain things which we either can't or which we shouldn't do.

We have previously discussed the question of the finish to the Concourse and it needn't be restated, you know it only too well. We note with regret your and Skipper's and Malcolm's contention that we will not get the finish specified from the Contractors, but your suggestion that we should terminate the contract insofar as the remainder of the Concourse is concerned cannot be implemented – at least not yet.

We can only terminate the contract on good legal grounds and these, as far as I can see, do not yet exist. As I mentioned to you on the telephone, if we get to a stage where the finish provided is so poor that you condemn it and the Contractors refuse to rectify it the situation would be quite different...

You can only advise and criticise their method of putting together the formwork and placing the concrete. As far as the final result is concerned however your powers are absolute and you can accept or reject and should the necessity arise in the Concourse we will certainly support you in taking any action you consider necessary to maintain the specified standard. If this action means pulling down completed work and the Contractor refuses to do so we can then invoke clauses in the contract, after taking necessary legal opinion, which may mean chasing the Contractors off the site.

Sorry about this but life is hard.[64]

Malcolm Nicklin of MacDonald, Wagner and Priddle wrote to Ove Arups on 30th May '… to fill in the gaps in the correspondence on the current folded slab formwork fracas.' Following a long discussion after the site meeting:

… actually we do not know what to do. We are in full agreement, that even if Civil and Civic were paid extra, we could still not get a satisfactory job, as I have already pointed out for you. The amounts quoted are quite ridiculous, we all agree. According to Ian there is not a lot of money in the extra reinforcement, and a statement that our requirements for the formwork quality should increase the cost ten times has no reasonable basis. It can only be considered as another example of Civil and Civic's wish to get some of their money back as well as a confirmation of their – now many times repeated – statement, that they are only interested to get out as soon as possible.

The question remains, whether we can stand back and watch them continuing with unsatisfactory work, without even a possibility for being paid extra. We all agree, that even against extra payment the quality would not improve very much – if it would improve at all – and also, that if they are not paid, it will be an impossible task to force them to maintain, what is achieved now...

If we refuse to accept their claim – unless they are trying to bluff – it will mean termination of the works in Major and Minor Halls. Whether they would stop also in the Concourse (possibly strike in sympathy) only time will show. It is possible, that this might mean some political uproar, which from the Committee's point of view might be undesirable up towards the election. Another risk is, that the Union might ban the site and boycott other workers...

It was suggested also to alter the requirements to the formwork and paint or render it all... (but) it sounds immoral to be forced to amend the appearance of a building to suit the contractor.

For once there is full agreement and sincere disgust between the whole site staff regarding the way this matter has been approached, and although we cannot visualise the political consequences we all feel like suggesting them to finish the course and pack up.[65]

Shortly after MacKenzie wrote '... when discussing the possibility of Civil & Civic finishing off the next few beams only and then pulling their flag down, Holland said he would take away all the formwork as he had designed it and it belonged to him! Leavey, somewhat aghast I think at this, intervened and said some residual value could be worked up for it...'[66]

Rigby of Arups in London wrote to Kelman that '... Holland's threat to remove form work off the site is in breach of clause 22 of the contract... (and) Civil & Civic's off the record threats to cut down the labour force and deliberately slow up the job... (is) in breach of their contractural obligations... if this slowing down process is put into effect... I think Nicklin should write a hot one to C & C throwing clause 26 and 54 at them...'[67]

Somehow, Nielsen, Malcolm Nicklin and Ian McKenzie did battle on site with Civil & Civic, and got good though not excellent quality concourse beams, but their relationship was like that of an unhappy married couple living together – with no prospect of a divorce for many months. 'Mr E. G. Wagner's feelings are, and have been for a long time now', wrote Nicklin to Arups, 'that the sooner we are rid of Civil & Civic the better for all concerned. He is not alone on this you can rest assured!'[68] Though to be rid of Civil & Civic was not to prove quite as straightforward as having them complete their work on site at the earliest opportunity.

In March 1962 MacDonald Wagner and Priddle had agreed with Civil & Civic that all subsequent outstanding claims in dispute would be held back and examined with the contract as a whole at a later date. This included claims by Civil & Civic on the cost of the folded slab formwork.

'Bob Kelman indicated that he was looking forward to the final episode of the Stage I termination...' wrote Malcolm Nicklin to Jack Zunz in London on 21st September 1962 'So are we, quite frankly, but this looks to be a way off yet...' MacDonald, Wagner and Priddle had asked Civil & Civic for a summary of all their claims and 'This shows that the contract sum they are seeking, with all the claims imaginable, is £3,055,000!!! Some £88,000 for interest on moneys tied up is just one of the claims yet to come... A bombshell exploded yesterday afternoon when Tom Walker rang soon after lunch to say that Civil & Civic had served notice that morning on the Attorney-General that the above claim should be resolved by arbitration...'[69]

In a memo written to Jack Zunz later that day, Nicklin thought that 'By putting this claim forward at this time and via the Attorney-General, it could be that Civil & Civic are looking for some publicity – perhaps even a "dog in the manger" act as they have not even been considered for Stage II. As you now know the Stage II Contract is nearly ready for signing, after which a formal public announcement will be made with a certain scream from the newspapers and all and sundry. Maybe Civil & Civic reckon this claim is a good way to join the bandwagon... If they won the folded slab claim... they could quote it as a precedent particularly if the Arbitrator found the work should be priced on a dayworks basis. If this was so they surely would plug for the whole contract then to be done on a cost plus or dayworks basis.'

Civil & Civic submitted three names as potential arbitrators.
1. Sir William Hudson – Chief of the Snowy Mountains Authority.
2. W.R. Nimmo – now retired but previously head of the Irrigation Commission in Queensland.
3. Neil Brown – ex-Chief engineer for Thiess Bros. now with Humes Ltd.

> ... and insisted that we agree to one of these or alternatively to none at all within seven days... Nimmo is "too old" really and deaf as a post as well... Sir William Hudson in his present heirarchial position with the Snowy Mountains Authority may be a little far removed from some of the practical details which will be certainly raised (perhaps this could be a good thing!)... if we do accept one of the three it would most likely be Neil Brown.[70]

Zunz sent a confidential letter to Nicklin in reply on 25th September:

> The choice of Arbitrator is most important… It is important, for us at any rate, that the Arbitrator, apart from having all the attributes legally and technically necessary for him to carry out his task, should have a very sympathetic architectural appreciation – he should be, if possible, an engineer/architect, rather than a pure Civil Engineer. I know that this is asking for a great deal but we must try and make the best compromise possible.
>
> Civil Engineers – a wonderful body of men – nevertheless have philistine tendencies as far as architectural matters are concerned and I cannot believe that our cause would be furthered by a man who is fundamentally insensitive to what we are trying to achieve. I know full well that theoretically an arbitrator should be unbiased but even arbitrators are human.
>
> I recently read that in this mildly lunatic world people who are both completely rational and totally insane are considered equally odd. I propose that we should conform to the mildly lunatic in that we should now use every possible dodge (legal of course!) to stall and delay the arbitration proceedings for as long a period as can be managed without damaging our cause. We here see no reason why we should be stampeded into agreement of arbitrator or for that matter for an arbitration date.
>
> … stalling on our part is not as lunatic as it seems. We have not devoted our time, in the way the contractors have, to preparing our cause. Obviously the more time we have the better.
>
> No doubt you will get the best legal advice – this is most important. I hope that such advice concurs with our view… namely, to try to finish the job before commencing arbitration proceedings and to use every legal dodge to achieve this end.
>
> … we think our cause is very good – we don't think that anything new has been specified or that any additional drawings or specifications have been issued to Civil & Civic since the 1st April this year… on the whole we have a very good case and their claim cannot be substantiated… [71]

With the preparation for the Arbitration getting underway, Nicklin found himself working longer than the usual hours, on one occasion phoning Zunz early one morning. Zunz wrote back '… let me say that we are very touched and impressed by your devotion to duty in being in the office at quarter past one in the morning. My admiration is unbounded.'[72]

Wagner and Nicklin had already met Leavey and Robinson of Civil & Civic on the question of the claim and choice of arbitrator '… After an hour and a half we had talked a lot, neither side had budged

an inch and we still appeared to be good friends at the end of it all!…
Basically we do agree on one thing, i.e.that Civil & Civic have
claimed that we have called for a standard of formwork finish higher
than that laid down in the contract documents and we claim that we
have not! Therein lies the argument purely and simply…'[73]

As the Arbitration was likely to raise many legal issues, and Jack
Zunz was at that time heavily involved in the development of the shell
design, he passed most of the work arising on the Arbitration to
Arup's Company Secretary, Roger Rigby. As well as being possessed
of a nimble mind, Rigby was also a cartoonist and artist of some
distinction, and when he travelled out to Sydney in December 1962 for
the start of the Arbitration hearings his handwritten letters back to
Jack Zunz were illustrated with little sketches, such as a barrister
holding aloft a boomerang with a little kangaroo squatting beside him.

Rigby wrote from Sydney on the tenth:

… I will spare you the horrid history of BA700, a flight that must have
marked up some record in the history of BOAC frightfulness. In
retrospect it had its comic aspects. The 5/- statutory bus charge took me
out from Victoria Airways terminal on the bridge into Pimlico, once
round Warwick square, back to Victoria Street and so round 3/4 of a circle
to the genteel front door of Victoria station. Thence we virtually
completed the circle by surging in a choking mob to the entrance of
Platform 17 (which is the nearest to the Airways building of course) and,
as the train was full, all the way down the platform to a point under the
bridge to Pimlico which we had crossed in the bus 15 minutes before. The
beauty of this farce was unfortunately wasted on my fellow passengers
who were either foreigners to London or lost in the fog.

After eleven hours of squatting (sic) at Gatwick we fell into a passing
train (no tickets of course) and went to Brighton, where I personally was
ushered into an Edwardian bridal suite of horrifying proportions. As we
had no luggage I slept in one corner of the vast damp bed and nothing else.

Boeing's need 400+ visibility for take off but next morning our Captain
was in a desperate mood. I put my trust in his long line of medal ribbons
and the mention in despatches on his Atlantic star, and so we got off.

As Frankfurt and Zurich were both fog bound we cut them out and
went to Basle and from then onwards it was largely routine apart from a
$1\frac{1}{2}$ hour delay at Tel Aviv because of the sabbath slowing down the petrol
dowser, and four hours at Singapore for a mechanical itch. I have a
souvenir menu card presented by BOAC in which I see listed the
succulent concoctions which we were always able to avoid for one reason
or another.

The end of this tragic comedy came at Kingsford Smith Airport when Ian met me with the news that had just reached him that Andrews the arbitrator had been refused permission to act by none other than Menzies himself. It seems that Andrews as a senior Commonwealth servant in Canberra can only accept gainful employment or in fact any task outside the line of his normal duty if he has Government permission. Everyone had thought that this would be a formality, but one greater than any of us could have foreseen had entered the arena: none other than Queeny. She is coming to Australia next spring and Andrews is wanted by Menzies as tour organiser. Maybe he has race horses as well as his Civils! Anyway Andrews is out.

Whilst Ian and I were contemplating this situation Malcolm arrived. He had come straight from taking Bob (Kelman) and family off the Castel Felice and the sight of Bob or of his 1300 immigrant fellow passengers must have had some unfortunate affect on Malcolm, because on the way to the airport he as near as dammit killed himself. Fortunately he was strapped in for his car did one complete circle and went 25 yards into another car. His back axle was written off, back windscreen gone completely, all the bumpers, trims, lights, etc. on his and two other cars smashed up, etc.

He got away with a bang on his head and although he looked normal at the airport, the reaction hit him a few hours later and he had to go to bed. However he is very much on the ball again now.

We went to the site (this was Sunday lunchtime) where were Ron Thompson and Skipper Nielsen who looks to me very definitely in need of a long holiday. Malcolm agrees.

Rigby later met the staff at MacDonald, Wagner and Priddle, toured the Opera House site – which he called 'the new Tramsheds'[74] and had briefings with Bowen, the QC retained by the Crown Solicitor for the Arbitration hearing, impressing on him '… we must leave no stone unturned to win this case or at least to minimise the adversity of the award.'

… the current position regarding an Arbitrator is that Professor Leavey of Queensland University has I think been agreed to by both sides. Whether or not he has accepted and can hold the first hearing before Christmas I don't know.

It is very pleasant here, about 80° most of the day. The Astra seems to be quite empty, and it is very comfortable and friendly thanks to the fact that I come in the wake of such distinguished former guests who have clearly left their marks on the receptionist if you understand me.

That damned Dexter is having his next test in Melbourne. His wife was on our plane from Singapore, she is a red head model.

Sydney bears such a resemblance in its life and manners to Toronto that I feel quite familiar with it, it is extraordinary.

The gorgeous specimen of bronzed demi god who sat at the next table to me at breakfast this morning ordered

Pineapple Juice, Grapefruit, Rolled Oats, Two poached eggs and rare fillet steak and coffee.

Rigby's letter to Jack Zunz on the 11th opened with the news:

Professor John Hardie Leavey, Brisbane University and Rhodes Scholar who was the Arbitrator as of yesterday afternoon is now no longer that man. He is just back from the States and is very busy and exhausted...

Now the suggestion by Civil & Civic is a Mr Williams. He evidently is a retired Commissioner of the Queensland Public Roads Department...

And then on the 12th:

Since yesterday there has been frantic activity by all the actors in an ever expanding cast. We were all down at the site last night, a glorious moonlit scene. At one end of the building were gangs of ex C & C engineers and foremen preparing their case and at the professional end of the site hut we were amassing information from the records.

Innumerable Arbitrators have been put up and shot down for a variety of reasons and the telephones have been jammed all over Sydney by our vocal peregrinations. However the current situation is that we shot down the last man put up by the other side. They are so desperate about this that they have now – reluctantly I think – agreed to a man put up by us, who we certainly didn't expect them to accept. He is Laws, a recently retired, but very active, chief engineer of the N.S.W. Govt department of public roads. He is well known to all the principals here and of course to the client and everyone is very pleased that we have got him.

... They were surfing at Bondi at midnight last night, it seems to be a 24 hour business.

Rigby's letter on the 13th assured Jack Zunz that the QC Bowen:

... has now had several very long sessions with all his witnesses and sources of information on the site and has got a fairly impressive grip on the situation. He can recite from memory the dates of pours of all the beams and give them their correct numbers, and I think he can also recite the major errors in most of the beams by number also...

... We are happy also with the Arbitrator. He is our nominee, knows the Macdas (MacDonald Wagner and Priddle) principals well, is a man of impeachable integrity, won't be flimflammed by smart lawyers, and is thought to be capable of appreciating what the folded slab means in terms of Utzon/Arup language. He is a Sydney resident, which means he will understand the importance of the project, and also is available.

Bowen was going to call for an adjournment following the first hearings, for a long case he had starting in January, and possibly would not be free again until May:

> ... This is suitable to us also I think and so I have encouraged the idea of such a lengthy interval. It will serve to dim the Arbitrator's memory of the super burnished appearance of the formwork which, is now being polished up for his inspection.

On the 14th Rigby wrote of Rider Hunt's position...'Their global target figure on claims and contract now stands (at) £2,600,000. I think this represents a difference between us of at least £250,000 probably more, so this is not a figure to be laughed off...'

Rigby's last letter on the 17th before flying back to London announced the news:

> The Arbitration has at last opened. After 5 minutes we had to move from one room to another, because no-one could hear anything. However, we are now happily housed on neutral ground in the APA building.
>
> Mahoney (representing Civil & Civic) turns out to be as unpleasantly smooth as Bowen said he thought he would appear to be. Bowen however has shown up very well in the cut and thrust of the opening sessions and we feel we are better represented than they are.[75]

On 20th December Kelman wrote to Jack Zunz:

> I am gradually beginning to find out what all this fuss over the Opera House is about. I must say it looks different from this side of the water!...
>
> Much frenzied time has been absorbed during the first few days on the great "Case", but Roger will tell you all about that. I have not yet been over anything like the whole of the site. The catacombs and dungeons need an official guide.[76]

Then, on 4th January 1963, Kelman wrote asking:

> ... What is my role here? From discussions with Mr Wagner I feel strongly that he wants Malcolm, or what is left of him, back.
>
> He feels I should take over from Malcolm, and we can have our Opera House back! He was happier before he even heard of it!
>
> ... It is now quite evident that (Civil & Civic) intend to deny us the use of the site for as long as is possible... [77]

On the 7th Kelman had a meeting with Civil & Civic on some of their claims:[78]

> I have had my first encounter with the Leavey-Robinson-Holland trio today. There is no doubt they are a tough trio, well informed and convinced of the justice of their claims. Even where these are the result

of much patient scouring of the Bill for small loopholes, the policy we have all pursued right through Stage I, of having what the building justified at any price, has certainly given them ample scope.

Even when we know perfectly well that a claim is cooked up to cover often huge expenses, it is almost impossible to refute their arguments. It seems we are left with the alternative of accepting the vast majority, or of refusing it on little or no grounds, hoping an arbitrator will see our point of view as well as theirs. Unfortunately he is likely to realise the expenses that C & C have had, the absurdity of the original Bill, the vagaries of our performance and I would think incline pretty much to the view that as the Bill was a travesty, fair and reasonable rates are reasonable and fair!

However, to go back to today's performance... (regarding costs incurred due to an increase in contract time).

Leavey went through his full song and dance routine emphasizing what good chaps they were to claim only the extension they needed, not that to which they were justified. The Aria, "Oh Wicked Engineer, Oh Fickle Architect" was given a moving rendition. Drawings were at least $2\frac{1}{2}$ to 3 years late, volume of work was doubled, calculated average monthly expenditure of £70,000 was maintained for almost full period so work must have been more; first real Concourse drawings issued March/April 1960 but requirements of wicked engineer invalidated honest contractors best laid program – more steel, beams to be poured in pairs, etc., etc.

We stood this one over until we have the full libretto in writing and with it all the other... claims.

Act II opened with the C claims...

C9. Extra cost due to reduced cover. This we referred back. It was piteous to realise how these poor chaps had been imposed upon, but we could not really be convinced in this case. However Peter Young said their returns do show greater costs for placing concrete into forms with $\frac{3}{4}$ in cover than in forms with $1\frac{1}{2}$ in. So! If we are still unconvinced – or rather convinced that we are being taken for a ride, what will an Arbitrator think. By the end of this job we will have exhausted Sydney supply of potential arbitrators.

Act III. Reinforcement. All our chaps agreed that reinforcement was their virtuoso performance on site. They did it well...

Act IV, F1. This is the dramatic content of this opus. Passion and character fuse into one great plot, and the primeval savagery of man stands revealed.

The Bill made no mention of patterning in B class formwork. The only opportunity they had of pricing patterning of any sort was in some C formwork to the soffits of bar beams. 40 squares at £36 odd. The difference from C plain to C patterned was about £19.19.0. Hence patterning as such cost nearly £20. I can almost hear Roger expostulating.

But they believe their creed; passionately... and they made their point well.

Patterning means lining of horizontal and vertical joints, it means vertical joints continue up from the sides of doorways and are equi-spaced from doors and corners. It means re-use is limited unless whole walls are repeats. Holland gave us a solo crescendo on this in which the horizontal semi-quavers were beautifully matched.

They admitted they would be delighted to be paid "fair and reasonable" rates for this work and that little gem, F7, "more patterned than patterned" rendered in trio is the excess of "fair and reasonable rates" syncopated into the principal theme of this movement...

As a sort of epilogue or perhaps it should be be considered a curtain call, Leavey advanced to the front of the stage and announced that more claims were to come. There would be something for everybody. When pressed to disclose the extent of this joy he admitted about 30 and promised these within the week to make Malcolm happy for his departure. I feel we have no guarantee that these will be the last. Remember Hitler and his "no further territorial claims in Europe"? If you take him as sincere you persist and go mad. If you don't, he wins. Or else you tell him where to go, and leave the whole mess to an Arbitrator, so that he can go mad.[79]

Kelman wrote to Zunz on the 12th:

... As we went through their claims it was evident that some were pretty far-fetched, but we realised that if we rejected these out of hand, an equal sum of money would re-appear under some other pretext...

but having discussed the whole issue with C & C. for several days one cannot help being influenced by their sincerity, when they speak of what this job has cost them. I also remember what certain early drawings cost us when the design changed during the production of the drawing. Their claim for £125,000 for general loss of productivity may not be far fetched. Leavey made the point that the only two parts of this job on which they made a profit of between 5% and 8% were the stormwater and cable duct diversions. Here they were able to go straight ahead...

(Leavey admitted that) the K Claim, under the heading "General" and comprising some £204,000 represents the margin over the total of all the others necessary to hold off their shareholders and it is in fact half their issued capital.

They will not let this thing go without a fight...

Do not delude yourself that there is any figure within the Stage I estimate and palatable to the Committee, the Minister or the Public which Civil & Civic will accept.

Storm canvas will be needed, and pretty well reefed at that. Arbitration will be our best port in this storm where we can shelter amongst larger vessels![80]

On 4th January 1963 Civil & Civic sent a long letter to MacDonald, Wagner and Priddle requesting an extension of contract time '... to the 30th of April, 1963... due to factors outside our control...' and quoted all sorts of reasons why this should be the case, including that 'the value of work carried out... is in excess of £3 million, as compared to £1.4 million in our original contract. This increase in the value of work by over 100 per cent must result in a corresponding increase in time...'

Hornibrooks, the contractor who were going to build the shells, had expected to move on site on the 1st of January, and they could not do that with Civil & Civic still there. Not least among the reasons for this was that Civil & Civic were paying over-award wages and Hornibrooks were not and could not, because their charter for the job was on a cost plus basis. When Kelman asked Holland for a '... firm program to get off the site, he hedged a little and then frankly admitted that his legal people had advised him not to leave the site until the Stage I contract was all settled up.'[81] Following this threat 'to "go slow" pending settlement of all the other claims, we have instructed them to finish by the end of February and if not we will terminate their contract.'[82]

The Arbitration hearing was due to resume in March, for which Arups found a new Counsel, John Kerr,[83] and MacKenzie and Nicklin flew back to London for a full briefing with all concerned to prepare Arup's case. Measures Arups resolved to complete included to go right through the files of correspondence on Stage I to compile '... a dossier of Civil and Civic's incompetence... and their admissions to such.'[84] Arups returned to Sydney in strength, their force including Ove Arup himself, Jack Zunz and Roger Rigby.[85] The Arbitration hearing got under way again still with Laws as arbitrator,

> 'a nice man' recalled Zunz – '(who) was hauled out of retirement to be the arbitrator.
>
> And this poor chap may have been a very good Commissioner for Roads, but of course he knew nothing about prestressed concrete. I mean, technically, he was totally out of step. And on the first day there was this scene, where Bill Leavey, the Managing Director... was in the witness box, and John Kerr was cross examining him. And John Kerr... is a big man with a grey mane of hair (and a) florid face, and he, like many distinguished QCs – a very theatrical sort of person – he tossed his grey hair back and said: 'Mr Leavey', he said, 'when you tendered for this project, did you make allowance for shipjacking these beams?' And there

was no reply. So he tossed his hair again and he said: 'I repeat my question, Mr Leavey. When you were tendering for this project, did you make allowance for shipjacking these beams?' So Bill Leavey said, 'Mr Kerr, I don't understand the question.'

So Kerr tossed his hair again. He said: 'Mr Leavey, I will repeat my question for a third time. When you tendered for this project, did you allow for shipjacking these beams?' So Bill Leavey says, 'Mr Kerr, I don't know what you're talking about – I don't know what you mean by shipjacking these beams.'

So he turned round to this poor arbitrator and he said: 'Mr Arbitrator, would you please explain to Mr Leavey what shipjacking these beams means.' So the arbitrator said, 'Sorry, Mr Kerr. I don't know what you're talking about.' So Kerr sort of shook his hair again, and he said: 'Mr Arbitrator, if you don't know what shipjacking means, and Mr Leavey doesn't know what shipjacking means, how do you expect me to know what shipjacking means.'... He turned round and said: 'Jack – what's it all about?'

You see, he'd come up from Melbourne the night before, to study the brief. So this went on in the mornings, until about midday and in the afternoons we'd meet without prejudice. There was Ove and I and Dusseldorp and Bill Leavey, sitting across the table, hurling insults at one another... [86]

On 13th March Zunz sent:

> ... a short report from the battlefield to let you know what is going on... Firstly, the Arbitration began on Monday on schedule... and the whole thing is, of course, a farce... listening to the lawyers examine and cross-examine makes one feel that it is really quite a difficult subject which they are discussing and not remotely connected with what we think the argument is all about.
>
> Yesterday when the Opposition put one of their foremen into the witness box, our Counsel objected to the principle of discussions between Clerks of Works and Foremen being construed as instructions to alter the quality of the work and so on. Opposition reeled on this development and after recess to this morning asked for an adjournment, so that the admissability of this evidence can be established. We are now in recess till the 1st April... [87]

Meanwhile Rigby was compiling the dossier on Civil & Civic: '... I have now collected into one vast mountain all this bumph and am sitting in the middle of it, only able to see the superstructure of the larger ships that pass the site office over the top of my paper crater.'[88]

With the hearing in adjournment Arups started talking with Civil & Civic about a settlement, but neither side was prepared to budge sufficiently to make an agreement. As 'the discussions had made much progress, but finality had not been reached',[89] the Minister for Public Works asked the permanent head of his department, Johnson, the Director of Public Works, to '... participate in the discussions between the Consulting Engineers and Civil & Civic.'

Johnson looked on the claims 'compared with the approach which the Department would probably have followed had the claims arisen under one of its contracts... I concluded... the Consulting Engineers had conscientiously and competently endeavoured to reach a basis of settlement which was fair and reasonable to both parties...' Johnson discussed the matter with the Crown Solicitor and Counsel and 'both stressed that it was most desirable that a settlement be reached if possible in preference to continuing with arbitration.' Arups wrote to the department '... expressing the view that settlement might be reached between the figures of £2.55 million and £2.65 million.'

> After discussion with the Minister, the conference was held in my office at which the following were present – Messrs Arup and Zunz for the Consulting Engineers, Dusseldorp and Leavey for the contractor, and Humphrey and myself for the Minister. There was considerable discussion and finally I stated that I was not prepared to consider the figure in excess of £2.58 million and that even this figure would require the Minister's approval. Mr Dusseldorp replied that if the Minister approved the figure he would refer the question to his own Board for decision so far as they were concerned. The Minister later agreed to the figure, this was conveyed to Mr Dusseldorp and during the same afternoon he conveyed to me his Board's acceptance.
>
> ... the Crown Solicitor and Counsel both regard the proposed settlement as entirely satisfactory to the Government. It is understood too, that the figure contemplated is below that at which the Technical Advisory Panel would be prepared to recommend settlement. It is also worthy of recording that from the calculations made by the Quantity Surveyors they are convinced that the actual cost of the work to the contractor exceeds the amount proposed to be paid.
>
> The following factors, in my opinion, fully justify payment of the sum mentioned:-
> 1. The heavy costs of litigation... Seventy odd other items are also in dispute... And it could transpire that the Crown would have to meet the greater part of the costs of the contractor as well.
> 2. Uncertainty as to the result, the Arbitrator might consider that the contractor is entitled to a higher, possibly a much higher, figure than the Consulting Engineers consider reasonable...
> 3. Waste of time... unless claims are settled the Arbitration could run for

another 12 months or longer... [90] the Consulting Engineers are concerned they would be prevented from directing their full attention to productive work and undoubtedly the completion of the Opera House would be delayed.

... I recommend that the Minister approve payment of the total sum of £2.58 million in full settlement of all claims by the contractor... (and) that the current Arbitration would be discontinued on the basis of each party bearing his own costs and sharing the Arbitrator's fee... [91]

Nicklin explained to the Executive Committee:

... that the difference of approximately £1 million between the original estimate of £1,511,000 and the final settlement related mainly to justifiable items arising from circumstances not foreseeable at the time the contract was entered into.

The amount of the settlement was approximately £40,000 more than the amount recommended by the Engineers, but offset against this was the avoidance of litigation which would undoubtedly have been costly in terms of money, time and effort.'[92]

The *Telegraph* quoted a 'high State Government authority' who said that 'The cost of building the first stage... exceeded the original estimate by more than £1 million... "only a small amount" had been in dispute with the contractor.'[93]

What a 'merciful release'[94] it is all over thought Rigby. Ove Arup wrote to his partner Peter Dunican letting him know they would all be heading back to London and 'We had a very successful party yesterday for all and sundry on the site. It is raining every day. – Love Ove.'[95] The morning after the party, Jack Zunz walked to the office of the architect, Harry Seidler on Macquarie Street to pay a courtesy call. Seidler's office was in the same building as Civil & Civic's and the debris from the party *they'd* held the previous night still littered the foyer.[96]

Nicklin wrote to Jack Zunz on 24th April with a copy of the executed Deed of Release officially closing Stage I and the Arbitration. 'Quite an historic document' wrote Nicklin. 'So it's all over! This is probably a fallacy of course as Stages II and III have yet to come but surely the first of the "big hurdles" has been jumped.'[97]

Zunz replied:

... We hope that you are now recovered from the shock of having at least the possibility of a tranquil existence. If you need some occupational therapy we can probably assist...

> Thank you for the transcript. Roger will probably prepare a Bible on how to avoid arbitration by prior indoctrination of site staff and we will send you a copy.[98]

The deed to close the Arbitration, four pages of closely typed legal script signed by Dusseldorp and the Minister for Public Works, Norman Ryan hereinafter, referred, constituted, deemed, thereto aforesaid and declared

> ... whereas it has been agreed between the parties hereto that all claims which have been made or which could be made by the Contractor in relation to the matters arising out of the Contract including the claim so referred to arbitration as aforesaid shall be settled and compromised by the Minister paying to the Contractor the sum of £537,551 17s 6d... in consideration (of which) the Contractor DOTH HEREBY remise release and forever quit claim unto the Minister and the Government of the said State all claims demands actions suits cause and causes of action or suit sum or sums of money compensation interest damages costs charges or expenses which the Contractor now has or hereafter may have or but for the execution of this Deed would have had against the Minister or the said Government for or on account of any matter or thing arising out of or in respect of the Contractor whether as payment for the works performed by the Contractor pursuant to the Contract or for extra works required by the Minister to be done or for damages or otherwise... [99]

The Arbitration hearing cropped up at Arup's next staff meeting in London:

> The May Senior Staff Meeting turned out to be a scintillating performance by Roger Rigby on The Sydney Opera House Arbitration – now successfully concluded, thanks to the hard work of everyone who went out in March. Jack Zunz gave us an admirably clear description of how the problems of Stage II were being solved. He also supplemented Roger's rollicking stories – with just the right shade of irony. Mr Arup ended the meeting, that will go down in the annals as the best ever, by pointing out that we ought to take great pains with our specifications. He was, too, slightly regretful that he had been unable to show us any of his slides – but those that accompanied Roger's travelogue – for he also described the journey – were magnificent. He will show them again and everybody will be able to see them. They are highly recommended.[100]

Utzon, referring to his dissatisfaction of the folded slab finish, wrote: 'The folded concrete beams under the concourse are an example of the unsatisfactory results (of concrete poured in-situ) a series of beams each different from its neighbour, and not a continuous even surface as visualised.' Utzon hoped later '... to conceal the defects and bring it up to a uniform and acceptable standard...'[101]

Civil & Civic poured their last concrete at the Opera House on 19th February 1963, the last two folded slab beams at the west end of the vehicle concourse and packed up and left the site on 10th March. Hornibrooks were informed they had possession of the site from 25th March, but even before that date were moving on to the site the steel for the cranes to construct the Opera House shells.

CHAPTER 9

THE DESIGN OF THE SHELLS

'And he gave the universe the figure which is proper and natural... Wherefore he turned it, as in a lathe, round and spherical, with its extremities equidistant in all directions from the centre, the figure of all figures most perfect and most like to itself, for he deemed the like more beautiful than the unlike. To the whole he gave, on the outside round about, a surface perfectly finished and smooth, for many reasons... he made it move with circular rotation... And since for this revolution it had no need of feet, he created it without legs and without feet... Smooth and even and everywhere equidistant from the centre, a body whole and perfect, made up of perfect bodies...'[1]

According to Utzon:

The Sydney Opera House is one of those buildings where the roof is of major importance. It is a house which is completely exposed. The Sydney Opera House is a house which one will see from above, will sail around, – because it sits on a point sticking out into a harbour, a very beautiful harbour, a fiord with a lot of inlets. This point is in the middle of the city and the city rises on both sides of the fiord so the Opera House is a focal point. This means that one could not design a building for such an exposed position without paying attention to the roof. One could not have a flat roof filled with ventilation pipes – in fact, one must have a fifth facade which is just as important as the other facades. Furthermore, people will sail around it, there are ferries sailing past and large ships coming in, – the big harbour is just outside and the large bridge nearby, so people will see it as a round thing. They will not see it as a house in a street, either along the street or across.

Therefore, instead of making a square form, I have made a sculpture – a sculpture covering the necessary functions, in other words, the rooms express themselves, the size of the rooms is expressed in these roofs. If you think of a Gothic church, you are closer to what I have been aiming at.

Looking at a Gothic church, you never get tired, you will never be finished with it – when you pass around it or see it against the sky. It is as if something new goes on all the time and it is so important – this interplay is so important that together with the sun, the light and the clouds, it makes it a living thing.[2]

Illustrating his idea for the shells, Utzon said:

> If you drop a big crystal ball on to the floor and then pick up the pieces the top face of each piece will have the same curve. This means that the pieces are in harmony with one another, they come from the same sphere with the same radius and therefore when they are built up in space we know that they will interact according to a natural law and that the composition is in equilibrium... We can now divide this into identical parts like slicing an orange. These become the ribs and then the ribs can be divided up into the smaller Y-shaped segments – all having the one common curve, the radius of the ball... You have here the precision of mass-production with the freedom you normally have only from handmade things.[3]

And of the interior of the shells Utzon said:

> The entrance into the foyer is low and suddenly you are in this soaring space, just as one comes upon the harbour suddenly through Sydney heads. Over all we put these light sails, just giving a feeling of protection and no more... Structure has disappeared in modern architecture for many reasons. Normally in a modern building you have a cardboard ceiling with all the piping and ducting up there, some columns sticking up, and you stand between these two horizontal planes. You don't know whether you are on the tenth or second floor and it doesn't matter. Here, I said, the span over your head is sacred – no installations can come through. That is very difficult, everything must be in the floor.[4]

While Ove Arup said of the Opera House:

> There is little doubt that the construction of Stage II is one of the most difficult building projects ever to be undertaken.[5]
>
> ... should the account not balance in the end, we shall have the comfort that we have been associated with the creation of the ninth wonder of the world – this is something in itself...
>
> I can assure everybody that the day this work is completed with its fantastic superstructure, the great concrete wings covered externally with Swedish Hoganas tiles of a beauty which does not fall short of the old china, with glass, steel and beautiful colours – then it will all appear as something extremely unusual – like a fairytale palace. And the situation on the peninsular in the wide harbour with its many pleasure boats, will underline the beauty in the building.[6]

At Ove Arup's first meeting with Utzon in 1957 'I had to point out to him that of course it was really the wrong shape for the forces that would be in these shells and that it would be very difficult to make, and he was very disappointed about it because he subscribed to this architectural tenet that structure and architecture or form and function or whatever you like to call it should be a unity.'[7] 'The interplay of surfaces made an assessment of structural feasibility by normal approximations difficult and of dubious value.'[8] It was '... one of those cases where the best architectural form is not the best structural form.'[9] 'I was very impressed with the basic simplicity of the planning and realised the immense architectural potential but... (told Utzon) that the sails forming the roof would be difficult to construct because they did not accommodate the basic thrust lines. There (were) moments which could not be absorbed by the thin concrete shells he had in mind... Utzon was quite willing to change his shapes in order to reduce the moments'[10] and they looked at alternative designs including a single roof without discontinuities over both halls but, '... any major deviation from the architect's proposal would destroy the essential sculptural quality of the scheme'[11] 'and it would not have been the design which won the competition... I therefore advised him to retain his basic idea, and we would somehow make it work.'[12]

David Isaacs of the Commonwealth Experimental Building Station at Chatswood in Sydney had visited Ove Arup and Ron Jenkins when he was in London in June 1957 and wrote to Ove the following October after looking at Utzon's 'beautifully prepared model of the proposed Opera House at the Sydney Town Hall'[13] to suggest 'It is clear that you are going to have a very interesting piece of structural design ahead of you.'[14] Isaacs let Arups know the station would be happy to advise on any 'special problems' that may crop up on the technical level in Sydney. Peter Dunican wrote back on Ove's behalf as 'Mr Arup is in Africa until the middle of next month' but thanked Isaacs for his offer of assistance, adding, 'I regard this as the most important structure that we have been engaged upon.'[15]

Ove Arup gave the overall control of the Sydney Opera House job, or 'job 1112' as it became known, to his partner Ron Jenkins, who was particularly skilled in structural analysis and had made the analysis of shell structures by what were at the time novel and elegant methods, his speciality.

Utzon's shells on the Opera House model were free shapes, like a sculpture formed by hand with plasticine or clay, and Ove Arup wrote to Utzon in December 1957:

... Jenkins and I are a little worried about your method of deciding the shape of the shells... The mathematical shape of the shells should be as simple as possible, both to facilitate calculation and to satisfy the eye... we must have a meeting to decide these matters as soon as possible... [16]

Utzon came over to London early the following January to talk over the shape of the shells with Ove Arup, Jenkins and one of Arup's structural analysts, John Blanchard. Blanchard was happy to meet Utzon who he found 'charming, absolutely charming'[17] when he went to lunch with Utzon and Ove at Bertorelli's Italian restaurant following their meeting.

On 14th January 1958 John Blanchard sent Utzon four drawings illustrating:

... the general arrangement of the shells. The shells are parabolas in elevation which we have tried to fit to your curves as closely as possible... you will note that they differ from the shapes as originally drawn.[18]

Utzon wrote immediately back in Danish to Ove in a handwritten, undated letter, the appearance of which he apologised for because '... my secretary has not yet arrived... Many thanks for the very beautiful "shells"... We are all thrilled with them. They are much better than the competition project.'[19]

In some notes on the structure sent to Utzon's house by Arups on 5th March, Arups explained that:

By thus defining the surfaces of the shells geometrically each point of the surfaces can be given spatial coordinates and a basis has been created for the calculation of the forces acting on the shells and the stresses created in the shells.

From a preliminary calculation it is obvious that the bending moments in the shells will be considerable owing to the heavy wind loads and it has been decided to provide the main shells on the inside with a series of ribs fanning out from the two supporting points and meeting in the ridge at the top.

It has also been decided to make use of the louvre plane, i.e.the surface closing the opening of the shell as a stiff membrane supporting the shell. It may even be necessary to connect the shells in some way to the internal structure of the Halls, but no decision has been reached yet. Extensive model tests will be required to arrive at a true distribution of stresses under varying loads.[20]

Arup and Utzon were armed with this information when they travelled together to Australia to present the *Red Book* scheme, and this brief synopsis on the shells was reproduced in the Sydney newspapers, Arup adding 'The structural design... (of the shells) is obviously quite a problem, and has only just been touched upon.'

In Sydney Arup and Utzon gave a talk at the Art Gallery, Utzon saying 'Australians going to the Opera House would get the impression of entering a cathedral', to which Arup added 'The Opera House is quite a new type of architecture. It could not have been done if we did not have electronic machines for the calculations.'[21]

The internal shape of the shells had to allow room for the auditoria and stages, and Utzon was looking at this in Denmark with Dr Jordan, the Danish acoustics consultant he had taken on. There was not room with the scheme as envisaged, and Ove Arup wrote to Utzon on 6th August 1958 following a visit to Utzon's office '... As far as the shells are concerned the positions of the supports have of course been radically altered and it will result in a somewhat different appearance of the shells.' The letter finished '... By the way, is there any news of my suitcase yet?'[22]

There were further refinements to the shape of the shells to cover the internal structures and Hugo Mollman of Arups travelled to Hellebaek to sort out some details. As the shape was governed by architectural considerations, Utzon was going to deal with it, and promised to provide Mollman with the information in a week, but Mollman wrote to Utzon on the 1st October 'This is now a fortnight ago and since then I have heard nothing more about the matter. This is now getting very urgent so I should be grateful if you could let me have the relevant information as soon as possible.'[23]

Then Utzon was off to Sydney again for the November visit with Jenkins when potential contractors for Stage I were interviewed. Utzon had stopped in India on the return journey and when Jenkins wrote to him on 11th December his letter opened 'I am sure you had a wonderful time in India. I am sorry it was not really practicable for me to join the party on that part of the trip.'

> Now that I have reported to my colleagues on the outcome of the Sydney visit, I am getting down very seriously to the problem of the shells.
>
> It looks as though we shall make use of the electronic digital computer and the Structurals Laboratory at Southampton University for all lengthy calculation, wind tunnel and structural model tests.

And Jenkins requested Utzon put him in touch with the shipyard in Helsingor 'to make perspex models for the wind-tunnel testing...

because they do such a marvellous job.'[24] Then Jenkins wrote Utzon a further letter on 13th January 1959, 'It would be very kind of you if you could find time to write to me about the questions I have asked in my letter of the 11th December regarding model making.'[25] At this time the 'side shells (were) to be elliptic paraboloids'[26] said Utzon to the engineers.

Meanwhile, work was continuing on the shells, which had started out as a pure (single skin) reinforced concrete shell, to which ribs were added for stiffness 'and when these proved to be inadequate a second skin was introduced so that there were two shells approximately four feet apart, strengthened by web members.'[27] Poul Ahm of Arup's team was in Hellebaek in August 1959, while Hugo Mollman was beavering away in England; Mollman wrote to Ahm at that time of modifications to the internal shell skin, his letter closing 'No doubt you are enjoying life in Hellebaek... and bathing and sailing in Jorn's boat. Who knows, you may even find time for some work now and then.'[28]

At the beginning of February 1960 'The shells consist(ed) of an inner and outer doubly curved membrane probably 3 in to 4 in thick, separated by intersecting systems of ribs at centres varying up to about 15 ft – 0 in.'[29] Kelman advised the site staff in Sydney. The Sydney staff needed setting out drawings for the shells, because items such as plant rooms, smoke extracts, fire curtain walls and lift shafts were related to the stage area which was related to construction that was then underway or soon to be underway on the podium, and the stage tower 'may or may not support the shells.'[30]

It was apparent at this stage, that to allow for movements in the shell structure due to wind load, temperature and so on that a concrete 'hinge' would need to be included in the design at the point where the shells sprang from the top of the shell columns. Ron Jenkins, who had called the Opera House 'something ahead of its time', wrote from Hellebaek on 24th June 1960 '... I am glad to say that Jorn accepts the concrete hinge idea... He not only accepts it but actually likes it, and we should therefore go ahead... (though) Jorn does not wish anything of the hinge to be seen above paving level.' Two months later, on 24th August, Utzon told Arups at a meeting in London at which Professor Ashworth was also in attendance that as far as he 'could judge, the project for Stage II should be completed by April 1st 1961.'[31]

On 14th November 1960 Ron Jenkins outlined in a memo the procedure that should be followed in tendering for the Stage II contract.

> There is no doubt that the tremendous effort we are having to make in the design of this superstructure will be reflected in the carrying out. There are not many firms in the world who would be suitable. It will be necessary to issue a description of the scheme to selected tenderers to give them about three months to work on it...
>
> The superstructure sub-contract may well be tendered for internationally. We should be very careful in making the short list to be sure that the firms selected are really capable of doing the job. We think we should have two centres for interviewing and answering questions – one in London and the other in Sydney. For the latter, one of our Partners should go to Sydney...
>
> We are still convinced that it would be very unwise to start the shell superstructure until our detailed drawings are quite complete.[32]

On 12th January 1961 the inner contours of the shells were finally fixed.[33] A structural model at a scale of 1/5 in to 1ft had already been made using the shell shape based on parabolas.

> The original version of the model was constructed in Denmark and was made of white Perspex. This material had less creep, slightly better elastic properties, and was less susceptible to temperature or moisture changes than transparent Perspex which is usually used for structural models. The model was manufactured by pressing warmed sheets of Perspex into wooden moulds made into the correct shape... [34]

Since late 1958 a team of engineers from Arups had been working

> ... in collaboration with the Professor and staff of the Civil Engineering Department of Southampton University, building and testing this model under various loading conditions, (and) writing and running computer programs on the University's Pegasus Computer for the geometric and analytical solutions and collating the results.[35]

Arups had also started carrying out wind tunnel tests on the shells at Southampton University using a separate wooden model.

Jenkins wrote to Utzon on 27th January regarding whether one of the concourse beams should be demolished or not, and the letter continued:

> I would now like to tell you the position regarding the superstructure. It may be that you and Professor Ashworth were under the impression that when we had finished our calculations and the model testing all that was left was for us to make detail drawings. Well, we have done the model

testing and this sort of work takes a long time not merely to confirm that the proposed structure is all right. We went to all this trouble because of the shells being structurally the wrong shape as we pointed out to you right at the beginning. In other words the structure proposed might not be sufficient. Now that we are plotting the stresses and deflections from the model testing we can see that something more has to be done in certain places. There are several ways of providing the extra strength that is needed and I and Hugo will have to come and see you to explain what has to be done and decide on the methods to which you have the least objection.[36]

Meanwhile, Waagner Biro of Vienna had been appointed to do the drawings for and manufacture the stage machinery for the Major and Minor Halls and Experimental Theatre.[37] On 6th February 1961 Hugo Mollman of Arups sent Waagner Biro drawings 'showing contour curves in the inner and outer shells' so they had the dimensions within which to fit their stage machinery. Mollman's letter finished, '... the curves shown on the drawings represent the centrelines for the outer and inner shell skins. You should allow an extra 3 in on the inside, corresponding to the thickness of the concrete.'[38]

On 27th February Jenkins wrote to Christiani and Nielsen in Copenhagen:

> ... During March or April of this year it is intended to invite applications from firms wishing to tender for the... Reinforced double shell superstructure (of) Sydney Opera House... (there are only) a very few firms who we are satisfied are capable of carrying out this rather difficult work, the start of which is anticipated in January 1962. We intend to issue information to the selected tenderers in April or May of this year... [39]

Lassen Nielsen of Christiani & Nielsen wrote back on 10th March:

> ... Unfortunately, we are at the moment very much pressed with work in connection with other large contracts on hand and regret, therefore, that we do not find ourselves in a position to avail ourselves of your kind offer.[40]

By that stage it was already apparent that there were serious difficulties with the design of the shells, and Utzon, who was concerned how this news would be greeted in Sydney, had rung Ove. Ron Jenkins already had a trip planned to Sydney, leaving on 7th March, and he wrote to Utzon on 21st February; 'I have noted your message to Ove about not spreading any alarm and despondency about the superstructure. In any case I would not do that... I shall not be ready to come and see you about the superstructure before I leave.'[41]

THE DESIGN OF THE SHELLS

As far as his trip to Sydney was concerned, Jenkins put a brave face on it and pretended nothing was wrong. On arrival he wrote a report for the Committee on the development of the design of Stage II:

... Because of the absence of scope for modification of (the shell) shape we found that these shells could only have adequate strength by making them into double shells; that is two thin shells, one inside the other, connected together by a system of ribs in two directions. This did not necessarily lead to a large increase in cost because with this system we could dispense with the originally envisaged separate and detached internal structures for auditoria and stage towers. With the double shell construction there are light weight auditoria ceilings suspended from the shells and the stage towers consist largely of the high shells themselves. This meant that we needed information about the loads the double shells would have to carry due to plant, iron curtains and upper stage machinery. M.A.N. were grossly misleading about the cost of this stage machinery and also in the estimated loads that would have to be carried. It is only recently that we have had information from the stage machinery sub-contractors which show that suspended loads are approximately two and a half times the M.A.N. estimate...

We have carried out a great deal of approximate calculation for the structural design of the superstructure, mainly by means of extensive programs for electronic digital computation. Owing to the limitations of storage capacity of these machines and the time it would take to program (them) it was impossible to carry out rigorous mathematical calculations for the stresses and deflections of this extremely complex superstructure and we decided that an approach by means of structural model testing was also necessary. We had perspex models made and the whole of the tests set up in the Civil Engineering Department of Southampton University. We sent the whole of our Stage II team to Southampton for a period of about nine months to carry out the tests and have use of the Pegasus digital computer at the same University. These tests consisted of reading over 1,000 electric resistance strain gauges under various load combinations of vertical weight and horizontal loads to simulate wind pressure. There was intricate apparatus required at the support points of the shells to measure vertical and horizontal reactions and the amount of rotation at the support points under various conditions. At the same time we had a set of wooden models made with a large number of connections to manometers for testing in a wind tunnel to find the wind pressure distribution for maximum wind velocities in any direction. This testing is now completed and we are in the process of interpreting the results. Certain requirements have become clear, one of which is that it is necessary to rest the shells on cast steel spherical bearings at the support points at the +42 level. We shall be able to report more fully on design and constructual methods in our next general report. It was indeed fortunate we can keep this testing in our hands because, with all the modifications that had to be made, it would have been impossible to have had it done as an independent exercise by some outside testing organisation... [42]

Jenkins also spoke to the Australian *Pix* magazine, which ran an article on the 'Opera House Roof' on 15th April entitled 'They're going to build it on hinges.'

Aircraft-building, ship-building, model testing – all architecture's latest techniques are being called on to build Sydney's famous Opera House roof. The designers have added an extra shell, pivoted the shells on hinges and hung tons of stage equipment inside them. The Opera House Executive will soon be calling for tenders to build the roof, and a start is expected within a year.

Many people have queried whether the shells could really be built to stand the gales which hit Sydney. They will, in fact, be strong enough to carry thousands of tons of stage equipment in addition to unheard of wind forces. 'An atomic blast would not shake them the way they will be constructed' said one engineer.

It is '... A building that would be astonishing in London or New York', says an observer in the current British Architects Journal. 'No one clambering about the scaffolding can avoid asking himself how a building so ambitious in scope and equipment, so lavish in structural expression, can be in scale with the city and State that is building it.'

Architects all over the world are watching to see how the problems of building this unique roof are to be solved. Until last month, nobody in Sydney could tell us how the shells were going to be built. Then Mr R.S. Jenkins of the consulting engineers on the project, Ove Arup and Partners, arrived from London with most of the final details. He is one of the world's top engineers specialising in shell structures.

How are the shells going to be built? Mr Jenkins answered: 'Some of the procedure has to be left to whoever gets the contract. I don't think we, as the structural engineers, should fix all of that in advance, but we have worked out the main details.

I felt from the first time I saw this beautiful and unique design of Utzon's that the shells could be built, but that it would be very difficult indeed. There is no other roof like it in the world that I know of, so it has presented us with a unique set of problems. We understand shell construction, but this particular job has been different.

So from the time we were appointed we have had a special group full time on the shells – sometimes up to a dozen in the team. After consultation the architect re-designed the shells. They are now aesthetically and structurally better than in the original competition plans. The small hall now has three shells like the large hall. You will notice that the shells look more alert and symmetrical – they do not flop over as much as some of them did...

We are still doing the final structural designs, but we have worked out the main points of how the shells have to be built. The whole job is very complicated and is something like aircraft construction. Model testing takes a lot of interpreting. We decided about a year ago as a result of the early model tests that each shell would have to be a double shell braced together to form a single roofing unit capable of standing the maximum wind velocities of the harbour.

The shells, ten of them, form the roofing system over these halls and the restaurant, but unlike most roofs which merely sit on top of walls, this will carry a huge tonnage of equipment. The shells have to carry the theatre equipment within the two buildings. We decided that it would be more economical to make them double (shells) and strong enough to do this than to have single shells with an entirely independent theatre building and roof inside', Mr Jenkins said.

'The shells will now be able to carry the auditorium acoustical roof, the steel safety curtains, all the scenery batons, and a floor above the stage to hold several things including air-conditioning plant. [The equipment will be suspended by ties attached to the inside structure of the shells. It will hang from the roof like the trafficway hangs from the arch of the Harbour Bridge.] We have designed each shell with an internal skeleton structure of ribs rather like the veins of a leaf. These ribs could be made of steel or concrete and whichever is decided upon will determine methods of construction. Ribs of steel tubing would be much lighter than concrete and this method appeals to me. I would rather like to see an Australian shipyard make the steel lattice just as though they were making the ribs of a ship...

Before the shells can be put up, we will need to order hinges of spherical cast steel, weighing up to 12 tons each, to articulate the shells at their support points and so carry the loads down into the rock foundations. These hinges are made necessary by the shape of the shells – virtually standing on points – and by the forces they have to stand; the wind pressures and other stresses. It will mean, in fact, that the shells will be able to rotate slightly on their hinges. This will take place during that part of the construction when the temporary supports are removed – once – after which there would be microscopic rotations due to temperature and wind, but nothing that anybody could see or feel.

To carry the huge load, their own weight and other forces, each set of shells is to stand on ten giant columns sunk 35 feet deep to rock foundations. The two carrying the front points of the largest shell are expected to bear a load each of 2,000 tons...'.[43]

Arups had sent specifications for the spherical shell bearings out to tender, and had received back quotes for spherical bearing assemblies including '... lifting eye bolts, securing bolts, sealing rings and greasing arrangements.' There were 16 bearings altogether to support the shells, which were of eight different kinds, and prices quoted included cost, insurance and freight for Sydney.[44]

On 10th April Waagner Biro wrote to Arups:

> With reference to our letters dated 21st of February and 10th of March 1961, we would like to know when we may expect the equations for the inner surface of shell 2 of the Minor Hall. ... We are forced to place the mechanical equipment as near as possible to the shell... These dimensions have not been given either on your drawings nor on the drawings of Architect Utzon.[45]

On 12th April Utzon telephoned London to ask when Ron Jenkins was coming to Hellebaek. Utzon was unhappy with the arrangement of the louvre walls, and had been developing the design along the lines suggested by Ove Arup, which meant a possibility of doing away with the louvre walls altogether.

Jenkins wrote to the Committee on the 20th:

> ... we recommend that we obtain tenders from two firms for the structural steel sub-contract and negotiate on a cost-plus[46] basis with Hornibrook, McKenzie Clarke Pty Ltd for the main contract...
>
> ... Stressed Skin seems to be the most appropriate classification for the type of composite structure... (I) described to the Committee... (with) the inner and outer shells (connected) by welded steel tubular latticed ribs... at the stage when the steelwork is erected it will be fully braced and it is anticipated it will be self-supporting under its own weight. It will have to act in conjunction with the concrete to support the final total weight and wind pressures...
>
> The Main Contractor will erect the steelwork, cast solid concrete in the lower parts above the bearings, case up the exposed steel and fix expanded metal between the ribs for forming the shells by concrete spray process. There will be rods left suspended to carry the light weight auditoria ceilings. The latter may be settled in time to include in this contract. The tiled external finish would be better included on a sub-contract... [47]

On his last visit to Sydney, Jenkins and Malcolm Nicklin had discussed the structural steel for the shells with Cockatoo Docks and Engineering Co. Pty Ltd and Stewarts and Lloyds (Australia) Pty Ltd.

> ... The Cockatoo firm appeared to be the best proposition. This was because the shaping and welding of the ribs is so much like building a ship. All the shapes would be laid out on the loft floor and then transferred to the telescopic jigs which occupy a large area. The tubes

would then be bent and laid out on the jigs and welded. The techniques for eliminating welding distortion were very reassuring as they have to be to satisfy Admiralty standards...

Our recommendation regarding the Main Contractor is, after five months more thinking, different from our memorandum to Mr Utzon, dated 14th November 1960, which we believe was discussed in Sydney during his last visit. In this memorandum we visualised tenders for Stage II from a small number of firms anywhere in the world, who were competent to do the job by our knowledge or as a result of enquiries. There are two principal factors which now make us recommend that we enter into a negotiated contract on a cost-plus basis with the one Australian firm we would have included in the list, Hornibrook, McKenzie Clark Pty Ltd.

We had already inquired before the visit if Christiani and Nielsen would be interested and the answer was in the negative. We are of the opinion that all competent overseas firms would consider the work too difficult to be rewarding without heavily loading their tenders. It is also quite possible that no response at all would be forthcoming from such firms. In our opinion the smallest cost will be obtained by the negotiated contract.

The factor of greatest importance to us is somewhat technical, and is to do with the implications of a design which has been often referred to as unique and difficult. As the result of our calculations and model testing we are now facing the problem with greater knowledge and a better realisation of the extreme difficulties that still lie ahead. We see the necessity of certain physical controls during construction such as temporary guying to definite forces measured on dynamometers and the use of Flat Jacks to fix the load coming down on the back stage wall to a predetermined amount. We shall have to feel our way during construction in some of these things. The point is that we shall really require the Contractor to join the engineering team in a more flexible way and to take a deeper and more intelligent interest than could be obtained by competitive tendering.

We are satisfied from our own knowledge and that of MacDonald, Wagner and Priddle that we can have no better firm than Hornibrooks with whom to collaborate...

When (I) was in Sydney (I) took the opportunity of describing the scheme to Sir Manuel Hornibrook and his fellow director, Mr Noe. Both of them liked the idea of the composite structure and fortunately were extremely interested in having the opportunity of doing the job.[48]

A note of gloom had entered Jenkins' correspondence, when he wrote to Alan Levy on 4th May after his return to London with the news 'I (am) going to Denmark next week to try and make progress with the superstructure.'[49]

In Hellebaek, all was apparently still on track for the double skin shell. A meeting was held in Denmark to discuss with Dr Jordan what sort of sound insulation the shells would provide as harbour noise would affect the acoustics of the halls, and '... Mr Jenkins informed Dr Jordan that the total thickness of the revised construction of the shells would be about 6 in, tiles included. The distance in between the outer and inner shells will be about 6 ft...'[50]

Then on the 23rd Jenkins sent a personal letter to Professor Peter Morice at the Department of Civil Engineering, Southampton University:

> The main thing we have learnt from the Opera House model tests is that the structure in that form does not work. We have therefore decided to make some considerable modifications to the external shape by making the tangent planes at the feet slope in the direction of the thrust line and not vertical. As things now stand this change will not be noticed by anybody if we do not exhibit the model at the Conversazione.
>
> We have therefore decided that we do not wish to propagate this false image and we have notified the Institution accordingly. I am sorry about this and hope you understand that we have to watch the considerable political factors underlying the Opera House.[51]

Malcolm Nicklin wrote from Sydney on 6th June, 'McDonald Constructions have been putting out a lot of feelers lately about the shells contract – we shall have to have a really good watertight story when the decision re Hornibrooks finds its way into the cold hard world.'[52]

However the Committee felt that the recommendation of a negotiated contract with Hornibrooks was 'abnormal.' Jenkins wrote to them on 13th June:

> ... We would say there is hardly any work in the world approaching the complexity of these superstructures that has not been carried out by some form of contractor nomination. We ourselves have used this method on about a dozen occasions. To give you two examples: Laings were nominated for some high blocks of flats for the L.C.C. at Picton Street, where new methods of construction were to be used, value £1.4 million; Sir Robert McAlpine were nominated for the Returned Note Building at Debden for the Bank of England, value £1.5 million.
>
> We have met costs plus fixed fee, target costs and agreed rates. One has to decide on the most appropriate financial arrangements for each particular case. What chiefly characterises these contracts without competition is the necessity of an unusually high degree of engineer-

contractor co-operation. It is important to realise that most of the highly complex work of Nervi, Esquillan and Candela has been done without competition. In these three examples, we see the results achieved by the highest degree of collaboration, since each has his own contracting organisation behind him. In the case of Sydney, we have to produce structures of even greater complexity by team work with a contractor not yet decided upon.

We appreciate that in a work with so much publicity there may be certain difficulties in explaining to the Press why a negotiated contract has been decided. We therefore put to you the following points, some of which cover matters raised in your discussions:

These shell-like superstructures are a great responsibility for us, and we believe the only method of obtaining the necessarily willing collaboration from the contractor is by a negotiated contract.

The construction sequence will be completely dictated by the design. Among other things, we have to ensure that the load is spread on to the foundations in strict accordance with the load-carrying capacity of foundations and columns already constructed.

Because design and construction are inseparable, we need team work with the contractor to a far greater than normal degree.

The construction will have to be carried out with extreme care – with a spirit of dedication would not be putting it too strongly...

It would be disastrous to have a contractor who was losing money on the job through cutting his tender to secure the prestige of carrying out the work...

Many contractors think they know what is required better than the consultant, and are quite prepared to put in sub-standard work to increase their profits. In normal work this can be controlled by supervision. Here, the very possibility must not be allowed to arise.[53]

To get the required standard, both in quality and form, it is our opinion that the profit motive should be eliminated from this contract...[54]

But making the tangent planes follow the thrust line narrowed the internal space of the shells. Waagner Biro wrote to Utzon on the 14th June:

... the altered shell contour causes a shortening of the forestage backcloth flies to approx. 48 ft up to 68 ft... (and) will disturb the accessibility to several mechanical plants of the portal zone, but definitive comments can be given only after the drawings of the exact shell contours have been supplied to us... [55]

And the day after that Jenkins wrote a private and confidential letter to Professor Ashworth:

... the superstructures have turned out even more difficult than we thought they would be at first. Between ourselves and you, Harry, this job is quite fantastic. All sorts of temporary stiffeners, shores and guys will be required. We should already be discussing practical problems with the Contractor who is going to do the work because provisions have to be made in the permanent structure for these temporary devices. It is not normal to have to go much into what are the contractor's problems in the design stage of an engineering structure, but in this case it is essential. Apart from all other considerations we really need a contractor appointed in the very near future. When I say team-work I do not mean it in the ordinary rather vague sort of way, but really categorically... [56]

Hugo Mollman wrote to Utzon on 31st July, enclosing two drawings showing:

side elevations of the shells in Major and Minor Hall when the shell surfaces are made up of parts of ellipsoids.

We have tried to keep the ridge curves as close as possible to the curves shown on the latest architectural drawings. It has not been possible to follow your curves exactly, but the differences are small. We want to emphasise that the use of ellipsoids simplifies the geometry considerably, and we hope that you will find the suggested shapes satisfactory.

Please let us know as soon as possible if you accept the new geometry as shown on our drawings.[57]

This was followed by another letter from Mollman to Utzon on 4th August:

We are at the moment working on the geometry and we have made a preliminary investigation of the parts of the shells where we previously had the louvre planes... (The intersections of the lines of shell 3)... give rise to some difficult intersections.

We have similar problems in shell 2. We enclose two sketches showing horizontal sections through the shells in these areas.

We have used circles as the cross-sections through the shells since we have not yet finalised the ellipsoids, but the problems are, in principle, the same.[58]

But the introduction of the shell geometry based on an ellipse had repercussions for Waagner Biro, who wrote to Utzon on the 17th:

... So far, our design work was based on the shell contours to Ove Arup's drawings No. 1112/Sk85, while those shell contours shown in your plans No.516-521, obviously reveal considerable narrowing of the stage area. We found this fact most surprising as Mr Peterson assured us that although the original parabolic shape of the shells is being changed into elliptic shape, the inside space of the stage is not reduced... Since the shape of the shells is of remarkable importance in respect of the stage machinery, we would appreciate clarification as to the divergences in contours. For the sake of the stage machinery we would rather welcome if the original shape according to Ove Arup drawing No.1112/Sk85, will be maintained...

We are expecting with interest your reply at earliest convenience.[59]

Peterson of Utzon's office sent a copy of the letter to Arups on the 22nd, adding '... they are a bit surprised that the inner shape of the Minor Hall... is much less than before.'

To which Mollman replied on the 28th '... The Contour drawings based on the circles are, however, not final drawings. They were made quickly to get a general picture of the new geometry... We are now working on the final geometry and are making Shell 2, Minor Hall, so that there is as much space inside the shell as there was previously...'[60]

Arup's report on the shells continued:

It became evident, however, early in 1961, both from the model tests and from calculations, that bending moments in some parts of the structure were more severe than had been anticipated. Moreover, the model analysis yielded results of load distribution to the foundation which could not be predicted by any known developed analytical method.

It was perfectly possible to cater for these forces and bending moments; it was also likely that theoretical proof of the model test results was forthcoming, but two things were quite clear. Firstly the structural design was an iterative process. By this we mean that the structural weaknesses shown up required strengthening and that the subsequent reshaping of parts of the structure would in turn alter the forces. This aspect, while known and predictable, was aggravated by the complexity of the structure and the length of time it took to investigate each alteration.[61] Secondly and more important, the architect expressed dissatisfaction with certain aspects of the shape of the roof, its internal appearance,[62] its method of construction and, above all, the louvre walls which he had never really liked.

We therefore decided with the architect to carry out a thorough reappraisal of the whole structure, regardless of inconvenience and the danger of throwing away years of work. We both wished to be satisfied that the best possible solution would be built.[63]

When Jenkins was confronted with not only complex and difficult to predict forces acting on the shells, but also an unhappy architect, he announced at a partners' meeting that he had come to a dead end on the shells. At this time Jack Zunz arrived back in London from South Africa.

Gerhard Jacob (Jack) Zunz was born in Germany, then came out to South Africa as a youngster and had most of his education there. Following secondary school, and a year at university studying Mechanical Engineering, Zunz volunteered for the South African forces during the Second World War. On his return he switched to Civil Engineering, then once he had finished his degree was looking for professional experience in Britain, but also found he was 'getting disturbed about the racial situation in South Africa, long before everyone else was.'[64] This was at a time when there was a tremendous upsurge of feeling of 'post war optimism, when people thought there would be a brave new world, and I was very disappointed, because I felt that the whole racial situation took a step backwards.'[65] Zunz recalled

> I had written from South Africa to three firms in the UK to seek work and, typically, Ove was the only person who replied. His letter, which was very friendly, said he didn't have a job for me, but if I did decide to come to this country 'do come and see me by all means'.
>
> The office of Ove Arup & Partners in 1950 was at No 8 Fitzroy Street, London, W1... At that time Ove was an outsider, not a member of the engineering establishment. He had only recently severed his ties with the contracting side of construction, and he was not a member of either the Institution of Civil Enginners or the Association of Consulting Engineers. He was interested in architecture, music and the arts, and he liked good food...
>
> Fitzroy Street on a sunny August afternoon was a quiet and pleasant backwater. There were hardly any cars, a few bicycles, and the odd barrow selling fruit of questionable quality. There were still the relics of war – bombed sites, shored-up walls – and the houses which had survived, however distinguished, had an air of genteel dilapidation. The sounds from open windows were those of sewing machines – Fitzroy Street was at the western end of the area occupied by the rag trade...
>
> To be interviewed by Ove was the experience of a lifetime. All the 'old hands' who were interviewed by him personally had a story – each one unbelievably different – of their experience on first meeting this remarkable man. Stories about Ove's often eccentric and unpredictable behaviour abound – they sound as if they should be apocryphal, but most if not all are incredibly true.
>
> Ove's office on the first floor occupied the width of the house. It was beautifully furnished with modern Danish furniture. A suspended structure of glass shelves supported on nylon wire hanging from the ceiling, ostensibly for plants, was more likely a foretaste of things to come.

In the middle of the floor was an open suitcase. His secretary, Kate, was dashing in and out seemingly engaged on intensely urgent and important matters. Ove told me that he was catching a ferry for Denmark and was really too busy to see me but was nevertheless very pleased I came! He exuded that rather kindly air which could tell you some unpalatable home truths, yet at the same time make you feel important and wanted. In this chaotic environment, we spoke of many things – the Korean War, which was a horrible topical preoccupation so soon after World War Two, of South Africa, which had recently been thrown out of the Commonwealth; we spoke about Britain's postwar problems – we spoke of many things, but not much about engineering or construction. After a very pleasant hour he said that he thought I was a nice chap and that he had enjoyed talking to me, but didn't have a job for me and that at that time he had a full complement. We shook hands and I walked out, probably no more or less confused than the many others who had had a not dissimilar experience.

During those first few weeks in London, my wife and I were living in the country with an uncle of mine, and no one was more surprised than I when, in the first post the following morning, I received an offer of work from Ove Arup & Partners. My salary was to be £8 per week (plus luncheon vouchers to the value of 2/6d [12p]). I subsequently learnt that Ronald Jenkins and Bob Hobbs had, shortly after my interview, asked for some urgent help on Hunstanton School, a competition-winning project which was one of the first (if not the first) structure in this country to be analysed by the then quite novel plastic design concepts... [66]

Britain had been 'terribly damaged'[67] in the war, and 'suddenly, by becoming involved in some of the new ideas in "social building" projects for people, particularly schools, housing and hospitals, there was a fantastic euphoria, and it seemed to release all the pentup imagination and emotion in people. So it was a very exciting time.'[68] In the middle of 1954 Zunz returned to South Africa to set up a branch of Ove Arup and Partners there with a friend from Witwatersrand University, Mike Lewis, and was in South Africa when the Opera House job came into the firm. It had always been understood between himself and Ove that he would return to London one day, and he came back in 1961 as an associate partner to work on the new BP head office in the City which at 400 feet high was then the tallest building in London. But just when he got back, it was 'at a time of great crisis, because Ronald Jenkins... who had dealt with the roof structure (of the Opera House), had come to a partners' meeting and said he had reached a bottleneck and could not see a way forward... Anyway, Ove came to me and he said he wanted me to take it on… which I did. And from then onwards, I really, more or less ran the Opera House job. Ove was of course, (still) very deeply involved, particularly on the political front.'[69]

Zunz found 'whenever anyone saw those sketches… of Utzons… they thought, well, this is… wonderful. It's something so unusual… so outside the norm of what one normally saw when one started a project, it was very exciting. And of course, with a great deal of awe, one wonders how one was going to put it together, because one hadn't built anything like that before.'[70]

Just before Zunz returned from South Africa, Ove had been to Hellebaek on other Opera House business and made a sketch which showed a fold in the roof. The sketch still exists on the back of a letter in Arup's files. It is quite different to anything that has ever been built and illustrated one shell that instead of having a rib, should have a fold underneath.

> I do not know whether the initiative came from Ove or from an expressed wish on Utzon's part to have the interior of the roof articulated. At that time our relationship with Utzon and his team in Hellebaek was warm and uninhibited. No one would think in terms of attribution we were all in it together. Utzon had never liked the walls which interconnected the shells, the 'louvre' walls, and Ove's sketch may well have been a response to this.
>
> Ove also told me that Jenkins had been in charge of the design of the roof structure and that he could not or would not interfere. He, Ove, was the Senior Partner, ultimately the boss, but he also had a mixture of awe and respect for Jenkins, who had in his own personal, private and aloof way, been the analytical, the technical and intellectual powerhouse behind the early development of the Firm. All of us early comers learnt a great deal from Jenkins. In fact, Jenkins' intellectual rigour coupled with Ove's creative philosophy provided a most stimulating and challenging atmosphere in which to work.
>
> It was only when Jenkins said that he could not see his way through, that Ove stepped in and sought the agreement of the other Partners to get someone else, in the event me, involved.[71]

The partners '… agreed that I should look at the whole situation completely afresh…' recalled Zunz 'I was specifically asked if something along the lines on which we had been working for two years or so could be made to work. And secondly I was also asked to look at (whether a type of)… construction… which would give some sort of folding internally could be made to work.'[72] The first thing that struck Zunz about the interconnected structure was that '… to my mind it didn't really work. It could have been made to work but I didn't think it would be a sensible way of building...'[73]

> We agreed to follow two parallel investigations – firstly to develop further the scheme which we had worked on, albeit in an amended form, to a shape where we would be certain that a viable solution had been found. Secondly we decided to investigate a rather different suggestion, where the inside of the shell would be formed by a series of fan-like ribs and where the louvre wall structure would, if possible be entirely reconsidered.
>
> This reappraisal took place during the summer of 1961 and resulted in the following conclusions:
> (i) The scheme which had been model tested and analysed for three years was workable but with some major amendments...
> (ii) The idea of "folding" the roof internally appeared to be possible. There were, however, several pre-requisites.
>
> Firstly, it was proposed to articulate the three sets of shells so that each set could act as an independent structure.[74]
>
> While the structural model tests and calculations which had so far been carried out would no longer be strictly applicable, they yielded useful basic information. However, the articulation of the structure meant that normal statical calculation could now be used. Secondly the structural and, if necessary, the architectural design would have to be adapted to a rather different construction method – greater emphasis was placed on the inter-relation of design and execution. Thirdly, we might have to face delays, since we virtually had to start afresh.[75]

Zunz had two people helping him, John Lethbridge working with him on the folded solution and Joe Huang[76] looking at the steel solution, with both proposals using the ellipse for the geometry. 'Because it didn't occur to us that (the geometry) was even on the agenda, because as far as we were concerned the geometry was frozen out. I particularly said to our people let's now, because we had spent so much time on the geometry, during the first two years, I said to our people, we have got to put all that behind us now. This is the geometry we are working with.'[77] But if it came down to the folded structure with ribs, '... repetition (of casting) immediately... comes to mind... And then we found we had no repetition because each of these ribs would be different.'[78] Arups then asked Malcolm Nicklin to see if he could find a large vacant site near the Harbour 'where we could lay the whole thing out.' It would have been very costly but 'What we intended doing was to cast these shells on a piece of land adjoining the harbour, lying on their side, so to speak on enormous timber beds on which adjustable forms would be used to form the ribs...'.[79]

As far as Arups were concerned the silhouette of the shells was sacrosanct and there was no question of changing it, but then one day in Arup's office at 13 Fitzroy Street when Zunz and Lethbridge were discussing the shells, John Lethbridge made a remark more or less off the cuff and as part of the conversation that the only way you could get repetition on a doubly curved surface like this was with a toroid (a shape like a car inner-tube) or a sphere. But they did not dwell on the subject and the conversation moved on to other matters.[80]

Utzon was booked in at the Athenaeum Court Hotel in Piccadilly on the nights of 29th, 30th, 31st August and 1st September 1961 for meetings with Arups to discuss the shells, but before he left Hellebaek Aage Petersen of his office wrote to Waagner Biro:

> Because of a slight postponement concerning development in the structural design of the shells for the Opera House, the meeting scheduled for September 11th seems to be of better value if it is postponed until after Mr Utzon returns from London with the final decision on the shell forms.
>
> As we do not know when Mr Utzon will return you will hear from us regarding a new date for the meeting immediately upon Mr Utzon's return...[81]

Ove Arup, Jack Zunz and Utzon were together at a meeting in Arup's London office when Zunz outlined to Utzon the two different shell schemes they had been working on. 'And those were both viable, and we had a meeting here. It was in Ove's office – I remember it absolutely clearly. There was only Utzon and Ove and I and... I took them through these two options, and Utzon was absolutely clear. He said... (regarding the ribbed scheme)... "I don't care what it costs, I don't care what scandal it causes, I don't care how long it takes, but that's what I want"... He had x-ray eyes. He wanted everything to be of see-through quality...'[82] 'He was absolutely crystal clear what he wanted... Utzon always disliked these so-called louvre walls. So he was very relieved when we came up with the idea of separating them.'[83]

And he preferred the folded solution as 'He felt that the integrity of a concrete structure left in its natural state was in keeping with the ideals of his concept for the scheme.'[84] 'We felt that his choice was quite right and that the concrete roof, despite all the possible effort required by all in starting anew, was much more in sympathy with the whole concept of the Opera House. We backed his decision very strongly.'[85] This was even though 'The steel structure, though difficult, would present no great novel problem in execution, but the fanlike concrete proposal, if possible at all, would require the closest possible integration of design and construction.'[86]

During those August meetings Zunz also recalled that 'during our conversations with Utzon mention was made of the lack of repetition... the problem is that there is no repetition. The only kind of geometry on which repetition could be used is spherical geometry, and we went on to the next subject because it was not a matter which we needed debated. We didn't say, *we didn't say,* can we make it out of a sphere? Because it didn't occur to us that it was even on the agenda.'[87]

Utzon headed back to Denmark to continue his work on the shells. He was to say later '... I worked like a sculptor; I tried to shape the things and I made many models. It came from model work, more than paperwork. You couldn't have this on paper because it would not be alive.'[88] The Japanese architect, Minoru Takeyama worked with Utzon at Hellebaek, and he recalled that in evolving the design for the shells Utzon would 'get wooden balls shaped like a Danish cheese and put them in a bathtub. Then by studying the angles at which the water cut the surface he was able to come up with the correct geometrical pattern... Utzon was full of self-confidence, yet at the same time always self-questioning. "Minoru, do you think I am doing right?" he would ask me. He compared himself to Hamlet. Sometimes he would get angry, but then he would only speak in Danish so only the Dane who was with us knew what was going on.'[89] Utzon had a spherical wooden ball made up at one of the local shipyards, cut it into pieces, and found that he could, in fact make up the surfaces of the shells from segments of the same sphere. 'One cannot make such a complex of forms without being clear on the geometry,' wrote Utzon later, 'without having found some form of harmony between them. I have worked a lot with various forms... for instance generated volumes made of ellipses and parabolas, but I ended up, by taking these forms from a sphere...'[90]

Ove Arup was in London when '... Utzon phoned from Copenhagen that he had solved the whole problem of pre-casting. It transpired that he had changed the whole shape of the shells by cutting each of them out of the same sphere.[91] So now they all are spherical, and the ribs follow meridian curves on spheres of the same radius, 246 feet.[92] That means that all the ribs are identical although of different length, and cut off at different angles at the spine end.'[93] The ribs could be divided into segments, the size of which were dependant on the lifting capacity of the cranes on site, then assembled like a giant lego set, Utzon later writing '... You will see that I have succeeded in getting these great complicated forms under control – and under control still with the freedom of the craft, paired, with the precision of the machine age...'.[94]

When Utzon chose the concrete fan-like structure over the steel structure, and was backed in his choice by Ove Arup and Jack Zunz, Ove rang Ron Jenkins who was at a conference in Holland to break the news. Ron Jenkins did not think the concrete fan proposal was possible at all. As Ove later wrote to Utzon 'I disagreed with some of my people about the feasibility of building the scheme as you wanted it – with inside ribs and without louvre walls. I thought it could be done and I also preferred this solution from an architectural point of view. So in spite of the disruption it caused I supported you against some of my own people...'[95] Jenkins stayed on at Ove Arups but dropped out of the picture as far as the Opera House was concerned, the overall responsibility for the project being taken over by Jack Zunz. 'I think it nearly broke Ronald's heart...' recalled Kelman 'because he realised in the long run, that it wasn't possible to design (the roof) as a shell at all.'[96] Hugo Mollman, one of Arups' most talented engineers and the associate partner responsible for the early shell scheme, had given himself body and soul in developing the geometry and design of the parabolic form, and when the decision was announced to go with the ribbed solution he'd carried on working for four weeks on the steel structure. '... They (Hugo Mollman and Ron Jenkins) were so heavily committed to that, as people do become, that they really weren't able to adapt to the idea of a ribbed solution with a spherical geometry. And they felt that the decision to go to that, was such a radical change, that it represented a sort of, vote of no confidence in them. Ronald Jenkins held on but Hugo Mollman just simply couldn't take it. He actually left the firm. (He was)... the only... casualty which I think we suffered.'[97]

Kelman wrote to MacDonald, Wagner and Priddle on 5th September:

We are at present going into the possible methods of constructing the shells and precasting appears to offer certain decided advantages, with crane capacity as a limiting factor. While we would like to think of (precast) units of about 25 tons, preliminary investigations here indicate that 10 tons or even less, might be the limit... We accept that a crane or cranes may have to be mounted on the existing structure, over the Auditorium seating and elsewhere... A tower crane on a track mounted over the Hall centre line, and working back from South to North is not impossible!! but almost so![98]

After Utzon headed back to Hellebaek after the August meetings in London, Ove Arup was in Naples from 4th to 11th September, then in Denmark with Utzon from the 25th to 29th. Utzon wrote to Ashworth on the 29th: '... Mr Arup has been with us this week and we have found a very ingenious and marvellous way of producing the shells and they are, finally, as we want them...'[99]

In tying down the shape of the shells, typical of the letters flowing back and forth between Utzon's and Arup's office was one written on 27th October 1961 from Knud Lautrup-Larsen of Utzon's office to Arups, enclosing drawings of a shell and swirls of circles intersected by straight lines.

After the telephone call yesterday from your Mr Lethbridge, we have produced the enclosed sketches "Plotting Sketch A" and "Plotting Sketch B."

The aim of the sketches is to show you that... the shell can be dimensioned in a rather simple way.

On "Plotting Sketch A", we have shown you our way of determining the inclination in the footpoint so that we get the appearance we want (pretty close to the longitudinal elevation you got recently)...

The basic facts for construction (on the drawings) are:

1. The radius of the sphere.
2. The inclination to the theoretical footpoint.
3. The latitude for lowest theoretical point on shells ridge.

From this geometrical construction you can determine the mathematical formulae which will give you all the dimensions you want...

We hope this will assist you in your further work, the result of which is looked forward to with the greatest interest.[100]

Ove Arup wrote to Ashworth on 30th October:[101]

Sydney Opera House

In the letter which you wrote to Utzon on the 5th October, a copy of which you sent to Ronald, you mention that you assume that arrangements could be made for Stage II to begin about the time that

245

Jorn and I come to Sydney in February or March 1962. I am afraid that this is too optimistic, and I think I ought to explain to you what the present position is. I am writing this as a private letter to you, because we are not quite out of the woods yet – although we see daylight ahead – and we would be in a better position to make a definite official pronouncement when Jorn and I arrive in Sydney. But of course we have nothing to conceal, and you may use this letter as you think fit and expedient. In fact we would welcome advice from you about how to handle public and official relations.

The design of the so-called shells has been beset with difficulties. As you know, when Ronald last visited Sydney we had arrived at a fairly definite scheme for the construction of these shells which involved the erection of a framework in steel which would be covered by an external and an internal concrete skin. There were, however, a number of outstanding architectural and structural problems which proved rather difficult to resolve. The former mostly revolved round the manner of closing the shells at the open end – the "louvre walls". Jorn has the whole time objected to an ordinary wall meeting the shell surface at this point and I feel certain that from an architectural point of view he is right. The latter are too complicated to go into, but any how our calculations proved that we could expect very high – in fact too high- stresses at certain points unless we were prepared to abandon the demand that the shells would spring vertically from the foundations, and Jorn readily agreed to this. However, it meant that our calculations and model tests to a large extent did not apply to the new shape, and it was therefore possible to consider other alterations at the same time.

The problem of the louvre walls was again examined in this light, and in the course of these very long discussions several old and new ideas were examined and some months ago Utzon made a suggestion which seemed to be a clue to a possible solution of our difficulties. As you know, one of the things which made the construction of these shells extremely difficult was that all the surfaces were different, so that there was no possibility of repetition, which is always the key to economical construction. If you examine Nervi's structures and domes and hangars they are all based on the repetition of precast units, and we had often discussed the possibility of using such a method with Utzon, but the fact that all the shells were different seemed to preclude this. However, in the course of our discussion Utzon came up with an idea for making all the shells of a uniform curvature throughout in both directions – in other words they are all cut out of the same sphere. This would mean that every segment of each shell was identical.

This is only a very short description of what happened because there are many other things involved in it, but it opened up new possibilities which we thought ought to be studied. As a result of these studies we have now produced a scheme, or at any rate a sketch scheme, which promises to solve all Jorn's architectural problems. He at least is wildly enthusiastic about it. It would also facilitate both construction and calculations. Construction – because all the main shells can be made from identical precast units, and calculation – because the present solution of the louvre walls – which really cuts them out altogether, makes it possible to divide the superstructure into three nearly independent units, a great simplification, so that we firmly believe now that we can avoid a repetition on a new model of the slow and expensive model tests. We are therefore very pleased about this development, but it means that we are to some extent starting afresh – although we could never have got so far without all our previous efforts.

The method of construction will of course be radically changed. We still very much want to collaborate with Hornibrooks and in fact we hope to send them a set of drawings with our recommendations for methods of construction and to ask them to send one of their technical experts to London, possibly in early December, so that we can discuss the whole scheme with them, and so that we can be ready by the time we come to Sydney to make a definite contract with them. We will, however, not need the collaboration of Stewarts and Lloyds or the Cockatoo Docks and Engineering Company. On the other hand we need to place an early order for some very large cranes... We have, however, an enormous amount of work to do here in the drawing office before we can forge ahead on the job, and do not want to repeat the mistake of starting the contract before we know exactly what we are doing.

This has been a difficult and unprecedented job – you have heard that one before. We had to grope our way to a solution, we needed the guidance of a rigorous analysis of the whole complex structure, and we had to "explore every avenue and leave no stone unturned" – at a disastrous cost to us, incidentally. That some avenues were blind and others almost impenetrable was probably unavoidable. In this case we saw the light through the woods in another direction than the one we were going, and we believe the quickest way out is to change course.[102]

On 6th October the Committee had telegraphed Arups to say the government had approved Arups' recommendation nominating Hornibrooks as the Stage II contractor. This was conditional, wrote the Committee on 3rd November, on the government being informed of the amount of Hornibrook's fee, and the 'proposed provisions in the contract, particularly with a view to ensuring that the government is charged only with proper costs of carrying out the work (with) reference to be made also to proposals to ensure completion of the work by the contractor within a reasonable time.'[103] The government had not yet signed a contract with Hornibrooks, but Hornibrooks could now start preliminary planning with Arups on how to build Stage II of the Sydney Opera House.

Manuel Hornibrook, the founder and Managing Director of Hornibrooks wrote to Arups on 17th November:

> ... we have taken immediate action to send our representative, Mr G. O. Boulton, M.E., M.I.E.(Aust) F.A.I.B., to London to discuss construction details and working methods.
>
> Mr Boulton has been our Chief Engineer for thirty-five years and now holds the position of General Manager and Director of this company. He has had wide experience in all classes of civil engineering and construction generally and is recognised as one of the most eminent engineers in Australia. For this reason our Board has appointed him its representative to discuss with you the technical aspect of the project. We are sure that with his experience he is admirably suited to undertake the work required... [104]

George Boulton was expected in London '... at 11.50 a.m. on Monday, 27th November. He will report to your office as soon as possible after arrival.'[105]

Ove Arup wrote to Professor Ashworth on 21st November:

> I am sending you herewith a letter which I wrote to you three weeks ago but did not send off. I was going off to Pakistan next day, and we were not certain that this letter would not alarm you unduly, especially as we were not able to send you any drawings at that time. However, I now regret not having sent it because I understand that our suggestion that the Second Contract should not start before September has caused some alarm and despondency, and it is much better that you should be in the picture.
>
> Since writing this letter we have progressed quite far with the new design, and it all looks very promising indeed. We have got a solution to the crane problem, which may be further improved upon but which definitely makes the whole thing feasible, and we are dealing with the details of tiling and dozens of other questions which require attention. Utzon is coming over today and we have arranged with Hornibrooks that they come here on Tuesday next.
>
> It also seems possible now that we can improve on the date when we can start on the site, but I must say that it would be very unwise to start before all our problems have been solved, and it would be also unwise to have two contractors on the site simultaneously because that would be bound to lead to trouble. Moreover an early start is not the same as an early completion... [106]

Utzon arrived in London before the letter went in that day's mail, and Ove added a handwritten P.S. 'Jorn wants me to add that the shells will look more or less the same as before, but that they will be still more beautiful, and we are looking forward to showing them to you.' Which was followed by a single line handwritten by Utzon, 'Warmest greetings from Jorn.'

Utzon wrote to Ashworth on 27th November:

... Back from London at last with a feeling that we have overcome the shells and you will get the most marvellous solution you could dream of. We were riding on two horses for a long time. The last six months the real ideal solution for everything technically and aesthetically was developed and it was even the cheapest way of making it you could dream of. We, therefore, gave up continuing with the first one which really has been dealt with for almost three years. Of course, all the work during these three years has been the background for arriving at this magnificent solution... [107]

At this time, Graham Gambie, a reporter with the Sydney *Sun Herald*, caught up with Ove Arup in London. Gambie reported that he had come to see Arup 'because of recent Sydney criticism of mounting costs in the Opera House project.'[108] The article was headlined 'I'M CRAZY TO BUILD IT.'

Against the streamlined finish of an office style in dark contemporary woods and white rugs, the large figure of Ove Nyquist Arup looks distinctly out of place. His suit reflects his 67 years, not the fashion dictatorially disseminated from Savile Row, and his wide red tie sets off his white hair. His speech is not old-fashioned. It has a challenging passionate ring... Mr Arup had read the criticism and he was weary of it...

'This petty criticism' Mr Arup said fiercely, 'just what type of mentality does it take? You know, personally I feel very virtuous and very good about this job. I don't care a damn – it's so ludicrous.'

Around his room is gathered primitive sculpture, sitting harmoniously next to larger-than-life Chinese wooden busts. One of the Chinese heads has a battered Panama hat perched precariously on it, but for what whimsical reason only Arup could tell. Next to this is an unusual white mask like a sharply silhouetted bull's head and it is not until you examine it closely that you realise it once was a shell from a model of the Opera House.

From an engineer, his unexpected unconventional ideas come as a shock. He eats most of his food with chopsticks, for instance – including ice cream when he can manage it. He has always encouraged avant garde architecture, and he was one of the founders of the Mars group in Britain which was formed with that idea in mind.

Sydney's Opera House finds him enthusiastic: 'There is no doubt that this is one of the most difficult jobs ever attempted in the world.' he said firmly. 'Even if it were just an opera house it would be a complicated business. But this thing, it's so much more than an opera house in a normal sense. All the opera houses in the world are different, but this is a kind of temple for Sydney – there's the question of civic pride…

Speaking for us, I would say we are quite crazy to take this job', he said. 'I'm not complaining, I'm just saying that's how it is. I never realised it would be so hard. I don't know of any other firm in the world which would put up with what we have had to put up with. It's taken two or three years off my life.

I think Utzon and I are possibly to blame in being too idealistic or too stubborn. Maybe we are a bit silly in refusing to compromise. But my excuse, if I need an excuse, is that in this particular concept, if you don't get the whole idea in the building, it could be disastrous.

I don't know how you could do anything to cheapen it without spoiling the idea. You could say "We'll use paint on the outside instead of tiles" – that would be all right. But with the structure there's such a difference. You just can't compromise. After all, why is this opera house being built? Because it's the most marvellous thing that's been built this century.'

Arup scoffed at reports that his firm would make an exorbitant profit.

'This is absolutely lousy as a business proposition' he said. 'We've got enough work – we can afford to do without this job.

There is this talk that suddenly we are getting enormous fees. But we're certainly not growing rich on this business. We've been at it for four to five years now and it takes an enormous part of our energy. You can only do this type of work if you have the enthusiasm for it…

We are always struggling to get an economical result. We are trying to save half a million on the shells by avoiding scaffolding, but this is involving us in design work that could cost thousands. It's better to do a good job – it's your reputation in the long run. If I wanted to make money I should be a barber or a stockbroker or something else entirely.'

Then Arup talked about Utzon, a friend of his, and said: 'Utzon cares less about financial gain than principles – in fact I'm worried about him. He's spent a lot of his own money on this. It's quite amazing that such a young architect has been able to master such a thing. I've worked with hundreds of architects but not one of them would compare with Utzon.'

Arup said that the strain of work on the Opera House had been so great that one of his associates had resigned.

'He couldn't stand it', he said. 'He was disheartened and he was not the only one.'

Would he tackle the job again?

'I'm not so sure. I'll give my answer on the day it's opened – that is, if I live so long.'[109]

Ashworth wrote a personal letter to Arup on 4th December:

> ... although both the Technical Advisory Panel and the Executive Committee approved your recommendation of procedure with regard to Stage 2, we have had some considerable difficulty getting acceptance from the Department and the Minister of Works, who, as you know are now cited in the Opera House Act as the Constructing Agency. I am quite certain in my own mind that much of the anxiety has had political foundation, as, of course, the recommendations you made and which we approved, cut across all the accepted normal contractual procedure in so far as the Department is concerned, thereby creating a position in which criticism is levelled at the Minister by many individuals. This, combined with the fact that in the next few months, probably about April, we are due to face another election, I am sure creates anxiety in political circles.
>
> Obviously nobody here is really knowledgeable or at all conscious of the vast amount of work and enquiry you have had to undertake with regard to the shell roof and I suppose the continued lack of authentic information out here tends to exaggerate such anxieties as do exist. To me personally, the satisfactory conclusion of Stage 2 is the point of no return and therefore should be started as soon as possible... [110]

Also on 4th December, John Lethbridge wrote from London to Jack Zunz who was in Hellebaek, with details of the weights of the shells and an estimate of the subsequent increased reactions on the shell columns. The letter closed 'If you alter the design – don't bother to come back!'[111] In Hellebaek Zunz had had meetings with Waagner Biro, who had 'complained of information which was requested and had not been sent... Waagner Biro require urgently the internal contours of the Major and Minor Halls to show the clearances in which they have to design. It was agreed that since final drawings giving exact contours might not be available until early next year the information should be sufficient to arrive at a final design leaving the dimensioning until the precise clearance drawings are available.'[112]

Utzon wrote to Ashworth on 13th December:

> ... (we had) a good fortnight with Mr Boulton from Hornibrooks, here in Hellebaek as well as in London and Sweden. The procedure of the manufacturing of the elements and the erection has been developed into something very good...
>
> Both myself and Ove Arup and his engineers are quite sure now that this scheme for the shells has come to an end and we are very lucky that we have been so stubborn because this last scheme, which as you know we have been working on the last eight to ten months, is rather revolutionary and elegant and its simplicity will save a lot of money.[113]

Jack Zunz wrote to Utzon on 14th December to let him know they were making a box for Utzon's new model of the Opera House, and that Ove Arup's son Steen would take it home to Copenhagen with him on the 23rd '... which means that you will be able to have it in time to put under your Christmas tree.'[114]

Ashworth wrote to Ove Arup early in the New Year:

> I am looking forward to meeting you and Utzon early in March... Although some feel it is a nuisance having the architect and engineer 10,000 miles away, in my view it has considerable merit in this particular job as it allows you both to get on with the real job of work and avoids you wasting time in all manner of local arguments, usually of a political origin. Disappointed contractors manufacturers, etc. put tremendous pressure on the local politician from the Premier down which of course both irritates and worries them.[115]

On 4th January 1962 John Lethbridge wrote to Waagner Biro enclosing drawings of:

> ... the geometrical contours of shell No.2 and the Louvre Shell in front of Shell No 2 for the Major Hall.
>
> We have to inform you that we have this week received information from Mr Utzon's office that the geometry of the Louvre Shell shown on these drawings is now somewhat altered. We understand that the alteration will provide more internal space for the stage machinery.
>
> The details of the final geometry will be sent to you as soon as possible...[116]

On the 12th Steensen and Varming wrote to Kelman regarding requirements for ventilation and smoke escape hatches, 'Do you know if Mr Zunz has found out how he can accommodate the openings we require in the shells? I believe he has discussed the matter with Mortensen.'[117]

The drawings of the shells with spherical contours were for real now and not just approximations of ellipses. The space under the shells for stages had always been tight and this made the situation even worse. Waagner Biro wrote to Utzon on the 17th that after studying Arups' latest drawings of the Major and Minor Halls:

> ... it has resulted that it is impossible to arrange the stage machinery in the specified scope in the new shell shapes. Above all the cycloramas, the panorama flies and the backcloth flies are concerned.
>
> ... The new shell shape causes (a) reduction of the height of the vertical stage building wall. But these walls are necessary for arrangement of counter-weight guides for the backcloth flies. ... Thus the

arrangement of the hand-operated backcloth flies is impossible. The loss of vertical wall area concerns also the flying galleries; they will be very narrowed or must be eliminated partially. As further can be seen from the sketches, the cyclorama of Major Hall and Minor Hall must be lowered caused by the narrowing of the shells.

... We like to point out that we have made utmost efforts for an acceptable compromise between the statical and stage-technical requirements. A reduction of the construction height seems not acceptable to us...

... since the final shell shapes will be fixed during your visit to London... we like to ask you to consider the minimum dimensions of the internal shell contours given by us. If this would be impossible we believe that this reduction concerning the upper stage equipment would be (for discussion) with Prof. Unruh... [118]

Waagner Biro cabled Utzon on the 24th 'When modifying design louvre shells between shells two and three please pay particular attention to necessary space for lifted safety curtains.'[119]

On 12th and 13th February Mr Hillinger from Waagner Biro had meetings in Hellebaek with Utzon. Utzon and Arups had been able to make some changes to the shells:

... up to the statical limits... e.g. Major Hall grid iron level approx. 5 ft on each side... The Louvre shells at Major Hall and Minor Hall have been displaced by 4.5 ft northwards (auditorium) in order to have space for the iron curtains... However the shell contours proposed by Waagner-Biro... and confirmed by Prof. Unruh have not been reached in the area of the flying galleries. The loss of vertical stage building walls still exists.[120]

The change in the internal volume of the shells led to many alterations in the design of Waagner Biro's stage machinery, not least of which was a need to narrow the height and width of the stage opening in the Major and Minor Hall. For example the width of the stage opening in the Major Hall was narrowed by 8 ft, and in the Minor Hall by 6 ft.

Waagner Biro wrote to Utzon on 27th February:

We are forwarding herewith several general and detailed drawings of the stage plant for your visit to Sydney... Since, however, the drawings do not correspond to the latest shell shapes, would you please destroy the drawings after use in order to avoid later errors.

In the meantime we are waiting for the shell drawings and dimensions of Messrs Ove Arup and Partners which are necessary for designing the steel structures (for the stage towers).[121]

Meanwhile George Boulton had written to Jack Zunz on 18th January to advise that D. C. Gore and R. F. Kynaston from Hornibrooks were booked on a Qantas flight and due to arrive in London on Monday 12th February:

> Mr Gore is a Director and Operations Manager of our New South Wales subsidiary, Hornibrook McKenzie Clark Pty Limited. He will be appointed to the management of the Contract. Mr Kynaston has been employed by us for some years in Brisbane and latterly in Melbourne where he has been Chief Engineer on a large construction project. He will be appointed next in charge to Mr Gore.
>
> We anticipate that Mr Gore will be able to return to Australia in mid March. If necessary, Mr Kynaston could stay some weeks longer to maintain liaison between your design staff and our planning operations in Sydney.[122]

Ove Arup wrote to the Committee on 23rd January advising that Jack Zunz and Utzon would be travelling out to Sydney with him in March, and staying for three weeks, and asked them to arrange a program of meetings to 'enable us to give a full explanation of the work still to be done – the procedure for Stage II and Stage III, with drawings showing all details and giving a clear picture of the Opera House as a whole...'[123]

Among the meetings planned, were with Civil & Civic, who had threatened to walk off the job as they felt they were not getting adequate remuneration for the work they were doing.

Then Utzon wrote to Ashworth on the 29th:

> ... It has been a most strenuous job for all of us this year. You might well feel that we have been very slow, I am not quite sure, but I suppose it was more or less our optimism that gave the impression that this complicated house was relatively easy to create.
>
> Mr Arup has been terribly stressed and has now to take a holiday and is sailing in three weeks to Sydney by way of the west coast of America...[124]

Ove Arup was quite ill, and according to his diary was:

Jan 8-19th	Away ill after fainting attacks.
Jan 22-25th	Spent some time with Utzon.
Feb 1-12th	Bad Gadstein Austria for treatment[125]

Jack Zunz wrote to George Boulton suggesting Gore and Kynastons' visit be postponed until after he returned from Sydney as Arups were currently producing 'information which will be necessary and useful on our trip to Sydney' and he wouldn't like them to arrive 'during the last minute rush.'[126] Boulton wrote back expressing his 'hope for (Mr Arup's) speedy recovery' but suggested Gore and Kynaston still come out because the matter of placing the crane contract was urgent if they were to start work at the Opera House site in August as scheduled.

> In order that our planning may proceed, – continued Boulton – we request you to advise us whether any alterations of consequence are contemplated in the design. Has a decision been made on the structural nature of the side shells and will they be precast or cast insitu? We are also interested in the proposed method and sequence of joining the erected segments for the main shells.[127]

On 9th February Zunz wrote to Ove Arup at the Hotel Elizabeth Park at Bad Gadstein, Austria:

> Jorn said that the latest drawings should be sent on to you. I am not so sure that this is a good idea but he suggested that if we didn't do it you would worry too much.
>
> The enclosed sketch was the bombshell which Buus brought with him on Monday. The hope is that the intersection shells (i.e. side shells) will now be made of a sphere of the same radius as the main shell. The structure as it is shown is unworkable because of the abrupt cut-off but we have already made some suggestions on how this can be overcome...
>
> As I mentioned to you on the telephone, this will mean considerable recalculation. I have stopped Hornibrook's people from coming and have suggested that they come back with us after we have been to Sydney.
>
> We are trying to make the scheme work – we think we can – and while Jorn (as ever) says this is the final scheme Buus says he really thinks that he means it this time... I have their solemn promise that there will be no further later demands...
>
> For the rest life carries on its usual chaotic way. I hope the weather is better now and you are having a good rest.[128]

On 12th February Ove Arup was in hospital in Austria with another fainting attack and on his return to England spent from 8th March to 9th April 'Convalescing at home.'[129] His partner Peter Dunican temporarily took over the reins of running the company.

On the 12th Zunz wrote to Boulton again requesting Gore and Kynaston to postpone their visit:

> ... we are very sorry about this but we do not consider their presence at this particular juncture to be of maximum benefit to the project...
>
> Our design has matured over the past weeks. There is no major alteration in the main shells and we are proceeding with our detailed

calculations and preliminary working details on the lines which we discussed with you when you were here. The geometry of the side shells has caused us considerable difficulty but is now taking shape. It looks as though it may be structurally simplified compared with what you saw. It is difficult to describe this in a letter but we will do so when we see you.[130]

On 6th March Ove Arup wrote to Ashworth a personal letter:

It was and is a very great disappointment to me that I could not join the others in the presentation of our new scheme to the Committee; but there is nothing I can do about it. According to the doctors there is nothing fundamentally wrong with me – in fact they are very satisfied with my general state of health – but apparently I have been doing a bit more than was good for me, and now I am punished for my sins by, for the time being, having to take things very easy, avoid worrying about anything, and be very patient – which is not as easy as it sounds.

The two bright spots in the situation are that I think we have now solved all the main problems in the design and construction of the main shells – a thing which has worried me for years, and that with Jack Zunz and his very strong team in charge I think the future of the job is assured, even if I stayed away from it altogether – which I have no intention of doing.

Since the change of design last autumn when we decided to try out the folded "shells" we and Jorn had to telescope what would normally have been a year or more of work into a relatively few months – taking account all the time of Professor Unruh, Waagner-Biro, Jordan Varming and the rest producing solutions and scrapping them again continuously.

I had planned to give you a fuller account of why we had taken such a long time and why we didn't get all the ideas straight away, but that would be too much like hard work, which I am supposed to avoid for the time being. Suffice to say that for this kind of problem the next best solution isn't really good enough...[131]

Utzon was working hard to have completed his *Yellow Book* to present to the Committee and Government in Sydney. This was another large book, which was a sort of updated edition of the *Red Book*, the size of a small coffee table top, illustrating the latest designs of the interiors and the spherical shell scheme. It had an ingenious line sketch on the cover, a swirl of circles drawn with a compass which if you looked at it for a few moments you could pick out the profile of the Opera House shells in the centre of the picture. Arups were preparing a *Black Book* for presentation at the same time, with engineering drawings of shell segments and elevations of the shell structure. Utzon was taking his *Yellow Book* with him on the plane and was to fly Copenhagen-New York, where he was to meet Zunz flying London-New York clutching his copy of the *Black Book*. Zunz took a later flight to New York because the *Black Book* was not ready, and left on a later flight with Utzon from New York to Los Angeles – fortuitously as it turned out because the American Airlines' flight they had been booked on from New York to Los Angeles crashed with no survivors at Jamaica Bay.[132] Utzon's arrival by plane in Sydney on 14th March was announced in the paper under the heading "UP IN CLOUDS OVER HIS JOB."

> An incoming Qantas jet liner circled Sydney Opera House yesterday to give the designer, Mr Jorn Utzon, an aerial view of work on the project.
> The aircraft's pilot, Captain John Sheilds, invited Mr Utzon on to the flight deck while the airliner twice circled the construction.[133]

It was the first time Zunz had been to Australia or seen the Opera House, and he drove with Utzon from the airport straight to the Opera House site for a brief inspection before going to their hotel in Bondi to sleep, telling staff that if there were any enquiries they were arriving at 1 a.m. the following day.

Zunz and Utzon had a busy three-week schedule in Sydney. There were meetings with the Committee, Technical Panel and government, tours of the site and meetings with the site staff and quantity surveyors, after which it was decided 'legal advice should be sought immediately by Crown Solicitors'[134] in regard to negotiations with the Stage I contractors Civil & Civic over claims. The presentation of the new shell scheme was made not so much to the government, but to the Committee and Technical Panel, and

> in those days of course, Utzon was a magician... first of all... his visual and verbal presentations were so superb, that he really carried all before him. And he had these people eating out of his hand... (so) these meetings were very successful. I mean, they asked pertinent questions, but at that time it was no more than a scheme, and we really... hadn't done enough detailed technical work to justify it right through and through. We felt that, in principle, it would work.[135]

In a meeting with the Director of Public Works, Jack Zunz 'repeated (the) request for (an) early signature on (the) Stage II contract'[136] otherwise delays would be faced, in particular in getting the order underway for the tower cranes. There were talks on the completion date 'sometime in 1965'[137] reckoned Utzon; the total costs, which 'might be still insecure'[138] reckoned Utzon again; potential contractors for Stage II, who were to be informed they would not have a chance to quote on building the shells; on stage lighting and the stage towers, which were to be designed by Waagner Biro and may be built early to act as part of the falsework to support the shells during construction.[139] At Hornibrooks' depot at Ashfield, Zunz and Utzon met Sir Manuel Hornibrook and D.C. Gore, saw a model they had made for the erection of the rib segments using an unusual device they called the 'erection arch' and discussed the draft of the cost-plus fixed fee contract. Following a meeting with the Technical Panel on the 22nd regarding estimates to go before Cabinet, whether the tile contract should go out to tender, that contracts for heating and mechanical services *could* go out to tender and whether Hornibrooks as an engineering contractor would be suitable to administer Stage III; Zunz and Utzon sat down to write a letter to Ove.

> We are sitting here just after a nice swim at 5 o'clock in the afternoon and intend giving you now a broad outline of what has happened...
>
> Firstly everyone here misses you pretty much and would have liked you to be here. Mr Haviland at the Executive Committee meeting asked us to convey to you their very warm greetings and wish you a speedy recovery. Broadly, both the technical panel and the Executive Committee have accepted our proposals for Stage 2, without any criticism whatsoever...
>
> Our discussions with Hornibrooks have been very fruitful. They have done excellent work and are very far advanced...
>
> Nobody seems to be shocked by the fact that the estimate is exceeded by almost double. We hope that the Minister's approval won't delay the signing of the Contract...
>
> Stage 1 is progressing satisfactorily but we have a lot of problems with the Contractor. However, we have full sympathy and support in all actions we have taken. The quality of the job and the final result makes us feel very happy. In fact every day we admire your folded slabs. So did Yehudi Menuhin the other day when he was taken over the site.
>
> Ruth wrote to us and said that you were looking well and that she was much more pleased with you now than she was before you went to Austria. Needless to say we are delighted. We play tennis, swim and in between times squeeze in a meeting or two with various parties...[140]

Ashworth wrote to Ove on the 26th:

> (We) were very sorry to hear of your indisposition and that you would be unable to join us in Sydney on this occasion. However, knowing you, I am quite sure you have been over-working and it will no doubt be good for

you to have a rest.

We have had a number of meetings of the Technical Panel and Joern and Jack Zunz have done their stuff with regard to Stage 2. Zunz gave apologies for your absence and I can assure you (he) did a first-class job in so far as the Panel is concerned...

Incidentally, another envelope (empty) addressed to me arrived with your letter... It would appear to me the typist has merely addressed and despatched two envelopes. I thought I would mention this in case there was a second letter which had been omitted from its envelope.[141]

The new design of the shells had not been made public during Utzon's visit to Sydney, the Sydney papers merely reporting Utzon had come to confer with the Opera House builders. Skipper Nielsen wrote to Utzon on the 18th April,

Mr Haviland asked me... whether he could get some material for a statement regarding the changes in the shape and method of construction of the shells... As it is obviously important to have all information available to put into the statement, I cabled you today for (a) briefing... Mr Haviland would like to have the material by the end of next week, so would you please answer by cable and if there is time also by letter...

When we rang and dictated the cable the conversation ran like this -

Malcolm: I wish to dictate an overseas cable to Denmark.

Office girl: Name and address, please?

Malcolm: To Jorn, J-O-R-N...

Office Girl: Utzon, U-T-Z-O-N?

Malcolm: That's right – Hellebaek, Denmark!

Office Girl: Yes! – And the text?

Malcolm: Haviland, H-A-V-I-L-A-N-D, Haviland requests for press statement next week reasons and extent of alterations to shells – ...

Office Girl: Golly, they are not going to alter them again, are they...

(We live in a big city!)[142]

Haviland issued the Committee's press statement on 30th April:

I have been approached by the Press frequently over recent months concerning statements being made that the designs of the shells of the Opera House have been radically altered.

These statements are not correct. The shells now finally designed are still the same main shape as in the winning design of January 1957 and are simply a refinement of the design shown on the plans prepared in 1958...

All the shells are now defined as separate portions of a single theoretical sphere giving a consistent and very satisfactory solution architecturally as well as structurally... [143]

In June when pictures of the revised shells were released, the *Telegraph* published pictures of Utzon's 1957 model and the new scheme with some quotes by Stan Haviland. On being tackled about the change in design:

> Mr Haviland said it was unfair to compare the new design with the original model of 1957. He said the model had been built from the freehand sketches submitted by Mr Utzon for the Opera House competition. Utzon may have won the competition with a structure which was completely impracticable to build, Mr Haviland said.
>
> Questioned by a Telegraph reporter, Mr Haviland retracted this statement. He said: 'No I did not mean the structure would be impracticable. I meant that from the start, we knew there would have to be a great deal of testing and research. The model was not a representation of the freehand drawings.'
>
> Telegraph reporter: 'But Utzon designed the model.'
>
> Mr Haviland: 'Yes, I know. But it was meant only to launch the public appeal.'
>
> Telegraph reporter: 'Was the public told it was not a representation of the freehand drawings?'
>
> Mr Haviland: 'No, but we were not trying to mislead the public. We have asked Mr Utzon to make a second model for public exhibition. The new model should be here in about six weeks time.'
>
> Telegraph reporter: 'Will this be based on the architectural drawings?'
>
> Mr Haviland: 'That is for you to decide.'
>
> Telegraph reporter: 'Are these last architectural drawings final?'
>
> Mr Haviland: 'Reasonably so.'
>
> Telegraph reporter: 'Would it have been possible to continue with the old 1958 design?'
>
> Mr Haviland: 'We did not ask. Mr Utzon recommended the changed design. He told us it would be stronger and more economic. We accepted his recommendation.'
>
> Mr Haviland refused to say how much the building would cost.[144]

Utzon too was interviewed by a *Herald* staff correspondent in Copenhagen about the change to the silhouette of the Opera House.

> The silhouette hasn't altered – said Utzon – Detailed drawings people are seeing now make the roof shell look steeper than on models and on the finished building. That is a matter of perspective. It is my design. Am I going to destroy it? What we have done is transfer the design idea into defined geometry. We knew what we were after. There's no established building technique for it.
>
> Saarinen's new building at New York's Idlewild Airport is based on freehand curves measured up and built in air in formwork, and concrete

was placed there in the air. We could have done this at one stage had the scheme been ready for it, but we believe that the additional discipline introduced by defined geometry makes sure that our much more complicated composition of forms is aesthetically under control.

There has been some misunderstanding along lines that the engineer had to take over and make something that could stand up. This is not so. We are working beautifully together. You won't be able to separate structure from architecture when it has been finished.[145]

Arups wrote to the Committee on 28th March to let them know negotiations with Hornibrooks were complete for the terms of the contract for Stage II of the Opera House. Hornibrooks were to undertake the work for a fixed fee of £75,000 which was less than 5 per cent of the estimated cost of the shells of £1,700,000.

The fee is relatively small – wrote Arups – having regard to the magnitude and complexity of the work...

All contracts of this nature require both parties to act in good faith. We believe that in the Hornibrook organisation we have the best firm available to do the job, and that all indications are that they are eager to carry out this most important project in a satisfactory manner.[146]

The government still had not signed the contract for Stage II, but with Gore and Kynaston leaving Sydney on 6th April bound for Arup's London office the real work was about to get underway of planning how to build the Opera House shells. Four days before they left, on the 2nd, Joe Huang wrote to Mr Hillinger at Waagner Biro in Vienna with new sketches of the Major and Minor Halls, adding:

Further to your telephone conversation with Mr Lethbridge approximately three weeks ago, we wish to confirm that it is necessary to change the geometry of all the shells due to the shifting of the footpoints. Fortunately, this change will only provide more space inside the shells with the possible exception of Shell 9, particularly between levels + 72 ft and + 112 ft...

We shall send you the revised internal contours of shell 2 and 9 as soon as possible.[147]

In the building trade, particularly the civil engineering trade, when the design finishes the construction can start. But the Sydney Opera House shells were so complex and so unlike anything that had ever been attempted before that the two were intimately intertwined. The design of the shells at the Opera House was still going on as they were being built.

CHAPTER 10

PREPARING FOR CONSTRUCTION OF THE SHELLS

On 16th November 1960 Ronald Jenkins wrote to Alan Levy in Sydney:

> We are now thinking, incidentally very seriously about which firms can be invited to tender for the shell-like superstructure. The more we look at it the more difficult seems the job. In due course I should like your opinion as to whether the present Contractors would be really suitable.[1]

The "present Contractors" did not get a look in, and Eric Wagner of MacDonald, Wagner and Priddle recommended Hornibooks as being in his opinion the best contractors in Australia to construct the Opera House shells. Hornibrooks also had an international reputation as being the top civil engineering contractor in Australia; in 1958, when Christiani and Nielsen were interested in quoting on the podium, they intended building the job as a joint venture with Hornibrooks.[2] Hornibrooks NSW subsidiary had quoted on the podium and put in a price of £1,616,060, the third lowest of the six quotes the government received and £218,031 more than the price put in by Civil & Civic.

Malcolm Nicklin wrote to Jenkins on 20th June 1961:

> You will recall back in 1958 when you interviewed prospective tenderers for Stage I the Hornibrook people advised that whereas the contract would be carried out (if successful) by Hornibrook, McKenzie Clark Pty Ltd. the engineering control would come from the parent company M. R. Hornibrook Pty Ltd. of Queensland. At that stage the latter organisation had a much better reputation than the N.S.W. firm and that still applies, although to a very much lesser degree, today.
>
> Without wishing to tip the scales against George Noe of the Sydney firm, a very good engineer but with due respect just a bit too talkative, we think it should be one of the Brisbane people who comes to see you in London and who will be entirely responsible for the overall control of the contract. You may remember the name George Boulton mentioned at the recent meeting with Sir Manuel... We feel that it would be wise if you were to give us permission to warn Sir Manuel (unofficially and verbally) of the way the wind is now blowing and for him to start thinking about

sending someone off to London. Of course we would tell him that he should hear officially from you in the very near future... [3]

Boulton travelled to London for a month for Hornibrooks' introduction to the shell scheme, on the basis that if Hornibrooks did not eventually get the contract his expenses would be refunded on a quantum merit basis. The government eventually reluctantly approved of Hornibrooks as the nominated constructor to build the shells – they preferred to put the job out to open tender – though they were still stalling on signing the contract. The reason MacDonald Wagner and Priddle recommended Hornibrooks in the first place can be traced back to the character of the man whose determination and drive built the company from nothing into a contracting organisation 'capable of undertaking civil engineering and building projects of any magnitude or nature.'[4]

Manuel Richard Hornibrook was born in Brisbane on 7th August 1893, the second son in a family of six boys and a girl. His parents had emigrated from County Cork in Ireland. Manuel's father John had a tea merchant's business in Brisbane and died of typhoid in 1903. The salesman and manager of the tea merchants robbed his mother of the business, so to help support the family Manuel went to work and at the age of 13 was taken on as an apprentice carpenter at H. W. Fooks Building and Joinery Works, though he received no wages at all during his first year and five shillings a week during his second. When he was 17 Manuel priced his first job when Mr Fooks was home ill, organised the work and completed it for half the contract price. When he was 19, Manuel entered a building partnership with A. G. Fooks, brother of H.W., but two years later following a disagreement on site, he had a fight with the boss's son – which he won – but decided it would be diplomatic to leave anyway and packed his tools and took the train home. Arriving at Enoggera Station looking decidedly the worse for wear, he was asked by the Station Mistress what had happened and when he told her she asked him to quote on a house she was about to build in Enoggera. Manuel won the quote, launching him on a career in the building trade.

Manuel Hornibrook never enjoyed a job unless "it was hard", and would stress 'It's not a matter of time; it is the will to do the job.' 'M.R' was proud of the fact that he never failed to complete a contract, 'It's not the jobs you start that count, – he was fond of saying – but the ones you finish', and nothing would incite him more than someone else saying 'It can't be done.' The company's plant and equipment division built cranes and all sorts of special construction tackle in their own engineering workshop, the design often the work of Manuel and later, of his engineer, George Boulton. In the 1930s, for construction of the 760 foot long, 138 foot wide Mackay Outer Harbour Pier in Queensland, the Hornibrook workshops designed and built a contraption with two 20-ton steam cranes that moved along the pier driving the piles in front of it as it went. But driving piles through the stratum of hard pipe clay was very slow, even with the largest steam hammer available on the market. After two weeks driving the first pile there remained 30 feet to be driven and one day the Chairman of the Harbour Board visited the site and remarked that at this rate it would take 20 years to finish the job. M.R. left the site, caught the first train to Brisbane and during the journey designed a new hammer. The new hammer fabricated in their workshop weighed 12 tons and had a drop that could be adjusted from one to five feet. It was on the site in Mackay 13 days after M.R. had left the job and proved capable of driving seven piles a day.[5] In the early fifties:

> The special hammer made for the No.1 Pier at Mackay Outer Harbour proved a valuable piece of equipment... It was used for driving the 3 feet 6 inch and 4 feet 6 inch diameter steel cylinders at Gibson Island (Power Station). A world record for driving cylinders of this type was established, only seven of the total number of 199 having to be airlocked.
>
> To enable the power-house to be built and the water-circulating system to be constructed, the area had to be enclosed with a coffer-dam of sheet piling driven to a depth of 45 feet. After the work was completed these piles had to be withdrawn for re-use on further sections. The extraction of the piles was extremely difficult as the salt water had rusted the clutches and the extractors on the market were not adequate for the job.
>
> So the Hornibrook workshops produced a steam extractor for the purpose. It was more than twice the capacity of any other extractor on the market and by using it, every length of sheet piling was successfully withdrawn.[6]

Though Manuel Hornibrook had no scientific training, he had a marvellous instinctive eye for structure, one of his engineers, Mr McIntyre remembering, 'He would look at a roof truss in some building and would say, "Those compression members are a bit light", or something of a technical nature. Without having been scientifically trained to determine which members were carrying compression his instinct was remarkable.' Charles Tranberg of MacDonald, Wagner and Priddle who knew M.R. for many years said about him, 'He was not only a contractor but he was a craftsman and construction engineer... I think it was because of his craftsmanship that he was a good contractor and a lot of his work could be described and indeed has been described as "copybook work".' Tranberg found Hornibrook 'could always visualise the plant required for the job and on many major contracts he played a major part in the conception of plant and designed special plant, methods and procedures.' M.R.'s motto was 'Do work on which you can look back on with pride.' As McIntyre recalled 'He was our worst headache. Even after an inspector had passed material, if M.R. considered it was not good enough he would condemn it.' Ironbark timber girders were used on the Mackay Pier, and one day M.R. visited the site and noticed a girder that was from another tree. He drew Archie McIntyre's attention to it, who assured M.R. that it had been condemned and would not be used. But this was not good enough for M.R. who got two men to burn it with an oxy-acetylene torch so there could be no doubt.[7] Nothing got Manuel Hornibrook going more than criticism of his work. During the war:

Allison engines were used in some of the U.S. Air Force planes. They were tested at the Eagle Farm air field. The work was on a 24 hour basis and the noise was very disturbing to residents of Ascot and Clayfield, so it was arranged to build an engine-testing stand. This was a massive concrete arrangement, built like a maze to try to contain the sound. A high priority project, the Hornibrook team worked all through one week-end to push the job along.

Early on the Monday morning General Connell, Commander of the U.S. 5th Air Force, came on to the job and reckoned the levels were wrong (which they weren't). He was a tall, broad-shouldered, raw-boned individual, fearsome in appearance and ever ready to brandish a leather riding-crop. After bullying the foreman he left for his Headquarters in Wickham Street.

About a quarter of an hour after the General's departure, M.R. arrived and received the foreman's story. On hearing it, Manuel Hornibrook, who never at any time was intimidated by anyone, got into his car and drove to the 5th Air Force Headquarters (he always drove himself) strode through the front door disregarding sentry and receptionist, along the passage, past the open office, with everyone staring at him, and without ceremony opened the door and entered the General's office. The very surprised looking general rose from his desk and asked the intruder who he was and what he wanted.

Manuel Hornibrook, prodding the General in the chest with his forefinger, said, "You might be a one star general in the U.S. Army, but I'm a five star General in my business; if you have any complaints you talk to me and not to my men." With those remarks he turned on his heel and stalked out.[8]

What also drove M.R. mad, were holdups on his jobs because of the unions. On one occasion in 1945 when the carpenters had downed tools on one of his jobs he said 'The Carpenter's Union Secretary needs a good hiding. If he likes to make it at the stadium I will do it myself... The Marquis of Queensbury Rules or bare knuckles will do me...'.

After becoming established building houses, the Hornibrook business soon moved on to civil engineering works, their first big bridge – of over a hundred the company was to complete in M.R.'s lifetime – was an eight-span reinforced concrete bridge at Howard in Queensland in 1925-26. Hornibrooks also tendered successfully for the Storey Bridge in Brisbane, with a channel span of 924 feet, at the time the longest steel cantilever bridge in Australia. J.J.C. Bradfield wrote the specification for the bridge as well as for the Sydney Harbour Bridge. When Bradfield was asked by a mutual friend, the Sydney builder James Wall, 'How are you getting on with M.R.?', Bradfield replied, 'He is perhaps the best contractor in the world, but he is also the most headstrong man I ever met.'[9]

M.R. would never expect his workers to do a job he would not do himself. In 1927 M.R. was in North Queensland

when he was called in to inspect the bridge over the Johnston River near Innisfail, the piers of which had been affected by molasses in the water.

Two divers at different times who had gone below to inspect the piers returned smartly to the surface, white-faced and shaken, because of a large crocodile lying on the bed of the river. They refused to return to the job.

M.R. decided he would have to go himself, so he donned the diving-suit and descended into the murky water to examine the piers, keeping a watchful eye for the crocodile. Sure enough when he got to the site he saw a large bulk of crocodile about 14 ft long lying close to the pier. With great caution he approached it to examine it more closely, and found to his great relief and amusement that the 'crocodile' was a large log.[10]

During the Depression, to keep his company going, Manuel Hornibrook realised a childhood dream by constructing Australia's longest bridge, the 'Hornibrook Highway' across Moreton Bay near Brisbane. It has 294 spans and is 8,806 feet long. M.R. personally took on the extraordinarily difficult task of privately raising the finance for the project during the bleak years of the Depression. The bridge was opened on 4th October 1935 at a toll of a shilling a car. It proved of national importance during the war years carrying military convoys, none of which paid any tolls![11]

The Hornibrook company expanded into New Guinea, Victoria and South Australia. Projects they completed included a hydro-electric power station in New Guinea, steel mills at Westernport Victoria and in the late fifties as a joint venture company called Hansen-Wilkins-Hornibrook Constructions they built the rocket bases for the Woomera rocket range in South Australia. Hornibrooks also built the Kings Avenue Twin Bridge and Commonwealth Avenue Twin Bridge over Lake Burley Griffin in Canberra. The British engineer, Sir William Halcrow, said the Commonwealth Avenue Bridge was the finest example of concrete work he had seen anywhere in the world.

Manuel's brothers all followed him into the business, Reg in 1913, Ray in 1918, Eric in 1919, Frank in 1921 and finally his eldest brother Gus in 1928.[12] Frank Hornibrook was transferred to Sydney in 1937 to establish a branch of the company in New South Wales. Their first contract was the conversion of the suspension bridge at Northbridge in Sydney to a concrete arch bridge. It had a span of 460 ft which was the longest concrete arch south of the equator at the time. Other big jobs the company did in New South Wales included the Iron Cove Bridge in Sydney and blast furnaces for Australian Iron and Steel at Port Kembla. In 1962 the Operations Manager of Hornibrooks New South Wales subsidiary, Hornibrook McKenzie Clark Ltd. was Dundas Corbet Gore, known as 'Corbet' to his friends.

Gore, 6 ft 3 in tall, weighing 14½ stone, "a pretty hefty fellow",[13] 45 at the time he started work on the Opera House, was born in the Queensland-New South Wales border town of Goondiwindi. Studying civil engineering at the University of Queensland in Brisbane when the Second World War broke out, Gore left his studies, travelled to England and enlisted in the RAAF where he was a navigator on bombers flying over the Bay of Biscay. Returning to his studies in Sydney in 1945, for his third-year practical experience in engineering in the summer of 1945-46, Gore found a job on the construction of the Iron Cove Bridge. The contract was run by Frank Hornibrook, and during the course of the job Gore met Manuel Hornibrook for the first time. Manuel Hornibrook was a familiar name to Gore as one of the 'Nabobs' of Brisbane society and as the constructor of the Storey Bridge. In fact during his student days and 'before I had any brains'[14] Gore and some other students had once clambered up the steel of the Storey Bridge, walked across on the top girders and clambered down the other side. Gore no doubt did not relate this escapade to Manuel, because when he graduated in December 1946 he was on holiday in Surfers Paradise when he received a telegram from Hornibrooks to say there is a job in Sydney if you want one, so he got on a plane and came down to Sydney. Gore's first job in New South Wales was working as site engineer on the construction of the oil refinery at Matraville. At the beginning of 1950 when Hornibrook started a construction company in New Guinea, Gore went there as their first manager, organising construction of a variety of jobs all over New Guinea, including bridges, airfields, houses, oil installations and roads.[15] Then in 1959 Gore returned to Sydney as construction manager for the New South Wales division of Hornibrooks, taking in all areas south of the Queensland border, with overall responsibility still for operations in New Guinea. In 1950-51 Hornibrooks had tendered on and won the contract for the Kings Avenue Bridge in Canberra, 'which was the first bridge built in Australia using major pre-cast pre-stressed concrete beams. When I say major, these were long and very heavy.'[16] Then Hornibrooks also won the contract to build the Commonwealth Avenue Bridge in Canberra. Half-way through this project Manuel Hornibrook asked Gore if he would take on the job of construction manager of Stage II at the Opera House.

When Ronald Jenkins had originally mentioned to Manuel Hornibrook in March/April 1961 the possibility of Hornibrooks being the contractor for the Opera House shells, all talk had revolved around a steel structure with a concrete skin. Then 'when George Boulton went over (to Arups) in... late 1961,' recalled Gore, '(Arups) were arguing whether they should be building it in steel or concrete. No one had worked out quite how... I remember when (Boulton) came back he said "you must be mad to use concrete, you have got to use steel, you will never support the weight." That was his opinion at that stage and he felt steel was the best solution and you put a concrete skin over the top of it.'[17] 'Little had been solved in a formal way by Arups at that stage or by Utzon… and (Hornibrooks) had a meeting to decide whether we would in fact take it on… there were… some risks involved as far as building was concerned. It was way out from a technical point of view and the lines were not all clear as to what we were expected to do and we didn't quite know if we were undertaking the impossible or not… We thought about it and then we said yes we would and then they asked me if I would do it…'[18] Gore asked if he could think it over. The job would be a fantastic challenge, but a career step sideways, because if he was construction manager at the Opera House site someone else would take over the job of construction manager for Hornibrooks New South Wales and the management hierarchy of the company would knit into place while he was stuck out on a branch line. Gore agreed to take the job on provided it did not affect his career path through the company, which the other directors agreed to. When the news was announced Hornibrook would be building the shells, 'I was told we were mad to take the job on, that if we could not get the Opera House to stay up our reputation as a builder would go down the drain.'[19]

Gore met Jack Zunz and Utzon briefly for the first time in Sydney in March/April 1962 when he had a chance to look at Utzon's spherical scheme in the *Yellow Book*, before setting off with Bob Kynaston for London via the States. In San Francisco they had talks with Adhesives Engineering Inc. and looked at some of their experiments using epoxy resins, which Gore was interested in using as a joint between shell segments, and at the University of Berkeley California they discussed the general concept of shell construction using pre-cast ribs with one of the world authorities on concrete, Professor Lin.[20] Then they flew to New York where they met some of the big construction contractors, including the builder of Saarinen's TWA terminal. They also looked at the terminal itself, which was in fact quite small, only slightly larger than the Opera House restaurant and nothing like on the scale of the Major or Minor Hall. In Europe they looked at tower cranes made in Scotland and France, and in Paris had a look at the Exhibition Hall which was of shell construction. The specification of the cranes for the Opera House depended on the lifting capacity at a certain radius, they had to be mobile and able to move backwards and forwards on rails, they had to be self-erecting, i.e. able to erect their own crane bridge on top of the podium, they had to be self-supporting because they could not be guyed to the Opera House or out in the Harbour somewhere, and their jibs had to be a minimum height above the rails to clear the Opera House shells. Whites seemed to have the best designed cranes and the most experience in tower crane construction, and Gore and Kynaston could physically see a crane working close to the size required for the Opera House on a dam site in France, so it was a White's crane that was selected to the relevant specification for the Opera House. In Hellebaek they stayed for two or three days in a hotel on the beach when 'it was Midsummer's Eve and all the witches came down and all gathered around the beach and sang songs to keep the witches away.'[21] They looked at some of Utzon's townhouses, and caught the ferry to Sweden to look at the Opera House tiles at Hoganas' factory.[22] In Utzon's office, which Gore felt was more like an artist's or sculptor's studio than an architect's office, Utzon was working on the shape of the shell segments, which tended to change as the forces were worked out and as Utzon was approving the appearance there would be some discussion between Arups and Utzon's offices. But by far the most time was spent in Arup's London office, in a job which had been expected to take one month and which they spent three months working on, still without finishing, 'to work out in parallel with the design an erection technique and (to) modify… the design to come to a practical conclusion at the end so that when the design was completed the method of erection… had been tied into it throughout.'[23] Provision had to be made in the design of the shell segments for attachments for lifting tackle, and for a method to hold the segments in place in the partially completed structure once they were lifted into position. This procedure was complicated by the fact that Arups were still feeling their way forward on the design – they had to keep modifying their design as the results of the structural analysis were completed – while all the time agreeing the final sculptural shape with Utzon's requirements. To say nothing of Utzon's modifications to the shape of the shells in line with his philosophy of never accepting a solution if a better one could be found. Regarding some of the work carried out by Hornibrooks and Arups, Zunz later wrote:

It is worth noting some aspects of the forces set up due to the construction sequence. This alone necessitated a comprehensive investigation into the state of stress of the structure at each stage as new units were added, falsework was removed and re-erected and so on. Here a model would be of little or no help at all unless of extraordinary detail and complexity. The extent of this problem only became clear during the year of planning with the contractor when construction procedures were evolved. To elucidate just one aspect of this investigation: a rib recently erected is decentred and therefore has certain built-in forces and moments. The next rib under erection is partially supported on this recently completed rib. During erection of this new rib a whole series of forces and moments will be induced in the completed rib, all of which have to be catered for. Since all 140 ribs are different, each one presents a new and different problem.[24]

Slippery pads would need to be inserted between the ribs as 'it is expected that $1/2$ in movement up or down or lengthways could be possible between adjacent ribs.'[25] Arups were to supply drawings showing the centre of gravity of each segment for Hornibrooks to work out their crane slinging. And Hornibrooks formwork must be designed, insisted Utzon, such that 'Chamfers on beams and columns must definitely not be used and all edges must be as sharp as possible.'[26]

Gore left London on 5th July to head back to Sydney, and that day Jack Zunz wrote to Malcolm Nicklin begging forgiveness for not communicating earlier as 'life has been a little hectic' as not only had they had Gore and Kynaston on their doorsteps but his able associate John Lethbridge 'had decided to take up another appointment.' Zunz added:

> … we cannot help but treat Hornibrooks as part of us from now on. We have placed them in a position of trust and we cannot treat them contractually in the same way as we would do under more normal circumstances. I have personally worked closely with Corbet over the past two to three months. Quite apart from his technical acumen and enthusiasm, we are all most taken with his attitude to the job and with his sincerity of purpose. While very often one talks about the desirability or otherwise of having a contractor in the design team, we feel that in this instance they are really with us. It would be very wonderful if we could maintain this relationship and attitude for the duration of the job.[27]

And when Jack Zunz wrote to Sydney a few days later on the 11th he described Gore as 'a much loved member of our team.'[28] On 17th

July Gore sent a letter summarising developments which closed, 'am arranging for a case of what I hope to be good Australian wines to be sent to London and I hope that Mr Bertorelli will serve them to the Arup table as required.'[29] Someone at Arups had written 'ah!' next to the paragraph in the margin, and when Kelman wrote back on various technical matters on the 24th he added 'The wine will be appreciated in the true sense of the word... But I think I shall have to make friends with Mr Bertorelli.'[30]

Zunz wrote to Gore on the 25th:

> The lateral stressing is being subjected to what may become an agonising re-appraisal. It all has to do with either designing the ribs for moments and torsions a little greater than hoped for or, alternatively, catering for somewhat larger forces than we have discussed with you. This doesn't apply generally, only in some of the longer members. I am telling you this to keep you in the picture but for the present no action is required.[31]

Gore wrote to Zunz the following day, that:

> ... as the publicity boys are now playing up in the papers that the first contract is complete, it will be essential to obtain permission to spend money on tests (for trials of rib segment erection) very promptly if there are further delays in (signing) the contract. This is a word of warning to get you primed for the battle.[32]

This was followed by another letter to Zunz on 3rd August '... I have a sickening feeling that the whole thing is grinding to a political stop.'[33] Hornibrooks' contract with the crane manufacturers had been conditional on signing a contract for their purchase by 31st July, but the government still had not signed a contract nominating Hornibrook as the Stage II contractors, and '... I think now that unless drastic action is taken, the initial crane order will be lost.'[34]

Gore's letter was followed four days later by one from Ian MacKenzie, passing on some information from Malcolm Nicklin obtained from Johnstone, the Director of Public Works:

> To start at the beginning, late last week Malcolm had occasion to contact Mr Haviland who mentioned after some hesitation that a Cabinet sub-committee had been set up to investigate the Opera House. He was very reticent about it, asking Malcolm not to mention it to anybody, would only say that he had to contact Professor Ashworth urgently.
>
> The sub-committee is now public knowledge (see enclosed newspaper cuttings) and the purpose of its investigations is taken to be costs. However, yesterday Malcolm met Mr Johnstone at a "get together"

1. Bennelong

2. Macquarie

3. Fort Macquarie

4. Fort Macquarie Tramsheds

5. Charles Moses

6. Goossens (left)

7. Elsinore Fort, Denmark

8. Jorn Utzon (left) and Norman Ryan, the Labor minister for public works

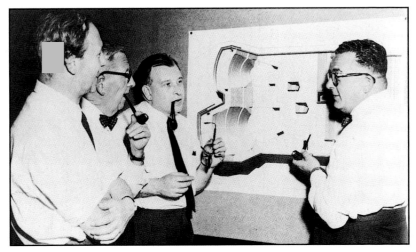

9. The competition assessors with from left to right, Leslie Martin, Cobden Parkes, Eero Saarinen and Harry Ashworth

"I had some friends in for cocktails and then some idiot mentioned the opera house!"
10.Cartoon in the *Sydney Morning Herald* on 4th February 1957 following the announcement of the competition winning design

11. Utzon's model of his competition design

"I said, it's just as well they haven't got that opera house up yet!"
12. Cartoon in the *Herald* on 20th February 1957

13. Joe Cahill signing the contract to build Stage 1, with Stan Haviland standing behind and Gerardus Dusseldorp on the right

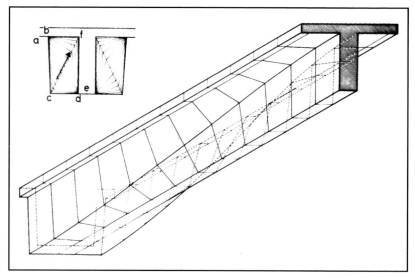

14. Isometric section of a concourse beam

15. Preparing the shuttering for the concourse beams

16. The completed concourse beams

17. Drilling for the concrete piers

18. The completed podium

19. Roger Rigby's letter
to Jack Zunz

20. Ron Jenkins

21. Model tests were carried out on shells based
on the shape of a parabola

22. The competition winning design

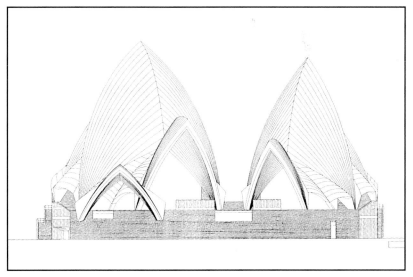

23. The design that was built

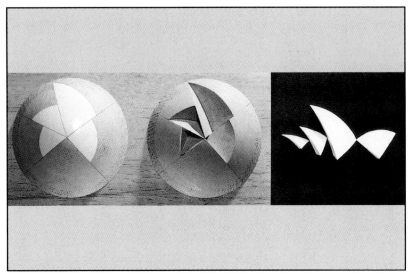

24. Hey presto an Opera House! After five years experimenting with various shapes Utzon finally chose to make all the shells as segments of the same sphere

25. Utzon's model of the spherical scheme clearly shows how each set of shells for the Major and Minor Halls was three separate structures

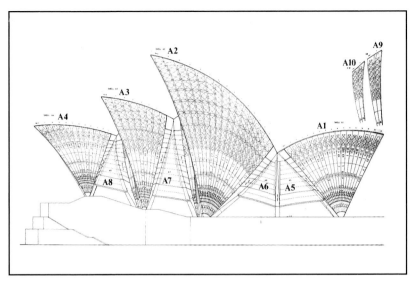

26. Drawing of the Major Hall shells before tiling, with the shell reference numbers

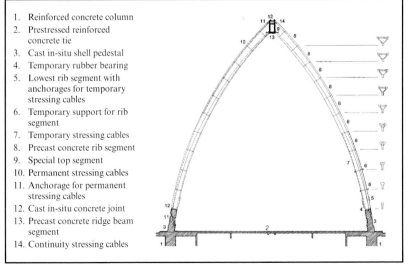

1. Reinforced concrete column
2. Prestressed reinforced concrete tie
3. Cast in-situ shell pedestal
4. Temporary rubber bearing
5. Lowest rib segment with anchorages for temporary stressing cables
6. Temporary support for rib segment
7. Temporary stressing cables
8. Precast concrete rib segment
9. Special top segment
10. Permanent stressing cables
11. Anchorage for permanent stressing cables
12. Cast in-situ concrete joint
13. Precast concrete ridge beam segment
14. Continuity stressing cables

27. Diagrammatic section through the shells showing a pair of ribs and the rib segments

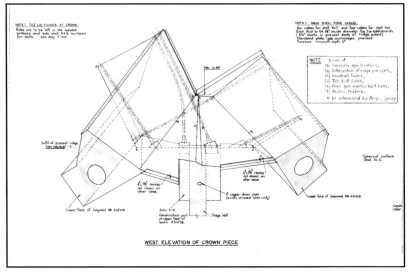

28. Many of the concrete elements looked like sculptures. This is one of the crown pieces

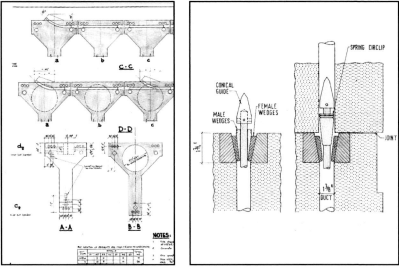

29. Lateral stressing ducts and longitudinal stressing ducts

30. The 'flying wedge' system allowed rib segments to be built like beads threaded on a string

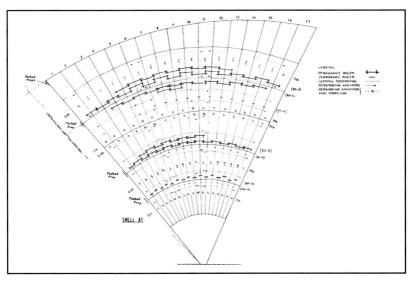

31. Shell A1 with lateral bolt and lateral stressing connections

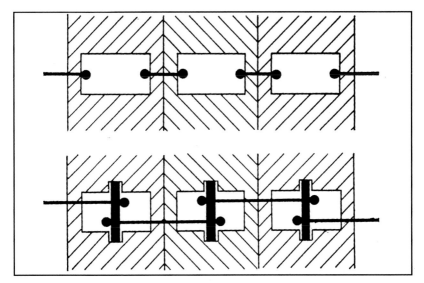

32. One of the evolutions in the bolt design was the change from
a short bolt passing through the edge of the rib (top) to a much
longer bolt passing through the centre-line of the rib (below)

33. Activity in the rib casting yard

34. Reinforcing for the shell pedestals was so thick you couldn't see through it

35. Placing the reinforcing for one of the crown pieces

36. From left to right Mick Lewis, Corbet Gore and Skipper Nielsen on site

37. From left to right Mick Lewis, Ove Arup and Jack Zunz on site

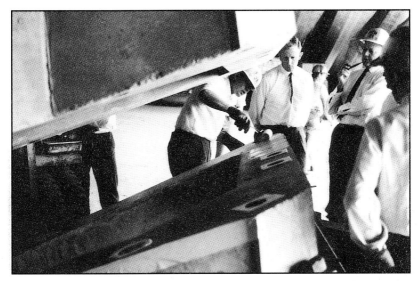

38. Making a test application of epoxy on a pair of
segments. Corbet Gore on the right with the pipe

39. A worker in one of the side shell segments

40. The stage walls rise above the podium

41. The Major Hall side shells with the erection arch on the right

42. The first ribs in place on the side shells

43. The side shell arches of A8

44. The first segment of a rib drops into place

45. Looking down on a rib under construction with a completed
rib on the left and the erection arch on the right

46. Lifting in a top segment

47. Temporary stressing underway

48. The Major Hall shells take shape

49. Progress on the Major Hall seen from the Harbour Bridge

50. Jim Inman riding on the top ridge segment of the highest Major Hall shell

51. Jockeying a top ridge segment into position

52. The completed restaurant shells

53. The completed Minor Hall shells

54. Laying tiles in a tile lid form

55. Tile lids hanging up beneath the concourse for curing

56. Fabricating a non-standard tile lid form in a concave shaped dish

57. Tile lids stacked on the podium ready to place on the shells

58. Tile lid erection underway

59. Once the fitting problems had been solved tile lid erection went ahead very quickly

60. Surveyors at work on site

61. The tiling nearly complete

62. Placing single tiles over the holes for the side-shell tile lid bolts

63. The patterns formed by shiny and matt tiles on the completed tiled shells

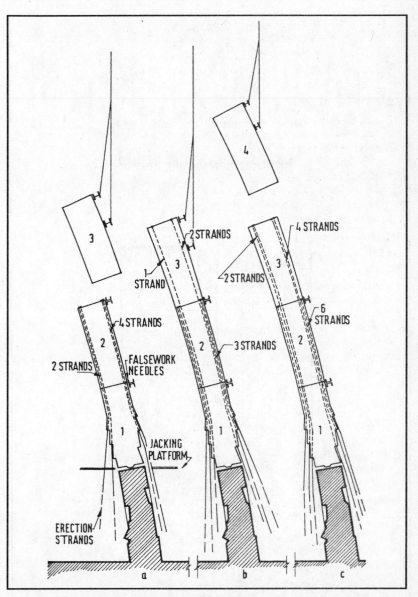

64. The temporary stressing system. Passing cables one at a time through a newly erected segment then stressing them locked the new segment into place while still maintaining a pre-stress on the previously erected segments

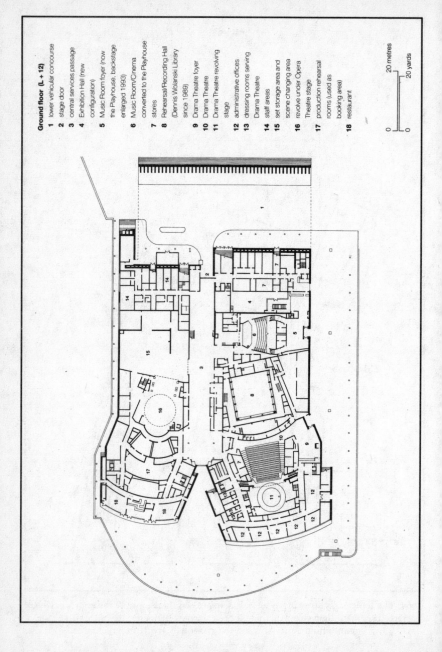

Ground floor (L + 12)

1 lower vehicular concourse
2 stage door
3 central services passage
4 Exhibition Hall (new configuration)
5 Music Room foyer (now the Playhouse, backstage enlarged 1993)
6 Music Room/Cinema converted to the Playhouse
7 stores
8 Rehearsal/Recording Hall (Dennis Wolanski Library since 1989)
9 Drama Theatre foyer
10 Drama Theatre
11 Drama Theatre revolving stage
12 administrative offices
13 dressing rooms serving Drama Theatre
14 staff areas
15 set storage area and scene changing area
16 revolve under Opera Theatre stage
17 production rehearsal rooms (used as booking area)
18 restaurant

0   20 metres
0   20 yards

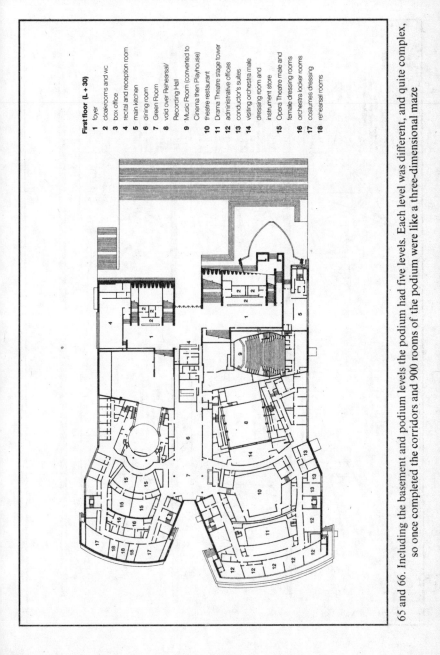

First floor (L + 30)

1 foyer
2 cloakrooms and wc
3 box office
4 recital and reception room
5 main kitchen
6 dining room
7 Green Room
8 void over Rehearsal/
   Recording Hall
9 Music Room (converted to
   Cinema then Playhouse)
10 theatre restaurant
11 Drama Theatre stage tower
12 administrative offices
13 conductor's suites
14 visiting orchestra male
   dressing room and
   instrument store
15 Opera Theatre male and
   female dressing rooms
16 orchestra locker rooms
17 costumes dressing
18 rehearsal rooms

65 and 66. Including the basement and podium levels the podium had five levels. Each level was different, and quite complex, so once completed the corridors and 900 rooms of the podium were like a three-dimensional maze

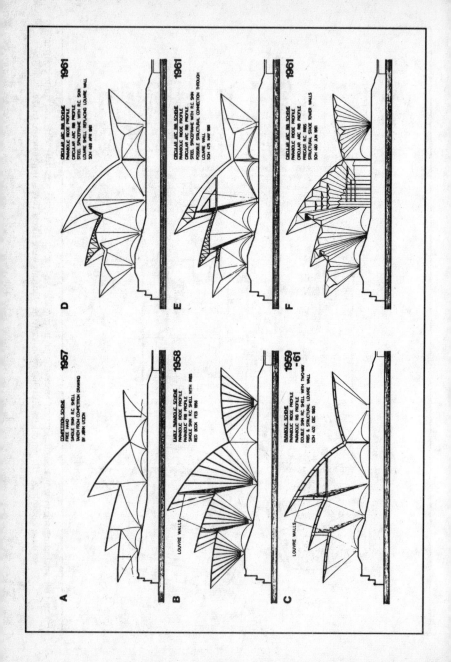

A

1957

COMPETITION SCHEME
FREE HAND
SINGLE SKIN R.C. SHELL
TAKEN FROM COMPETITION DRAWING
BY JORN UTZON

B

1958

EARLY PARABOLIC SCHEME
PARABOLIC RIDGE PROFILE
PARABOLIC RIB PROFILE
SINGLE SKIN R.C. SHELL WITH RIBS
RED BOOK FEB 1958

LOUVRE WALLS

C

1959 -61

PARABOLIC SCHEME
PARABOLIC RIDGE PROFILE
PARABOLIC RIB PROFILE
DOUBLE SKIN R.C. SHELL WITH TWO-WAY
RIBS & STRUCTURAL LOUVRE WALL
SCH 402 DEC 1960

LOUVRE WALLS

D

1961

CIRCULAR ARC RIB SCHEME
PARABOLIC RIDGE PROFILE
CIRCULAR ARC RIB PROFILE
STEEL SPACEFRAME WITH R.C. SKIN
LOUVRE SHELL REPLACING LOUVRE WALL
SCH 408 APR 1961

E

1961

CIRCULAR ARC RIB SCHEME
PARABOLIC RIDGE PROFILE
CIRCULAR ARC RIB PROFILE
STEEL SPACEFRAME WITH R.C. SKIN
POSSIBLE STRUCTURAL CONNECTION THROUGH
LOUVRE WALL
SCH 475 MAY 1961

F

1961

CIRCULAR ARC RIB SCHEME
PARABOLIC RIDGE PROFILE
CIRCULAR ARC RIB PROFILE
PRECAST R.C. RIBS
STRUCTURAL SHADE TOWER WALL
SCH 460 JUN 1961

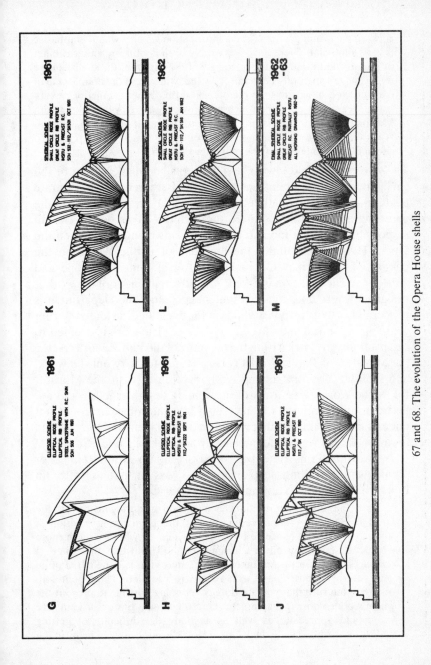

67 and 68. The evolution of the Opera House shells

277

cocktail party and got some extra information which I would emphasise is very unofficial. There have apparently been doubts, by either cabinet or its sub-committee, on the adequacy of the design of the shells! These doubts have apparently been raised by the switch from the double skin of concrete and steel trusses to the present form. Either cabinet or its sub-committee (I am not sure which and have no means of checking with Malcolm) want a report on the shells from an independent non-Australian consultant. The sub-committee is expected to report to cabinet today so there may be more news soon.[35]

The government had always had concerns about the design of the shells, this was the main reason they had entered into a separate contract with Arups rather than the usual arrangement on the construction of buildings where the architect takes on the overall responsibility for the job and appoints his own engineer. When the Opera House came under the umbrella of Public Works on the passing of the Sydney Opera House Act in 1960, Johnstone had written '... The question is asked: when the remainder of the work is designed, where does the government come in? The Department is concerned as to its responsibilities in the event of disaster to the roof through faulty design or structure.'[36] As '... The work is deemed to be an authorised work within the meaning of the Public Works Act... the Minister for Public Works is empowered to carry out the work, and shall be the Constructing Authority.'[37] Yet Ryan, the Minister for Public Works, was firmly of the opinion that the shells could not be built, all his advisors were telling him the same, he could not understand how they could ever be made to stay up and they looked to him as if they were held in place by 'invisible sky hooks.'[38]

Ashworth at this time was on a six-month world tour after obtaining a travelling scholarship, and was at Arup's office in London. He wrote to Haviland on 9th August:

... Numerous disturbing rumours have reached me during my travels, the latest being that some investigation of the engineering position is suggested. I cannot conceive how, or by whom, or what useful purpose would be served by any such suggestion. (Meanwhile the Stage II contract had still not been signed and)... unless this is done in the quite near future serious delays with regard to completion are bound to occur... I am sure that you are doing everything possible to prevent the whole work coming to a complete standstill. Should this occur I am sure you would appreciate as well as anybody the difficulty of getting underway again... The Sydney Opera House was the envy of many in the places I have visited, and it seems most unfortunate to me that some in Australia should be endeavouring to talk us out of one of the finest buildings architecturally speaking that Australia has had.[39]

Also on the 9th, Haviland wrote to Ashworth:

... the situation has changed almost from day to day... I received (yesterday) from the Minister a letter, a copy of which is enclosed.

In the meantime, I had learnt of the appointment by Cabinet of a Committee comprising the Minister for Local Government, Mr Hills, and the Minister for Lands, Mr Compton (Haviland and Cobden Parkes had been called in to see the Government Committee and)... Both Bill Laurie and John Roderick,[40] speaking on the telephone to me since the interview with the Committee, have expressed doubt as to the outcome of the second opinion proposition but it is fixed so firmly in the mind of members of Cabinet that it is advisable to fall with it. Hence the concurrence expressed by me at the interview.

... It will be up to you now to explain the situation to Ove Arup in a way that they should not see any objection to it. The nomination of the second firm should be your own, avoiding any appearance of your nomination being suggested by Ove Arup. The sooner that you can manage this job the more it will be appreciated, particularly if it is holding up the Stage II contract.[41]

The letter from the government addressed to Haviland raised the concerns of the Cabinet sub-committee over costs and;

The stability of the works proposed in Stage II, namely the shells superstructure or roofs... in view of the novel design of the work, the method of construction, and the very great cost involved, it should not rely on the advice of one firm of Consultants, but that another Consultant should, in collaboration with the existing Consultants, examine the data available to them, the development of the design, and the decision as to the most appropriate procedures and method of construction, with the object of reporting to the Executive Committee their views on the present proposals of Messrs Ove Arup & Partners.[42]

Zunz recalled that the government 'suddenly realised they had seen no detailed drawings and virtually all they had were some sketches and verbal reassurances. What they really wanted to know is if what we were doing was sensible'[43] particularly because at that time the failure of a bridge in Melbourne had placed severe pressure on the New South Wales government to be seen to be exercising proper management and control over the project. Zunz was due to go on ten days holiday with his family, and the night before leaving 'I had a phone call from Mr Ryan at 2 o'clock in the morning. It was a very bad line, but Mr Ryan was very polite and he said "Mr Zunz, we would like you to come to Australia immediately to attend a Cabinet sub-committee meeting, and would you please bring Mr Utzon along, because the whole project is in jeopardy.'"[44] 'And I phoned up Utzon and we arranged to go. Ove was ill, as he had been really for most of that year, but because of the seriousness of the situation Peter Dunican persuaded him that he should go as well'[45] and Zunz cancelled his holiday and they all went. Ove Arup and Jack Zunz flew out from London together and met Utzon in Hawaii

... where we had dinner together. We agreed that because of Ove's frail condition we would not ask him to do anything except as a matter of last resort. Utzon and I would deal with the matter as best we could.

Having flown through the night and over the dateline, within two hours of arriving we were whisked to the cabinet office to meet a very formidable array of ministers and officials, headed by the premier. He welcomed us and explained the government's difficulties and that, because of the complex technical nature of the project, he and his colleagues required further information and reassurance that we were actually capable of building the opera house and that it wouldn't fall down, and that costs would be contained.

Utzon and I were just about to open our mouths and reply when Ove piped up and said: 'Oh well, I'd better deal with this.' And then he rambled. Unfinished sentence followed unfinished sentence. There was an array of trained stenographers to record the proceedings and I watched these girls trying to catch it all. Gradually their writing became slower and slower until after about 10 minutes it stopped. Although he didn't finish any sentence, if one listened carefully one could get a picture of what he was saying – rather like an impressionist painting. It all made good sense seen as a whole. He went on for forty minutes, and then just as suddenly as he had started, he stopped. There was a deathly silence. I suggested that to have formal reassurance on technical matters, we should seek an opinion from Yves Guyon, a very distinguished French engineer. And the crisis was over. Ove had blown it away with his extraordinary speech which no one could record. He had painted a picture. Whether the premier and his colleagues understood and agreed to what he said or whether they were fearful that he would start all over again no one will ever know, but he had won the day.[46]

Though as Ove Arup pointed out to the Technical Advisory Panel he 'was agreeable to the proposal although he pointed out that it would be an almost impossible task in view of its complexity and the amount of time already spent by his team on the project.'[47]

Utzon and Arup's visit had been announced in the Sydney papers on the 18th, which reported 'They will discuss engineering problems and the mounting costs of the Opera House',[48] but the main purpose of the visit was taken to be costs, even though it was also reported that 'In the meantime (the government) has held up the signing of a contract for the shell roof.'[49]

Reporters leapt on Utzon as soon as he stepped off the plane, who said 'Mr Ryan had telephoned him last Wednesday night to ask him to fly to Australia',[50] Utzon adding 'But the talks are quite normal. They are to discuss the beginning of the second stage.'[51] And regarding the Opera House costing more than expected Utzon said 'I have all the costs with me, but the whole business is very complicated. Unless a person had a thorough understanding of all the factors involved he would not appreciate the figures... the government should employ a public relations man to keep the public informed about Opera House developments.'[52]

As always the press also wanted to talk to Ove, who of course obliged. 'Since his original sketch Utzon has constantly been improving his design... Any designer worth his salt would...', Ove told the papers, 'This is what Mr Utzon has done.'[53] 'Mr Arup said because of the revolutionary design of the superstructure, the method of construction had to be solved at the same time as the final design was being evolved... the Opera House represented a very daring and difficult, novel form of construction never tried before. "This is the most complicated and original building ever attempted" Mr Arup said.'[54]

Though the day after the Cabinet sub-committee meeting, the headline on the front page of the *Herald* was 'OPERA HOUSE COST NOW £12.5M. Heffron Tells Of Big Increase'.[55] And there was not one mention of possible construction difficulties on the roof in the ensuing long article.

Haviland wrote to Ashworth on 29th August:

... How time flies! A lot has happened between times. I received at home yesterday your card from the Isle of Skye... When the Minister first telephoned Zunz, there was quite a reluctance on the part of both Zunz and Utzon to come. No doubt Zunz will tell you of his telephone conversation with me next day. Happily all in that connection worked out for the best; although Arup in the discussions spoke at some length, he was very appropriately supported in brief by Zunz and the members of the Cabinet Committee were very impressed. We have reason to be grateful for their help.[56]

Meanwhile the government belatedly approved letting the crane contract as a sub-contract outside the main roof contract.

On his return to London, Ove Arup wrote to Monsieur Guyon, a Frenchman who was 'probably one of the best-known and most respected civil engineers, at that time. He was particularly known for his work in pre-stressed concrete and we knew him well and had a great respect for him.'[57]

> ... We now have a scheme for the building of the superstructure (of the Opera House) we are happy about... The (superstructure)... has been generally referred to as "the shells", but this is somewhat misleading. The present design is based on a series of hollow arches or frames constructed of precast units, and tied together with prestressing.
>
> This whole job has constantly been very much in the public eye in Sydney, and there have been various attacks on it in the press... There have lately been suggestions in the Press that the Opera House when built would not be stable. This is of course not founded on any facts at all but it is the sort of thing which is likely to worry the clients... we have been thinking that it would be a good idea if you would be willing to have a look at what we are doing, and would tell us whether in your opinion the way we are going about the thing is reasonable so that if the matter should crop up through the Opposition asking awkward questions in Parliament, we could tell the Government that we had in fact consulted a person of your calibre, as to the soundness of our methods... [58]

Guyon replied:

> Coming back from Sydney where I had been called for the jacking of Gladesville Bridge,[59] I found your letter of September 4th about the Opera House... It would be with pleasure that I would have a look at the design... I am due to go to London in the first fortnight of October. I (could)... have a look at the design at your office during this trip and that I give you then a definite answer.[60]

After looking at the design Guyon 'grasped the concept immediately'[61] and wrote to Arups on 25th October that the 'scheme now being designed is practical and capable of achievement' though it was not until a year later on 21st October 1963 that Guyon completed his formal recommendation on the question put to him by Arups on whether 'the theoretical and practical investigations which have been and are being carried out... are adequate for ensuring, the safe erection of the structure.'

You have provided me with some drawings and specimen calculations and I have had two meetings with you as well as some correspondence relating to technical details. My conclusions are as follows:

The structural scheme is basically sound and attainable provided the members are of the correct dimensions and reinforced adequately...

I indicated to you that I wished to do further calculations to establish the order of magnitude of the forces and to compare these forces with the material which has been provided to resist them. Here I have been hampered by the magnitude of the task in that it is impossible for me without many assistants working over a long period to investigate all parts of the structure under all loading conditions in the same way as you have done. This would be an enormous task and outside the terms of reference as I understand them. On the other hand I have had several meetings with you where you have shown me the calculations you are doing and some of the results. I, for my part, have taken one or two small sections of the job and compared the results you have shown me with an approximate analysis of my own. From this investigation I am satisfied that the theoretical studies which have been made are sufficiently comprehensive to provide a sufficiently detailed knowledge to construct the structure. The designs which I have made approximately, compare reasonably well with those carried out more rigorously by you and indicate that the magnitude of forces have been catered for... The erection procedure which has been devised is in my opinion sound.[62]

Mike Lewis passed Guyon's report onto Public Works in a confidential letter. On 14th November 1963 Zunz wrote to Lewis:

Monsieur Guyon 'phoned from Paris today to say that he was going to Australia in ten days' time – I think it is something to do with the Gladesville Bridge – and he wondered whether there was anything he could do on our behalf. I said 'no' but that it would be a good idea for him to see you and to be shown round the site... he now knows something about the job generally and it would be interesting for him to see (it). We don't think any more than necessary should be made out of the second opinion which he has given and I know that Ove feels very strongly about this so that it should be played down as much as possible. I would question therefore the wisdom of arranging a meeting with him and Johnson. At the other end of the scale he might be able to give us some useful advice on the site.[63]

Meanwhile the delicate and complicated task of planning the construction of the Opera House was continuing. The building would have to stand up to the highest wind gusts that could ever possibly occur in Sydney, not only when the building was completed but during construction. Arups had requested information on possible wind loadings to the shells and on the 20th September 1962 Malcolm Nicklin wrote to John Nutt in London with a summary of his findings. According to his enquiries with the Sydney Bureau of Meteorology winds that could be expected on the east coast of Australia did not vary to any great extent with latitude 'Therefore it is possible to transpose the maximum gust recorded off the Queensland coast (125 m.p.h.) to Sydney.' Sydney's main weather station was on Observatory Hill 500 yards from the Opera House at the south end of the Harbour Bridge so records taken at the station could be applied directly to the site.

> The highest gust recorded is 153 m.p.h. in 1876 which lasted $1\frac{1}{2}$ minutes. However, this was recorded on an old machine and has been corrected to 115 m.p.h. on modern equipment. The old machines however, tend to average and it is probable that the gust was much higher than the figure computed of 115 m.p.h.
>
> In 1940 a short gust (approx. 10 seconds) of 95 m.p.h. occurred. For longer duration winds, a velocity of 85 m.p.h. has been recorded for 12 minutes and 42 m.p.h. for 11 hours. Neither of the above occurred under tornado conditions.
>
> A tornado at Narrabeen, 16 miles north of the station was estimated at 300 m.p.h. one at Brighton, 8 miles south at 200 m.p.h. and one at Swan Hill in Victoria at 180 m.p.h.[64]

The tornado that hit Narrabeen had cut a swathe of destruction including stripping the trees from a hillside. But in tying down the design of the shells it was apparent that Arups could at last see some light at the end of the tunnel, Zunz writing to Gore on the same day 'We still have some formidable problems but I am sure we will solve them satisfactorily.'[65] Arups staying in touch all the time with Waagner-Biro to ensure they could shoe-horn their stage machinery into the space beneath the shells, Kelman writing to them on the 21st enclosing:

> ... duplicate copies of our drawings 1112/10-21B showing internal contours of shells 2 and 9 of the Major Hall. We confirm that this set of contours is not based on the final geometry, but that of shell 2 can be used to design the final stage tower without any risk of touching the ribs of the final shell, provided that an additional clearance varying from 0 to 12 inches from the neutral line to the extreme north end of the shell is allowed...
>
> We also confirm that the contours of shell 9 can be used for the final design of the proscenium wall, provided that an additional 6 inch clearance is allowed.[66]

The cranes were to be mounted on structural steel bridges supported on towers spanning over the existing substructure of the podium. For the structure to support the weight 'We will stiffen the side walls' wrote MacKenzie to Kelman 'probably by means of vertical steel sections fixed to the free edges.' And regarding loads of the towers to the concrete foundation piers of the podium MacKenzie continued:

> With all due respect, following all the sleepless nights we have spent after trying to justify increased pier loadings from 12 ton to 20 or 30 ton rock for you, it comes as rather a surprise when you query a mere 50 per cent overload on 3 piers!! Actually these are the least of our worries. The 165 tons results from an out of service condition in a 90 m.p.h. gale and consequently is only a temporary loading. The maximum sustained loading will be about 80 tons and usually is rather less than this.[67]

And all the while the design of the shells was still moving ahead:

> We discussed the construction of the side shells with Mr Utzon by telephone last Friday – confirmed John Nutt to Utzon's office – As we mentioned then, we can incorporate the stepped boundary plane and the continuous top surface in our analysis without great difficulty if the beam spacing is maintained at 7 ft 6 in...
>
> The voids would be formed by cutting the inner skin by small circle planes parallel to the meridian circle. This would give a rectangular shape of void on the inner skin and the end faces would be parallel, though they would not be radial to the side shell sphere.[68]

Utzon's office needed the internal shells' contours for their own work:

> ... Although we appreciate that it is extremely urgent for you to have these contours – wrote Joe Huang to Prip-Buus on 4th October – and that we have been trying our best to produce them, we regret that they will not be ready until at least the end of next week. That of shell 4 may be a little bit later.
>
> We hope that you realise the reason for our delay is due principally to the many tricky problems restricting our freedom to move the footpoints of the shells. However, after a great number of trial and error adjustment exercises, we think we have solved most of these problems, and once the final geometry is fixed, we see no reason why the internal contours of all the shells cannot be produced within a very short time.[69]

While the practical problem of building the Opera House could never be lost sight of:

> We are going through the dimensions and will, in fact, revise our drawings to agree with your dimensions unless we find these to be incorrect. – wrote

David Dowrick to Gore – Discrepancies appear to have been due to evening off to the nearest 1/8 in. We agree to your going ahead with the fabrication forms to your dimensions.[70]

While on 12th October Jack Zunz wrote a personal letter to Stan Haviland:

I should like to inform you about some developments which are presently taking place. Firstly, Jorn has no doubt told you that he proposes to come to Sydney early next year, together with some of his assistants, in order personally to supervise details and completion of the Opera House.

We have for some time intended to follow a similar course and have now decided to set up our office on the site at about the same time. Michael Lewis will be in charge of our office – he is an Associate Partner and has been in charge of our South African office. We will also send at least 4 of our team working on the project. They are among our leading lights and will form the nucleus of the office to assist in completing the design, the details, and the supervising of structural and civil engineering work. Furthermore, Bob Kelman, whose trip has been authorised by your Committee earlier this year, will arrive in Sydney early in December. He will now probably stay for 12 – 15 months and his knowledge of the project, after a continued association with it for 4 years, will be very valuable on the site.

We propose to continue our collaboration with Messrs MacDonald, Wagner and Priddle. We have appreciated their advice and assistance very much and they have looked after us very well indeed. They have expressed their willingness to continue working with us and agree heartily with our proposals for setting up our site office.[71]

And to dispel any lingering doubts that the Opera House shells would ever be built, at last, on the 18th of October, the government signed the Stage II contract with Hornibrooks. *The Sunday Telegraph* carried a picture of 69-year-old Sir Manuel Hornibrook captioned '… master builder with a tough background' with an article headlined 'HE'LL PUT THE ROOF ON OPERA HOUSE.'

A bareknuckle fight between a teenage carpenter and his boss' son led to the start of a huge Australian construction empire which came into the news in Sydney this week. The carpenter, a young fellow named Manuel Hornibrook, won that scrap in Brisbane 50 years ago, but decided to quit anyway, and go into business on his own.

Last week, without even bothering with the formality of calling tenders, the New South Wales Government awarded one of the many Hornibrook companies the £1.8 million contract for the unusual roof of the Sydney Opera House. Some people said Hornibrooks won this top-prestige job because their group was the only one in Australia equipped to handle such a difficult task. Sir Manuel Hornibrook, 69-year-old ruler of the empire, wasn't so blunt when I interviewed him in the boardroom of his Sydney office this week.

'It would sound egotistical to say we were the ONLY company who could do the job', Sir Manuel said. 'But off-hand, I can't think of anyone else.'

That statement pretty well sums up this master master-builder. He is NOT egotistical. But he's forthright, honest and proud...'I'm a carpenter by trade', he told me. 'But I've got a lot of horse-sense – and that's what counts.'

He's honest when he says he is 'not a good enough organiser' to be able to retire or when he discusses the financing of the Opera House job. 'Some people say our fee of £75,000 is too small, that we have cut our price and will lose money on it' he said. 'But I reckon we'll come out all right.'

He is proud when he discusses his humble beginnings and his immense achievements... Young Manuel chose 'the building game' for his career, and had himself apprenticed as a carpenter to a Brisbane building company – at 10 shillings a week. Drive and ambition made the boss' son jealous of the young carpenter and led to that bout of fisticuffs.

'We didn't mince words', Sir Manuel recalled, 'we just got stuck into it.' 'We both came out with a few wounds, and I decided it would be better if I left. I picked up two other men and a boy and started out on my own.'

At first the 19 year-old businessman concentrated on shop fittings and small building jobs. Then he built a few houses, then some municipal drainage works. 'Later we got on to bridges', Sir Manuel said. 'I always liked bridges.'...[72]

Under the contract, the government were to pay for the site office at Bennelong Point, the salaries of all Hornibrooks' construction and office staff and the entire cost of building expenses including all plant and materials for a fixed management fee of £75,000.[73] Hornibrooks had the option of purchasing plant at written down rates at the end of the contract. The expected time for completion of the Stage II contract was two years and three months (excluding tiling). 'In the world of big construction, Sir Manuel is known as a man who loves meeting challenges' had written the *Sun Herald.* 'Reckoned as something of a perfectionist, his careful approach to his building jobs has sometimes meant shaving his firm's profit. At least he has made sure of £75,000 this time.'[74]

The *Sun Herald* also caught up with Corbet Gore: ' "We don't under-estimate the many problems to be faced and overcome once the work has begun." he said. He regarded the construction of the Opera House roof as the biggest challenge in his life as an engineer, "It will either take a few years off or put a few years on my life," he laughed. "To me this is the most fascinating engineering job in the world today.'"[75]

Meanwhile Hornibrooks had sent their time and progress schedule through to Arups outlining their construction program on the shells. 'We have received your Stage II program now.' wrote Kelman to Gore.

> It is a wonderful piece of gamesmanship and must put you points ahead. At first we wondered whether it was the new internal shell profile or part of the stage tower on a triangulated system. Whatever it is – it is a masterpiece!
>
> Is there any chance of your issuing an explanatory manual together with it or even a sort of simplified edition for the benefit of consultants. Please do not think we are not grateful but we just cannot understand it. Malcolm says you think we are holding back on you. We assure you this is not so... [76]

'I am sorry that you cannot follow my time and progress schedule,' wrote Gore to Zunz:

> Perhaps the following description may assist. The schedule actually combines the ordinary bar graph with a critical path analysis thereby, we feel, getting the best of both worlds. Consequently, we have a time scale at the top horizontally across the page and the time of any one operation is the horizontal projection of the line representing the operation so that the angle at which any line is drawn is for convenience of layout only and the slope distance does not represent a time interval. The dotted vertical lines represent the same point in time and again are put in for layout convenience only...
>
> ... the actual function of design and fabrication have been for convenience separated on the chart. The small circles shown in the action lines on the graph represent points in time where a particular phase commences or finishes, the same as in the critical path analysis. I hope this clarifies it for you. If not, you could call in Stephen Potter as a Consultant or I'll make a special trip to London. [77]

Civil and Civic though were still in occupation at the site and showing no inclination to leave, and as Hornibrooks could not start work until they did so Gore added '... due to the alteration of work that can be done on the site prior to 1st January next, this program must suffer the fate of other programs and be re-done.' [78]

Even though Zunz and Kelman did not understand Gore's program Blanchard apparently did, for when Hornibrooks finally sent a revised edition in March the following year he wrote to Gore 'Thank you for the copies of your program which have proved most helpful.' [79]

As if there was not enough to hold up the job, Zunz found himself writing to a freight company on 24th October:

> As explained on the telephone this morning, the above import is purely a wooden model of the roof of the new Sydney Opera House sent to us from the Architect, Mr Jorn Utzon, in Copenhagen. It has been sent to aid in the preparation of detailed working drawings. It has no commercial value whatever, nothing is being paid for it and there are therefore no relevant invoices or documents. Accordingly we are returning the form in connection with duty payable and we should be extremely grateful if you could manage to clear this model through Customs as soon as possible.[80]

And as if he did not have enough to worry about keeping 45 engineers occupied on the structural design of the shells and the production of 1200 drawings that would be required for the job and the Arbitration hearing with Civil & Civic which was starting shortly, Zunz also worried about crane bridges.

The three giant tower cranes to be used on the Opera House site ran on rail tracks supported by crane bridges built on top of the podium. The bridge spans and supporting towers to be fabricated from steel were quite awesome structures in themselves. Hornibrooks worked with Ian MacKenzie for the general layout and design and the final details were carried out by an outside structural engineer, Mr Otten. Zunz was not keen on the design of the crane bridges, or the fact that the detailed analysis was carried out by Otten. In his opinion the crane bridges were too heavy and 'over-designed'. Zunz enquired of MacKenzie 'Why have the bearing points for the staunchions been located in this way? Could not the crane bridge spans have been made interchangeable? Would intermittent welds instead of continuous ones have saved costs? Should there be sand boxes in the rails? In fact Babcock & Wilcox the crane manufacturers will have to check the design of the towers and bridges.

> Quite frankly your criticism seems to me to be very wide of the mark, – wrote MacKenzie to Zunz on the 24th October – possibly, because you are unfamiliar with Australian practices...
>
> The general principles of the layout and the design were prepared by Bob Kynaston in conjunction with myself before Otten carried out the detailed analysis. I have every confidence in Otten – he was schooled at B.H.P. and afterwards worked with Dorman Long and in Arups while overseas on a post-graduate grant.
>
> While I do not know what you based your initial estimate of weight on I should be surprised if you allowed adequately for the support beams

and towers which have proved necessary in practice. Possible locations for these supports are very limited both because of the existing structure and by the necessity to complete the class C areas at the northern ends of the halls with a minimum of interference.

The crane bridge spans *are* interchangeable as far as possible and so in fact are the support towers.

I will not comment on your view that Babcock & Wilcox should check the track and supporting arrangements. However, could you please ensure that their comments, if any, are transmitted to Sydney as speedily as possible...

The question of intermittent verses continuous welds seems to be splitting straws... [81]

Gore also wrote to Zunz. The fact that the crane bridges were possibly over-designed was:

... a wise precaution for a structure which will be subject to considerable handling and to some extent mishandling on a construction site.

We have allowed for operating all three tracks simultaneously and this is necessary if No. 2 crane is to erect at the No. 1 shells concurrently with the No's. 1 and 3 cranes erecting at the No. 2 shells.

Deflections have been kept less than the minimum figure stipulated... We are quite happy for Babcock & Wilcox to inspect the design although quite frankly we cannot see much point in it. [82]

Zunz wrote back to MacKenzie with words to the effect of how dare you criticise my judgement, which spurred Corbet Gore to write to Jack Zunz:

I am writing this as a personal note as I do not wish it to be fed into the system. I have been somewhat disturbed at the correspondence concerning the tender on the crane bridges as I feel that this, coupled with the 12,000 miles separating us, is the type of incident which tends to drive a wedge between our two organisations and this concerns me at the beginning of a job which is going to require our complete co-operation if it is to be successfully carried out.

I have absolutely no desire to deny in any way the rights of Arups to review, criticise or check and we have been particularly careful to work in close co-operation with Ian MacKenzie and Malcolm Nicklin throughout the complete design of this structure. We had complete liaison with Ian on the location of the bearing points for the staunchions and I understood that he was in contact with Bob Kelman on this...

... we deliberately did not include sand boxes in the rails in with our structural details as these will be made of timber on the job...

This perhaps clears the details away but I am a little concerned with the criticism of the steel detailing...

Now I don't doubt that any Engineer on going through the detail drawings produced by another can, on the face of it, find minor details which he feels could be improved. This is doubtless true of your drawings as well as ours but I cannot help feeling that the detailed criticism from your office of these drawings was pretty minor in character and certainly not of such magnitude to justify the furore that has been caused. I think that my staff, when you consider that these drawings were produced at a time when we were restricted in our activity due to the late signing of the contract, did a very good job to get a complete design out to tender the day after the signing of the contract...

Well, I have now said my piece and can now forget the matter. Perhaps in the future, with a little closer liaison between us, such similar situations can be avoided. The presence of Bob Kelman should facilitate this... [83]

Which Zunz in his turn replied to:

Thank you very much for your note of the 16th. I am very pleased that you wrote to me about this matter. I think too much has been made of what is a relatively minor problem and I know that you agree. On the other hand it is as well that some of these views are aired at this early stage because there may be matters of principle and it is as well for us to understand one another.

I don't want to reiterate things which have been said many times before because you know them all. Your company's selection was the result of two requirements; firstly to have a contractor available as early as possible to assist in the formulation of a construction scheme with all its consequences, and secondly to have the best contractor in Australia. On both these counts our association to date has convinced us that the choice we have made, inevitably on recommendations without detailed knowledge, has been the right one. You know, in other words, that we are extremely delighted with the work you are doing and above all with your attitude towards the job...

I think that all the people concerned with the production of the drawings and details of the crane bridges did an extremely good job in the time available, in fact we were surprised by the rapidity. We specifically made our comments known as being cursory and we said we were sticking our necks out by making them relatively uninformed but we wanted to get them back to you as soon as possible. From then onwards I daresay people's feelings were hurt – unnecessarily so...

We will certainly not allow any wedges to be driven between our organisations – in fact we think you are wonderful, crane bridges and all. [84]

On the same day, Jack Zunz wrote another letter to Gore:

... The problems relating to the erection arch are, we hope, gradually resolving themselves. If they are not we're in trouble and I'll tell you why.

We have done most of the detailed calculations for the shell arches (the octopus ribs are not quite so advanced) of the Major Hall. To do these calculations we have had to assume a system of building. As such they have been prepared on the assumption that the erection arch scheme works and the stress distribution in the various components will be vastly different if another erection sequence were to be adopted.

In telling you this we don't wish in any way to bring pressure to bear on you in your final recommendation. If necessary alterations can be made and probably very quickly. On the other hand it would be very useful if we could reach finality on this score shortly so that as many of these major decisions are put behind us and our working drawings will be subjected only to unpremeditated amendments if you see what I mean.[85]

To drop the roof segments of the Opera House shells into place during construction, the traditional method would have been to build a scaffolding on top of the podium to provide a solid support. In practice this presented several difficulties, in fact supreme difficulties because of the geometry of the inside of the Opera House. The weights were high and the strength of the scaffolding would have been enormous. And the ability to adjust an ordinary bird cage scaffold system into position during rib erection raised many question marks. At the same time a web of scaffolding would preclude the use of the area beneath the shells for workshops, changing sheds or any other use and make it very difficult to survey rib erection when the inside of the shell was blocked with scaffold tube. Also scaffolding would have been very difficult to erect on the louvre shells to place the rib segments on the overlapping shell above. To say nothing of cost. To erect the Opera House shells using scaffolding including planking, ladders and platforms Mills Scaffolds priced the job at £146,500 and Cyclone Scaffolding at £304,350.[86]

To erect the shell segments, recalled Gore,

... on George Boulton's trip, it had been suggested that there would be an outside arch with the segments hanging from it – over the top of the building. And this had considerable difficulties, because each time you moved it, you had to take the whole thing down and weld up another piece of the right angle and put it in. And that seemed to me to be a rather slow and tedious process... [87]

So Gore thought, why not have an erection arch on the side, between the already constructed side shells and the rib under construction, to support each segment as it was dropped in. The idea tickled Ove Arup's fancy, and he got right behind Corbet Gore with his support, but some of his engineers were not so happy with the idea. The arch was a completely unstable structure with no visible means of support at all other than that it was guyed onto the already built section of the shell that was under construction. It had a ball joint on each leg at the bottom where it rested on the shell pedestal and a ball joint at the top which meant it could move in any plane at any time and swivel to adjust to the shape of the rib ahead of the one that was under construction. Telescopic sections were added to the arch to increase its length as the length of ribs increased as they advanced up the shell. 'People thought we were mad really.'[88]

Some of the Arup engineers were concerned about the amount the arch would flex, particularly on the longer ribs, causing them to corkscrew slightly out of their true position on a surface of a sphere. It was the control of this flexing that was the main source of discussion between Arups and Hornibrooks concerning the arch and typical of the correspondence that took place was a letter from C. Wymer of Arups to Bob Kynaston on 5th September:

… the radial loads applied to the steel arch are different from those I used in deflection calculations of the steel arch whilst you were here in London.

I have enclosed a summary of the problem, and some figures to indicate the magnitudes with which you will have to deal. In general, the radial forces are reduced but the Bending Moment diagram is such that bowstringing in some cases (eg. Rib 16 Shell 2 Major) will be difficult or impossible.

It may well be that you have taken account of the tangential component of the dead load, but judging from your figure of 27 tons maximum (presumably for Rib 16 Shell 2 Major) for the bowstringing force, you have based your calculations on the radial component only.[89]

But Gore was not going to be deflected so easily, replying on the 24th:

it would appear that these deflections are only obtained when we are erecting ribs containing more than 11 segments. Now we can reduce these by bowstringing the arch for these particular ribs. This would mean that by applying an initial bowstring force to each half of the arch, the positive deflections could be neutralised. Bowstring force would have to be released at approximately 9 segments so that it would not increase the negative deflections. In this way, the total differential deflection at a point three segments up would be in the order of $^3/_4$ inch but if bowstringing was not used the total differential deflection would be approximately $1^1/_2$ inch and it could well be that this is quite acceptable to you, in which case bowstringing would not be necessary.[90]

Hornibrooks subsequently wrote a computer program: '… which, amongst other things, will give us accurate reactions at the crown and at the spring of the erection arch for all ribs under all loading conditions. We anticipate this information should be available shortly.'[91]

With the ability to anticipate deflections of the arch under load, the way was clear for its fabrication to go ahead. An eight-foot high working model was first made to test the theory with a model of an Opera House shell before the full size erection arch was manufactured. In fact four full-size arches were manufactured, two for use in the Major Hall and two in the Minor, fabricated from TIA grade high tensile steel rolled in the U.S.A. and built at Thirlwell & McKenzie Engineering Port Kembla. The cost of all four arches came to a total of approximately £90,000. Hydraulic jacking points were built into the arch to allow for adjustments to rib segments when the arch deflected.

Later, when erection of rib segments was well under way with the arch in use, an enquiry to John Blanchard from Stephen Harris of Ove Arups Sydney[92] on arch deflections received a reply which started:

> The medieval schoolmen spent years disputing how many angels could stand on a pin. A similar dispute raged in the early years of Stage 2 as to what contribution the strain energy of the diagonal bracing made to the deflection of the steel arch…
>
> You will note that I have omitted the remark made on previous calculation sheets that the deflection at the top of the segment under erection is adjusted to zero. This was a slip, presumably it is governed by the deflection and rotation of the top of the segment before.[93]

Despite all the difficulties, the erection arch worked well in practice and the erection tolerance of $\pm\frac{1}{2}$ inch at the top of the ribs was generally achieved.[94]

In the latter half of 1962 there had been an immense volume of correspondence between Corbet Gore and Arups London office to tie the design of the shells in with the erection procedure. There were still so many details to button down that Gore visited London again from the 10th to 17th December for an intense program of meetings, working most days from 9 in the morning till 7 in the evening, including Sunday, with Saturday morning designated a 'rest period.' A whole host of subjects was discussed, from deflections of the erection arch and details of the side and main shells, to matters concerning the cranes and tiling and strengthening of the foundations. Gore left in time to be home in Australia for Christmas with his family just before London was paralysed by its heaviest snowfall since 1881. Before he left, he was asked to the Arup Christmas party attended by over 700 people at the Napoleon Suite of the Café Royal in London, and was treated along with the rest of the congregation to a speech from Ove Arup:

> To-day I am faced with the usual Christmas Party problem: Can I be serious, or shall I just try to be funny? My inclination is towards the former – very likely it is only an attempt at rationalising my inadequacy as a purveyor of amusing or witty nonsense – but in a way, as I am getting older and see this firm of mine grow into a many-headed monster, I feel a certain urge to talk to the monster and remind it of what it was created for and how it ought to behave in future – in short – the sort of moral uplift which parents and old people are fond of inflicting on the young, and which possibly benefits no one…
>
> … Loyalty is of course a great thing – teamwork is necessary, team-spirit even, but not group-think, not Big Brothership. We must not strive to produce or take on yes-men. Let us remain a collection of oddities, if you like. The loyalty and team-spirit which is a condition for happy and efficient collaboration must be given freely. Loyalty to a group is only good if it transcends the group, if it is loyal to something greater, to certain principles and attitudes, if it is based on a common endeavour, rather than self-righteousness or smugness. My country – right or wrong – is not the right slogan.
>
> … I've nearly finished now – I will only mention that we have tonight broken a rule which we have stuck to all along, that of not inviting any guests to the party other than the wives, sweethearts, husbands and boyfriends of the staff.
>
> The reason for this rule is obvious: on these occasions we want the staff and partners to mix and get to know each other as much as possible, and if the partners had obligations to outside guests, this would be made still more difficult.
>
> However, tonight we have as our first and only guest Mr Gore from Hornibrooks of Australia, the contractors for the Sydney superstructure. But Mr Gore is actually a very important member of the team working on Sydney, so it is natural that he should be invited. And anyhow, it is nice to break the rules sometimes.[95]

Also at the party was Mike Lewis, who had recently arrived in London from Arup's office in South Africa. Lewis was good friends with Jack Zunz, who he had met when they had taken a BSc in engineering at Witwatersrand University in South Africa, and he had stopped in London to get a grounding on the Opera House job before travelling out to Australia to establish Arup's office in Sydney and look after the Opera House site. Lewis had established Arup's South African office with Jack Zunz, but was unhappy with the political situation in the country and once the office was thriving reasonably well started to get restless and was not willing to stay on indefinitely.

> And then this job came up which had been, sort of, bedevilling the whole of our office, and I was asked if I would be willing to go to Sydney to look after that end of the work... And it struck me as a very interesting possibility. I had a look on the map to see where Australia was, I have to admit that, and I certainly didn't envisage a city like Sydney, but I knew enough about the job to know that it was... one of the most challenging one could hope for...
>
> (after arriving in London) the work here, the three months that I had here, to get to know the Opera House, was also quite telling in a way. Because I came from an office which was small – we had a staff of about thirty in Johannesburg. They had a staff of something like fifty or sixty working on the Opera House, and I said, there is no job in the world that justifies that number of people, it's just these lazy Poms. They can't do it properly, and all that sort of thinking. By the time I'd left here, I thought we didn't have enough staff to do it... so, it was quite a conversion course that I had to undertake to get to know the job. And we were by no means through with the design of this project...[96]

Every architectural detail of the inside and the outside of the shells would have to be agreed with Utzon. On 24th November Zunz had visited Hellebaek with Mike Lewis to see Utzon to go over a score or more items, from the 'Tile lid detail at (the) open end of (the) shells' and the 'Ridge detail at (the) junction of (the) main and side shells' to '... a detail of the stair flights which are converted to ramps at the springing points of shells 10, Major and Minor Hall.'[97]

Some questions on details had been tied down during Arups meetings in December with Corbet Gore: '... At top of fourth segment Utzon agreed to carrying water out by benching in each rib rather than taking it down 3 inch pipes to just above pedestal... (and) Utzon agreed to providing 2 feet 6 inch diameter permanent access man-hole in soffit of ridge member at Rib 1 for each shell (for access to the ridge at the top of the shells)... (Also) Mr Utzon does not wish anchorages for the normal stressing to be visible at the open ends of the Main and Louvre shells unless this is unavoidable. If they must be visible they should be recessed on the side face of the rib away from the diaphragms.' But other matters were raised '... Hornibrooks to confirm loads from erection arch on to penultimate ridge-piece... Arups to allow and detail for this connection. Ridge pieces with cylindrical soffit and of constant depth. Joints to be radial or great circle depending on Utzon's requirements... Tiling on Shell 1C to be discussed (with Utzon). Arups have prepared sketch for discussion...'.[98]

But Utzon was in the process of closing his office down to move to Australia. 'Utzon wasn't very good at communicating by letter', recalled Zunz, 'and I was extremely concerned that we weren't getting decisions out of him that concerned the roof structure.' Zunz had dozens and dozens of people working on the Opera House shells in Arup's London office, and Utzon's office had closed down. It was during a crucial part of the design and 'I had one or two fairly sharp exchanges with Utzon because I just felt we weren't getting the right kind of leadership on that front. I didn't want him to show us how to design the structure, but I did need him to resolve all the matters concerning the tiles and the panels of the tiles, because that in the end determined the joints in the shells and the structure where they occurred. In the end I managed to persuade Utzon to agree to come via London on his way to Australia.'[99] Utzon had a connecting flight to catch so Arups booked a room in a hotel at London Airport for a meeting. Zunz took with him a list of handwritten notes of 'Matters Affecting Utzon' covering 63 items requiring Utzon's attention on two lists A1 to 36 and B1 to 27. Also attending the meeting was Mike Lewis, Joe Huang and Ove Arup. The meeting took place on Boxing Day, when the weather was still freezing after the cold snap that had set in just before Christmas and 'Ove was quite ill at the time. The room we had was so cold that Ove put on a hot bath and he sat with his feet in it to keep them warm. He wasn't well at all.'[100] And they set to work to button down the matters requiring immediate attention for the design of the shells. They included questions:

A.7.   Inclination of shell 1 – new position.
A.12.   Ridge detail, tiles?
A.17.   Jointing in ridge member either radial or parallel between ribs (when seen from below).
A.22.   Backstage wall – pattern of formwork and quality.
A.29.   Depth of joint in tile surface.
A.35.   Details at bottom edge of tile lids.

And Zunz had jotted down some answers in the margin – 'Edge detail of louvre shells as for main shells' and depth of joint in tile surface '¼ inch deep not less', with a list of which Arup engineers were to attend to which item, David Dowrick – pre-stressing main shells, John Nutt – pre-stressing side shells, Geometry – Joe Huang, Analysis – Peter Rice and Tile Lids – Ted Kowalski.[101]

Then Utzon caught the plane out of London for an extended journey to Australia. He eventually arrived in March when Jack Zunz was in Sydney for the Arbitration hearing. When Utzon was on the flight from Tahiti to Sydney a radio message was received on the flight deck that Utzon had been invited for lunch with the Queen, so he was whisked straight from the airport to lunch on Sydney Harbour with Her Majesty on board the *Britannia*.

After the Boxing Day meeting Jack Zunz and his family, along with the Lewis', went together to Austria for a week's holiday. Zunz took the opportunity to have a day in Vienna with Waagner-Biro. Then Mike Lewis left for Australia, stopping in Tel Aviv where he stepped in front of a bus and was knocked down, breaking one leg very badly and sustaining other injuries. He was still in hospital there, in plaster from the chest down, when Jenkins, Rigby, Ove Arup and Jack Zunz travelled out in March for the Arbitration hearing, and they stopped in Tel Aviv to visit him.

When Jack Zunz returned to London from his skiing trip in Austria in January, there was a letter waiting for him from Utzon from the Windjammer Inn, Miami with a sketch at the top of Utzon lying down with his feet sticking out of the bottom of the bed. Utzon wanted to change the details of the ridge and the side shells, and explained that he was in bed as 'the flu overlapped me again.' The letter closed 'Thank you for good meeting, warmest greeting to Ove... I hope he didn't suffer from the meeting.'[102] Utzon had wanted to increase the height of the openings in the side shell for the glass walls. When the letter arrived Zunz had been in Austria '... but Ove phoned me having had a meeting with all the people in the office.' Zunz wrote to Utzon, 'We all agreed that your proposals for shells 5 and 6 might help the situation. On the other hand the delay would be serious and, as agreed, we are now continuing with the original design.'[103] But on opening the letter from the Windjammer Inn, Ove had been quite prepared to make the change and had contacted the Committee, so that he found himself writing a letter of apology to Harry Ashworth on 22nd January:

> I gather from Nicklin that you and the Committee have been somewhat upset by my telephone conversation about the alteration which Jorn wanted to make to shells 5 and 6, and that you did not gather from my account what the alteration was about. I am very sorry that this should have happened, especially as there was no need for it because Jorn has now sent us a telegram to the effect that he does not want the alteration made after all, and I am sure he will be very sorry that I have worried you about the whole question.
>
> ... it was only a fairly minor alteration to the side shells which would I think have been an improvement, but which would mean the re-design of the whole of the 'bridge' consisting of four shells in this area which form the structure supporting the two main shells 1 and 2, and which would be the first part of the superstructure to be constructed. In view of the upheaval which the alteration would have caused I think that Jorn's decision not to go on with it is justified, and there is no more to be said about it.[104]

A second letter arrived from Miami in which Utzon asked if the supporting column of the octopus arch could be moved to stand in the stage tower. 'I found on my return that the foundation drawing for this new column has already been issued to site...' wrote Zunz to Utzon, 'Ian MacKenzie is here however and he feels that the difficulties of placing additional piers if the column is moved would be insurmountable and we have therefore decided to let it stand'.[105]

By this time Bob Kelman had been in Australia for a few weeks after travelling out by liner. On the 18th December he gave a progress report to a meeting of the Executive Committee on the work completed for Stage II:

> Due to the way in which each section of the design of this structure is dependent on all the others, it is difficult to say exactly what stage we have reached at a particular time. In attempting to give the Committee some idea of what has been happening in London it will probably be best to give a brief outline of the manner in which the whole problem has been tackled.
>
> Arups now have about 45 people employed on the job, divided up into 6 or 7 teams, each concentrating on a particular aspect of the design and each dependent on information being produced by another group.
>
> The design has been considered in three principal sections – main shells, side shells and the supporting structures. To each of these, three phases of design exist.

The first is the basic structural theory. The second is the production of drawings showing what is required – the outline drawings – and the final phase is the working out of all details.

At present most of the basic structural design is completed for both main shells and side shells. This has been a long, laborious task involving extensive use of computers for calculations of both stresses and shapes. The three dimensioned curved shape is not easy to define on drawings, but the bulk of this work is done. The remaining calculations are mostly related to problems of erection and stressing.

The second phase, involving the production of working drawings is well under way. The main shell ribs are done and the more involved abutments, ridge beams and side shell arches are in hand.[106]

These drawings were starting to come through to Sydney, John Nutt writing to Gore on the 18th February:

We are sending by separate cover the precast formwork details for the Major and Minor Halls shells 5 and 6. Checking of these dimensions is a long and involved job and we have been as thorough as possible in doing this. However, there is always the possibility that errors in data input to the computer might escape all our normal ways of checking. We are doing all we can to eliminate this source but a check along these lines will not be available for some time. However we are not pessimistic about this and are quite confident that all will be O.K.[107]

While the job of looking into every variable that could crop up during construction continued. John Blanchard sent Corbet Gore a graph prepared with the advice of his heating engineers to give 'some idea of the variation of temperature in the main shell ribs during construction when the tile lids are not in position... (and showing) how the rib would cool off... (if) the air temperature were to drop by 20°F either suddenly or uniformly for 2 hours.' And advised in the same letter that 'Unfortunately the top three ribs of shell A2 are not man enough to carry a 90 m.p.h. wind during the construction stage... These ribs will therefore need to be propped (and possibly tied) off shell 9 during construction. We are still working on the simplest way of doing this.'[108]

On 7th March Yuzi Mikami at Arups London office wrote to Jack Zunz in Sydney:

We have found that there has been a mistake in the process of computation on Minor Hall side shells 5 and 6. The lowest part of the shells adjacent to arch 5-6 was made approximately 13 inches higher than that of Major Hall's, in other words each arch leg is more than 2 feet longer than Major Hall's along its inclined surface. I enclose a sketch showing this.

I can have no doubt that this is architecturally very serious, since all the other dimensions in Minor Hall shell outline are smaller or at least the same compared with Major Hall, and it will be clearly seen from Central Passage + 42 level especially when standard height glass boxes are built underneath the shells.

... John Nutt's group has already carried out a number of drawings and schedules... using the computed result. The situation is somehow similar to that of when the alteration to Major Hall shells 5 and 6 was suggested.

There would be three possibilities on this:-

1. To carry on as it is; this could be done only with the full consent of Jorn Utzon himself.
2. A practical minor change (which was to widen the tile lids and make the box beam and cantilever internally wider). This can be done without losing any time.
3. To re-compute the whole of the shells and re-do the drawings and schedules. This is no doubt the best architecturally but would delay our issue of information to the site three to four weeks according to the estimate of the people concerned.

Please cable your decision immediately as the work is still going ahead.[109]

Zunz cabled back on 14th March:

RE MINOR HALL ARCH 5-6 PRESENT POSITION NOT ACCEPTABLE STOP REGRET BUT MUST REDRAW TO SAME MINIMUM CLEARANCE AS MAJOR HALL STOP HORNIBROOKS ARE AGREED TO DELAY STOP UTZON AGREES...[110]

On the 14th Gore got back to Blanchard regarding the question of high winds on the construction of shell A2:

Paragraph 2 frightens me somewhat and we would like details of just what sort of propping is necessary as soon as possible. It is not going to be an easy job, so please give us your full information on it at your earliest, particularly the extent of loads to be carried...

(The letter continued) For your information, we have erected three segments on a trial scaffold, glued them together and pulled the stressing wires through. This was not a complete test in that, being the first one up, it went somewhat in fits and starts. However, the indications are promising and we hope by next week to be able to assure you that lifting gear, epoxy and flying wedge strand systems are all working well.[111]

The day before, Zunz had written to London:

... I wish you could all see the trial segments, which Hornibrooks have made. They are erecting a few and to see the emergence of something real after all the months of sweat is a great thrill, and it is really a pity that you cannot be here to see it. We all think Hornibrooks have done a good job so far.[112]

It had taken 18 months from the first mention of concrete rib segments in 1961 to the stage when it was possible to make an erection of trial segments. The use of epoxy (a special formulation similar to Araldite) for jointing between segments was its first application in any building project, though epoxy had been used in the United States to bond metal plates to concrete railway sleepers and to glue concrete curbs to road surfaces. Corbet Gore wrote that the

> Structural use of epoxy was born of the Architect's requirements that the joints between the precast segments should be as small as possible so as not to be visually prominent. The constructional advantage lay in the fact that an orthodox concrete in situ joint between segments would need a day's curing before stressing and so only one segment per day could have been erected.
>
> On their way to London in March 1962, (Corbet Gore and Bob Kynaston) called at San Francisco to discuss the jointing principle with Professor T.Y.Lin at the University of California, Berkeley. Professor Lin's recommendation was to stress the bare concrete segments together without a jointing compound. It was felt, however, that such a technique would inevitably cause the concrete to chip which would be architecturally unsatisfactory. Hornibrook located and had discussions with a Californian company specialising in epoxy resin and its use in construction, and the information so obtained was taken to London.[113]

Allowance was made for the strength of epoxy in design in its use as a joint filler and stress distributor.[114] Hornibrooks were reluctant to use this new material about which so little was known in a building which was planned to last hundreds of years, and they embarked with Arups on an extended testing program. Subsequently, quite by chance, Arups discovered that epoxy jointing of pre-cast concrete units was being made at that time on a road bridge in France at Choisy le Roi and they visited the builders, Entreprises Campenon-Bernard, in Paris to learn what they could from them of their own application of the technique. Shear tests on thin epoxy resin joints were carried out at the Cement and Concrete Association in England by crushing pre-cast concrete cubes joined with epoxy resin. In 1963 Hornibrooks arranged for a series of trials at the University of NSW to find the best techniques of surface preparation of the concrete and resin application. The treatment decided on, which became an industry standard, was to grind the matching surfaces of rib segment ends just enough to expose the aggregate not more than seven days before jointing. To clean the surfaces before the epoxy resin was applied they were wiped with dewatered absolute alcohol. The most efficient way of applying the glue which took place on the shell itself just before the segments were stressed together, was to spread it on the lower face with a spatula or grooved scraper and on the upper face using a paint roller. Two different formulas of epoxy were made, one for summer and one for winter use as the epoxy thickened in cooler temperatures. Polythene was taped round the edge of the segment to prevent the glue running onto the finished concrete surface when the pre-stress was applied. Tests had also established that the strength of the joint was substantially increased when this pre-stress was applied during setting.

The erection sequence for the segments of the ribs could have gone ahead whether epoxy was used for the joints or not, but it would not have been possible to erect the ribs without the ingenious temporary stressing procedure evolved by Hornibrooks with the assistance of Arups. Gore saw as the most awesome task that faced him in the construction of the Opera House shells the safe erection of a pair of ribs before they could be permanently stressed along their length, across the crown and to the existing structure. To hold the rib segments in place was like working with beads on a string or a finger with many joints, but in this case the beads weighed ten tons each – which amounted to 120 tons for the 12 segments on the longer ribs – and they soared to a height of over 150 feet above the podium. Gore described the procedure:

For this purpose a completely new technique of prestressing was initiated and developed by Hornibrook. The purpose of the erection stressing was twofold. Firstly, it served to pull the epoxy glued joints together for greater adhesion and secondly it added to the support and strength of the rib during erection and jacking operations. There were nine erection strands all told in each rib and they extended from midway up segment 1 through to the top cut-off segment. By destressing three strands at a time and passing them through the last segment erected and restressing them, at least six strands could be kept stressed all the time. As new segments were erected, the erection stressing proceeded by this leapfrog action. Three erection strands were located on each of the three corners of the segment cross section. A system of 'flying wedges', which were fixed to the head of the strand, was developed and anchorages made and cast in to the top of each segment. The flying wedge was dimensioned to pass through the anchorage as the released strand was pushed up through the last erected segment. Once through, 'collets' with an external taper to fit the segment anchorage and an internal taper to fit the flying wedge were slipped into the anchorage. The strand was then pulled back on the collets and stressed against them. Later, when the following segment had been placed, the strand was released and pushed up ready for a repetition of the operation. This leapfrog stressing operation was an integral part of the erection of each segment. An overall stress of about 200 psi was obtained by this temporary stressing operation which gave sufficient rigidity to the erecting rib and ensured effective pressure across the setting epoxy joint, and only in a few instances did the wedges jam. In all of these instances the strands were eventually freed.[115]

The development of the temporary stressing procedure alone had taken months and sometimes 'was discussed and planned for days on end'[116] in Arups London office (Fig.64) During the erection of the prototype ribs:

> Many lessons were learnt which proved invaluable when production commenced on site.
>
> The problems which were investigated at that time and successfully overcome were bond breaks between segments, (during casting), locating spigots for positioning and aligning adjacent segments, finish of forms, manufacture of forms, methods of introducing voids in segments, methods of forming bolt holes in segment flanges, methods of forming ducts for cables, concrete quality, and steel placing and disposition.[117]

The use of epoxy for the rib joints in the Enfield tests 'worked so efficiently', found Gore, 'that we have had trouble in wrenching the segments apart after we have finished with them. The concrete itself parted before the glue.' When work got underway on site unions negotiated an extra 10d. an hour payment for carpenters and labourers working with epoxy resin on the ribs.[118]

The day-to-day task of communicating between Arups London and Arups Sydney, between Arups and Gore and between all concerned and Utzon kept the momentum going to get construction of the Opera House shells underway. 'I must chide you gently for referring in your cable to "arch ribs"', wrote John Blanchard to Bob Kelman on site on 19th March, 'we don't have them, only arches and ribs. This is why I must produce a dictionary of nomenclature this week.'[119]

'What is the maximum load Waagner-Biro will be permitted to suspend from the ridge beam of a completed shell?' asked Corbet Gore of Kelman, and 'we are more than somewhat curious about the weight of the first precast segment of Arch Ribs 8-10 Major Hall and the distance of its centre of gravity from the hall axis. This appears to be the worst case for our cranes and needs looking into – could you please find this one out soon.'[120]

John Nutt announced he would be on his way 'I shall be leaving England on April 23rd for Sydney by the S.S. *Northern Star* of the Shaw Savill Line and due to arrive in Sydney on May 29th. I hope I shall be uncontactable during that period. All cables, telegrams, telephone calls and personal visits will be unanswered.'[121]

The first structures for the shells to be built above the podium would be the stage walls for the Major and Minor Halls:

> This is to advise you that we have checked the strength of the Major Hall stage wall under wind forces and consider it to be safe, in a free-standing condition, for winds up to 85 m.p.h. – wrote Gore to Arups London.
>
> Only two gusts greater than this figure have been recorded at the Sydney Meteorology Station – one of 93 m.p.h. from WNW in January 1958, and another of 95 m.p.h. from the W in October 1940.
>
> Unless you require otherwise, we will not tie this wall back during construction. Would you please confirm.[122]

'We have a letter from Hornibrooks... which questions whether the side shell slabs could be cylindrical', wrote Zunz to Kelman, 'as far as I can recall we tentatively agreed that it would be O.K. but Buus was going to check with Utzon. I would be inclined to be fairly firm on this one because with the surface being broken up by the precast beams we see no reason why these should not be cylindrical. We can understand the insistence on having the tile lids spherical.'[123] Yes, Utzon got back, the side shell slabs could be cylindrical.

Gore had felt:

> ... since leaving London that one loses touch with the overall trends of thinking on the design of the project and, consequently, it would be an advantage if somebody could sit down and keep us up to date on these trends.
>
> However, as a practical solution to the transmission of information, I would like to suggest as follows:
> 1. Any question or statements which requires answer or immediate action at the other end should be separated in the letter to a paragraph

by itself. It thus stands out in the text and is easy to allocate to one person to accept responsibility for the necessary action.

2. Could you indicate against this segregated question or statement the priority you require for the action. I would suggest that we might give –

Priority 1 as meaning a cable reply or a letter by return mail.

Priority 2 as meaning a reply within a week.

Priority 3 as meaning a reply in due course but no immediate urgency.[124]

Blanchard got back about propping the stage wall against wind, writing to Kelman:

… I have checked the case when the wind is blowing from the south… with a wind speed of 85 m.p.h. i.e.a pressure of 34lbs/sq ft I calculate that the steel stress in the starters is about 33,000 lb/sq in. We regard this as satisfactory, especially as high winds from this quarter are unlikely, so… would you confirm to Hornibrooks that there is no need to tie this wall back during construction.[125]

Rib segment weights were calculated with a standard concrete density of 155 pounds per cubic foot. 'Local aggregates can give concretes up to 160 feet – sometimes in excess of this', wrote Kelman to Zunz, 'also the excessive compaction in the segment will tend to push the densities up.' The weight of the segments was critical for crane lifting capacity and the design weight of the structure. Should we look at a 'less economical aggregate to get the density below 155 pounds?'[126] asked Kelman. David Dowrick wrote back with a list of segment weights outlining that segments could weigh up to 11 tons 'accurate to within $\frac{1}{2}$ ton'[127] which was already outside the anticipated crane-lifting capacity of ten tons.

Mick Lewis had arrived in Australia on crutches. He made a slow recovery from his accident but was left with a permanent limp. He put a brave face on it though, writing to a lecturer at Witwatersrand University on 8th May, 'It has taken me about 80 days to go round the world only because I was unfortunate enough to have an argument with a bus in Tel Aviv.'[128] Before the accident, Roger Rigby had written to Jack Zunz at his hotel in Seefeld Austria asking him to warn Mick to have his story ready when he reached Sydney.

As you know, the first question on arrival will be 'What do you think of Australia.' The answer to that one will make or mar Mick's whole sojourn in Australia.

During the war an American Admiral on his first visit to India arrived in Bombay and was asked, 'Well Admiral, how did you find India?' and he said, 'I got off the ship and there she was.' This would not be enough.

During the Ottawa conference also in the war Churchill decided to visit Niagara Falls. They asked him what he thought of them. He had to remind the press that he had first seen them in 1906 before most of those present had been born but added 'The principle appears to be the same, the water falls downwards.'[129]

No construction had taken place at the Opera House site since Civil & Civic had left and Lewis' impression was, 'When I arrived here it was rather marvellous, there was just a sort of open podium like a Greek amphitheatre. There was nothing happening on the surface it was just this podium and the water.'[130]

Later, on the Opera House site, 'Leaning against his office window, which looks out across the full majesty of Sydney Harbour, almost at water-level', Lewis told the *Sun's* reporter 'we are building a dream here. Our job is to make that dream – the roof – come true.'[131]

Lewis bought a plot of land on Middle Cove overlooking the Harbour and Utzon offered to design a house for him, though not long after he wrote in a memo to Poul Ahm 'I am not at all sure whether I should be sad or happy, but Jorn is far too pre-occupied with the Opera House to design my house – he is even having difficulty in producing the drawings for his own.'[132]

John Nutt arrived in Australia at the end of May and the papers interviewed him as soon as he arrived. 'This design has no precedent...', Nutt told the *Daily Telegraph,* 'I can see the building giving the Harbour a feeling of unity because the roof arch describes the same curve as the Harbour Bridge. This makes the roof both aesthetically and structurally exciting – possibly one of the most interesting building projects ever... All the major problems of the roof's construction have been solved, but there is still a lot of routine work.'[133] The *Sun* carried a picture of John Nutt and Corbet Gore with the model of the erection arch. Zunz wrote to Nutt from London, 'I gather that you are settling down nicely but I must say that the photographs in the newspapers somewhat flattered you!'[134]

John Nutt was an Australian engineer who had led the design team on the side shells in London. He had been educated at Queensland University, and in 1956 at age 21, appointed to an Assistant Lectureship at the University of Manchester, England. For five years he carried out research on stresses and forces in building structures, receiving a doctorate in the process and taking part in the early use of the electronic computer on the analysis of structures. In the early fifties, the Manchester firm of Ferranti Ltd marketed the first commercial computer in the world which had been designed in the Electrical Engineering Department of the University and the university staff had access to a development model of what became the Sirius computer on which the analysis of the Opera House roof was carried out. On joining Arups in 1960, he worked on many complex technical projects including the definition of the wind forces for the tallest buildings at the time in Europe which were at the Barbican in London, and the transmission of noise and vibration generated by the underground railway and isolation of the acoustics of the Barbican Concert Hall and the Guildhall School of Music. Still only 28, when the new team for the Opera House roof was assembled under Jack Zunz in 1962, he was an early member.

The cross-section of each rib varied smoothly from a solid 'T' at the pedestal to a hollow open 'Y' at the top. Although the ribs were of different lengths they all had the same cross-sections at the same distance from the pedestal,[135] so it was possible to pre-fabricate them. Every rib had at least 3 segments, and there were 224 ribs, so there were 224 of rib segments 1, 2 and 3. Then there were 190 of rib segment 4, 170 of rib segment 5 – and so on to rib segment 12, only two of which were required for the pair of longest ribs on the tallest shell of the Major Hall. At the point where the ribs cut off at the ridge plane a special short segment was required, each pair cast to a critical length, and there were 224 of these.

Hornibrooks produced a table of segment quantities listing every rib segment from 1 to 12 plus top segments which came to a grand total of 1,592 and asked Arups 'would you kindly confirm the following schedule is correct.'[136] This was for the Major and Minor Halls only and did not include the restaurant or side shells. Besides over 1100 working drawings issued to site, Arups wrote 3,000 schedules, including lists of reinforcement details and instructions on stressing operations.

On 20th May Corbet Gore wrote to Arups:

> With reference to the Manual of Procedure, Volume 2, page 24, Note A, the columns have to be connected to Arch 6 – 2 after the first stage of stressing.

> Can this be delayed until the arch ribs are permanently stressed and rib 1 of shell 2 is also erected and permanently stressed? If so, at what age must the concrete be before rib 2 rib 3 etc. are erected?[137]

The Manual of Procedure was 'a marvellous document relating to nomenclature and drawing systems generally'[138] prepared by John Blanchard. The Opera House job had generated its own particular vocabulary and one of the functions of the manual was to ensure for example that a crown piece could not be confused with a ridge beam or a top segment, everyone was clear on what a louvre segment was, a side shell box beam could not be mistaken for a side shell arch segment and outlined that a pre-cast diaphragm was 'idiomatically a pre-pre-cast diaphragm.' Containing 'a comprehensive explanation of the nomenclature to be used, the geometry, the general system of drawing numbering and resumé of the information which will be prepared',[139] 10 copies were sent to Hornibrooks, they were in general distribution in Arups and they were also sent to Utzon, the Clerk of Works, the Quantity Surveyors, Committee and anyone else that it was felt ought to have one. It would also come in useful 'providing a rapid briefing for newcomers to the job, and for explaining the principles to strangers.'[140] The 'Manual of Procedure Volume II' was also produced which covered the erection sequence and special precautions that were necessary during the sequence of the erection of the main and side shells. John Nutt wrote to Blanchard from Sydney on receiving his copy:

> I have been reading your manual on how to build an Opera House in two (Vol. 1 and 2) easy lessons. It makes wonderful reading. For the record, on page A4 (Vol.1) paragraph A9 'The side shell slabs are pre-cast to a cylindrical surface to 245 feet – $11\frac{1}{2}$ inches with straight tapered sides', and the next sentence is unnecessary. Also, on page B5 (Vol.1) paragraph B7, the "ABP" is parallel to and at a distance of half the width of rib O at the vertex, from the centroidal plane of rib O"; not as shown. Diagram should be amended accordingly... [141]

Corbet Gore too wrote to Arups London after he had received and studied his two volumes of the 'Manual of Procedure', and asked, 'A general comment is that can we assume that the procedure laid down involves all the operations necessary but not necessarily in chronological order?' Then he raised over 30 points of detail including:

F28 – Remarks
Side shell scaffold takes part only of the radial component. During

erection of segments, there is a tension force on the tie due to the dead weight of the segments.

Should not some cables be stressed either before or during erection and others stressed during the stressing operation in the arch rib?...[142]

S2 a) – Tolerance for length is O.K.

Tolerance for thickness of +1/8 inch –0 could not be guaranteed without wall ties, particularly as internal forms are chords between diaphragms and the Architect does not desire to have ties on to the finished face of the forms. The same objection would be to a tolerance of +1/8 inch in other cross sectional dimensions.

We consider that $+\frac{1}{4}$ inch should be obtainable in these ribs though, naturally, we will endeavour to obtain the tighter tolerance...

Referring to Note c) (iii), this tolerance cannot be guaranteed. The 3 inch joint is put there so that discrepancy may be taken up and, whereas we have done our best to meet all other tolerances during casting and erection, we have no control over the accumulative tolerance in the 3 inch joint...[143]

To incorporate the changes and updates John Blanchard brought out a 'New Edition' including a revised appendix showing 'the restrictions which apply to the timing and order of erection.' The manual opened:

The purpose of all drawings made in this office is to convey information to the Contractor to enable him to construct the Opera House!

Since we are only part of the overall design team, however, we have to liaise very closely with the Architect, who must approve in principle everything that we do...

This means that before final working drawings can be issued, many sketches and scheme drawings must be produced to convey our ideas and suggestions to all who may be interested.

As this preliminary information is approved, final working drawings are prepared, but it often happens that they cannot be issued to site as final 'WORKING DRAWINGS' because parts of the drawing may not have been given final approval outside this office, or maybe we ourselves are not able to give final approval. In cases of this nature, the drawings are issued as 'PRELIMINARY'...

General information included: (For typical shell numbers see Fig.26).

A2) The main part of Stage 2 contract comprises the roofs of the Major Hall (A), the Minor Hall (B), and the Restaurant (C). The letters A, B or C are prefixed to drawing numbers or code numbers of structural elements to indicate the appropriate hall. The Minor Hall is roughly a replica of the Major Hall at approximately 0.78 of the scale but a precise geometric similarity between the two halls does not exist...

A3) Each of the Major and Minor Halls has four MAIN SHELLS numbered 1, 2, 3, & 4 from the south. Shells A1 and B1 cover the entrance foyers, shells A2 and B2 the stages and shells A3 and B3, A4 and B4 cover the Auditoria and Bar Areas...

A4) Each of the Major and Minor Halls has eight SIDE SHELLS in four pairs numbered 5, 6, 7 and 8 from the south...

In general drawings have been prepared for structural elements of the western shells only, the corresponding elements of eastern shells being identical but to opposite hand...

A5) The Major and Minor Halls each have two LOUVRE SHELLS 9 and 10 projecting southwards from Shells 7 and 8 respectively. They are similar in construction to the Main Shells but smaller in extent. Their function is, in conjunction with vertical glazing, to fill the gap between main shells 2 and 3 and the underlying side shells.

A6) The ARCHES are the hollow members formed at the junction of the side shells with adjoining shells. They are also described as SIDE SHELL ARCHES or conversationally as 'OCTOPUS ARCHES'[144] but the term Arch Rib is never used.

A8) The Arches are of a complicated, continuously varying, generally hollow cross-section, and are circular on elevation...

A9)... The Side Shell Slabs are precast on the flat with straight tapered sides. Each long edge is supported on a Side Shell Beam so that it deforms to the correct cylindrical shape under its own weight. The slabs extend from one arch to the opposite arch...

A10) The two lower portions of each main and louvre shell are of solid insitu concrete and are known as the MAIN SHELL PEDESTALS or just PEDESTALS...

... Springing from each pair of Pedestals is a series of radiating RIBS, the MAIN SHELL RIBS (these are never referred to as arches or arch ribs)... Each rib consists of two HALF-RIBS which are identical, but to opposite hand and are circular in elevation. The half ribs are separated from each other at the ridge by the RIDGE BEAM...

It should be noted that although each half rib lies in a plane, this plane does not intersect the Hall Axis Plane at 90°. Therefore, the corresponding half rib on the other side of the shell does not lie in the same plane but in the reflection of that plane in the Hall Axis Plane.

A12)... During erection, and until the post-tensioning of that rib is completed, the segments are hung from steel NEEDLES.[145]

These needles are supported at one end on the previously constructed rib and at the other end on a STEEL ERECTION ARCH. This is a trussed steel arch supported on the pedestals and tied back to the completed portion of the main shell. It is so constructed and articulated that it can be moved successively in to a new position and extended so as to take up the correct shape. The lowest two ribs of each shell are supported by an extension of the side shell scaffold.

Each rib is supported on the Pedestal through a TEMPORARY HINGE. This enables the partially built rib to be rotated to correct any misalignment that may be developing... for certain of the smaller shells, in order to reduce weight, the depth of the stem of the rib (and therefore the total depth) of the section has been reduced by either 12 inches or 18 inches...[146]

A17)... during construction of a shell whilst only the first few ribs have been erected, it is necessary to support the top flange of Rib 1 laterally from the side shell arch through FLAT JACKS at intermediate positions. These are deflated and removed, according, to a pre-determined schedule, as construction proceeds.[147]

A27) Horizontal thrusts from the shells are resisted by the TIES. These are groups of 1.1/8 inch diameter (generally) strand in ducts in concrete encasing laid on the floor slabs at springing level (between the shell columns). The strands are post-tensioned progressively as the shells are constructed according to a sequence laid down by the Engineer.

A28) Stage 2 contract includes the completion of unfinished items of Stage I...

Changes in stage machinery requirements have necessitated a redesign of the structure in the stage areas and the floors here are to be constructed according to a new set of drawings. This will mean the removal of half of the floor that has been constructed at level +45 in the Minor Hall and some alterations to the floors at lower levels in both halls.[148]

On site work was at last getting underway on Stage II, and scaffolding and reinforcing for the shell pedestals and stage walls sprouted from the flat surface of the podium like fresh growth after an atomic blast. On 3rd June Corbet Gore wrote to Jack Zunz as:

I thought you might like to have a note indicating how we are going.

Industrially, the situation has settled down and it's calm enough at the moment – I don't doubt there is a storm ahead on the subject of wages but I feel that this period of calm has been helpful and certainly there is a good relationship between the men on the site and the Management...

The stage wall[149] was a bit slow to get started as the steelwork was out of position and there was quite an amount of demolition work to be done before we could get going. However, it is squared and cleared up now and I will be looking for better than a lift a week. We have already poured a 12 foot lift right across and will be pouring another 12 feet right across during this coming week and from thereon it should be routine so that the forms can be released and go across to the Minor Hall.

The Tower Cranes are being erected ahead of the schedule we laid down. No. 1, which is just outside my window, is just about to jack itself on to the bridge and should be travelling out along its bridge fully erected by the end of this week. It will be of great assistance in all the work going on in the stage wall and stage pit areas...

The Whirler Crane in the Casting Yard is in full operation and, although I say it myself, is a beauty. She is now busy settling octopus rib forms. A lot of time and money is being spent on the lagging and lining of these forms but I am forced to admit that the plywood does give an excellent result and our fibreglass lining looks to me as though it is going to be the 'goods'. They are the best forms I have ever seen quite frankly, and there is no reason why perfect strips should not be made each time...[150]

The erection arch, as you know, went out to tender and we are very happy with the detailing being done by the successful tenderer...

Our computer program which is now complete (I am just waiting for the results) indicates that the loadings previously considered were in fact higher than we were actually obtaining and I will send you the complete results as soon as David Evans comes back from Adelaide. However, the crown reaction appears to be in the vicinity of 30 rather than 50 tons which may enable us to save additional money on the arch. The program, and I know little of these things, apparently caused some excitement in I.B.M. as it was too big for the Sydney computers – apparently the biggest of its type they have yet seen in Woomera.[151] I shall now have to go and read up a textbook so that I can boast intelligently about it...

John Nutt has arrived of course in a blaze of press publicity which is something akin to the treatment accorded to Elizabeth Taylor and I think Mike Lewis has settled in. It is certainly good to have him here.

Now I must go out and watch my crane being jacked on to the bridge. Best regards to all the boys... [152]

Not long after Zunz wrote to Lewis and Kelman:

... we had a call last week from the (N.S.W.) Agent-General's office asking whether it would be possible for us to arrange for the Premier to inspect the Royal Festival Hall. We did this and at the same time asked whether he couldn't spend a few hours looking at our offices and meeting the people working on the job and see the work we are doing here. He agreed to do this and together with Mrs Heffron, the secretary, and his press agent we toured the Festival Hall and subsequently 13 Fitzroy Street and were joined there by a hoard of newspaper men who had been briefed by the Premier's press secretary. The industry and tidiness on the floors which were inspected by the Premier was quite staggering and 'before and after' pictures would really have been very funny. Anyway all went very well and we think it was quite useful in letting people know the effort we have put into this.[153]

In July 1963 Kelman and Gore flew to London to look at some outstanding issues on the construction. Mike Lewis sent a memo to

Jack Zunz regarding Gore's planned absence: 'He is needed here, so please do not keep him in London too long.'[154] With the Arup engineers in London, Kelman and Gore went over 26 'Points for Discussion' which were listed and 'to be read in conjunction with Manual of Procedure Vol. II.'[155] They ranged from examining the forces exerted by the erection arch on the ridge during construction, to attending to differences in expansion in the structure if parts of it were tiled (more reflective) and some not. But the meeting created just as many questions as it answered, and an Arups list of outstanding work as at 1st August included among many other items:

Analysis

Redesign of Ridge Beams (include. re-examination of shell bolt loads).

Finalise flat jack loads.

Examine need for tension anti-creep connection between shells 4 & 8.

Prepare Sirius (computer) program for assessing significance of deflections measured on site.

Details & Design

Check shear and wind on all pedestals.

Determine position of continuity cables in ridge beams.

Details of lateral prestressing.

Finish details of lateral bolts, pads, flat jacks and packed props.

Incorporate new pedestal hinge.[156]

Many of the items listed concerned work that was already underway in Sydney on the formwork for the shell segments. Each was given a priority of 1, 2 or 3 and nominated anyone of 12 engineers who would take action on each item.

In July a meeting was held in the Architect's office on site attended by Utzon and his staff, Mick Lewis and the Arup's staff and Bob Kynaston with the Hornibrook engineers and foremen as Corbet Gore was in London.

Mr Utzon opened the meeting explaining the importance of accurate concrete work for the rib elements, based on his previous experiences of the folded slab and an inspection of the ribs erected in Enfield. He pointed out that standing under a rib, the soffit lines could be lined up by eye from almost any position and therefore, any inaccuracy would be very noticeable. He indicated on a sketch, the areas of the rib soffits as well as the edges which would be exposed and where a first-class quality of work would be mandatory, and requested that sample segments should be set up on the site so that these edges and surfaces could be clearly marked.

Mr Utzon indicated that certain areas of the inside shell soffits would be covered by the stage towers but apart from that, all other areas would be exposed...

As for the Bar areas, Mr Utzon indicated that he did not consider it possible to obtain a perfect off-form finish on the walls, but that all slabs and beams must show the same standard of workmanship as the ribs. He pointed out the reasons for this:

That it was his aim to convey to the patrons a feeling of consistency when they move through the building and therefore, the character of materials must be the same throughout.

As for the other situ work on site, Mr Utzon underlined the instruction previously given for Stage I: that no repairs to concrete surfaces were to be carried out except where necessary for structural reasons.

In case of any repairs being required, only a minimum of cement should be applied and kept as far back from the finished surface as possible. This was also to apply to the anchorages in the folded beams where he intends to apply some special treatment.

The meeting concluded in a site inspection where Mr Utzon gave examples of faults which are to be avoided.[157]

To achieve Utzon's exacting demands for the concrete finish, the plywood for the forms was accurately sanded to shape then coated with a layer of fibreglass and polyester resin which gave 'a thick hard smooth surface resistant to vibrator bruising and easy to strip.'[158] At that time top-grade concrete was considered to have a strength of 6,000 lb per square inch, but Arups specified a concrete strength for some shell segments of 7,500 lb per square inch.[159] Hornibrooks did a lot of experimenting with aggregate mixes and cement and found they could produce a concrete mixed day to day on site which consistently gave a strength of 8,500 lb per square inch – way ahead of anything else that had been achieved at that time. To achieve the strength was:

A combination of the aggregate, the balance of the various sizes of aggregate, the amount of cement and the wetting additive used... You used water but you put the chemical agents (wetting additive) in the water which enabled you to reduce the amount of water per pound of cement. The strength of the concrete is dependant on the amount of water. The less water you use when mixing cement means the stronger the concrete so the better you could make the water go round the better you are. But the philosophy here was quite different in that in view of the restricted places we had to put the concrete and the finish required by the architect it was necessary to place (the) concrete in a sufficiently fluid state (to) get the finish.

And so I made a rule with Arups that any concrete poured would have what we termed the three inch slump. It was a measure of the viscosity of the concrete if you like. The popular philosophy was to use (the) additive to reduce the amount of cement in the mix and therefore save money. The net result of doing that if you start off with a one inch slump and add the additive and take the cement out (is) you finish up with a cheaper mix but with less cement and a one inch slump and I wouldn't have that philosophy. I said no, look, we will design a concrete with the strength required (that would) have a one inch slump and then we will put additive in to get a three inch slump. Because (in this) building it was essential (because) if I didn't have workability in the concrete (I) couldn't get the finish.[160]

Some of the forms were seven feet deep, of narrow section, complex and heavily reinforced, and on site Hornibrooks were using a maximum of three-quarter aggregate for the concrete. To get the concrete through the forms and into all the little corners and crannies and still achieve a high finish meant the concrete had to be very heavily vibrated. Often in concrete that is vibrated too much the aggregate separates from the water giving an uneven finish 'but I say that if your concrete is well designed that it can take as much vibration as you care to put in it.'[161]

To ensure a colour consistency in the concrete throughout the job, Gore specified the aggregate and cement was to come from the same supplier for the length of the contract. And to show Utzon the sort of finish that could be obtained Hornibrooks did a series of tests at their Enfield depot on slabs of concrete about 18 inches square.[162]

In the roofs of the Major and Minor Halls and the restaurant there were 2,194 precast elements including rib segments, crown pieces, ridge beam segments, side shell arch segments, side shell slabs and pedestals. Only the pedestals were cast in-situ in their locations on top of the podium, all the other elements were cast in moulds or 'forms' on site then assembled to build the roof. Once some wharf sheds built in the 1880s at the south-west corner of the Bennelong Point site had been demolished by a company called Whelan the Wrecker, Hornibrooks set to work to lay out a casting yard.

An important requirement for the precast concrete was that the surface finish should meet the exacting aesthetic requirements of the Architect. A further need was that casting should be to very fine tolerances since the whole geometry of the shells could be thrown out by inaccuracies. Fine tolerances were also necessary for the myriad number of interconnecting ducts, bolts, etc., all of which had to match their neighbours when segments were erected.

> If accuracy in erection was to be maintained, it was essential that each rib segment should be cast against its mate whilst the latter was held accurately in the correct geometrical position. In this way any deviation from its correct plane of the end of the segment was compensated by a corresponding error of opposite direction in its mate. In this way, when segments were stressed together separated only by a narrow glued joint, the erected rib would accurately reflect the rib as cast.[163]

Rib segments were 15 feet long and weighed approximately 10 tons each. They were all cast from just three different shaped moulds or 'beds'. Each bed, had a length of 75 feet, i.e.five segments long, and was arched to reflect the spherical shape of the 246-foot radius of the Opera House shells. The bed was about 10 feet high at the centre. A frame 75 feet long constructed to the shape of one side of the rib which held the 1-inch thick hardwood ply of the form was mounted on wheels and controlled by hydraulic rams to allow the bed to open and close for fitting precast bulkheads and reinforcing and for stripping the forms. Concrete buckets were transported from the mixer by forklift trucks, then the concrete was poured into the form (Fig.33).

> Running down the centre of the casting yard was a 15-ton Whirler crane which was designed and built specially by Hornibrook for this job. The crane had a 15-ton maximum lift and was capable of handling 10 tons at 100 ft radius. It was used to lift segments out of the beds and place them in the initial storage area for curing... [164]

The first 75 ft long bed had tapering sides to reflect the shape of the rib on the outside surface of the shell of the Opera House as it widened between the pedestal and the crown like lines of longitude on a globe between the poles and the equator. The second 75 ft long bed had slightly wider tapering sides, and so on for the third. Segments from the first bed provided the lower portion of any rib in the Opera House, then the height of a particular shell determined how many more segments from the other beds were required to make up the necessary length: rib top segments required special external end forms to allow the skew cut off plane to be correctly orientated.

The longest ribs in the Opera House – at the opening of the biggest shell of the Major Hall – are made from 13 segments from three beds (five plus four plus four) the fourth (top) segment cast in the last bed having a shear cut off plane to orientate it to the side of the ridge beam. Although only three beds were necessary, in practice further duplicate beds were made to speed up rib production. Gore wrote:

Since five segments were being poured at one time and since the segments had to strip separately, it was necessary to separate them with precast end bulkheads painted with bond break on one side. The end bulkheads were cast in a subsidiary casting yard mastered by its own monorail hand-operated crane... These bulkheads contained all the stressing anchors and also two locating dowels so that when the segments were jointed together in the air, they would be accurately located. These dowels had to be designed in order that they would locate the segments but still allow the segments to be stripped from the soffit. Bulkheads had to be cast to extreme accuracy as the main forms closed on to them and leaks and distortion could result from any misfits.

In preparing the bed for pouring, the end bulkheads were first set up in their correct positions (at 15 ft intervals). Then reinforcing previously made up into cages in special timber jigs was crane handled direct to the moulds. Extreme accuracy of bending was necessary since cover generally was only $3/4$ inch and in the top flanges particularly available space was crowded with ducts, bolts, bolt sockets and anchorages...

In an effort to minimise weight the Designers restricted the dimensions of the concrete within the precast units to as great an extent as possible and, as a result, concrete had to be placed in extremely difficult areas highly reinforced and filled with stressing ducts and fittings.

Some idea of the difficulty of the placing conditions can be seen in the fact that in the large segments all concrete for the stem had to pass down a reinforced side wall $2\frac{1}{2}$ inch thick for a distance of some 8 ft.

Vibration was effected largely with external vibrators mounted on plates on the steel form frames. Vibrators were moved along the bed as the concrete pour proceeded. Areas such as the segment stem and prestressing anchorages were further vibrated internally... it is significant to note that the casting yard was instructed to place concrete at not less than 3 inch slump. Even at this slump, the concrete was to reach a strength of 6,000 psi. There is no doubt that the high quality of finish obtained was made possible by not attempting to fight low slump concrete into the restricted formwork.

Before any rib was stripped from the mould, it was accurately surveyed from survey posts permanently located at each end of the forms and pins were placed in each segment in an accurately known position which could be picked up during erection... For ribs containing more than five segments the No.5 segment when stripped was lifted from the mould and set up in the new mould as a starter segment. In this way the joint between segment 5 and segment 6 was matched...

As was the case for main shell ribs, end bulkheads (for the top segment of a rib where it cut off at the ridge beam) were separately precast. These presented some difficulty as no two were the same and their side edges were not perpendicular to the plane of the bulkhead. It was found that, after some training, a tradesman carpenter could effectively construct these using three-dimensional co-ordinates defining the plane at each side of the bulkhead...

Side shell arch rib segments were also cast to the same principle of matched contact faces. Although one side of the side shell arch ribs was in fact identical in shape to the main shell ribs, the other side was the warped surface transition between side shell and main shell geometry.[165]

Zunz explained that 'the space between side shell and the main or louvre shell is filled by a warped surface described by two points which move up each circle at the same speed and are joined by straight lines'.[166] The warped surface shape was different for each segment – and Hornibrooks made a special adjustable form with a hinge and a top surface of thin plywood that could be flexed to create the warped surface:

A number of subsidiary casting yards handled other components such as side shell beams, side shell slabs, main shell crown pieces and side shell arch rib crown pieces. All were comparatively straightforward jobs of precasting. The side shell slabs however, being only $2\frac{1}{2}$ inches thick and 7 feet 6 inches wide and up to 20 feet long were very flimsy. They were cast in a cylindrical mould and to prevent damage were handled by a specially designed and built vacuum lifter (powered by a Volkswagen engine) which was effective for both stripping and erection...[167]

The first units were cast in August 1963 although at this stage the casting yard was not completely set up. During the initial few months of operation, production figures suffered from -

1. extremely wet weather;
2. intense industrial unrest; and
3. design details not being finalised.

The last factor made necessary continuous modification of detail forming arrangements and it was not until the casting yard had been running for some six months that the job was able to settle down into a routine production run.[168]

Segments were numbered to ensure they would be assembled on the shells with their match-cast mates. However production at the casting yard was soon some way ahead of the construction phase on the shells and when space for storage ran out on site the segments were trucked to the grounds of Her Majesty's Prison at Long Bay Gaol for secondary storage.[169]

With production underway in the casting yard Bob Kelman wrote to Jack Zunz on 23rd August concerning a detail of 'lead flashing at the bottom end of segment No.1' but also with 'A note of human interest! Skipper is getting married, we think, on Saturday 7th of September. I thought you may like to send him something on behalf of OAP London in view of the long and faithful service he has given the job, and the good relations which have always existed between him and our people here.'[170]

Meanwhile, on the side shells Arup engineer D. Michael in London wrote to John Nutt in Sydney:

> You are correct to say that we are giving too much information in defining the co-ordinates and offsets of the ducts in the warped surface part of the precast diaphragm. Your suggested remedy provides the required minimum number of dimensions. I feel that to produce the information to draw a dimensionally correct untwisted warped surface is not possible, as the offsets are not simply obtained but are affected by the diaphragm inclination on the arch elevation in the same manner as ducts in the soffit...
>
> I have plotted the warped surface $4\frac{3}{4}$ inch (or modified value) line at the joint face and the inner face 9 inches away on graph paper and checked the offsets as schedule. They seem to me to be very reasonable. The $\frac{1}{2}$ inch error which you quote never occurs. It is more likely that accumulative errors have produced the effects which you observe. If the V, G co-ordinates were 1/8 inch out and the V, G offsets 1/16 inch out in the same direction, both very possible, and the form were 1/8 inch out we have an accumulated error of nearly 3/8 inch before any errors of the calculating technique are involved.[171]

Zunz wrote back to Mick and Bob about Skipper's great day:

> It is a pity that we have probably missed Skipper's wedding. We had naturally intended to send him a gift and good wishes but in the heat of the moment in my absence the matter was overlooked.
>
> Could you please send him a gift and good wishes on behalf of the firm. We leave the choice and amount to be expended to your unquestioned taste and discretion.[172]

CHAPTER 11

THE GUNPOWDER PLOT:
A CHANGE TO THE SHELL COLUMNS

To build the forms for the shells Hornibrooks advertised for joinery-boat builders. *The Daily Mirror* ran an article on the request under the heading 'NOW IT'S PLAIN SAILING'.

The Sydney Opera House contractors today sent out a call for boat-builders. Appropriately they are wanted to help with the sail-like roof...

The supervisor, Mr R. S. Wood, said today forms were being manufactured for the roof arches. He said the arches would be like half an upside down boat hull. The system of setting them out was the same as the setting out of a boat and for that reason boat builders would be ideal for the job.

Mr Wood said the reinforcing for the first shell was already in position. It would give the public the first impression of how the shells would look.[1]

The reinforcing for the first shell was for the in situ pedestals at podium level that were the springing point for each shell. They were fan shaped, the length along the top of the fan and consequently their height was determined by the number of ribs on that particular shell as the base of each first rib segment was 12 in wide. They were built to withstand immense stresses and typically could be 12 ft by 6 ft wide at the base and of solid concrete except for the ducts for stressing cables. The concrete was extremely heavily reinforced, the weight of reinforcing alone in the larger ones being up to 15 tons. Indeed they were '... so heavily reinforced', recalled Gore, 'that we were a bit apprehensive that we would ever be able to place concrete in them at all. The reinforcement was so thick that if you put a sparrow inside them, it wouldn't find its way out: I have a photograph... of the reinforcing up, and you can't see daylight from one side to the other through the mass of reinforcing'.[2] (Fig. 34).

But before the concrete could be poured for the shell pedestals and the first precast segment could be placed, there had been some work to do on the shell columns. The Opera House shells effectively stood on stilts, because the point at which they sprang from the podium was up to 50 feet above the bedrock and the column itself could extend many more feet underground to a foundation of adequate bearing capacity. Even before turning the first sod the position of the columns had been in a state of flux, Ove Arup writing to Utzon on 6th August 1958 following the change from his freehand sketch scheme to the scheme based on a parabola '... As far as the shells are concerned the positions of the supports have of course been radically altered.'[3]

When the first plans had been prepared for the podium the shell columns had been designed to support a lightweight shell structure, plus a margin for what was considered the maximum load a shell structure could impose. With the introduction of the double shell 'skin' connected by a steel lattice it was apparent that the columns built so far would not support the increased loads, and in March 1960 Kelman discussed with Hugo Mollman the shell column alterations that were likely to be needed. Not long after, 'A meeting was held in the office on the 12th April 1960, in order to discuss the problem of Shell Columns.' When Kelman '... proposed we should face the fact of having to enlarge columns now and do so before any further work was done. Only four columns in the Central Passage now require any demolition.'[4]

The introduction of the spherical hinge in the top of the column for the steel shell scheme meant a further change to the design, while the decision to go with the concrete fan shells meant a re-writing altogether of the book on shell columns. On 27th September 1961, with the new shell scheme looking like it was going ahead, Jack Zunz rang London from Hellebaek asking that work be stopped on construction of shell columns and Kelman telegraphed MacKenzie on site to pass on the news. 'Why do things like shell columns always have to happen to us?'[5] lamented Ian MacKenzie in a letter back to Bob Kelman. Arups produced a 'Summary of Adjustments to be made to Columns and Foundations on the basis of Loads Submitted April 1962.' It listed 'adjustments' needed to columns for the Major and Minor Halls, possible changes to the foundations and floor slabs to cater for tie forces and under 'Use of openings for Springing Details' mentioned Column 5 in Major Hall 'MacKenzie to move joint slightly Northwards and to leave bigger pocket' and, 'Column 10 has been cast with original hinge pocket.' The summary noted that column 18 for the Minor Hall 'could be altered N.B. (columns) 18 and 19 will be poured very soon.'[6]

Gore had wanted to get on site as soon as possible to start work on the new columns to avoid a bottleneck when work on erection of the shells started, and since a Certificate of Practical Completion for the Major Hall podium was expected in September 'this prevents Dusseldorp objecting to site entry' wrote Gore to Zunz.[7] But Kelman advised Gore 'By all means get everything ready to go, but we feel it might be a bit unwise to start on site until Civil & Civic are off. It well could start a lot of damaging rumours which we can well do without at the beginning of the job.'[8] But word was already getting about, so much so that the Committee prepared a statement

> ... as a reminder of the history of the Opera House project and to present in their true perspective particular circumstances which are at present the subject of much uninformed discussion. It is understood that rumours are afloat that the supports for the concrete shell roofs are not strong enough. This would be laughable if it were not for the fact that apparently credence is given to them in some quarters. The fact is that there is a safety factor of plus three.[9]

But Arups were stalling, Gore could not have started work on the columns even if he had wanted to. In October 1962 Arups were still discussing with Utzon the locations of the footpoints of the shells, and column sizes, and Blanchard wrote to Gore on 8th November that '... details for columns above the foundation piers should be completed by 31st December but general details for the Major Hall will be ready by the end of November.'[10]

On 31st October Arup engineer David Lowes in a letter signed by Joe Huang headed 'Additional Foundations' addressed to Ian MacKenzie which commenced 'Dear Malcolm', advised

> We have thought it advisable to substantially alter the formerly proposed method of supporting the shells. The object of the revision has been to achieve a reasonable degree of fixity at the shell springing points without also introducing large horizontal forces at intermediate floor levels. This approach has led to the adoption of long columns designed to resist both bending and compression, as well as prestressed ties between the shell springing points to increase the stiffeners of the system. Where there appear to be distinct advantages the columns will be detached from intermediate floor levels until the erection of the shells has been completed, and then reconnected...
>
> The Architect has provisionally approved of these new rectangular columns.[11]

Arups reckoned '... the cost of strengthening the foundations and substructure would be about 5 per cent of the total cost of (Stage II)' and the procedure of

> Strengthening of Foundations is necessary in order to carry the higher design loads imposed by the shells. This will entail providing additional concrete piers under some of the additional columns and the sequence will be:- Break through existing walls to provide access for percussion drilling rig, break through floor slab, drive steel cylinders, excavate and get out until 20 ton rock is reached, test rock foundation, concrete pier while withdrawing cylinders, concrete pier cap, reconstruct floor slab and wall. Some of the piers will occur outside the sea wall and will be driven through the sea and seabed in which case the cylinders will not be withdrawn.
>
> Some of the columns themselves will require strengthening which will be achieved by casting new reinforced concrete round or adjacent to them. Strengthening of some floor slabs between the springings of the main shell arches is also required to carry the larger design tie forces now imposed. This will be obtained generally by laying post-tensioning cables on the existing floor slab, casting a new slab round them and tensioning.[12]

On 13th December Arups prepared an 'Agenda (for) Pedestals, Foundations, Strengthening Sub-Structure and Other Sub-Structure Work' for Gore to discuss at a meeting in Arups' London office. Among other things the Agenda advised '... temporary demolition of walls and slabs will involve extensive propping... Some additional foundations and possibly underpinning of walls may be required in the Major Hall area... Some columns in the central passage may be demolished and replaced by load bearing walls.' All columns 'will eventually be made rectangular, some structurally and others decoratively.' Laying the extra ties on top of the existing podium increased the level of the podium and 'may involve the strengthening of existing floor slabs in some areas.'[13]

A 'Summary of action required after December 1962 meetings with Gore' included the notation, 'Arups stated that columns 2, 3, 7, 8, 12, 13, 17 and 18 must be allowed to move laterally at all intermediate floor levels (even where columns are not otherwise being modified.) This could be dealt with by cutting out slabs and propping until shells are built.'

For the moment all this talk had gone on behind closed doors, but when Ove Arup was in Sydney for the Arbitration hearing the *Sunday Mirror* carried a front page story on the 17th March with a large photo of Ove gesturing with his hand and quoting him in the caption 'This is a trial-and-error job. I dare not estimate the eventual cost.' The article, headlined 'PLANS RUSHED FOR POLITICS', reported

A major blunder revealed yesterday in the construction of the Sydney Opera House will add a fortune to its cost. Twenty reinforced concrete columns built to carry the roof cannot support the load. This is because the roof design was changed last year, after work on the base of the building had begun…

But Mr Ove Arup the 67 year old consultant engineer for the job said yesterday this work was negligible.

'It is only one of a million troubles', he said. 'The Opera House is being built on a trial-and-error basis. If the planners had been given five years to design the building, instead of being rushed into it for political reasons, about £2 million might have been saved on the ultimate cost.'…

Two engineers on the site, who asked to remain anonymous, said the extra columns were only one of many secret changes in the Opera House plans… One said the great sails of the roof, weighing 21,000 tons, might have collapsed if the original design had been carried through.[14]

The following day Zunz wrote to London:

I understand that Roger has sent to you the *Sunday Mirror* with our front page news. It was of course a complete distortion and even allowing for the widest interpretation of what was said by Ove is quite the most tainted bit of journalism I have experienced. No doubt the repercussions will come shortly but at the moment we are dreaming up ways of building a few nameless newspaper reporters into the pedestals. Unfortunately they are so full of steel already that we might have to resort to some of the new bored piers![15]

The rival *Sun Herald* quoted Gore as saying in an article headlined 'Opera roof blunder denied.'

"A major blunder? That's baloney!… The extra cost will probably be about £6,000 – a 10 per cent rise on the original cost of the foundations." – The article also quoted Malcolm Nicklin – "This is just one of a number of modifications of the Opera House design worked out over the years".

The engineers said the additional columns were being built because four extra shells had been included in the revised version of the roof. It had originally been intended to have louvre panes of glass between the adjacent shells, but the designer Mr Joern Utzon, had decided instead to use small shells as louvres. The extra columns were necessary to support their weight.

"There is nothing unusual about changes and modifications," Mr Nicklin said. "Look at St Paul's Cathedral. It took 15 years to design and 300 years to build… "

Mr Gore, who is currently supervising the trial runs for the erection of the roof at Hornibrooks' Enfield depot, told *The Sun Herald* the design of the Opera House was so revolutionary it was inevitable some mistakes would be made. "This is something out of the ionosphere. We have never seen anything like it in this country before," he said. "It was only too easy to 'knock' the Opera House and everybody who was working on it. If anybody wants my hide, they can come and get it," he added.[16]

And in the *Sydney Morning Herald* the following day Ove Arup

described as a complete distortion a report in a Sunday newspaper that 14 supplementary columns being built to rectify a 'major blunder' would add 'a fortune' to the Opera House cost.

Mr Arup said he had been misquoted. He denied a statement in the article that the original columns could not support the roof, and added: "There is no blunder or crisis. We know exactly how we want to go about this stage."

He said that when the State Government asked that construction of the Opera House begin in February, 1958, he had requested a postponement in the belief that "it was unwise to start the job before the drawings were made. It is a very bad thing to have a competitive tender when the design is not complete." he said. "We had to put the foundations in before we knew the loads."[17]

Of the original columns, 19 out of the 20 were already 70 per cent complete. On 1st May Bob Kelman wrote to Jack Zunz from Sydney.

Hornibrooks are investigating the possible use of explosives to trim back some of the existing shell columns. Before you have a fit as I did, I know that explosives have been used for breaking set concrete out of a ready-mixed mixer drum. I feel if this was possible trimming back columns should be child's play and hence agreed to the proposals. We tried it out last night. While the immediate visible effect was not very remarkable, it does appear greatly to reduce the hours spent on the jack picks.

The magnitude of this work in re-building these columns is fantastic and could slow the whole progress of Stage Two down, unless dealt with pretty drastically now. For this reason Corbett is bringing in a demolition expert as a sub-contractor, and we have discussed the possible political effects of using explosives with the Public Works Department representative at our site meetings. He has phoned back this afternoon after discussion with the Director of the Public Works Department. They have no objection and leave methods to our discretion... [18]

And MacKenzie wrote to Zunz on the 7th:

... This whole business of demolition of existing concrete is taking on alarming proportions – the difficulties really have to be seen to be believed.

> The high strength concrete plus the quantity of reinforcement makes the task almost impossible. Two men with jack picks took nearly 2 weeks to cut away just 1 yard of concrete on Shell column V before blasting techniques were adopted. Even now, with a team of specialist demolishers on the job blasting the concrete, there is months of work ahead...[19]

But Zunz did have a fit when he heard explosives were being used for demolition on the Opera House without his prior notice. Kelman wrote to him, also on 7th May:

> It rained all March. We had 10 inches in the last five days of April. It rained all last night, so what better way of being awakened to a steady deluge than your dulcet tones over the International Phones (via Vancouver) gabbling away like an enraged Chinaman.
>
> Second effort via Yugoslavia was quite intelligible and I will instruct Hornibrooks to desist from the use of explosives. So far, apart from making the Commanders of two Manly Ferries wonder if they were being fired on from the Point, no damage is done...
>
> I cannot help feeling that you are being over conservative with your worries about micro-cracking...
>
> We would appreciate a final verdict on this as soon as possible, because Hornibrooks required to have Columns 3, 4 and 5, 8, 9 and 10 completed in four weeks time... [20]

Arups in London had taken advice from various organisations, including the Royal School of Military Engineering '... and last but not least all right thinking members of this organisation. We are all unanimous in feeling very strongly that the use of explosives should not be allowed.'[21] And Zunz wanted to know what effect the vibration and shockwave would have on the podium structure. Corbet Gore wrote to Zunz:

> I have been in touch today with Mike Lewis regarding use of explosives in column stripping and while appreciating your decision as to whether they may be used or not, I can assure you if we are expected to strip columns by hand we have no hope of meeting our existing program and that the cost would be in the order of six times the cost of using explosives... [22]

And Lewis, whose letters to Zunz now had unusual titles like 'Gunpowder, treason and plot', sent Zunz a memo on the 10th May entitled 'Blood and Thunder.'

> The time is 4.30 pm and Hornibrooks office has been vacated as a result of a telephone call from the *Daily Mirror* (heaven preserve us). They have received a call to say that the Opera House is going to be blown up at 4.15 pm. Now that the time has past I feel free and happy to write to you in

this connection. It is probably a hoax originating from the workers, who are at present on strike – this is the third work stoppage since I have been here.

Regarding the use of explosives for "constructive" purposes, we must thank you for a most entertaining and informative salvo of cables. The up to date position is as follows:-

Hornibrooks are continuing with the complete demolition of columns 3, 5, 8 and 10...

Bob was present at last night's firework display and says that the process is not unlike peeling a banana, and appears to have little effect on the surrounding structure. The complete demolition of each column is going to reduce the amount of labour and time expended by a considerable amount and in this working man's paradise this is going to result in some economy, even though we will require more concrete in the final column...[23]

Gore recalled about the hoax:

... everyone was on strike, so the site was deserted, except for the staff who were still working... I was in my office and this great policeman came in and told me they'd had an anonymous phone call saying there was a bomb. He said: 'I don't think there's anything in it, but I think it would be safe to... get people out.' And (the bomb) was timed to go off at quarter past four. So we got the blokes... (and) the girls out of the office, and we were all standing down on the broadwalk here, watching our watches to see if anything went off at a quarter past four, and of course the siren went off. The people nearly fell in the harbour, because the siren was set automatically to go off at knocking-off time...[24]

Kelman wrote to Zunz:

All is quiet at present on the Western front! In the words of the popular song we are Praising the Lord and keeping our powder dry!

I refer of course to your letter of 8th May making such a booboo about our fireworks. I know Mick has written to you at some length on this, but the subject is so close to my heart I cannot resist a few words.

Mick will have told you we carried out some experiments with impressive equipment, using black powder. Our friend, John Smith (and as far as we know he is not trying to remain anonymous that is his real name!) from the Department of Mines undoubtedly knows what he is talking about. He has stated that concrete is able to stand displacements of up to 100 thousands of one inch due to a shock wave...

Please understand that we are not being unnecessarily carried away by the pressure of the job in attempting to find a solution to this problem...

By the way I am looking forward to meeting the... "right thinking members"... of our organisation![25]

To assess the effects of explosives on the structure Arups recorded tests with a vibro-graph, a technique they'd employed previously to assess the effect of vibration on buildings from nearby railways. After experimenting with gelignite, the results of which were 'both magnificent and startling with large sections of concrete flying in all directions.' To 'avoid possible damage to adjoining structures' various experiments were tried and black-powder was reckoned to be most suitable for demolition. 'The manner of application of explosives was to drill suitable holes in columns at approximately 12 in centres around the perimeter to a depth of 3 ft which had the effect of shattering the concrete and same was then removed by Jack-Pick, the reinforcing steel being burnt off as removal proceeded.'[26]

And in reference to Kelman accusing him of '… gabbling away like an enraged Chinaman' and likening column demolition to '… peeling a banana' Zunz penned a poem to the Sydney staff:

Your learned friend one Corbet Gore
We know has dropped his bombs galore -
And now in peace with powder dry
We thought he was a modest guy.

But no – his new acquired fame
Is like that of a well known dame.
Who wouldn't want to watch the hose
Peeled off the limbs of Gipsy Rose?

Today the methods are the same,
In essence rather than in name,
And while Miss Lee brings female guile
And song and laughter and a smile,
Our Corbet uses pick and kelly
But most of all he uses "gelly".
Old custom now makes place for new
Reluctantly we say "adieu"
To Gipsy's string and her old zipper
Make way for Gore – the Sydney stripper.

And even if we gasp and moan
By cables and by telephone -
Confucci say "You must remember
Guy Fawkes is not till next November."

But please in future let us know
Before you puff and puff and blow
With fuses, bombs and then with fire
On well cured, solid "mud and wire."[27]

Although Hornibrooks timed the explosions to go off during the rush-hour when it was expected the noise of traffic on the bridge would mask the sound, passing ferry passengers were aware of a dull boom emanating from the bowels of the Opera House and it was only a matter of time before the word got out: The story was broken by the *Sunday Mirror,* who boasted 'The first intimation of trouble with the roof supports was given in an exclusive *Sunday Mirror* story more than three months ago.'

> Sixteen of the 20 key piers designed to support the roof of the Sydney Opera House are being demolished. (Hornibrooks)... have called in explosives experts to carry out the demolition.
>
> A spokesman for the firm said today that G. Bayutti and Co. was doing the work because it was feared that indiscriminate blasting could weaken the entire structure.
>
> The project engineer for M. R. Hornibrooks, Mr R. F. Kynaston, said last night that the revised scheme would add £40,000 to the estimated cost.
>
> "But in the long run the revised plan will save a terrific amount," he said.
>
> "I don't know how much it will be but it will certainly run into six figures."...
>
> The consulting engineers Ove Arup and Partners decided that it would be quicker and cheaper to build the roof in pre-cast segments. (Compared to the original shell design).[28]

Kynaston conducted reporters and photographers round the site and the following day the *Herald* published two photographs with an article head-lined 'CHANGES AT OPERA HOUSE.' The picture on the left illustrated one of the original columns tucked discreetly against a wall ready for blasting and that on the right the web of reinforcing for one of the new columns thrusting up through the centre of a room and punching a hole through the concrete ceiling like Jack's beanstalk. Once shuttered and cast the shell pillars were no longer a mere column but a massive rectangular buttress the size of a good-sized bridge pier, dropping down through the rooms of the podium, as often as not right through the centre of them, to be left standing there like a giant immovable bedroom wardrobe left by careless removalists. In the article Kynaston was quoted as saying the work of constructing the columns will probably delay completion of the building by 'a few months.'[29]

In a report on the columns sent to Public Works on 31st July Arups advised the Director 'This demolition was quickly and economically

executed using explosives in a new technique developed on the site'
and sent a schedule of costs outlining costs incurred in demolition and
strengthening columns minus the cost that would have been incurred
anyway if the columns had been built from scratch and concluded: '...
the additional cost of strengthening the columns is seen to be
approximately £57,000, we are satisfied that a substantial saving has
been effected by changing the basic concept for the construction of
the building.'[30]

The following day in the *Herald* an article headlined '"SAVING"
ON OPERA HOUSE' reported:

> A new technique developed to erect the roof of the Sydney Opera House
> would save £135,000, the Acting Minister for Public Works, Mr. P.D. Hills,
> said yesterday.
>
> This estimate included £57,000 to demolish and replace 16 of the
> 20 columns built to support the roof.
>
> Mr Hills said the work would not delay the completion of the project...
>
> Originally it was planned that the shells which make up the sail-like
> roof of the Opera House would be paraboloid in shape.
>
> Mr Hills said that by modifying the shells to a spherical curve a pre-
> casting technique could be used.
>
> This meant the concrete members could be cast under factory
> conditions instead of building them in position, supported by scaffolding.
>
> Mr Hills said the saving was possible as the forms used to cast the
> concrete could be re-used.[31]

Ryan the Public Works Minister had been overseas when Hills made
the comment on a saving and when he returned he was asked by an
Opposition MP Mr Taylor in the House whether the cost of
removing columns would 'increase the cost of the project' to which
Ryan replied: 'I can inform the Hon. Member that the cost of the
alterations involved will, in fact, effect a saving in the total cost of
Stage 2 of the work...'

> MR HUGHES: As a supplementary question, I ask the Minister for
> Public Works whether he can explain how erecting columns and then
> pulling them down, instead of doing the right thing in the first place, can
> cheapen the cost.
>
> MR P.N. RYAN: I have not had the opportunity of carefully analysing
> all these matters, but it should have occurred to the Hon. member for
> Armidale that it is possible, by modification in design and an alteration in
> procedure, to make an economy. That is normal practice and frequently
> occurs on big projects. It might not be obvious to the Hon. member, but

anyone who has been engaged in building or has any knowledge of building practices and procedures understands that this is possible and frequently happens. I understand that this is so with the alterations at the Opera House.[32]

And just when it was thought the work was nearly complete, at a site conference on 2nd October:

... Mr MacKenzie reported that Mr Kynaston and he had agreed that Bayutti's sub-contract could be terminated when the complex demolition work had been concluded in approximately two weeks. However, a cable had since been received from London advising that some further demolition was required on shell columns I, VI, XI and XVI.[33]

Everything would have been all right if Bayutti's had stuck to just demolishing columns:

I refer to your letter of 22.5.64, blithely headed "+51 & 66 Level Ties", wrote Kelman from London to MacKenzie in Sydney on 9th June.

Now when the Resident Engineer wishes to notify the consultants that he has (unwittingly, of course) allowed a demolition experienced contractor to mine much of the structural steel out of a critical portion of the structure, one would expect more sensation than is provided by your letter.

This is, in fact, so calm, so matter of fact in tone that I cannot believe in the awful implications which you yourself provide.

Surely the purpose of an R.E. is to stop these mining exercises... I can imagine a scene as the R.E. walks up to a driller, slowly removes his pipe, looks at the rusty heap of spoil at his feet and says, "Be sure to let us know if you are hitting any steel in this concrete.".

"Concrete!" the man cries. "Struth, mate, I thought the stones and sand were just impurities in this imported steel stuff."

This is not really good enough. It is no good enlarging anchorages to get the steel in if as soon as your back is turned these blokes dig it all out again![34]

A later 'Firm estimate' of extras on Stage II put the 'Removal and Replacement of Columns and Adjacent Slabs' at $303,308.[35]

CHAPTER 12

LATERAL THINKING

The concrete was successfully poured in the first of the heavily reinforced shell pedestals, and the way was clear for the placing of the first segments:

The first of 2,250 pre-cast roof segments for the Sydney Opera House was lowered into position today – reported *The Sun* on 22nd November – A concrete block weighing 12 tons, it is part of the first of the roof shells. Construction workers and engineers began hoisting the segment at 6 am. Two hours later it was lowered into the base of the first roof shell.

The segment is part of one of six ribs which will converge to an apex at the top of the Major Hall stage wall to form arches. These arches will provide the base from which the roof shells will fan outward and upward to a maximum height of 221 feet above sea level.

A special tower crane is used to set the segments in position. A director of the construction company on the job, Mr Corbet Gore, said the crane was one of the largest in the world. It had a capacity of 20 tons. 'The weather was perfect for the positioning', he said. 'There was hardly any wind, which was important.'[1]

'Today we witnessed an extremely momentous happening at the Opera House', wrote Mick Lewis to Jack Zunz the same day,

the first precast segment for 5/1W was erected into place. There was a great deal of flurry from the press and some television photographers were on the site from 6 am when the operation started. You will be receiving press cuttings as they come to hand, but I thought you would like to know that it all worked out very well! Completely without snags. The formwork for the arch pedestal has, unfortunately, deflected 5/8 in at right angles to the boundary plane and we have introduced a $\frac{1}{4}$ in compensation into the position of the first segment.[2]

There are a multitude of decisions which crop up during the course of construction on any major building project, almost by the hour. The design of the Opera House roof was so complex that the decisions to be made were multiplied to an extraordinary degree. Those decisions have to be taken based upon an intimate knowledge of their impact on the forces, stresses and deflections to which the structure is subjected. That knowledge is contained in the thousands of pages of calculations and the hundreds of drawings undertaken during the design. Familiarity with the design is essential because a minor error can easily escalate into a major catastrophe, or at least delay and compromise the construction program. An answer has to be found to each decision quickly, frequently under the immense pressures of site with a score or more workers hanging on your word and a heavy concrete element hanging on a crane. The full consequences of these decisions can be assessed quickly by only a few key people with an intimate knowledge of the design, but the design was being carried out in London, 12,000 miles away.

Jack Zunz made a decision which was fundamental to the successful construction of the Opera House. He decided to send a few of his key designers to Sydney for the duration of the construction.[3]

John Nutt was already in Sydney acting as the point of liaison with the builders because in London he had the responsibility for leading the group which designed the side shells. Joe Huang and Peter Rice had recently arrived in Sydney from Arup's London office. Zunz recalled:

> Both were part of a plan to send some key personnel, familiar with at least some of the design principles for the roof structure, to Sydney to assist Michael Lewis. Both Rice and Huang left London before the designs were fully resolved. In Rice's case he wanted to work on the Opera House site. He had not previously had any site experience. Ian MacKenzie was the senior Resident Engineer and Rice became his (invaluable) assistant with particular responsibilities for the roof. Huang was, alas, diverted sooner than I had hoped back to his native Malaysia to carry out a new hospital project.[4]

Huang, who joined Arups in 1956, was familiar with large precast structures after experience gleaned in Arup's industrialised housing group. In 1960 he joined the Sydney Opera House team working on the podium structure, and then on the roof structure. He had a particular involvement in the definition of and the application of the geometry of the shells. His exceptional skill in mathematics was put to good use in solving the complex equations which gave the intersections between the spheres and planes which form the surfaces of the roof and define the shapes of the precast units.

Peter Rice had an intimate knowledge of the structure and design of the shells. Michael Elphick found:

> ... Peter was a complete breath of fresh air in a lot of ways... But he's a classic Irish-man, almost like a caricature... His father... was very high up

in the education system in Southern Ireland and so Peter had a very pleasant education. He sort of did, English and Irish and he did poetry through the medium of Irish and Welsh... (some) godforsaken thing... And when he finished his schooling career which was, if you like, more arty than crafty... he thought he'd like to be an aeronautical engineer. And so he went up to (a University in) Northern Ireland... (where) the aeronautical engineering buildings were terribly drab and... so depressing, but the civil engineering buildings were nice and bright so he became a Civil Engineer...

So he really started his mathematics at University level. And then... he went to England and started to work with Arups... But because he started maths (at University) he missed all the basic maths and seemed to just jump in at vector algebra and matrix algebra and that sort of thing – he had an entirely different approach to doing things... (If he was solving a problem) Peter would sit down and get his pencil out and he would write out the rules of how he was going to do it. He would make his own rules up for the thing and then he'd just do it purely by logic from his rules with complete checks and plays all the way through it. And he would come up with the answer, you know...

But it was just that completely different attitude. It was almost as if, you know, as if you jumped somebody in at the upper level. And he learnt the principles before he learnt the detail, if you like.[5]

Rice had been involved in the wind-tunnel tests of the model of the Opera House at Southampton University since 1958 and had been willing to carry on working on the project where Ron Jenkins and Hugo Mollman had not. He would quietly observe the work that was underway and write to London anytime he noticed a change that could be useful in the construction or structure, much to the gratitude of Jack Zunz who wrote,

I want you to know... that we appreciate your comments and interest and look upon you to continue to pass on to us all forms of criticism whether constructive or destructive. You have so much detailed knowledge of the behaviour of the structure and know your way round the calculations so much better than anyone else that we would like to know that you are following the progress and developments right to the end... [6]

Rice wrote to London on 29th November after an 'historic week' on the site with the placing of the first shell segments and raised a dozen or more points where detail changes would be necessary in the design, particularly to simplify reinforcement placement in the shell segments which Hornibrooks had found took six days to place in the forms. The Sydney office would redesign the reinforcement details to make it simpler, Rice advised, and also mentioned that:

When cast the arch pedestal was 5/8 in low. 3/8 in of this was taken up in the 3in concrete joint so that the 1st segment was $\frac{1}{4}$ in low. The 2nd segment however is, or appears to be, 7/8 in low. An extensive survey is going on at the moment to discover how this is and what happened. My own theory favours movement in the 3 in grouted joint which has not been grouted yet. We shall however find what is wrong and correct it by some form of rotation of the segment at this joint, though this will be difficult. It is obviously early to jump to emphatic conclusions after one segment has been erected, but a tentative one suggests that we may have extreme difficulty meeting our tolerance requirements. One thing I had not realised is that with the 2 in threaded head on the bolts we will be in some difficulty fitting them in. I do not wish to labour this point. But I am worried. Very worried...

The pace here is beginning to speed up, and I too enjoy the job more.[7]

Joe Huang was settling in as well, though even some of the other engineers had trouble keeping pace with his ruminations. 'After discussing the shear problem in the pedestals with John, Ed and Peter', Huang wrote to John Blanchard on 29th November,

I am now convinced that the "exact solution" which I did in London was not 100 per cent correct, because I have ignored the boundary conditions. As we all know, for a given section, the shear stress due to bending in the direction normal to a boundary is zero and consequently the shear stress at a right-angle corner of the section must be zero. From this we gather that the shear stress increases from the boundary to a maximum at the centroid. The shear stress created by torsional moment, however, has the reverse effect, i.e.it is maximum at the boundaries and diminishes until it is zero at the centroid...

The conclusion that we get out of this discovery is that we have over estimated our combined shear stresses which is something to our advantage...

After having inspected the steel already in position for pedestal A2, I honestly believe that the links have to be either reduced or revised before any concrete can get to the bottom of the pedestals. However, these revisions will be done on the site and will not in anyway reduce the strength of the pedestal...

I have now settled down in Sydney and found accommodation on my own. It is situated on the other side of the river and every morning I have to make a short trip by ferry to work, which I enjoy tremendously...[8]

Blanchard wrote back to Huang that 'I am glad to see you have settled in comfortably, although I do not understand why you do not buy a yacht.' And neither could Kelman, who had a yacht moored at Lavender Bay on the other side of the Harbour and used to sail across in the morning... It embarrassed me, because I was always late. ... I used to sail past Corbet Gore's window at the end of the Opera House... moor down at the Man o'War steps here, and come ashore... I remember taking my secretary back across the Harbour by water one evening. She was quite delighted.[9]

Rice wrote regarding 'our attempts to assess the errors in position' of the first segments.

We have taken a week to reach a firm decision on how to correct it. Even this decision was far from satisfactory as in the end it was little more than a best guess, based on a lot of conflicting information. This is obviously intolerable and we cannot go on in this way. We have with Corbet had a major re-consideration of how we survey and set out the arches and this is to be incorporated immediately. We are also considering some changes in the erection technique and sequence...

When trying to assess the error in A5 1/2W we used XYZ co-ordinates to points p, q, r and t. The point r we found to be useless because we could not properly define it.(Point) p also, being on the boundary plane was liable to error. The other two, q and t, are undoubtedly the best and most consistent. We tried to work out the orientation of the upper diaphragm plane from the co-ordinates of p, q and t but this was no good because we found that the possible error in orientation of the diaphragm in the forms swamped the effects we were trying to measure...

Another possibility being actively considered by us at the moment is to build the whole arch and then rotate it back into position when complete. This would involve a considerable change in detail, an effective hinge would be required at the 3in joint, and a significant temporary prestress (800 kips?) would be needed to avoid damage. We obviously will not do this unless we have to. Equally obviously the arch erection will have to be speeded up...

Although things look ominous at the moment things often do in the beginning. There are many special conditions about this first segment which can be corrected and improved, and if we can devise and get some kind of scheduling to assess errors we may not be too bad. I hope so.[10]

A letter from David Dowrick in London on diaphragm drainage holes also mentioned

... the likely invasion of Arups (Sydney) by Peter Dowrick who has crossed the Tasman for his first University vacation. It's tough when my young brother sees the job before me! I have recommended him to introduce himself to you all so please be kind to him, especially Peter.[11]

The job was winding down for the Christmas break, which would give the engineers some breathing space to think about the misalignment of the side shell arch segments.

In January *Construction* magazine ran an article on the Opera House entitled 'Putting Sails in Unchartered Space.'

> The secret of what is happening there on the foreshore of Circular Quay lies in the character of the man doing the job, D. C. Gore, Corbet to his friends.
>
> Solidly built, he is the antithesis of what might be expected. With a thousand and one details to be watched, and with an almost nightmarish number of major problems yet to be solved, Corbet Gore goes on his way unhurried and calm. His unpretentious desk in his construction office is clear of litter, there is not the slightest trace of nervous tension for his work is so planned that he always has time to think, even if some of the thinking is done as he drives to and from work.
>
> "I have a good staff," is the way he answers the question. "We are here from eight to six for six days a week and that should be enough. I don't take my work home with me and in the evenings I like to relax with TV and on Sundays work about the garden."[12]

Arups too were under no illusions about the contribution of Corbet Gore who:

> was brought down to look after the Opera House and was the director of the company on site. For sheer skill, coupled with an ability to manage people and for getting the Opera House shells built, he deserves all the credit. He's a very quiet, self effacing man, but without him, we could never had done it. We were proposing to build something which was very unusual and very difficult, and unlike most constructors, he turned round every problem and treated it in a positive way. He didn't find ways for not doing it, but treated a problem as a problem to be solved, which is unusual. Corbet conceived some very interesting ideas on how to put the Opera House together. We had some ideas, of our own, for instance how to handle the concrete elements, but they were ill thought out. It was Corbet who came up with the ideas for the special lifting tackle. Then the idea to cast the segments with matching surfaces, which had a most profound effect on the very quality of the look of the Opera House, was also his. Certainly the decision to go ahead with these proposals was ultimately ours, but the concepts were his.
>
> I could name a hundred and one other different things. By his personal example, with the long hours he put in and his leadership on the site, he really kept the job rolling forward. Not least in his capacity in dealing with the men, because it was a time, if ever there's not a time, when there was a great deal of industrial unrest in the construction industry. Australia is rather renowned for its industrial problems in the construction industry. And he dealt with it all magnificently.[13]

Even at this stage the design of the structure had not been completely tied down and there were detail changes still to come that would effect the casting of the rib segments. Some of these alterations were to allow for lateral stressing ducts in the ribs following the changeover from the Rice Structure to the Baker Structure.[14]

> The Rice Structure was the condition of the shell structure before it was stressed together laterally and therefore a certain amount of movement could take place between ribs. The Baker Structure was what we called the structure when the lateral stressing had been applied and stressed...
>
> The decision was made that we ought to stress the ribs together permanently, so that then had to be analysed and Alan Baker had a program which he'd developed himself at University which was able to analyse this structure. Earlier on the structure would have been too complex, we'd have had too many unknowns in it to have analysed it. The program that Peter Rice had written and was used on the Rice Structure could only cope with a hundred redundants, a hundred unknowns, if that. Peter Rice moved onto site, so the analysis of the new structure, the stressed together structure, was taken on by Alan Baker.
>
> Early Rice computer analyses were an extension of techniques used in traditional calculations by hand and were at the limit of the capacity of the computers at the time. The Baker Structure was a refinement of all the work that had gone on before on the Rice Structure, and was only possible because of newer more powerful computers.
>
> (The Rice Structure) had the lateral connections in the form of the bolts. So it was strong enough. But you would have got movement, you had the wind and of course temperature. And I suppose there were other long-term fatigue capabilities of the bolts. That was an unknown and of course rather difficult to test.[15]

Arups and Utzon's office embarked on enormous and extensive parallel investigations leaving no stone unturned in a quest to find a way to waterproof the joint between ribs in the Rice Structure to allow for movement.[16] Arups favoured lead, Utzon preferred copper.

> Lead caulking was the ultimate outcome of a bitter struggle and emerged victorious largely because it could permanently resist movement... Kelman wrote to Zunz from Sydney on 10th February,
>
> The Baker Shell, now trussed like an Edwardian Dowager, cannot breathe. Its ribs lack relative freedom, and if the inter rib joint is to be grouted as a shear key, the justification for the lead is gone. This is of course, wonderful ammunition for his lordship, who may possibly be waiting for the whites of our eyes to show, but who has as yet held his fire![17]

But Arups stuck to their guns, and in the end it was lead that was used for the caulking.

The main thrust of the design on the Opera House shells, the effort, the number of people involved and the major part of the work, went into the design of the ribs and the side shell arches. A relatively minor effort, but an absolutely essential one, involved the design of the lateral bolts. To prevent the fan of ribs from opening out like the ribs of a paper fan with no paper to hold them together, the ribs of the Opera House were held together by lateral bolts. The lateral bolts were just that, a nut and a bolt. What could be simpler, but nothing was simple on the Opera House and the bolts eventually used pushed forward the scientific frontiers of the day.

The bolts holding the ribs together were buried in the structure and could not be inspected once the Opera House was completed. Their role was critical – they could not fail – and they had to resist corrosion in Sydney's salty atmosphere for at least the design life of the building which was 300 years, with no possibility that any moisture condensing on the metal could absorb any substance and drip onto and stain the adjacent concrete. The bolts had to have an ultimate tensile strength of 70 – 90 tons/sq in and be able to stand thousands of stress reversals through the life of the building.

In the Rice Structure, each rib would have been free to move up and down relative to its neighbour up to one inch on the longest ribs, so rocking washers were fitted under the bolt heads so 'ribs and bolts were, in effect, alternate links in a chain.'[18] With the advent of the Baker Structure, ribs could move relative to each other during erection, but not on the completed building; so whichever structure was used the bolts had to allow for initial movement during construction. For example the longest ribs compressed by nearly half an inch due to 'elastic shortening' as the concrete itself compressed during final stressing. Also

> The shells are, in fact, assemblages of inter-connected tubular concrete ribs, fanning out from a single point of support on each side and meeting at the ridge; rather like two cupped hands laid finger-tip to finger-tip. And, during erection, the ribs must be capable, like the fingers, of independent movement. In fact, at this stage, this independence is the crux of the design, allowing for movements due to wind load, differential creep and unequal thermal expansion.[19]

A redesign of the bolts was necessary because long bolts had a greater resistance to fatigue than shorter ones (Fig.31 and 32). The new design had to make use of the original bolt pockets as the size of the pockets was limited to that of the earlier design since they had to fit between the ducts provided for the longitudinal prestressing cables. The original intention was to have the ribs bolted together at the edge of the rib, so all the bolts would be 2 ft 6 in long. With the new system, the bolts passed approximately through the centre line of the ribs so the bolts became progressively longer the higher they were up the shell with those close to the top of the highest shell 8 ft long.

An extensive search was set in motion to find a suitable metal for the bolts. Stainless steel was out because it was not sufficiently corrosion resistant. 'Nionel' was looked at, an alloy of nickel, chromium and iron, and so was Delta Bronz. Hornibrooks went to the Austral Bronz Company in Sydney who recommended an alloy of a mixture of copper, lead, tin, iron, manganese, aluminium and zinc which they called 'Manganese bronze'. Finally the search narrowed down to a choice of two materials: K-Monel 500, a copper-nickel alloy, or a titanium alloy containing 4 per cent aluminium and 4 per cent manganese. For the fabrication of the bolts Arups went to Frederick Mountford of Birmingham who specialised in corrosion resistant fasteners. As far as corrosion was concerned, titanium was the best material available – virtually everlasting.[20]

The saga of the design of the lateral bolts is best told by recourse to the original documents. 'As a general comment on the supply and manufacture of these bolts we must make every effort to get as many guarantees as possible from the firms supplying and making them as this will impress on them how important it is that they be right',[21] wrote Peter Rice to Corbet Gore on 1st May 1963. It had been known the bolts would be used in early 1962, but due to the research involved in finding a material that was up to the job, and outstanding questions on their detailing, Corbet Gore found himself in London on 18th July 1963 discussing the bolts:

> since it is going to be very difficult to get the materials most urgently required to Sydney in time to meet the construction schedule...
>
> Initial supplies of completed bolts must be in Sydney by 1st November 1963 for use on the first ribs of shells 1 and 2 of the Major Hall...
>
> (U.K. sources were quoting a delivery time of 20 weeks for K-Monel and Mountfords needed a further two weeks to have them machined)
>
> Should it serve any useful purpose, Mr Gore offered to call in at International Nickel in Canada on his way back to Sydney next week.[22]

International Nickel Canada were the main supplier in the world of K-Monel.

Kelman had written to London of the demoralising effect amendments to drawings was having in Sydney. Zunz wrote back on 16th September:

> ... I have never tried to withhold the true position as regards alterations of designs and working drawings from Corbet. In fact I have done quite the reverse. I have advised him time and time again that in the initial stages the construction may have to be carried out to the rate of production of drawings because our design was not far enough advanced. On numerous occasions we have issued drawings knowing only full well that certain aspects of the design had not been completed and Corbet has never been unaware of the situation.
>
> We hope that this will now come to an end but there is one major exception. Your detail, Bob, of the lateral bolts "in action" has set the cat amongst the pigeons. The efficacy of the whole assembly is now in doubt and we are frantically reconsidering the whole issue. We are having a meeting with G.K.N. Fasteners this week. We will give you details as soon as possible, but in the meantime for segments 1-5 (A1 & A2), we have no choice but to carry on with what you are doing.[23]

Zunz wrote to Gore on the 23rd:

> (We) hope you will continue to be patient and understand the difficulties we have to overcome.
>
> I am writing to you in connection with the lateral bolt assembly which has now reared its ugly head. We have had a continuing process of designing and redesigning governed by the results of our calculations, construction needs and availability of suitable materials. When we came to what we thought was the end of the process, Peter, who has been dealing with this problem, packed his bags and flew to Sydney. As a result of some observations of Bob's we have now reassessed what we thought to be the final design. Some weaknesses in the design have become apparent and in Peter's absence we have had to put other people on to it to pick up the threads (figuratively not literally!).
>
> We are now working very hard to improve the detail and while we hope that there will be no major amendments to the ribs it is likely that minor ones will follow. These may of course involve you in some further modifications to the formwork, but this is all I can tell you for the moment. In the meantime, you must proceed with the information you have and unless we find any major snags we don't think it ought to matter anyway for the first few ribs which you are now proceeding to cast. Please bear with us for the moment... [24]

LATERAL THINKING

Zunz then wrote to Lewis and Kelman on 3rd October

... Peter is of course centrally involved in this issue and it is a great pity that he is not here just at the present when this crisis has arisen. On the other hand we have to do the best we can and if after Peter's arrival in Sydney you, he, or we jointly or separately consider it desirable for him to personally rummage through past calculations it might be worth considering his coming back here for a week or ten days. Don't take this too seriously at the moment, I am merely thinking aloud...

The bending moment set up in the bolt is excessive and Bob's sketch illustrates this very forcibly. In addition, however, the axial extension of the bolt due to the change in geometry causes very substantial fluctuations in stress and over the short length of the bolt we are now advised that these fluctuations bring us into the fatigue range. Thus the fluctuating stresses would have to be limited... Theoretically we really want universal joints which is a tall order on a structural engineering project...

In having this uneasy feeling that we are really applying the knowledge and experience of a mechanical engineering device to civil engineering structure, I am conscious of the uniqueness of the problem. Conversely this uniqueness should not let us cloud our common sense and experience...[25]

Kelman outlined the technical reason for the increase in the length of the bolt in a letter to David Dowrick.

... Assuming movement after installation will not be more than $\frac{1}{2}$ in and that when installed there is no moment, my calculations indicate that a movement of $\frac{1}{2}$ in involves an alteration in alignment of approximately 1°. The co-sine of 1° is 0·99984 and assuming the Young's Modulous of about 15 million, the stress thus induced is well under 3,000 pounds per square inch. The obvious answer is to increase the bolts size until this is not serious...

In the light of all these potential changes we have instructed Hornibrooks to block out for 5 in square bearing plates in the lower six segments...[26]

Zunz wrote to Lewis and Kelman again on the 15th:

I wrote to you on the 3rd to outline our dilemma because not only do we want your help technically in understanding the problems we face and how we see them, but we also need your and Hornibrook's understanding. We have now reached the end of our deliberations and while I have cabled you and spoken to you on the 'phone last week, I thought it would be best to have a weekend before writing to you explaining all the gory details.

To continue where we left off in my last letter and to paint the picture for you somewhat more clearly, it has always been my intention to provide belt and braces for the lateral connections. In fact these were the words which we have always used. As the design progressed we were being driven more and more into a corner where the lateral stressing appeared to introduce incalculable effects and where in the end what with time running out and a good deal of analytical evidence facing us, we accepted a belt only in the form of bolts. Admittedly we decided as a matter of policy to provide a very firm belt in allowing a substantial factor of safety but in the end we relied solely on the bolted connections.

We were faced then with the choice of proceeding with a bolted connection only, roughly along the lines indicated to you in our previous letter, or introducing lateral stressing with or without the bolts knowing that the effects of the stressing are not so far fully understood. All this of course has to be measured against the reality that events have caught up with us and that rib 1 shell 2 was about to be cast. We therefore put our heads together and in making the decision which inevitably has far reaching consequences, we took advice from many members of the firm including some not directly connected with the job.

Without exception we all felt that lateral stressing was a good idea if correctly controlled and we all admitted that we weren't quite sure of the quantitive effects of such stressing. We also felt that bolting was necessary during erection and during decentering. There is no question of a permanent attachment of the rib to its neighbours at this stage. We were left with the following possibilities:
1. To use bolts only.
2. To use bolts to a lesser specification coupled with lateral stressing.
3. To use bolts to the full specification coupled with lateral stressing.

We decided on the third possibility which really brings us back to the initial brief, namely to have belt and braces. The thinking therefore is that if radial and tangential shears are such as to make the lateral prestressing locally or wholly ineffective (which we don't believe) the bolts are adequate for the safety of the structure. On the other hand we also believe that lateral stressing does give us a better structure on the whole. We are studying the various effects of lateral stressing. Our details will then allow us to omit it in parts of the structure if our calculations finally show it to be inadvisable and again if during construction some unforeseen measures have to be taken there is no reason why horses shouldn't be changed in midstream. This is an extreme view and shouldn't be taken too seriously at this stage but it illustrates to you the flexibility which we will have built in...

We have looked into the calculations to find out the order of shears which are developed and we know that these are of substantial magnitude but when spread over the length of a rib they can probably be dealt with. The localised shear force has come about because of the limitation of our calculations where more numerous attachments prove beyond the capacity of the computer...

> In making this change, which is rather a drastic one, I realise full well that we may be setting the contract back for a period which only you and Hornibrooks can establish. The seriousness therefore of making this alteration is known to us. On the other hand you know that Hornibrooks were forewarned about the possibility of having their enthusiasm tempered until sufficient information became available. In fact looking back over the past year it is a surprise to me that we haven't had to substantially delay operations before today and while this may be poor compensation for those having to be burdened with all the ramifications of amending the formwork and so on, it is nevertheless a thought worth bearing in mind. Our apologies therefore to you and Hornibrooks – we are hopeful that from our side this is the last of any major modifications...[27]

Technology was advancing with the Opera House, but sometimes not quite fast enough. The slow computers of the day sometimes could not crunch through the numbers quick enough to produce answers to the many complex structural analyses required on the shells. Or the programs were not available to do it, so Arups had to write them from scratch.[28]

When Rice arrived in Sydney, after thinking the matter over he sent two long letters to Jack Zunz discussing aspects of lateral stressing, in particular the effect of expansion in a rib or ribs due to heating on one side by the sun, and the effect this was likely to have at the lateral stressing points:

> ... I have discussed some precautions which I feel we should take with this scheme and I have attempted to relate aspects of the problem of multiple stressing to the erection sequence. I have in addition suggested one modification in thinking which could if necessary be worked into a complete solution.
>
> I hope you will accept these comments in the spirit in which they are made, I am acutely conscious how difficult, vexed and delicate is the problem of lateral stressing, and I feel, if such a thing be possible, very humble in discussing the problem at all. I would like also to say that in spite of many words to the contrary I too appreciate the benefits of lateral prestressing and I have spent a lot of time in the past trying to devise a satisfactory solution. I have not, until we received your letter, considered multiple stressing of a kind now being used.[29]

What would happen, ruminated Rice, 'under symmetrical temperature increase of one rib relative to its neighbours...'? Can 'the top section, or that nearest the ridge... be held, without deflection'? Probably not, so the 'ridge beam may deflect', but what effect would this have and '...

what is the approximate value of the deflection needed at the highest stressed joint.'? Rice's letter continued:

Under unsymmetrical heating, that is differential heating of one side only as could occur when the sun shines on the inner face of one half of the shell, (as could happen at the open end of the shells) the nature of the force and deflection in the ridge member will be complex...

We may find that we have less real safety than we imagine if a form of progressive failure is possible.

If we consider again the case of an internal stressing point (i.e. a bolt or lateral stressing cable anchor) we have found that a radial force will tend to be developed, when one rib is heated and the remainder are not. These forces will tend to be accumulative, when summed from one end, i.e.They will all be in the same direction. If we now think of the top rib (say 16 Shell A2) we can easily see that they will produce a torsion in this rib. It would seem to me that very little relief will be available for this torsion, from strain energy considerations. Where does it go? And can we be sure that no severe cracking will occur in the webs? If cracking could occur in the webs, would it matter?[30]

These were just some of the many points Rice raised and 'I do not think I have exhausted all the problems which could arise...'. 'I accept that there may be no positive answer to them and that one must be guided by experience. However, I am sure we should find an order of magnitude for each of them and satisfy ourselves that we are operating in the right range...'[31]

Rice's second letter continued:

Herewith Part II of my thoughts on lateral connections.

I hope you find them not too disturbing, or arrogantly presented. I am trying to help.

... in the work we have already done on the temperature condition, we found that when part of the shell was covered by tile lids and part of it was not the temperature variation across adjacent ribs was not dissimilar to that existing across the glass wall.

... We could leave the lids off progressively, and by measuring concrete temperatures and temperature variations transversely across the ribs ensure that we had almost covered the same temperature conditions as those expected across the glass wall.

... The final stress condition (in the shell) will be a function of the temperature difference existing between ribs at the time they are stressed.

... The sun, as we know, can cause quite sharp temperature differences from one side to the other and from one rib to another and there may be some sense in stipulating that lateral prestressing may only be done in the shade, or early in the morning, or when the ribs are under some sort of covering.

… You say in your letter to Mick and Bob, that the lateral bolts are to be retained as a safety device. However, your recent enquiries have indicated that there is a real possibility of fatigue failure in them. I would therefore suggest that to make them more realistic as a safety device, a radial shear key is used which would not be damaged by tangential movements…[32]

This then exhausts my present thoughts on lateral stressing, I hope that you have not been at any time offended by my approach. I do not for one moment think that these observations will come as a surprise to you in London. I only feel that placing them on paper at this time may be of some benefit.

I had a very fine holiday on my way here. Sydney is a very pleasant place, quite impossible to dislike it. We have found a little house along the coast, near Ed and John. It begins to look as though I shall be healthy and brown in spite of my reluctance. Sylvia is arriving tomorrow with the children, I will be a happy man then… [33]

Zunz wrote to Lewis on 4th November

When we went through our recent purge about lateral bolts money was of course no object! We didn't at the time make any comparisons because we felt that the problem was so difficult that cost consideration could only be a side issue.

… While the accurate figures are not yet available it would appear that the material as presently specified will cost approximately £80,000 ex U.K…[34]

Arups original estimate for the lateral stressing for the shells, including pre-stressed cable and bolts *had* been £20,000 and this had now suddenly jumped to £90,000. Lewis found the figure of £80,000 'comes as rather a shock.'

I do not think there is any need to raise this before the Technical Panel until we have firmly established what we are going to do and how much it will cost. In any event, it is essential and I doubt very much whether anybody will fuss about it.[35]

On the 8th Zunz wrote to Mountfords:

We have received your letter of the 7th November. The shipping dates you quote would mean that the bolts would not be available until early March in Sydney if they are airfreighted.

This late delivery may have very serious repercussions. Expenditure on site is now being maintained at a very substantial rate and non-availability of these bolts would bring a section of the job to a complete standstill…[36]

And Zunz begged Mountfords to do everything they could to urge their suppliers to cut down delivery times.

On site Hornibrooks were sweating on the revised drawings for lateral connections on the segments to keep casting of rib segments underway. The subject was a frequent source of discussion at the weekly site conferences and was jotted down under the heading of 'Unresolved Design and Construction Problems.'

16.10.63. Lateral stressing and lateral bolts, drawings on their way from London.

23.10.63. ... Lateral stressing and lateral bolts – insufficient details have been received for work to proceed. This matter is UNRESOLVED AND URGENT.

30.10.63. Lateral stressing and lateral bolts. Information is virtually complete for first five ribs, subject to receipt of drawing 4051C, which was despatched from London on 24.10.63. However, details for subsequent ribs still urgently required.

6.11.63. Lateral stressing and lateral bolts. Drawing 4051C has been received but information still incomplete. URGENT AND UNRESOLVED.

13.11.63. Lateral stressing and lateral bolts. RESOLVED.[37]

Zunz wrote to Lewis on 19th November:

It is probably just as well to give you the full story in small doses. I am not withholding anything from you but the full financial repercussions of the changed design of the bolts is only just coming to light. We have a fairly accurate estimate of the material costs which are £53,000 (Sterling). The manufacturing costs though are as yet unknown but could be as much as £100,000 (Sterling).[38]

Meanwhile the GKN Research Laboratories at Wolverhampton had agreed to construct a test rig for Arups for fatigue loading on the bolts and rockers, agreeing to carry out the work for no charge. '... It will be possible to simulate 100 years of building life in about a week's testing... Tests will be carried out on the most severe condition.'[39]

Orders were deferred for bolts not urgently required '... so that we can change the detail if necessary, after we have gained the experience of erecting the first few ribs...'.[40]

Arups sent the specification of the new bolts to Sydney, which had a 1½ in diameter shank with a 2 in diameter thread, and Kelman showed it to Hornibrooks:

... who have had a fit. Seriously, is it appreciated that we now have to place a bolt with a 2 in diameter thread on the end through adjacent flanges, each of which has a tapered hole tapering to a maximum of $2\frac{3}{4}$ in. This in fact, means we have now limited the tolerance to $\pm$ 3/8 in...

It gives me the horrors, but at the moment I cannot think of anything to do about it.[41]

Gore wrote to Zunz on 19th December concerning the planned contract time for the roof shells of two years

... I realise that from a design point of view you are somewhat in a corner with these lateral connections and I know that there is no deliberate attempt to reduce tolerances just for the sake of reducing them and, as I stated in my letter of 4th November, it is a different thing to aim at a tolerance than be limited by a tolerance. Our experience on the few segments that we have put up, and admittedly they are octopus segments which are more awkward to handle and align, is that it is extremely difficult to work to $\frac{1}{2}$ in. In fact, by the cumulation of errors of concrete surfaces, survey, etc., I doubt if we would know whether we were within a $\frac{1}{4}$ in at any time.

Consequently, with both your schemes 1 and 2 for the long titanium bolts, I think we will be facing erection difficulties which could well be insurmountable and at least could make time of erection considerably longer...

Unless the tolerances available allow the segments in the main shells to be erected and placed in position like a brickie laying bricks, then the two years could stretch indefinitely. You can perhaps see from this why I am getting cold feet from the lateral bolting details...

I am sorry to upset your Christmas like this and naturally if there is no other way out then we will give it a go, but I can foresee repercussions both construction-wise and from the political angle of time of completion.[42]

Mountfords then had a fit when they heard the design of the lateral bolts could possibly change once again to reduce the bolt diameter. Not least among the points they raised was that '... The titanium material is probably by now all ground to final dimensions and being heat treated.'[43]

Bob Kelman was due to return to London shortly, and on 2nd January he wrote a personal note to Jack Zunz:

This is a sort of end of term report, or summing up. To me, as the year is about to change and my term (or sentence) to expire, it feels like a sort of last will and testament.

The job is very far from being in the position I/we visualised it would be when I left London fourteen months ago and our relations with the Master leave much to be desired. All this could have been foreseen, but a much more disturbing aspect was not.

I mean by this the split with the Colony. Colonials have always tended to act on their own initiative where necessary. Ian has done this for years. I found it necessary when I came and each succeeding arrival, often contrary to his expressed wish and intent, has rapidly found himself at loggerheads with the imperial direction.

This has become a standing joke here. As each new arrival appears his attitude and convictions change almost quicker than the colour of his knees!

The situation now is that we feel you regard this office as something of a nuisance, whose attitude and recommendations are frequently a considerable embarrassment to the smooth functioning of the drawing office.

This should not be so, and the fact that it is so should give rise to thought, especially as the people sent here are not all irresponsible and have all laboured mightily in the conceiving of this monster. (The possibility that all have in the past been so far below club standards that, with admirable English diplomacy they were turned into Remittance Men and banished to the Colonies, I pass over – not, however, without some misgiving!!)

The reason for this change of heart could conceivably be that they do not consider the ideas conceived in the sanctuary of the drawing office can stand up to the exigencies of the site conditions. It may be hard to think up a satisfactory lateral bolting detail, but I am sure it is going to be a ruddy sight harder to get an unsatisfactory one into place on site.

Lateral bolts are, of course, the prime example of a detail we think has got out of hand and is now divorced from all site constraint, but ridge access and the small question of drainage holes are examples of the Home Office's complete preoccupation with design, untrammelled by nasty reminders that these have to be built.

Neither Peter nor I are able to accept the arguments put up against access from ridge to ribs, although I agree that the later modifications have even further restricted their purpose. I have always thought, and still do, that to build an unmaintainable building is foolish and deliberately to restrict access to the few areas where fixings and water-proofing could be inspected is irresponsible. After all the Rolls Royce is a very fine motor car, but we are trying to build one on which you can neither open the bonnet nor take off the wheels!...

And concerning drainage holes in the segments:

Your comment that "we don't understand what is difficult about building in a small hole etc." argues strongly that it is time you came again and saw for yourself!

The reason why it is not only difficult but b...... impossible is that the matching holes are in the internal steel forms and once these forms are in

350

place neither an intelligent gorilla nor a technically trained o'possum can get down to check whether the plastic liner fouls the steel, and while something approaching the former may well be available on site the latter probably lacks the physical strength to bend the steel out of the way!...

While I have the highest respect for some of the "expert advice" you are prone to take in your intellectual mecca, some good practical advice is often available from the people who actually have got to get the job done – witness our use of explosives!...

We are suffering on this job from having a contractor who is willing, and sometimes carried away by his enthusiasm, to help us achieve impossible results. If Corbet had said in the beginning that the whole thing was a sort of fool's nightmare we probably would not be so ready now to demand that little bit beyond what he has estimated he could, with loving care achieve.

I have written the foregoing in confidence that you know me well enough not to be offended. It does worry me that in putting these views I may be adding to the worries you already have and of which I have a fair appreciation, but somehow we must be able to build the job and if we here are to be of any help at all we must be taken seriously.

Wagers are practically being taken here on my behaviour when I return – as to whether I remain a colonial spokesman or suffer a reversion. My private hope is that I never see a Sydney drawing again, but it is said alcoholics feel this way too, after a bad bout!

We remember the old service motto – "Nil Bastardo Carborundum" – and remain cheerful, as well as wishing you all a very Happy New Year.[44]

David Dowrick wrote to Mick Lewis on 10th January:

We have just issued (drawings) 1112/F83 and Sk962, both of which concern the packing of the lateral gaps between ribs. As the shears between ribs are often higher than can be dealt with by prestress and friction alone, keys must be provided on the flanges as shown in F83. Early ribs are satisfactory as cast, but the key recesses should be incorporated as soon as possible and not later than the interface between ribs 5 and 6 on shells A1, A2, B1, B2. They should extend from top to bottom of each rib... [45]

The same day, John Blanchard wrote to Peter Rice:

Your very lucid and helpful memos of 23/24-10-63 have not been neglected and as Alan Baker's mammoth task of analysing the laterally stressed structures draws to an end, I am in a better position to comment intelligently on the points raised therein.

Allan has analysed the Baker Structure (as the laterally stressed shell is named) for each of the Major Hall shells using his partitioned space framework program...

For Shell A2, he has also analysed the Rice Structure (i.e. the bolted shell) for self-weight of rib...

As you may have suspected all this was a formidable task, the first load case of each structure takes three hours (of computer) machine time and each subsequent case about half an hour. There is a vast brute mass of input data to prepare and the welter of output that emerges periodically takes weeks to collate and plot. (Copies of these graphs are being prepared for you and will be sent when complete). However, Alan has developed a pretty smooth technique for handling these complex analyses and has become particularly adept as a diagnostician in detecting irregularities in the output and determining the input error responsible. An interesting error of this kind occurred on A2 where the Y co-ordinate of a node near the pedestal on one rib was punched with the wrong sign, so that this particular node was situated over the harbour instead of in the shell. The effect of this was as if Hornibrooks had omitted to put in one segment of that rib since the members meeting at this node were several hundred feet long and did not carry much load. The bolted structure objected most strongly to this treatment as the dead load on this rib had to be carried in tension up to the ridge beam which spread the load back to adjacent ribs. The laterally stressed structure, however, was much more accommodating, the omission producing quite minor disturbances.[46]

Blanchard explained the analyses used that had reached the conclusion shear keys would be required between ribs, and went through the other points Rice had raised.

We are not proposing to analyse for unsymmetric temperature... the ridge beam should be flexible enough in the east-west direction to accommodate even the full free deflection without any distress...

Yes, the torsions in Rib 16 are high, but not too high for David to have his arm twisted and accept them.

We have not yet looked at the effect of temperature variation along a rib, but this can easily be done (given the shape of the temperature curve).

You are quite right, loss of prestress due to temperature fall is significant especially on Rib A2-16 (it would be!) but is not much greater than the Dead Load thrust and is no real embarrassment. But we are going to analyse for wind here to see what support is supplied by lower ribs, in which case we can also investigate unsymmetric temperature.

I agree that it would be worthwhile taking temperature readings in ribs adjacent to the leading edge of the tiling. You seem to imply that the tile erection should be halted for this; whether this is desirable should, I think, be decided on the spot in the light of circumstances, but I should have thought one of the natural breaks in the erection would have sufficed.[47]

R.K. Elms of Arups London wrote to Mick Lewis on 29th January:

> I have been looking into the possibility of pre-loading the lateral bolts in order to reduce fatigue and hence, bolt diameter. The answer seems to be that we can reduce the diameter to about $1\frac{1}{4}$ in throughout providing the nut can be tightened sufficiently to induce a prestress in the bolt of 24 Tons/sq in. This will mean applying a torque of approximately 7,500 lb in. to the nut. Would you get Hornibrooks' views on this and on ways of controlling this prestress.
>
> Having discussed this all round, we believe that the best answer from a design point of view is to preload the bolts after lateral prestressing and before the appropriate tile lids are placed... [48]

Meanwhile it transpired in fatigue tests carried out at Cambridge University that K-Monel '... has more favourable resistance to fatigue than Titanium. The manufacturers of the Titanium have fallen behind with their order and we are attempting to cancel, or at least delay, manufacture until we know whether we can switch over to K-Monel altogether...'.[49] Elms wrote to Mountfords passing on the results of the fatigue tests, which '... seem to show that the fatigue strength is much better than we assumed and that a reduction of bolt diameter is possible. Our intention is to reduce (the diameter of) all bolts, except urgent ones, to 1 in diameter for both shank and thread.'[50]

But availability of titanium was much better than that of K-Monel, so where it was impossible to get hold of the K-Monel in time titanium bolts were delivered to maintain the erection schedule on site. But then Mountfords found they could not get delivery of sufficient high-grade K-Monel (Type D) and some bolts would have to be made with a lower grade K-Monel (Type B), which meant bolts in three materials being delivered to Sydney. Altogether on the Opera House shells there would be a total quantity of over 700 bolts and they would be in eight different lengths from 30 in to $97\frac{3}{4}$ in long. Also, bolts of the same length in some locations on the shells were subject to higher stresses than those in other locations. So Arups instructed Mountfords which bolts could be made in which materials and when the bolts were despatched. Titanium bolts were marked with a green band round the shank and the letter 'T' stamped on the end, 'grade D' K-Monel bolts would have a red band round the shank, while the lower 'grade B' K-Monel bolts would not have any special mark except for the letter 'M' stamped on the end face. Arups produced a schedule for Hornibrooks to show which bolts could be used where on the shells. All this rigmarole was quite apart from the fact that bolts were urgently required on site to maintain the construction schedule and bolts were being progressively shipped to match that schedule.

In November 1964 Corbet Gore received a letter addressed to Hornibrooks in Sydney from Mr R. Hutson of East Greenwich in London, to which Gore replied:

> Thank you for your letter and we greatly appreciate your consideration in writing to us regarding the box you found in London. From your brief description, it would appear that the components you found are part of the structure for the roof of the Sydney Opera House. These components were being specially manufactured in England for shipment out here, and were probably en route to the docks when the case fell from the lorry...
>
> Thank you again for your thoughtfulness in writing to us as the construction of this project could well have been delayed if new parts had to be made in England and shipped out. As a matter of general interest, I am enclosing an aerial photograph of the site showing the construction of the Opera House at its present stage. I hope it will be of interest to you.[51]

Mountfords assured Gore '... We have telegraphed and written to Mr Hutson asking him if he can tell us where we may locate the box which he saw falling from the lorry, as this is almost certainly one of the boxes included in our consignment... shipped per S.S. *Doric* and from which consignment one case was reported missing. Needless to say we shall take all necessary action at this end to recover this case and the contents, and re-despatch to you at the earliest opportunity.'[52]

To produce the original bolt design with a $1\frac{1}{2}$ in diameter shank and 2 in diameter forged and threaded ends, Mountfords ordered $1\frac{1}{2}$ in diameter bolt material and commissioned Garringtons to design and manufacture forging tools and a special furnace and to carry out forging trials. So this cost was included in Mountford's final bill. The $1\frac{1}{2}$ in diameter bolts were machined down to a 1 in diameter straight shank with threaded ends and Mountfords offered to sell the excess metal swarf when they could and issue a credit. This they estimated to be in the order of £3,000 to £8,000.[53]

In the entire order of lateral bolts for the Opera House there were 742, of which 208 were titanium. Of Mountfords final bill of £98,967, £74,850 of the cost was in the anchor plates and rocker washers. The anchor plates were simple thick rectangular plates of K-Monel drilled with two holes. They weighed 49 lb each; there were 606 of them and they cost £48 each. The rocker washers, also in K-Monel, weighed 14.3 lb each; there were 2,532 of them and they cost £18 each.[54]

But would the K-Monel type 'D' 1 in diameter studs used in the most critical locations in the Opera House sustain a proof stress of 54 tons/sq in under a pre-loading of the bolt to 7,500 lb in the nut under accelerated corrosion tests? Blanchard wrote to Sydney 'Dear Mick, Allah is merciful sometimes. I enclose a copy of a report on corrosion tests for the bolted assemblies.'[55]

The report from the City of Birmingham Public Works Department Industrial Research Laboratories on a Sydney Opera House K-Monel bolt assembly supplied by Frederick Mountford confirmed 'The assembly sustained a proof stress of 54 tons/sq in and satisfied the specification requirements.[56]

To allow for the lateral movement between ribs during construction a number of slippery pads were placed along the length of the rib to act as a sliding joint. But with the change from the Rice to the Baker Structure there was the question of whether to stick with the original expensive pads designed for the Rice Structure and expected to last for the life of the building or go with a cheaper one that only had to last for the construction phase. Blanchard wrote to Nutt in Sydney:

> Obviously the slippery pads are needed during the construction stage since without them the deflections due to dead load and prestressing are restrained, and unacceptable stresses are set up thereby.
>
> (though) when the Baker Structure has been formed by grouting and laterally stressing (the ribs) the slipperiness of the pads is no longer apparently required...
>
> when we had to order the pads we were still not sure if the Baker Structure would work and we had therefore to be prepared to build a pure Rice Structure. Indeed, although we have no reason to suspect the Baker Analysis, we still like to have the possibility of building the Rice Structure in reserve...
>
> As you know, our design philosophy is to visualise the possibility that although the Baker Structure will remain intact initially, eventually a local shear failure may occur in the inter-rib packing due perhaps, to some abnormal temperature distribution. Although this failure is probably not directly self propagating, it will permit some relative movement between ribs. This movement occurring daily and assisted by enhanced corrosive conditions could lead to a fatigue failure of the lateral strand. Breakdown of the inter-rib shear connections would then spread

with increasing speed, and the structure would degenerate (in the mathematical sense) to something like the original Rice Structure. Our safeguard against this, admittedly remote, possibility, is to design all members and the lateral bolt assemblies for the theoretical stresses and deflections arising in both the Baker and the Rice Structures.

Now admittedly we do not know whether the structure would degenerate completely to the Rice form, but we feel that with the slippery pads remaining active we are more likely to finish up with a structure that we know and, in our twisted way, even like, than in the limbo of some intermediate and imperfectly understood structure.[57]

The pads for the Opera House, ordered specially for the job, were made by the Glacier Metal Company in Wembley, London, 'Europe's largest manufacturer of plain bearings.' They were required to have an anticipated life of 100 years and like the bolts, could not corrode in any way to leave stains on the adjacent concrete. The specification for the pads was 'two metal plates of bronze or stainless steel with a sandwiched inert material (the Glacier-du pads used polytetraflouroethylene – commonly known as PTFE or teflon) with a coefficient of friction never greater than 0.1 or 0.12 and permitting a shear movement of one inch... (they) should carry a normal load of 126 kips without exceeding a concrete stress of 2 kips/sq in.' Over 900 of the pads were used on the Opera House and they had a typical size of $8\frac{1}{2}$ in x 20 in.[58] As the Stage II construction drew to a close and Arups worked out the quantities required to finish the restaurant, Blanchard wrote to Rice there would be '... some spare "x" (size) pads at the end of the job which your children could take to school to show to teacher.'[59]

CHAPTER 13

WEIGHTS AND MEASURES: CONSTRUCTING THE SHELLS.

Jorn Utzon had inspired Ove Arup to take on the Sydney Opera House shells, Ove had handed the platter to Jack Zunz and now Zunz was working with his engineers to put those shells on paper in a form that could be built. But there were those who said the Opera House shells were impossible and could not be built. Candela had said so, Sydney engineers were saying so, and Ryan, the Minister for Public Works thought so. Maybe, just maybe, it could be done in steel, but concrete, you would have to be mad. Hornibrooks' most senior engineer, George Boulton, had said as much and so had other Sydney builders. To inspire others to follow you in an act of madness you have to be either a great man or a fool. But Jack Zunz was no fool. He was also an easy man to follow. His confidence never wavered and his presence inspired confidence in the other engineers. As John Nutt wrote many years later:

He led the engineering team and gave it vision and direction. He was the bridge with the government, the Opera House Committee and the architect. He was able to maintain the trust of the client which is essential if a project is to be successfully implemented. There were political issues which surfaced in a blaze of publicity. He had to deal with these and give the designers room to take their technical decisions without the pressure which would lead to error. He was the guide on engineering matters for the architect. Unlike a normal structure, on the Opera House, analysis, design, construction and architecture are intertwined. Jack Zunz was the focus of this inter-relation between engineering and architecture where both come together to take on that indefinable quality of greatness which is a characteristic of this building.

He brought to the job a confidence which was firmly anchored in an innovative engineering skill founded on deep technical knowledge and a creative attitude. He understood instinctively the human element and how to draw client, architect, engineer and builder into a team with a common and visionary purpose. He was courageous and optimistic, always finding a solution when difficulties arose. That requires an instinctive understanding of construction and architecture, of politics and human relationships, and a meticulous attention to detail.[1]

As the focus of the work moved from the drawing office to site, the design decisions which had occupied the engineers for so long were to be tested for buildability. However for a time when construction started it seemed like the Opera House might not be buildable after all.

The accuracy of the construction of the Opera House was critical, and the precision of its assembly was dependent on many factors, including accuracy of casting, accuracy of erection, deflections during erection caused by movement of the erection arch or scaffolding and the effect of wind, temperature and other factors before or at the time lateral stressing locked the ribs into place.[2]

A segment out of place if not corrected or without correcting the adjacent segments would lead to cumulative errors that would throw out the whole geometry of the structure. This giant lego set in which the pieces weighed ten tons each and was being built like beads threaded on a string had to have a completed surface that was a sphere of radius 246 ft.

Six months after the placing of the first segment, the octopus arches of the Major Hall side shell met at the crown above the apex of the stage wall. And

> ... we have come to the rather agonising realisation that we are unable to complete this structure within the tolerances prescribed by the design – wrote Mick Lewis to Jack Zunz – This has become patently obvious by examining the intersection of the arches at the crown piece of the Major Hall...
>
> We are satisfied over here that the inaccuracies do not have any structural significance but we are seriously concerned over the repercussions in the attachment of the side shell tile lids, and the eventual geometry of the main shells...[3]

Though the main shell ribs would be erected with the erection arch, the side shell arches were being built on a conventional scaffold and it was the scaffold that was the culprit. Rice wrote to Zunz:

> ... Explanations as to why the scaffold should move are, I am afraid, rather futile. We have tried but all reasonable explanations fail. I can only say that it has moved and that the movement has been unpredictable. Certainly the scaffold for the remaining arches has been considerably modified, and strengthened, but in future I think we will be relying on jacking a good deal more.
>
> The Brontë-like gloom of this letter I can perhaps relieve. The difficulty is not that we are unable to achieve the tolerances we have specified (or most of them) in manufacture, but rather that we have not

achieved them to date. I am very hopeful that in the future we can in fact achieve them with proper control... [4]

Lewis found that the technical traumas and difficulties were 'within our limit to solve and Corbet Gore and I used to make a plan that when things got really bad, we would go and have lunch at the University Club, and finish a bottle of claret. And that would help solve a lot of them.'[5] But

Our greatest problem, that we could not crack – you know, just sitting around the table – was to determine where these elements stood in space. Because, once you directed them onto scaffolding – scaffolding is not rigid. Once the load comes on to the scaffolding, the scaffolding moves – be it only a small amount – so how do you place these elements onto the scaffolding so that they will be in their correct position in space.

If you didn't get them in the correct position in space, as you built onto it with those shells... fanning out... eventually they wouldn't fit. There was no tolerance for that. And we spent six weeks – the first elements we put up, we spent six weeks with the surveyors trying to determine where they were. And we then realised that we've got to solve this, because... it'll take us twenty years to get this roof up at this rate... [6]

However there was sufficient confidence amongst those members of the London design team on site in Sydney to believe that solutions would be reached.

Normal methods of construction using a plumb-bob and a level such as on a conventional rectangular building just did not work here. The segments had to be placed in their correct position in three-dimensional space and that could not be done if that position in three-dimensional space was not known beforehand. Then a procedure had to be evolved so it was possible to orientate the segment into that place when it was erected. Hornibrooks had their own surveying instruments and surveyors, but this placing of segments in space was outside their experience in construction. To see what the industry in general had to offer, Peter Rice placed an ad in the *Herald* for surveyors at the Opera House.

Michael Elphick started his career in surveying articled to a surveyor in Castlereagh Street Sydney. After working diligently for that 65-year-old gentleman for three years Elphick was bored and had itchy feet and decided with some friends to tackle an unclimbed peak called Mt Anne in South West Tasmania in winter. '... we missed out on our air drops, which is a bit sad. So we ran out of food

– and to cut a long story short, we had quite a good time and climbed our mountain, but lost a lot of weight.'[7]

While in Tasmania Elphick dropped into the Hydro Electric Commission and secured a job with them for a year or two as a surveyor on dam sites in South West Tasmania 'getting my bushwalking paid for.' Elphick returned to Sydney to get his qualifications then worked on the Snowy Mountains River Scheme for a while before returning to Sydney doing setting out work for the expressways and on multi-storey buildings when

> one day I happened to open the *Herald*, and there was this advertisement saying that... Ove Arup and Partners wanted a surveyor for measuring deflections of the shell roofs of the Sydney Opera House. And at this stage I was completely oblivious of the thing called the Opera House. I had paid no attention to it whatsoever. It was outside my sphere of worrying. And I had a look at it and I thought "Well, they'll only ever build one of those." And so I went down to have a talk to see what it was about.
>
> (Elphick was interviewed by Peter Rice) And I think sometimes there are people in this world who you click with, and Peter had a bit of a talk to me and then we walked out round to Farm Cove... and he said "How would you go about it?" And I thought, "Oh, I don't know." So I thought (the) first thing I would do is climb all over it to have a look to see what it looks like. And I think I was the first... surveyor who got his feet off the ground... (while) everyone else is saying, "Oh, well, stand back here and measure it... " from the other side of the harbour or something you see.[8]

Elphick described the site from a surveying point of view as consisting of two basic units:

> The Podium, a concrete structure about 400 ft x 500 ft x 50 ft high supported by a network of 3 ft diameter concrete piers. This is of wall and slab construction with many expansion joints, consequently parts of it move continually due to temperature effects, and the slabs deflect up to 3/8 in. if loaded with a vehicle such as a fork-lift. The shell roof is independent of this podium structure, being supported by its own series of columns which pass through the podium to a separate foundation below.[9]

Elphick felt that he got the job on the basis, that he had gone and clambered over the site, though Rice 'was very clever mathematically and didn't really care who the person was, as long as he could work with them... he wanted someone he could mould and educate to his ideas... And I think that's what was important, because you virtually had to throw away the rule book in a lot of things... it was a case of a mutual learning situation.'[10] On site Elphick found 'a lot of time was spent just with Peter... because he'd been so much on the design, just trying to get a feeling for the thing. And – thinking – you know – what might be needed here and might not be needed there... the real problem was that the problems (were) so great in certain areas, that there wasn't room for pettiness... And so for this reason there was... a lot of give and take. You know (the engineers and construction team) lived the job for the time I was (there). Well, we all did... It was a funny little world in a way.'[11] Elphick found that the 'higher echelon' such as Corbet Gore and Mick Lewis would fret sometimes when he took Peter Rice and some of the other engineers on one of his bushwalks. Lewis thought '... we weren't going to come back. He feared that he'd come in on Monday morning (and) the whole site staff would be overdue on a bushwalk...'.[12]

Elphick saw as his basic survey task:

(To) provide dimensional control in the casting yard, i.e.make sure that the forms were plumb, position the "match up" segment correctly and establish reference points on each segment which would be used to assist the final positioning of the ribs.

Establish reference points on the partially erected structure. The first few segments of each rib would be positioned by dimensions from these reference points.

Check the position of a rib as it was being erected to enable the engineers to keep the whole rib in its best position. This involved not only finding out the rib's position, but predicting where it was heading so that corrective measures could be taken early, or at a convenient time in the erection sequence.

Measure the movements of the rib during erection, including the effects of permanent stressing, release from the erection arch, and creep deflections over several months. The purpose of these measurements was twofold – it enabled the consulting engineers to check their calculations by comparing the final deflections of a rib with their predicted results and to assist in determining where to place a rib, so as to leave it in its best position.

For speed in construction the roof was erected in many different places at the same time. Should any operation be held up due to a technical difficulty, the erection crews would move to another section, thus preventing loss of time on the job as a whole. As a direct consequence, the survey staff had to be prepared for sudden changes in program. To allow for this, very tight survey control over the whole site was necessary, and because of the construction of the podium, a regular check had to be kept on permanent survey stations to see whether or not they were static.[13]

Rib segments were picked up by a tower crane hooked with a special Hornibrook-invented slinging gear that could swivel the segment in any direction to orientate it to drop it into its position on the shells. That position could be close to horizontal above the side shells or near vertical at the springing point. Segments would then be attached one at a time from pedestal to crown, each one joined with epoxy resin to the one previously placed and held tight by the temporary stressing cables and in position between the previously erected rib and the erection arch. But the erection arch was flexible and could deflect more than three inches. And the ribs were very flexible because they were of thin concrete and very heavily stressed. Also with a rib the shape of a great circle with a radius of 246 ft if you rotated it a very small amount, an eighth of an inch on the inside and an eighth of an inch on the outside, then it moved sideways at the top three inches. 'And if it did that (once stressed) it would actually twist itself and snap and fall apart.'[14] Gore was only too well aware of this, and that a rib segment could kick out under stressing and snap like a green stick, so precision in surveying was imperative.

To calculate the position of six or eight points on a rib took two weeks with an electric calculator. So to locate the segments in three dimensions in space in the complex geometrical structure of the shells Rice suggested to Elphick he write a computer program to check the sightings made on the ground with the co-ordinates of the structure. Australian General Electric had a computer at York Street in the city but 'none of the people who wrote computer programs down there had any idea of mathematics. If you talked about vector algebra'[15] their eyes glazed over. So Elphick brought in Tony Cramm, a civil engineer who had written programs on structural analysis for a Masters project at the University of New South Wales and between them they wrote from scratch a three-dimensional program for the geometry of the shells, working through 'the wee small hours'[16] of the night at AGE in York Street. Each segment was given a code number to establish its hall, its shell, its rib and its segment number, and the code was written with a felt pen beside the surveying nail in the segment. The theoretical position in space of all the segments was established in the three-dimensional program. Four survey positions were set up in the Botanic Gardens and around the shore of the Harbour so that the moment segments were up, the surveyors could immediately sight them with the segment code number and jot it down on a table. The readings were picked up by cab to feed into the computer program which would run that night at AGE and in the morning the results would come back with the exact erected position of the segment and whether it was half an inch or a quarter of an inch out so it could be adjusted if necessary.[17]

All the work of setting up the program with systems and controls on site, teaching the other surveyors the procedures and trying out the ideas took time. But by a stroke of good fortune 'we had a three months crane drivers' strike and it was the best thing that happened. We went flat out in that three months. There were no problems at all. And by the time the strike had finished, we were ready to go... And Hornibrooks weren't too unhappy about it either because it enabled... (their erection procedure to) get refurbished and tied together. And, you know, a good strike every now and again is pretty handy.'[18]

The surveying program for the shells was run 900 times during construction. If the position of a segment was found to be out there were various ways it could be corrected. The epoxy joint for the next segment could be made slightly wedge-shaped by shimming to introduce a corrective angle change. It was also possible to make adjustments to completed ribs. During construction the rib rested on a hinge on top of the pedestal and it could be rotated about the hinge to its correct position. Or after final stressing of a rib, but before connecting it to the ridge segment some needles supporting the rib to the erection arch could be removed to relax the rib so it would rotate at the top. The slight change in orientation of the rib could be taken up in the 3 in concrete joint between the top rib segment and the ridge segment. For limited adjustments to the structure as a whole the reactions exerted by the side shell on the main shell in construction could be adjusted by altering the hydraulic pressure in the flat jacks.[19]

By learning and measuring what was happening and making the right predictions a straightforward system was established for erecting the main shell ribs; but the biggest problem, and the baptism by fire for Elphick because it happened right at the start of the job, was with the side shell arches. These arches (or 'legs') which formed the primary supporting system of the entire structure, were like no arch that had ever been seen before but like an arch under torture. The six arches supporting the biggest shells of both the Major and

Minor Halls sprang from the pedestals at an angle then curled and twisted through space, nearly turning themselves inside out before meeting at the crown (Fig. 43). Elphick thought the problem with the intersection of the first arch was 'that each night the steel scaffolding got colder and it shrunk a little bit and then everything came down. And the next day when it warmed up again, the concrete didn't move up again. And if something compressed (in the scaffolding or supports)... it just stayed there, so it kept creeping down... And so they had to push (jack) it back into position. Now here they're really pushing very big forces... so that was the problem... where to in fact push it from and how to do it... Later on Arups came (up with)... a marvellous solution to this which was a surveying nightmare.'[20] Instead of grouting up each joint for the side shell arch as they went, two or three of the joints were left open. If, for example, one side of the arch had ten segments between pedestal and crown, the first joint at the pedestal would be left loose, so would that between the fourth and fifth segment, the seventh and eighth segment and that at the tenth at the crown, so the arch was in three pieces resting loosely on its birdcage scaffolding. 'And the idea of the thing was we'll keep everything nice and flexible in space and then you can push it all in the right position and then we'll tighten it all back together.'[21] The side shell arch segments were hollow with a roughly rectangular space inside of about 3 ft 6 in square. From the pedestal to the top of the crown above the stage wall was a height difference of 75 ft, but the arch sloped so its actual length was closer to 100 ft. The arch was surrounded by supporting scaffold so survey points could not be sighted from the outside, so the surveyor would climb into the hollow arch segment at the top and clamber down through the arch with his survey instrument to take his sightings from the top of the pedestal. '... they wanted things to within an eighth of an inch or so, and everything's sort of floating around in space, and it was fairly difficult.'[22] The jacking acrossways was being done with the surveyor inside like an Egyptian mummy in its tomb, and the first segment sat on a shear pin (hinge) on top of the pedestal. So 'if the level of the instrument started going off severely, you'd know that the shear pin was failing and you might as well just (say your prayers)... there's nowhere to go, you're inside it you know... And that type of operation often took about 14 hours. Because they might start jacking and they might have a jack burst, or that sort of thing. And then you'd have to stop... and build up some more scaffolding. And you're only moving a small amount at a time, because if you're moving big loads... you can't just make it move. You move it up a quarter of an inch and then tie it off and so on...'[23] Sometimes for these jacking operations Elphick – who was pretty bony anyway – had to lie on the concrete for five or six hours to get the sight line through his instrument and it would get very cold when the work was done at night so he would wear a boiler suit and pack the pockets and spaces with polystyrene foam.

For the jacking of the side shell arches the surveyor inside the arch would sight onto a target at the top with a grid on it marked with right and left and 'radial direction', 'normal direction' and so on. The instrument would be set up pointing at the starting point on the grid then as the jacking operation got underway the grid would move across the cross hairs. The grid was marked in this way because the surveyor may be laying down and could not get behind the eye-piece and was taking the reading with a mirror 'so you had no concept of any direction' or which was right or left.

> Peter (Rice) was doing the job one day and... they started the jacking and Peter said, "Righto, ready to start." So all the riggers started and they increased all the jacks by a quarter of an inch... and they said: "How's it going, Peter?" He said, "Right, it's moved down a quarter of an inch." And of course all the jacks had come up a quarter of an inch, you see. And so the riggers said, "Oh, bloody Peter's got his arse up again," – I should have explained to the riggers how things happen, because, you know, that was not possible, you see.
>
> So, he said, "Right-e-o, jack now, quarter of an inch again." Peter said, "Yeah, down another quarter of an inch." Quarter of an inch again. Down a quarter of an inch. And you must be getting close, and Peter said, "No, you're going in the wrong direction." And they said, "Oh, rubbish." And he said, "Anyhow, it's still moving." They said, "We're not jacking." Of course what had happened was that was the last 200 straws that broke the camel's back.[24]

The scaffolding had started to fail under the concrete arch as it was being loaded more and more in the wrong direction 'and at that stage it was starting to crumple slowly.'

> And so they did what was a brilliant technical manoeuvre, which was probably stupid, they swung the crane round and hooked it on the end of (the arch). So here we had a crane which had a twenty ton capacity at fifty

foot radius hooked on the end of something weighing four or five hundred tons I guess at least, which was slowly collapsing. But it held it while they could rush in and get in the RSJs to weld it up again... if Paul (the other surveyor) had said it was going down, (the riggers) would have listened you see. And so that was a case then of myself really failing, because I should have explained to them what the procedure was so they would know that type of mistake couldn't happen, or they'd double check, you see... and after that there was no problem.[25]

Elphick also recalled:

A slightly different problem occurred on site. If a line of sight passed within several inches of a scaffold tube or similar metal object, the effect was to deflect the ray and this deflection varied depending on the temperature of the day, position of the sun, etc.

In one particular case on a line 200 ft long, swings of up to 12 in were observed at varying times of the day due to the line passing one inch from a vertical tube about half way between the points.

This effect caused a major headache in siting stations to survey the East side shells A2 and A3, since it was impossible to see to these shells without looking through the central scaffold tower.[26]

Sometimes with things like the scaffolding you'd have to take sort of executive decisions. Like, I had troubles on the Eastern side here, when we had to measure a whole lot of things there and the scaffolding was always in the bloody way... and they wouldn't co-operate there. So the only solution to that was come in one Sunday. And I don't know what happened, but some vandals came in and undid the scaffolding and it all fell in the harbour. And so we got our work done that Sunday... It's amazing what vandals will do.[27]

One night Elphick was down below with Harry, another of the workers, when they were jacking one of the side shell arches. Elphick was just making sure none of the support props became unladen. The Acrow-props, which are a screw prop, had several layers of 6 in square by $\frac{1}{2}$ in thick steel plates on top with a rubber sandwich in between so that when the prop was hammered up the rubber would give a bit, there was a preload there and a bit of give so there was no point load anywhere under the arch.

Anyhow, so this is going on, but if the (arch) became unloaded, well then some of (the steel plates) could fall out, and then you might have a chain reaction occurring, and so it was important to watch what was happening...

Anyhow, Harry and I were just wandering round doing this and just keeping track and suddenly there was a bit of a yell up on top and a loud bang, – it was about eleven o'clock at night... There was a big light up at the top and there was... light streaming through the scaffolding, but it was all fairly dark. It was sort of, a real black and white newsreel type scene. And I looked up and there's all these things coming out of the sky towards us... from a couple of hundred feet above...

My immediate reaction was to turn and run like billy-o... which would have been a waste of time anyhow. I looked out of the corner of my eye and there was Harry standing there, looking up, with a cigarette in the corner of his mouth. And it suddenly hit me what he was doing. He was looking for the rubber pads – he was going to dodge the plates but not worry about the rubber pads... And so I did exactly the same thing, I stood there... you could pick the two because they fell differently – the rubber pads bounced and the steel ones went "clunk". And anyhow, when I went by he said, "If you'd have run, sonny boy, you'd have been rat shit." I said, "Right, Harry."

... I learned a whole lot there, you know. This was why this guy had lasted so long, because he knew what to do at the right time and he didn't expend energy when he didn't have to. So it was a very strong (memory)... I can still see those things falling out of the sky now, which... (is), interesting, because it was a while ago.[28]

When the side shell arches did not intersect correctly on the first side shell of the Major Hall, John Nutt and Peter Rice evolved the system of placing the first segment on a hinge on top of the pedestal and building the rest of the arch in sections then jacking them into place. As John Nutt describes it:

We decided to build the arch on a feather bed. We introduced 'soft' supports between the rigid concrete arch and the flexible scaffold so that the precast elements, when bolted together, would uniformly squeeze out the liquid epoxy to give a tight uniform joint between the segments. The soft bedding prevented the arch from breaking these joints before the prestress was applied across the joints. The softness accommodated the rigidity of the concrete arch. When all the segments were assembled, the arch was jacked into its correct final position and stressed onto the pedestal.[29]

However part of the first arch was already built and it was three inches out of place, and for three weeks the engineers wondered what to do with it or even whether to pull it down. Eventually it was decided to leave it in place and 'The side shell was built to accommodate the... extra inclination but the first main shell rib adjoining (the arch)... was built in its correct position with the result that there is an unusually wide joint showing between the arch and the rib. Instead of the one inch gap which was intended, the gap here varies from one inch to $3\frac{1}{2}$ in along the length of the rib.'[30]

By far the greatest part of stressing at the Sydney Opera House was done with 0.6 in stress-relieved strand supplied by the Somerset Wire Co. Ltd. of the UK. The strand was delivered to site in two-ton reels. The reel was set up on a stand and the end was pulled out with a small $\frac{1}{2}$ ton winch across a 200 ft long bench to its specific length for a particular rib, then cut off with a grinding disc. To make wider diameter stressing cables the 0.6 in strand was wound up into multiple strand cables on site. Ducts ran through holes at the joining faces of the rib segments. 'In the case of main shell and side shell ribs, cables of up to seven strands were winched up through 3 in ducts fed from the bottom.'[31] The permanent stressing operation of a rib involved a team of seven men, some at the top and some at the bottom, communicating by telephone on the longer ribs as they were unsighted over the convex curve of the shell. The anchorages for the cables in the shell pedestals and first ribs are architecturally expressed. The nine cables for the temporary stressing were smaller and though primarily intended as temporary strands for use in segment erection, ultimately a decision was made to leave them in after permanent stressing had taken place. The ribs were strong enough to take the extra stress and they gave extra strength. Once the rib was permanently stressed from the top cut-off segment to the pedestal and to its other half across the ridge segment, it was released from the erection arch.

During stressing of the ribs large numbers of temporary and permanent stressing cables 100 ft or more long trailed from the base of the shells and over the top and sides of the podium during construction like streamers garlanding a departing ocean liner. During temporary stressing one problem presented itself: while the first segments of a rib were being erected there were nine long tails of strand trailing from the first segment. As the strand was pushed up the rib these tails of course reduced. However, nine of the normal type of hollow spindle jacks would have been needed for each rib being erected at any given time or, alternatively, one jack would have had to be threaded on to each strand many times. What was required was a straddle jack into which the strand could be fed from the side.[32]

A worldwide search was set in motion to find a suitable jack. Hornibrooks wrote out a specification for a straddle jack and while touting it round different manufacturers, one of their suppliers suggested they try a company in Vancouver Canada. This company had made a straddle jack previously for another job, so using a similar technique they were able to manufacture the special jacks. Hornibrooks imported six 'CCL Mark 8 Twin Jacks' specially adapted for stressing operations at the Opera House that could fit over and grip a strand at any point along its length (Fig. 47). Each weighed 81 lb and were 33 in long, so were no lightweight to lug around the site. All told during Stage II '108 miles of 0.6 in stressing strand were used. It has been estimated that the contract involved approximately 30,000 individual stressing operations.'[33] There were about 20,000 0.6 in stressing strands in the roof. In addition there was the 1.1/8 in diameter strand used in the shell columns ties and 0.276 in wire used to stress the top rib segments across their cut-off planes at the ridge.

The ducts for the stressing cables were simply a tube through the concrete. There were 12 running the length of every rib, they were up to 200 ft long on the longest ribs and including the ducts for the lateral stressing there were 'In all… 41,000 individual ducts with a total length of about 70 miles.'[34]

The grout was a sand and cement slurry pumped through the duct to seal it right along its length to prevent any chance of the cable rusting and to 'lock them in and hold the stress on them.'[35] If for any reason there was a break in the cable the grout ensured 'that the prestress force of that tendon is not lost over the entire length of the tendon.'[36]

A grout mixer and high capacity pump were set up in a central location and grout was circulated from this point to the bases of the shells through a ring main. Grout could be taken from the ring main at any point into small portable tanks and pumped from them into the ducts with small easily controlled portable pumps. Pumps of 300 psi capacity were used to push the grout against a static head of the order of 200 psi.

At each of the three corners of the segments were located three 1-3/8 in ducts, one 3 in duct, dense reinforcing and a multitude of lateral ducts, carrying bolts and lateral stressing cables. With grouting it was inevitable that leakages from one duct to another and from ducts into the open would occur. As soon as this was realised, protective measures were built into the segments at casting. Nevertheless, it was still necessary that all ducts be water tested and external leaks detected and sealed with epoxy. In cases where leaks between ducts occurred, simultaneous grouting was arranged. Even so some grout leaks still occurred and removal of the stains on the finished concrete surface proved difficult...[37]

The basic procedure was simple enough, the grout was pumped up from the bottom of each rib through the duct and was blocked off at both ends when it ran freely from the end of the duct at the top of the rib.

But Arups checked to see if the grouting had been effective in the ducts and 'discovered to our horror, that in this 100 ft height... the grout was suspect... in the top ten foot of every cable duct and at intervals along the upper portion of the duct.'[38] To get an idea of how the voids were forming 100 ft long clear plastic tubes with a steel stressing cable inside were laid against the side of one of the shells, pumped full of grout and allowed to set then inspected to see what was going on. 'And we then discovered a phenomenon which nobody had ever come across before, was that, when you pump grout... the process of pumping the grout up the slope... caused a kind of sedimentation of the cement particles – separation of the cement from the water and the water all went to the top. And the water, by whatever means, drained out of the structure leaving a void.'[39] In the upper sections of the tube, where there was any restriction in the diameter – as happened in practice where the split collets remained in the anchorage pockets of the 1.3/8 in temporary stressing cable ducts – 'Below a number of the restrictions it was noticed that separation of the grout column took place – the stiffening grout arching across the duct allowing water to collect immediately below the restrictions. This separation never took place in the lower portion of the duct.'[40] Stressing ducts in buildings are normally close to horizontal but at the Opera House they were mostly at very steep angles and for the grout to reach a height of 150 ft on the longest ribs required a pressure of 350 lb/sq in applied at the pump. 'Field tests for shrinkage'[41] successfully carried out by Hornibrook before the start of construction 'did not accurately reflect the high pressure conditions present in the ducts themselves.'[42]

Arups 'then had to develop a means of preventing... (the grout separation occurring) for future ducts as we went along.'[43] In experiments all sorts of additives were tried to prevent the water separating from the sand/cement mixture, and the most successful was found to be Methocel, a synthetic methylcellulose polymer made by Dow Chemicals, supplied in powder form which was dissolved in water before the cement was added. It was a similar additive to one commonly used in soft ice-cream to hold its shape and prevent it from melting. The grout initially used on the Opera House roof was a 'low bleed' grout of a type in general use in the building industry. A low bleed grout is one in which the water separation along the length grouted is one per cent or less of that length. The Methocel grout was a 'no bleed' grout in which literally no bleed occurs. The larger ducts carrying the majority of the cables were satisfactorily grouted using the low bleed grout, it was only in the smaller diameter vertical temporary stressing ducts where there were some problems. However, after the first voids were detected, Methocel grout was subsequently used to grout all cable ducts on the Opera House.

On the ribs which had already been grouted with low bleed grout 'approximately 84 ducts were comprehensively investigated by drilling holes at 2 in, 12 in or 40 in centres along their complete lengths of 80 ft to 150 ft.'[44] Other ways of locating voids in ducts included X-raying the ribs. Another method measured the pulse count through the rib using gamma rays. A radioactive material of 137 curies was placed on one side of the concrete and the rate of transmission of the rays through the concrete measured on the other side as a pulse count on a scintillation counter. 'A void would give an increased count.'[45] The device was 'quick to locate large voids and it was particularly useful in the Opera House investigation in locating the head of the grout.'[46]

The fact that cement particles in sand are too large to penetrate the air spaces between the individual wires of a 0.6 in strand led to the trial of another ingenious technique. A radioactive fluid of '100 microcuries of sodium/24 carbonate with a half-life of 15 hours'[47] was dissolved in four gallons of water and pumped at high pressure into the strand itself. The time taken for the fluid to penetrate from the bottom to the top of the duct along the interstices of a strand 150 ft long was from 10 minutes to 17 hours. The radioactive fluid would collect in the grout voids and could be located by running a geiger counter along the surface of the rib.

This led to another interesting experiment of trying to seal voids in ducts by pumping a very thin epoxy mix up the reinforcing strand, but it was not possible to formulate a sufficiently thin mix for this purpose and the fluid would only penetrate a metre or two along the strand.

Arups felt that small voids found intermediately along the length of a duct '… do not present a corrosion hazard.'[48] As an insurance against the larger voids at the top a small modification was made to the top rib segment and 'ducts were grouted in a two-part operation.'[49] Two holes a foot apart 'were cast into the duct'[50] at about five feet and six feet from the top of the segment. Methocel grout was then pumped up the duct from the bottom of the rib in the usual way 'until a grout flow came from the first hole. After 24 hours, grouting from the bleed-hole immediately above the head of the grout took place until it flowed'[51] from the duct at the top of the rib. Filling of the top voids in the already grouted ducts was done through 'a hole drilled laterally into the void.'[52] 'All drill holes were sealed with epoxy.'[53]

The investigation to find the cause of the grout voids at the Opera House, and a remedy for them was very thorough. John Nutt wrote a technical paper to alert the industry in 1967 once Arups and Hornibrooks had found an effective solution. Most of the summary on grouting reproduced here is taken from that paper. Once the Methocel grout was adopted, there were no instances of further voids found on the Opera House.

Meanwhile, Kelman was still occasionally mystified by communications from Sydney:

> Dear Arthur,
>
> The following cable came on the 21st May:
>
> LT LOVARPART LONDON
>
> ATTENTION KELMAN BOB CAN YOU AUTHORIZE TWO EXTRA MILLS SCAFFOLD ARTHUR OPERABUILDERS
>
> Now it was addressed to LOVARPART. It was dated the 12th and arrived on the 21st and was completely – yes, completely incomprehensible even to me!
>
> Naturally I had the text checked. The whole organization of the British GPO was thrown into this. International telegraphy faltered and almost failed while resources were diverted to this mystery.
>
> No cable on the 12th May could have had those identification letters. Confusion spread to Sydney and strikes broke out on the Opera House. Still the mystery remained.
>
> Then on June 3rd the clouds burst. 12 should be 21. It had arrived on

time. Honour was satisfied. Our countries went back to cricket and the rain here was resumed.

Have you seen a quack recently? Do these attacks come often? Do you send telegrams like this to other people? Does your family know about it? Do *you* know about it?

Please, Arthur, I hope you are well, but I am worried...

WHAT ON EARTH DOES IT MEAN!![54]

Crimp's answer was '... all you have to do is cable back "YES"'. He said he was not responsible for the alteration to the cable address, which should have read OVARPART, and that he suspected a GPO typist with other things on her mind. Crimp had been pestered by a scaffolding contractor salesman and just wanted from Kelman a confirmation that that particular part of the scaffolding contract was already filled. Kelman wrote back – YES – but with reservations. Mills had built the scaffold for the trial rib erection and

As you know, Mills made one heck of a mess of that scaffold. Their first effort was to erect it 90° wrong in place. I had this dismantled to jolly cries of "Oh, of course, if it is wrong, we must get it right." So they put it up again – not only 90° disorientated, the other way, but opposite hand to our drawing. There were no jolly cries this time – only very glum looks when I pointed this out, as it was almost complete. So I let it go.[55]

The scaffolding needed some further corrections and bracing and Mills had put in a claim for extra payment:

However, it is impossible not to feel some sympathy for anyone who is brought innocently into contact with this S.O.H. and so gets caught. They have undoubtedly lost heavily on this, and I would not feel the sum involved is worth making an issue of.[56]

And there was the never-ending battle to have accurate drawings dimensioned in three planes passing in a smooth flow the 12,000 miles from London to Sydney. The task of drawing and dimensioning some of the complex shapes of the Opera House shell structure on paper tried some of Arup's draughtsmen to the absolute limit. Zunz wrote to Sydney that when a draughtsman had completed the drawings for several top rib skew cut-off segments they were 'suicide material'[57] and 'we have had several resignations recently.'[58] Subsequent changes to drawings could likewise be the last straw for a frazzled draughtsman. Zunz once wrote to Lewis concerning drawings for ridge tiling:

Firstly, the ridge lines remains unaltered, namely 16 in away from the centre line of the Hall axis (see attached sketch 920A dimension A). Because the angle varies from shell to shell dimension B will also vary. If we therefore accept that the 16in dimension remains fixed – and if this is altered this office will be strewn with corpses – the outside surface is now dimensioned.[59]

Any errors or inaccuracies on drawings could have major repercussions on site. 'Nobody in London appears to have any real conception of how difficult it is to achieve the tolerances asked for throughout almost every aspect of the job',[60] wrote Ian MacKenzie in a memo to David Dowrick after some errors occurred on drawings. 'Every dimension on every drawing must be checked, and then the drawings must be checked again, if necessary, for missing information... All this is aimed at saving not just an hour or two of construction time, but days.'[61] And because the carpentry and setting out involved on some of the top segments could take 5-7 days 'I can only insist, beg or plead for accurate and correct drawings.'[62] David Dowrick maintained that dimension 'B' on rib segment drawings was unnecessary but 'the errors we are getting are not the $\frac{1}{2}$ in which you suggest is the accuracy we can expect but a staggering 6 in or more', wrote back Ian MacKenzie if the 'B' dimension was left out.

In particular one with an error of just over 6 in was a segment made up with special care since we had just become aware that all was not well in the earlier segments. If we had any segments with *all* dimensions correct to $\pm \frac{1}{2}$ in you would have had a golden licence from me.

Perhaps the worst feature of this whole affair is the psychological aspect. The effect on the morale of a carpenter who finds dimensional errors on drawings greater than the tolerances he is expected to achieve should not be under-estimated. We have here a situation where a carpenter may be working for several days on formwork and blockouts associated with the anchorages and cables. He finds numerous errors of an inch or so in dimensions and each time the answer given him is to ignore some dimensions or change others. This carpenter might then be transferred to setting out lateral bolts. It is very, very difficult to convince him that the dimensions are now correct and he must achieve an accuracy of ±1/8 in or less. The result is what you would expect.

Hornibrooks' comment when I passed on to them the gist of your letter was to the effect that "if they cannot work out these dimensions in the design office how can we be expected to build it in the field". There were other remarks which I have censored. I am afraid I cannot help but agree with them.[63]

A sentiment shared by Peter Rice, who also wrote to London that month

It is hard, maybe impossible, to persuade carpenters to work to limiting accuracy with woolly drawings, particularly when they contain inconsistent dimensions. Even Bob might be touched to find the reverence with which engineers are treated, especially when they are in the green lands of England.

Control is an ever present personal problem and the finest weapon we can ask for is accurate and consistent drawings. It may be an unpleasant exercise and we can but ask, but please. One bad drawing can affect the morale of more than one segment.[64]

But once formwork was accurately in place and the concrete pour could go ahead it was a sight for sore eyes. 'I have just returned from watching the casting operation of Pedestal A2 west and since my heart is filled with joy I feel that it is timely for me to communicate with you,' wrote Lewis to Zunz on 1st July.

I watched with growing consternation as each heavy layer of steel was applied to this reinforcing cage until eventually it was not possible to see through the reinforcement. Every person that I have showed around the site wanted to know how we were going to get the concrete in and I shrugged this one off with the comment that we would paint the steel to match the concrete and leave it out altogether.

Hornibrooks have a gang of something like 15 men doing this concreting; there are approximately twenty form vibrators and ten poker vibrators in use and standing on the scaffolding one has the feeling that if the formwork were less robust it would surely be launched into orbit. Consequently the concrete appears to be flowing into place with remarkable ease and I am confident that the concrete will be good and the finish up to standard.

Seeing this operation in progress reminds me of the Standard Clause in the South African Specification where we insist upon the presence of a European supervisor during all casting operations and usually find a group of indolent-looking Africans each with a tamping rod in hand gazing vacantly into the sky until they are prompted to spring into action...[65]

Though with little apparent progress on site and not much more than the side shells rising above the podium there were still those who felt it was not too late to call the whole thing off. One reader of the *Herald* proposed 'that consideration be given at once to the question whether the project should not be entirely abandoned because of the uncertainty in cost and time of completion, and because the design has been altered in so many respects that it no longer satisfies the original requirements.'[66] Another proposed '... a satisfactory solution to the problem. Bennelong Point, with the lack of passing traffic and noise, is an ideal venue for a hospital. The present foundations could, I believe, be used with modifications for the erection of a modern hospital.[67]

While an officer from the American cruiser U.S.S.*Providence* visiting Sydney, on looking up at the Opera House sails under construction with the first ribs in place, asked 'All right, but what are those curved things.'[68] While Utzon still maintained his insistence that those 'curved things' must always be treated with the love and care that was their due, writing to Arups on the handling of segments and tile lids that 'these components are finished articles and therefore careful handling is just as important as perfection in manufacture.'[69]

In early October the London office heard from Jack Zunz, who was in Sydney with Ove Arup on a visit. The memo, addressed to Bob, John, David & Co. was

> just a note to tell you that life here is as usual quite hectic. The 5-6 complex has been de-centred and it is a very strange and wonderful world which is being unfolded. Apart from the inevitable lapses the quality of the work is quite superb and equal to anything I have ever seen.
>
> I gather too that the morale both on our side and on Hornibrook's side is high which, having regard to the tremendous difficulties, is I think a great compliment to all concerned. John (Blanchard), of course, has been here recently but I wish you could all see some of your handiwork.[70]

The memo finished with a handwritten note: 'May I add, whatever trepidation and tribulations and what not you have gone through – it has been worth it. Yours truly appreciative and grateful, Ove Arup.' Kelman wrote back:

> Your note, endorsed by Ove, came yesterday and pleased everyone a lot. It was a nice sort of touch and gave most of us a real feeling of the satisfaction and wonder you obviously felt at seeing your baby grow up.
>
> I probably have an advantage here in imagining what it is like. Even propped up on its steel maze it was an impressive proposition![71]

But to bring Zunz back down to earth again, before he left Sydney he received a letter from John Blanchard enclosing '... two copies of (drawings) SK1018 and 1021, horrific documents relating to main shell loadings.'[72]

For all sorts of reasons the weights of some of the shell segments had increased over their original design weight (even though Zunz had allowed a 10 per cent buffer) and the loads on the side shells and shell columns, particularly on the smaller shells, was going to be too high. 'I write in haste to catch you before you leave so can offer no constructive suggestions except to try everything to lighten the tile lids and to reconsider our decision to omit voids – (spaces or holes in the concrete),' closed Blanchard.

Though Zunz was already aware of the problem – he had written to Blanchard from Sydney on the 16th and the letters had crossed in the mail. '*Design Loading*: This is urgent and most important' wrote Zunz to London:

> Firstly, the weight of the tile lids has been checked again and the figures... are correct. In addition to that the segments of the shell are heavier than designed... With regard to the arches they also have turned out to be slightly heavier than anticipated... It is absolutely essential that someone looks at this problem right away to try and evaluate the cumulative effect of all these minor items... [73]

Zunz wrote a less light-hearted memo to Kelman, Blanchard and Dowrick on the 22nd:

> I cannot say that I enjoyed receiving your cable about the situation of the total weight of the roof. In fact it is almost the sort of nightmare I have been trying to stave off for the past two years. Anyway we have got it, we have got to get round it and that we will surely do somehow or other...
>
> Shells A4 and B4 which are amongst the worst affected must be looked at again very thoroughly. Work here has not yet commenced but some of the ribs on B4 are due for casting in about 3-4 weeks' time...
>
> Please therefore look into the ties, the pedestals and the ribs of A4, B4 as well as (and this is important) the effect on the arch system A4 and A10. Please treat these in sequence of construction generally and advise Sydney urgently because work on this will not now proceed until revised information becomes available.
>
> I have introduced voids in all remaining ribs of A1 and B1 and, for that matter, in all other segments still to be cast where previously David had allowed these voids to be omitted.
>
> Approximately 5 per cent of all tile lids have so far been cast and we are introducing light weight sand for the remainder. We estimate that this will bring the weights of the tile lids back to those originally calculated...
>
> If you have any other really unpleasant stories to tell me, Janet has my itinerary for the return trip.
>
> I look forward to seeing you all again,
> With kind regards, Jack. [74]

Peter Rice wrote to John Blanchard asking to have some points clarified:

> 1. How do you define the ultimate load of the ties? Is this against cracking of the concrete and, if not, at what load do you expect the tie

to crack, for we consider this to be the most important criterion.

2. When you speak of ultimate load it is obviously necessary to know how the basic tie force will vary.

Is it very sensitive to load distribution, to the amount of load carried by side shells, to temperature, to lateral stressing? In other words, how likely are we to encroach upon the safety factor for reasons other than the weight increase?

3. What is the effect of cracking on the shells and columns – i.e. a relationship of movement of the tie to

change of stresses in the arches and ribs.

4. If cracking is likely, where will it happen and when it is likely to occur? A graph of rate of application of tie force would be ideal.

We will of course be measuring movement of the column heads which will give us a warning... [75]

To measure any movement in the tops of the columns Rice talked to Michael Elphick who invented

these upside down plumb bobs. The problem was that... the shells stand on columns and the columns are about fifty feet tall and they go right down through the building, so you have an arch sitting on a column... between the columns there's a beam, so that as you put more things on the roof, these are going to push apart from the tops of the columns. So this tie-beam between the two had (about) a hundred cables, each with a hundred tons on it preload. And so they'd tighten up the cables as they put (more weight) on the top. It's like – if you imagine an A-frame roof with a tie across the bottom (which is) standing on tall columns – that you've got to tie the tie up as you put tiles on the roof.

So they said, "Well, what we really want to know is how much these columns are moving in and out." I said, "Oh, what accuracy do you want?" "Oh, we want about a thousandth of an inch." So I thought, "That's pretty interesting." And so the easiest way was then we drilled a hole through all the floors from the bottom to the top. [76]

The surveyors anchored a length of 50-foot long piano wire in the basement of the podium, which passed up through the holes in the floors. At the top they cut a 44-gallon drum in half and welded a tube in the centre of the base then drilled a hole in the bottom of the drum beneath the tube. Then they formed a big block of polystrene into a doughnut shape to use as a float which was dropped into the drum with the tube in the centre. Once the wire was run up through the tube and held in place on top of the float with a bit of wood across the top and the drum was filled with water 'the float lifted up with about a hundred pounds upwards thrust... But there's no mass, so it wouldn't oscillate. So it would just go up and just go wham...'[77] The surveyors could then use an inside micrometer to measure the distance between the top of the column and the wire 'which was easy... Because you could just walk out the door and just measure it and walk back inside and have a cup of coffee... which was far better than some complicated surveying technique.'[78]

The surveyors had employed a principle familiar to anyone who has seen a toilet cistern, and from then on in correspondence on shell column loads Arups frequently referred to Michael Elphick's 'upside down plumb bob.'

Blanchard sent to Sydney some additional information 'showing the loads on the main shells in a little more detail' and some analyses fed into the computer of the effects on 'the shells themselves and the substructure' if lighter weight tile lids and rib segments were used, as well as 'the calculated weight of the structure that you were actually building until recently... if the weight of the tile lids had not increased... (which was of) no practical use but may have some philosophical interest'.[79]

Lewis wrote to Kelman and Blanchard that he had agreed with Zunz to

> examine in detail the importance of the additional loading on both shells 1 and 4 and advise us if any major surgery is necessary. The strength of the ties could be increased by gunniting additional layers of steel or buttressing walls below the +42 level. We are not enthusiastic about either possibility.
>
> (introducing lightweight concrete for tile lids) seems to result in only a marginal improvement of the situation and we are examining durability and porosity of tile lids cast using lightweight sand. If the introduction of this material increases the hazards of corrosion or damp penetration then we should rather attempt to deal with the additional loads in some other way.
>
> Our investigation is proceeding and we will probably have some sensible conclusions within a month. By this time Jack will have returned and you can decide finally what you want to do. The tile lids which have already been manufactured could be used in specific areas of the structure where overloading is not important.[80]

Blanchard wrote to Lewis to tell him 'what we are doing this end with regard to the load increases... A4 and B4 Ribs... changes are necessary in the top segments... A4 and B4 Pedestals will be redesigned and redetailed... A4 and B4. Ties will be redesigned and redetailed... A4 and B4 Columns will be checked...'.

Side Shells have been checked and found capable of carrying the increase of main shell load. We have still to check whether they can also carry the additional weight caused by omitting the voids at the crown. The other outstanding problem, which I think we are not yet in a position to solve, is the effect of auditorium loading on the side shells in addition to the increase of main shell loading... [81]

MacKenzie had earlier written of one of the column ties 'I am inclined to put in some type of anchor because it seems to me that there is a risk of the tie overturning...'

I have visions of the tie flipping over to thump against the underside of the cantilevered gallery beams and catapulting the occupants of the rear seats on to the stage. This might be quite in order for pantomines such as Peter Pan, or even a spectacular success in some of the lighter operas, but I doubt if it would be appropriate for Lucia di Lammermoor.[82]

Kelman 'greatly appreciated' the note. 'I think it ranks as one of the truly great comments on this historic (or hysteric!) task! Jack and I had fits when we savoured its comic gravity.'[83] Kelman then went into a lengthy technical discourse of possible ways to provide for thrusts from columns.

Not long after, Arups London sent to Sydney a revised erection sequence for sections of the shells 'consequent upon segment weights being greater than expected' to minimise possible loads on the structure during construction, with revised times between what period one erection sequence could follow another on particular shells. In some cases these times were five months.[84]

When Ryan the Minister of Public Works had got wind of the problem with loads, Ove Arup in person received an anxious letter from him to which Ove replied:

I have given a good deal of thought to your request for a letter which will give you the assurance that we have done everything in our power to ensure the stability and permanence of the Sydney Opera House, and that you need have no fear about the safety of the building.

This assurance we gladly give you, although it should be unnecessary to do so, for we are naturally fully aware of our responsibilities in this respect, and would not dream of taking any risks on this score.

I understood from you, however, that you would like us to implement this statement with some information about what steps we have taken to ensure the safety of the bulding, so that you could make use of this information in case the Government were subjected to questions in the House about such matters... but I frankly do not know where to start and end...

It has, I think, been made clear to you that this building is structurally very complicated, and the solution has only been reached after years of toil by a great number of high-powered engineers...

The questions which could be raised in the House would, I am sure, be quite elementary, and would have nothing to do with the real difficulties we have encountered and overcome...

The position is that you have chosen us as your professional advisers. If you yourself should doubt our professional ability, which I know you don't, then your right course would be to get rid of us and appoint advisers whom you trust. If anybody else criticises us on technical grounds then your right course would be to refer them to us for an answer to their criticism, and we should have no difficulty in disposing of it.

I don't know whether this letter is what you want and need, but I have tried to explain our position...[85]

Ryan replied '... I wish to assure you that at no time have I entertained the least doubt as to the professional competence of your firm.' And asked for a description of the shells to explain what was 'occurring on the site so far as the erection of the structure is concerned... and a clear statement as to what has been done to ensure their stability... it is not sufficient for me to say, if questioned about them, that I do not know but I am confident that the Consulting Engineer has done his job properly.' Ryan asked for a report on the stability of the shells and promised to send 'Departmental officers... (to) discuss the matter further with Mr Lewis.'[86] To allay the Minister's fears, Jack Zunz wrote a 30 page 'Report on the Roof Structure to the Minister for Public Works, Government of New South Wales' published in May 1965 which included two pages on its 'Structural Stability.'[87] Though when he received it the Minister was unhappier still. The report concluded by saying 'It is probably true to say that the construction of the roof for the Sydney Opera House is on the boundaries of what is technically possible.'[88]

But it was not just difficulties in the structure that could be caused by over-weight. Lewis wrote to Zunz on 24th November:

It is strange that I should have told you in this morning's telephone conversation that everything is relatively quiet on the job. It seems that this has set in motion a number of problems. The most difficult one was presented to us by Hornibrook this afternoon. They have discovered that on practically all of segments 4 and many other segments in isolated positions the crane is heavily overloaded in attempting to lift these segments.

It seems that if we are able to reduce the density of the concrete to 125 lb cu.ft. they will be able to manage the erection without calling for an Act of Grace from the Department of Labour and Industry.

The situation is frankly rather desperate and if the lightweight concrete attempt fails then they have little alternative but to introduce some sort of lifting pole to assist the erection of these segments.[89]

Jack Zunz described the availability of a suitable tower crane as the keystone of all the early design decisions. The size and weight of the roof segments depended on the lifting capacity of the cranes. They were built by Weitz & Co of Lyons in France. Weitz was a German and he had developed the cranes for Germany's reconstruction program after the war. The cranes Hornibrooks chose for the job were the Weitz 280B, costing over £50,000 each, including spares, the largest crane of its type on the market.[90] They were ordered through Babcock & Wilcox in London, the Australian agents for Weitz, and erected on site by a team of riggers brought over from the UK and France. Babcock & Wilcox called them 'Whites' cranes to save mentioning the war.

Before a segment was lifted it was slung from a device called a needle beam which supported the segment in position between the erection arch and the existing structure.

But because the erection arch was erected parallel to the existing rib and just outside the line of the new segment to be erected, the segment had to be presented to the arch – or to the shell – in the attitude in which it would go into place. In other words, you couldn't put it in and turn it round and swing it round like you can normally on the sling. So we had to develop lifting gear which enabled us to position the segment in its actual orientation before we put it in. And this was done by a series of steel beams and chain blocks, which enabled us to suspend the segment from the crane hook, in precisely the same attitude as it would be in the shell.

They worked very well and the chain blocks gave us very good control for final adjustment when the segments went into position. And of course epoxy had to be put on the segments and we had to wrap plastic around each side of the joint to stop any spillage of epoxy getting on the concrete to preserve the pristine nature that Utzon wanted.[91]

The crane jibs were left loose at night so they could move on their bearings like a giant weather vane in the wind. One night the project superintendent George Ellis was fast asleep in bed when he was woken with a phone call from a new security guard who was doing the rounds on site.

"The big crane jibs they're revolving," said the guard. "Yes, that's good" said Ellis. "What do you mean? There's somebody switched it on or something" said the guard. "No, it's revolving in the wind" said Ellis, "It's like a weathervane. The jib will go into the wind, like a ship on the water on anchor. If it was rigid it would blow over. That's good, it's revolving round. So good night. Thanks very much.".[92]

But one night the cranes nearly did blow over which caused a bad fright because it was right at the start of the job and got in all the papers. The cranes ran on wide tracks like a giant railway carriage, and when they were unoccupied not only were the jibs left loose but each wheel had to be anchored and tied to the rails. It was at a time when there were some industrial problems on site with the Builders' Labourers and other unions and

for reasons best known to themselves, on the Saturday night when they knocked off work, instead of dogging down the fore wheels on the two cranes, they dogged down two diagonal ones and didn't do any others and didn't tell anyone. And that wouldn't normally have been a problem, except that we had a southerly buster that night, and of course the full force of the wind hit the crane jibs before they had time to move round into the wind. And both the cranes jumped the rails but fortunately the two dogs held and we were able to pick them up and jack them up. But it would have been a very serious thing if those two cranes had fallen down at that stage of the game, which was quite early on.[93]

Michael Elphick recalled an incident between the crane drivers and the dogmen. The dogman was responsible for seeing a roof segment was slung correctly when it was picked up by the crane, and then would actually ride the segment standing up on it and holding onto the crane wire as it was lifted, swung round and lowered into position on the shells.[94]

Well, sometimes different people didn't get on very well with each other. And of course there... could potentially be conflict between the crane drivers and the dogmen. Now the crane drivers had a very difficult job, because they were manouevring very heavy things in amongst people – and sometimes – you could literally ask the crane driver, "Down an eighth of an inch", or "Move to the North a sixteenth of an inch." And they would literally do it. And they couldn't see what they were doing, because they'd be reaching over the top (of the shells) and there's... two hundred foot of jib out and (they had to move the load in such a way) so it wouldn't pendulum...

And so I thought they were marvellous, you see. But of course, the dogmen may get a little bit short, because they're the people on the receiving end and a bit rough. And one of the dogmen wasn't getting on very well with one of the crane drivers, and a considerable amount of abuse was going backwards and forwards between them on the two-way radio. So anyhow... (once the segment was in place) everyone would walk down, but the dogman would jump on the hook to go back down to the bottom, you see. So he jumped on the hook to go down. And the crane went round, and instead of going down, it went round and round and round, it went out over the Harbour and then lowered the hook down until it went into the Harbour and then picked him up again then dropped him into the Harbour again for everybody to see, then gave him a 360 rotation round to dry him off a bit and dropped him heavily on the concrete, you see.

The dogman wasn't very happy about this, so... when he picked himself up off the concrete, he went like a hairy goat towards the crane and started climbing up the tower inside the tower crane. You go up the ladders inside. And the last thing you do when you get there, to get into the cab, you went through a sort of grate on the floor inside, you see. Anyhow, when he got up to the grate, the crane driver – and of course (we were) on the shell and you could look straight across at the cab here, because it was fairly close... The crane driver without any great aplomb, dropped his trousers and urinated over the guy below, you see. 'Didn't make the chap very happy at all. So it took a bit to persuade the man to come down and what have you after that, and there had to be a guard to... get the poor crane driver out of the site that evening... But they were drinking together a few nights later, so I guess they sorted their differences out some way. But it was a beautiful little scene... [95]

The cranes too were the source of much angst on site because of strikes. When asked what he thought was his worst moment on the Opera House Corbet Gore replied it was 'finding the Builders' Labourers Federation',[96] who would go on strike at the drop of a hat 'any excuse they could think of.' The 1960s were a time of full employment in Australia. Workers could switch jobs just how and when they pleased and could always find another one and unions asked for whatever they wanted and frequently got it. Gore reckoned Jack Munday, the secretary of the Builders' Labourers Federation, made sure the 'Opera House was built as slowly as possible and as expensively as possible'[97] while the builders' labourers said that 'never did one job give so much work to so many for so long.'[98]

Hornibrooks had an immediate introduction to the trouble that lay ahead when they first moved onto the site. They wanted to lay off the site watchmen who immediately called a stopwork meeting because they claimed they were being replaced by 'armed and uniformed patrolmen.' Nobody would be allowed to enter the site until the stopwork meeting ended. 'Our members are fighting for their livelihood' said an organiser for the Miscellaneous Workers' Union. 'The Union will not tolerate the use of guns at the Opera House. It believes in culture, but not by force of arms and the use of uniforms foreign to those of the police of this state.'[99]

Workers went on strike for height allowances or because of a dispute over the position of the clocking-on machines. When some workers were sacked for refusing to clock-on other members of the unions immediately went on strike.[100] One builders' labourers' strike went on for five weeks over a £2 a week pay rise. During the construction of the podium workers had received 55 shillings a week over the award rate, and as Gore wrote to the Director of Public Works,

> There can be no doubt that the root cause of these stoppages has been the campaign by the Unions for a site allowance in keeping the over-award payment made by Civil & Civic Pty Ltd during the Stage I contract, although various other excuses have been given. There also can be no doubt that this job has been selected by the Union specifically as the job on which industrial trouble will be formented, in order to bring pressure for increased wages and conditions throughout the construction industry in New South Wales.[101]

In the first 15 months of Stage II there was an average of one stopwork meeting a week with a resultant total loss of 57,000 man hours, 4,000 of them during a claim by workers for more toilets.[102] Union action also took the form of deliberate 'go slows' and the 'withdrawal of key personnel from the site and the deliberate prevention by the Unions of the recruitment of replacement labour.'[103] Following a week of planned absenteeism on 25th May 1964 all dogmen refused overtime to complete a concrete pour on a section of the arch crown of the Major Hall – one of the most critical points in the structure of the shells – and the job was completed by staff personnel. The two dogmen responsible were immediately dismissed. The following day the Builders' Labourers Federation went on strike midway through a concrete pour and two other unions came out in sympathy.[104] Mick Lewis could not believe it, 'It is doubtful whether more than two weeks' effective work have taken place in the preceding two months' he wrote shortly after.[105] Lewis was from a country where there were literally no strikes, in South Africa there were no unions, and now he found himself in a country that was absolutely bedevilled by them. He recalled one incident when a worker was instructing a mobile crane driver to lift a segment, who says

> ... "Okay, she's ready to go." And the crane driver says: "Have you slung it properly?" So the chap says, "Yes, I've slung it properly." The crane driver says: "If you say that's slung properly, then you don't know what you're talking about. I'm not prepared to lift that load." So the other says, "You'd better call the Project Manager... ".
>
> Eventually, each tier of management comes until you've got the Project Manager on the job, and the Project Manager says: "I've looked at that slinging. It's okay, ready to lift. You lift it, and if you don't lift it, you're fired. That's the final word."
>
> He says: "Okay, I'm off." And every crane driver on the site as he made the signal, walked off with him. You know – it was like a comedy.[106]

When the wheels on the cranes jumped the rails and they were jacked back on again the crane drivers went on strike and only came back when it was agreed they would not have to lift any loads unless the wheels were locked to the rails, or move the cranes along the rails under load, which meant it would take double the time to erect the roof segments.[107] A crane strike in early 1964 went on for three months, and in a separate instance following the disruption of the concrete pour on the arch crown[108] 200 men went on strike for two weeks after 'The men, mainly members of the Builders' Labourers Federation and the Building Workers' Industrial Union, stopped work after the dismissal of two dogmen whom they said had been victimised.'[109]

Hornibrooks took the unions to court on several occasions, and one time the Commonwealth Industrial Court made a 'no strike' order against members of the Federated Engine Drivers and Firemens' Association working on the Opera House.[110] But still the industrial unrest continued and throughout Stage II a week or two without strikes was like a short period of calm in a habitually stormy sea.[111]

Meanwhile, back at the ranch, the business of designing and building the Opera House continued. The engineers asked London for the drawings and calculations for the entrance canopies[112] as

> Utzon is now calling for an off-form finish to the top side of these canopies as well as to the underside and we are looking into some method of obtaining this by pre-casting... The drawings will be of help initially but we will need the calculations to determine what additional work is required to complete the transverse beam and to judge any change in section shape.[113]

The canopy calculations had been completed by Joe Huang, and, like many of the tasks completed by Joe, were very complex, but Kelman could not find them. Re-doing the calculations was not a task to be taken on lightly, so Kelman took the obvious course of action which was to ask Joe where he had put them. Joe wrote from Malaysia, where he had moved to to set up a new Arup office,

> I have to work my memory so hard to try to think where I put the calculations for the canopy. After virtually fifteen minutes I am pretty certain that I put them together with the main calculations for the concourse beams done by Peter Skead. Should you find that they are not in this file, I am sorry to say that we have lost them.[114]

Meanwhile MacKenzie, who over five years earlier had believed he would be stopping at the Opera House for eighteen months before travelling to his home in New Zealand, now found himself recalled to London.

> 'Your impending departure is epoch making', wrote Kelman to MacKenzie 'SOH minus MacKenzie seems nothing at all, but O.A. + MacKenzie will be nice. I will have someone to ask about all the awkward questions the (Resident Engineers) ask!
>
> I certainly never expected the bar areas to be built without you watching over them. I shall pray.
>
> I do hope you don't find this place too depressing. To arrive in January is grim. The sun doesn't appear until about June; the world is black and damp – perhaps we will go back together!![115]

Kelman wrote to Joe Huang on 21st December

> I am pleased to say we have found your calculations – Eureka! They were with a miscellaneous batch found at the back of a correspondence filing cabinet. However, I believe even Scotland Yard has this trouble sometimes!
>
> A very Happy Christmas to you... [116]

And to Ed Perry in Sydney on the same day,

> After a purge which has made de-Stalinization look like spring cleaning we found – quite by chance – Joe Huang's calculations on the Canopies.
>
> I will send these and two prints of relevant drawings (which I think I previously and erroneously said had gone) when the local GPO has recovered from its present acute indigestion.[117]

At this time too it transpired that it would not be a good idea to use lightweight concrete for some of the segments, even though 'I am a member of the Lightweight Concrete Committee of the Reinforced Concrete Association',[118] wrote Jack Zunz to Mick Lewis. The construction of the shell roofs of the Opera House in concrete was already at the structural limit of what could be achieved, and Zunz did not like to contemplate the slight loss in strength using lightweight concrete would entail, and its long-term strength was unknown.

> If it were deemed necessary, despite all this, to seriously consider using lightweight concrete <u>because there is no other way</u> – we would have to carry out a good deal of checking of our calculations. This is a dismal prospect and I don't at the moment know where it would begin and end. One thing however is certain and it is that it would mean continuing building at some peril because of unknown structural effects – a responsibility which makes me shudder and one which we cannot contemplate without further investigation.[119]

On 22nd January Lewis wrote to Zunz from Sydney,

> We have just received the calculations for the balconies which were despatched by sea mail and this, we believe, must be the fate of the canopy calculations.
>
> Please do your best to prevent this sort of thing happening because we are really quite embarrassed by the delay.[120]

On the same day Kelman wrote to John Nutt from London, 'At last I have had printed all I can find of Joe's calculations for the canopies and have sent you these, at least as much of them as I can. I also enclose two prints of each drawing.'[121]

When Kelman was passed on the letter from Lewis he wrote back on the 27th:

> I am sorry the balcony calculations went by Sea Mail.
>
> However, I think this has not yet been the fate of the Canopy Calculations. We had a terrible job to find them at all and then getting them copied seemed to paralyse the system, so that they went off a few days ago.
>
> There is nothing – except standing instructions that all Sydney mail goes by air – to guarantee that they have not gone by sea of course.[122]

It was not just the side shells where tolerances were a concern. As the main shell ribs were being built Lewis found 'We are experiencing some rather curious behaviour on the part of the structure and find that practically all of the ribs in their erected shape seem to adopt a radius of approximately 1 ft smaller than the prescribed 246 ft.'[123] If the ribs could be thought of as having a 'C' shape the C was closing up slightly like a bow when an arrow is drawn. On the shorter ribs built so far this was having the effect of the completed rib being $\frac{1}{2}$ in low at the ridge. As Lewis pointed out in his letter, when the rib segments were temporarily stressed together with epoxy resin joints the change in shape 'could be due to the unequal pressure on the rib and top flanges caused by cantilever action. A wedge of approximately 1/32 in at each joint would be sufficient to cause this behaviour.'[124] Lewis continued '… we are still proceeding along the basis that each rib should be erected in its true geometric position regardless of the behaviour of its predecessors. As you see from the above remarks this is not always attainable.'[125] Which was a spur for Peter Rice and Michael Elphick to set to work to anticipate when this was occurring so adjustments to the rib segments could be made progressively as they were placed.

On 1st April Gore wrote to Zunz '… I understand that congratulations are due on your becoming a full Partner. This is a very well earned and justified appointment so please accept the best wishes of Bob Kynaston and myself.'[126] Zunz thanked him for his letter and his good wishes and wrote 'I hope the date of the letter was of no significance.'[127]

The bar areas that Kelman was saying a silent prayer over in the hope that they would be constructed all right without the presence of MacKenzie *had* been due to be constructed as part of Stage I but had been deferred to Stage II when it was apparent Civil & Civic were unwilling or unable to achieve the required concrete finish. The bar areas are the floor levels and flights of stairs beneath the glass walls that lead to the bars in the north foyers of the Major and Minor Halls.

The balconies of the bar areas stand right above the Harbour like the bridge of an ocean liner and command sweeping views to the Harbour Bridge and along the length of Sydney Harbour to the Heads. When the competition design was announced Professor Ashworth said to a reporter, 'The view and atmosphere on these harbourside foyers probably will have no equal in any Opera House in the world.'[128] Though Lilian Craft of North Sydney believed 'One feature of the new Opera House will appear unnecessary, indeed repugnant, to many – namely, the liquor bars. What possible effect can these have upon the enjoyment of opera, except a harmful one?'[129] Though when the question of a name came up for the building, Joseph Anderson wrote to the *Herald*: 'Sir, – I suggest that the Opera House might be popularly known as The Schooner, an allusion to its beautiful design, to its quayside location and to the refreshment (supplementing the spiritual) to be obtainable within its walls.'[130]

In preparation for the start of the work on the bar areas, the Architects and Engineers outlined some general instructions

> This section of the job is regarded as the most important section of the whole building insofar as the standard of finish is concerned. The finish must be uniformly as high as possible. Any defects or minor errors will be very noticeable since the ceiling height is low. There are numerous curved and straight lines both continuous and discontinuous which can be readily lined up by eye. It is most important that these lines should be individually true as well as bearing the correct relationship to each other. The practical implication of this is that while accurate setting out is of importance, the final approval of formwork will rest basically on a visual check.[131]

One day Utzon was in the bar areas when the formwork was going up. Gore was there and so was Bob Woods, the carpentry foreman supervising the work. Utzon was talking about the importance of an exceptional finish and Gore said to him 'You know you architects are all the same. We builders produce good off-form concrete and all you do is bag it (rub it with a hessian sack soaked in runny cement), paint it or cover it with a false ceiling.'[132] Utzon picked up a piece of ply that was lying on the floor and wrote on it in pencil 'To Bob Woods and Corbet Gore, I, Jorn Utzon, undertake never to cover this concrete but to leave it in the completed building as it comes off the form.'[133]

To achieve the pristine finish Utzon demanded no effort was spared. The carpenters put '... polyurethane strips on all the edges of all our formwork so as to act as a gasket so that when the form was closed up they were absolutely watertight and you got no water runs down the side of the concrete. You can get water runs in the side of the concrete and water can leak out and run down and leave a mark... And we had to stop air bubbles which you can get on the side of the form...'.[134] When the concrete is poured sometimes it'll enclose an air bubble which forms a round bubble in the concrete surface. To prevent it happening 'We did that with a very fine mist spray on the form just ahead of the concrete as it was being poured. (It) just gave enough moisture on the surface of the form... so that you didn't enclose an air bubble...'.[135] Also,

> The other thing about that bar area which people don't realise... is that you have the circular beam that runs around the top of the ceiling, and

then there is a series of beams that run radially in, and the geometry of the thing was such that each one of those has a twist. You can't see it with the naked eye but the geometry in fact has a twist in it of $\frac{3}{4}$ of an inch or so... so each (beam) had to be made with that twist. (And) There is no applied finish on any section of concrete that we did. It is all off form.[136]

Utzon later wrote when the work was completed,

... the bar areas will show the structure with its ribbed ceilings and walls formed in concrete without any treatment... the concrete stands with an even and precise surface and the sharp and straight edges clearly define the geometrical concept, a series of radial concrete beams, with their soffits forming a huge cone.[137]

Kelman need not have been concerned about the work going ahead without MacKenzie. The off-form finish of the Opera House bar areas is one of the most even and smooth that has been achieved anywhere in the world in reinforced concrete. During Stage III Yamasaki, the Japanese American architect who designed the World Trade Centre in New York, was shown around the site by David Littlemore, and he climbed up on a chair and ran his hand over the surface of the bar area beams, saying 'I have never seen concrete – natural concrete of such quality – such absolute proof in all the several surfaces.'[138]

When Arups had backed Utzon's choice of the ribbed concrete solution with precast elements for the shells they knew it could be built, but were not sure quite how it could be done. When Corbet Gore had travelled to London the first time to plan a way to build it he too did not know how it would be done, but he had faith that somehow or other, given time, using the resources of Arups and the Hornibrooks organisation, that eventually a way would be found how to do it. And once the die had been cast and the work rolled forward, Arups and Hornibrooks were quite determined that they would not and could not fail. As each difficulty arose in the design and construction, one by one they were overcome, even if at the time no known solution existed. There was no way to analyse the Rice Structure with lateral stressing, but Baker had written a program that could be adapted to the task. There was no existing bolt in any known material that was suitable for the lateral rib connections, but they found one. How could a rib be built up with elements in space? They found a way. To put those elements in space to the tolerances that were required was impossible. A survey program was written from scratch to do it. The shell segments in some locations were too heavy for the tower cranes to lift. Well we will just darn well have to lighten the lifting tackle and get special permission from the Department of Labour and Industry to lift them.[139] The weights of the elements had exceeded their design weight and would overload the structure during construction. Well we must fine-tune the erection sequence so the structure would not be overloaded.

With the major design and construction difficulties conquered, during the periods of industrial calm the pace of work picked up and if it never quite reached the pace of a brickie laying bricks it was not unusual for the riggers and erection crews to place eight shell segments a day with a record on one occasion of 14 segments placed in a day. As the shells rose from the podium 'Sydney people, like the inhabitants of one of those towns with an uncompleted cathedral in the Middle Ages, have grown used to living in the shadow of a vast edifice that year by year slowly pushes its way upward into the sky.'[140] The editor of the *Herald* John Pringle lived opposite the Opera House on the other side of the Harbour '... and used to gaze at it each morning and evening in a mixture of agony and ecstasy. Indeed for a time I became so obsessed with its progress that I could tell at a glance each day as I passed it on the ferry what piece had been added to its complex bulk the day before.'[141] As the precarious-looking shells took shape an aerodynamics expert wrote to the *Herald* advising 'people to ring the weather bureau before going to the opera.'[142] Others were just as stern in its defence, so much so that the BBC journalist Trevor Philpott touring Australia said 'Sydney people defend it like a mother defends an idiot child.' Philpott said he had spoken to workmen and construction experts on site and 'claimed several of them had told him that even now they had still no idea whether the Opera House would stay up when completed or whether it would just collapse'.[143] This was quoted on Philpott's program on British TV which had an audience of ten million. Ove Arup was too big a man to be worried by petty uninformed criticism, but he was still driven to say in a speech in London on the Opera House that 'he felt like a participant in the Battle of Waterloo trying to describe the centre of the affray.'[144]

Although Gore's relations on site were not the best with some of the more militant elements of the workforce, that was not the case with the carpenters, who rose to the challenge of crafting the intricate formwork for the shell segments and sanded them to a superb smooth finish, taking great pride in the work they did. There were a lot of Italians working on the Opera House, who were 'traditionally concrete people' and 'very enthusiastic... very interested' in the work and 'good people.' They 'caught a lot of fish off the wharf at lunchtime'[145] and would set fish traps in the Harbour beneath the podium. Though Kelman did not have such luck 'we used to try and fish at lunchtime, and I remember Michael (Lewis) promised us a frying pan if we ever caught a fish, but we never did.'[146] On another occasion, recalled Kelman,

> there were a lot of rats on Man o' War steps... and finally I thought we'd better deal with this. So I brought a .22 rifle into the office and I kept it beside my desk, and every now and again I'd have a crack at these rats on Man o'War steps. And one day... the Director of Public Works came down, and Michael Lewis was showing him through the office, and he was so petrified that if he opened my office door he'd find me aiming a rifle out the window (that) when he did open the office door, the first thing he said to the chap was, "Oh, Bob's probably shooting rats -" – something like that. He was so (sure) that that's what he would find, that he immediately burst out with that, before he needed to, but I was sitting calmly at my desk working... There was a lot of fun in the early days.[147]

What was not so much fun one day was when an apprentice on a ferry carrying workers from Circular Quay to the Navy Docks on Garden Island took a pot shot at the Opera House with a .22 rifle and 'it went right through the window beside Ian MacKenzie's head.'[148] Elphick remembered MacKenzie as a New Zealander with

> very acquiline features and a big deerstalker pipe. He was the most calm person I have ever met. Somebody would come rushing downstairs in a complete panic saying: "There's a crack appeared somewhere." You know – panic, panic, panic. "Concrete spalling off -" you know. And Ian would sort of reach round and look for his matches and tobacco and pat his pockets and check that his pipe was there, and then he'd sort of stand up and walk upstairs and then we'd go to the site of the damage or whatever it was and he would slowly fill his pipe and take a few puffs and say, "mmmm. That's very interesting." And then turn round and walk back downstairs. And then you'd say, "Well, what do you think, Ian?" He would say, "Oh, it's very interesting, isn't it." you know. And two hours later he'd probably come up with the solution of what the problem was. But he'd be thinking about it, but he couldn't – no matter what – he wouldn't panic.[149]

The only time Elphick ever saw MacKenzie react suddenly was when the shot came through the window and 'he went straight backwards off his chair onto the floor faster than anybody I've ever seen...'[150] The story made the papers, which was published with an awestruck-looking picture of Ian MacKenzie next to his office window with the bullet hole in the glass. Later a '16 year old youth told police he'd fired... one bullet at a bird and the second into the water... The youth told police that he had a new rifle and was crossing the Harbour in a ferry when he decided to try it out... Police took possession of .22 calibre rifle.'[151]

One Sunday MacKenzie came down to the Opera House site with his family and they brought the dog with them which they were subsequently very concerned about because 'it ate some rat poison, but it didn't seem to suffer any.'[152] MacKenzie remembered that one time two workers had a race through the inside of the hollow side-shell arches.

> there were two identical sides, because the shells are symmetrical, and you could have a race by... scrambling up to get into the side shell and then along the side shell, scrambling up the arch to the ridge, squeezing through an 18 in diameter hole that was about three meters long, along the ridge, down the corresponding side on the other side and back down and back out again. It was a real squeeze. You could just about get stuck in these damned holes, in fact... [153]

There would be food scraps lying around the site and possums would get into the site from the Botanic Gardens and take up residence in the hollow shell segments. Various people would be scrambling up through the holes in the arches on legitimate business such as the surveyors, and occasionally they would come across a possum which would come 'screeching past' which was 'very disconcerting.'[154] Hollow precast segments were also stacked around the site before they were assembled and in winter, with the sunshine coming in, the workers 'used to sit in these precast elements and have their sandwiches. Which meant that the possums used to come and collect the remnants. And one of the workers got bitten by a possum... They almost had a union issue as to whether the site should be cleared of possums.'[155]

On 5th April 1966 the top ridge segment of the highest Major Hall shell was lowered into place. Jim Inman, the dogman who rode the segment up, carried a notice 'would you do this for $44 a week.'[156] Hornibrooks built a small scaffold at the top, raised their flag and an Australian flag at the top of the shell and celebrated with a topping out ceremony. However next morning the flags had disappeared 'some students or builders labourers pinched them.'[157]

On 17th January 1967 the last shell segment of the 2,194 was lowered into place at the end of the ridge of shell A4 above the top of the harbourside foyer of the Major Hall, three years and two months after construction of Stage II started. 'LAST RIDGE SEGMENT ERECTED TODAY HOORAH'[158] cabled Mick Lewis to Jack Zunz.

When Ian MacKenzie left for England in 1965 shell construction was still underway, then when he returned to the site in 1967 the roof structure was completed. '... it was really awe-inspiring... to see the structure complete after eight years... that was really something, when you could stand down in the bottom... and you looked up 200 feet clear up to the top of the shells there, and realised that was about the height from the water up to the deck of the Harbour Bridge – just that huge volume there.'[159] John Nutt felt 'The best time in this building was before the insides went in when the outside roof was there all by itself and you looked up and you got a bit frightened. In fact it was overawing, you got used to the drawings and things at a different scale and when you see it at full size it really is quite a powerful effect.'[160] Kelman too thought it had 'a magic about it. I can remember in the early days when the shells were up and there was literally nothing inside them, and you could walk out onto there in the evening, just as it was getting dark – there was quite an extraordinary feeling about it, almost like an Egyptian tomb or something. It was very impressive indeed.'[161]

CHAPTER 14

THE TILES

Talking of the Opera House roof, Utzon said 'There is no doubt it must be white, because the roof has so many forms and white is the best to show the shades in the different kinds of lighting in a harbour-city like Sydney. The light will change quite a lot here, and all these shades would be seen at their best on a clear white surface. Furthermore, the surroundings are rather dark. This roof will be very sensitive. Unlike a building which has only light and shade, it will be a very live sort of thing, changing all the day long...'[1] 'In order to express this liveliness, these roofs are covered with glazed tiles. When the sun shines, it gives an effect which varies in all these curved areas. We know it from these vigorous shapes as we actually experience them, we can see them as if we were sailing around the building. The jagged silhouette will change its character, so that the House from being rather vertical in its expression, will become more horizontal.'[2]

The Opera House is a creature of the light, which seems to come to life when the sun shines on the shells. Almost without exception, a visitor to the Opera House will climb up the wide steps of the podium and reach up to run their hands over the tiles of the shells. If a father has his son with him who is too short to reach he will lift him up so he can touch the tiles, and say something to him like 'It's like the tiles on the bathroom at home.'[3]

When Utzon's competition scheme was published in 1957 and it was announced that the concrete shells would have white tiles, J.R.L. Johnstone of Beecroft wrote to the *Herald,* 'It's overfinished roof with many curved surfaces all covered with white tiles will be a glaring monstrosity.'[4] 'And how is it proposed to retain the pristine beauty of a glistening white tile roof in the midst of grimy harbour smoke', wrote Mrs Macquarie of Potts Point, 'when, with daily attention I cannot keep my light coloured window sills and door free from a grey film of dirt?'[5] While Mrs Coleman of Willoughby suggested: 'Sir, – I have been a professional colour artist for more than 30 years and consider myself an authority on colour.

I am not expressing an opinion on the architecture of the proposed Opera House, but – the suggested white tiles! This will give the impression from the Harbour and foreshores of either an Army camp or a circus. May I say that white can be very ugly if used in a big way. Touches of it can be most effective of course.'[6] To which Phyllis Shillito of Sydney replied: 'I suggest to your correspondent Mrs Coleman that when the Opera House is built she watch the effect of the ever-changing sky on the roof of white tiles at various times of the day and year. This experiment will offer her a new and exciting experience in colour.'[7]

On his return trips from Sydney Utzon collected a variety of handmade tiles in Japan and China in different textures, colours and glazes to take back to Europe to study. He knew they were long-lasting and weather-resistant because Islamic mosques and tombs that were hundreds of years old were still covered in their original tiles and gleamed like new. Of normal tiles Utzon said 'they give you an impression of paint; but several years of research by Hoganas... has given us exactly the tile which can match what I saw in the East.'[8] Hoganas' factory was about two hours journey from Utzon's home, by ferry across the sound to Sweden from Helsingor, then a ten-mile drive north along the Swedish coast. Utzon originally approached Hoganas at the end of 1957[9] and looked at their standard tiles but 'We soon found out that they could not meet the requirements even if certain glazes and qualities were of interest.'[10] Utzon looked at other manufacturers and could not find a tile anywhere that gave him what he wanted, so he came back to Hoganas, who, 'In order to study the influence of the curvature of the shells on the shapes of the tiles a scale model of two shells... was made, (which Hoganas believed) has been of great help to the architect in his judgements not only about the influence of the curvature, but also about colours and surface textures.'[11] Tile samples were made, but then it was decided the shells would be made of precast segments and a decision was made not long after that the tiles would be on separate precast panels or 'lids' that would be attached to the completed shell structure. So 'a new series of tile samples were made in different colours and surface textures... for the edges of the lids, white, black, brown and blue tiles have been the subject of our studies. Some trial lids were made for these studies both with filled and unfilled joints between the tiles.'[12]

Information filtering through to the Sydney public on the Opera House was sketchy or non-existent, particularly as Public Works had ordered a ban on all consultants talking to the press, no doubt reasoning that no information was better than any information. Any information that was given was released in carefully worded press statements. Such was the paucity of information available on the Opera House, that the public had no idea what was going on, which was not surprising as many of those very close to the scheme did not know what was going on either and were waiting in the wings on tenterhooks for Utzon's next divine flash of inspiration. When some information did become available, by accident or design, the press fell on it like a pack of baying wolves. This was the case when news came to hand in Sydney, after years of speculation of the tiling that would be used on the shells.

In Sydney on 23rd June 1962 the *Sunday Mirror* announced in an 'exclusive' some 'shock changes... in the design of the Sydney Opera House roof.' Not only will 'Its sleek lines... be made plump' i.e. in the change from Utzon's competition scheme to the spherical shell structure, but also 'It will be covered with black stripes... Instead of the soaring white shells Sydney was promised, the roof will be a prefabricated patchwork... Mr S. Haviland... in an exclusive interview yesterday with the *Sunday Mirror* (said) "The black ribbing has been introduced as a feature... It will make the Opera House stand out... The segments will be in off-white tiles, with black ribs of tiles running down between each segment."'[13] The *Daily Telegraph* published a plan view of the spherical scheme 'showing the pattern of black stripes on the "sails",' and quoted Haviland as saying "the black ribbing... would improve the appearance of the Opera House... It will make the whole structure more spectacular. When (Mr Utzon) came to Australia he told us to just about scrap his original design. He said he would improve on it as he made detailed designs. The black ribbing has been the most outstanding change so far". Mr Haviland said the tiles for the roof shells would be each four inches square. The black ribbing would be arranged in diamond shapes running in lines from the base to the top of each "Sail".'[14] While the *Sun* assured readers '... the licorice-all-sorts black vertical stripes that have been added to the modified sail-roof could, on Mr Haviland's own assurance, be supplemented next year by horizontal and diagonal stripes.'[15]

THE TILES

The *Herald* asked George Molnar what he thought of the new design. He said the lines would accentuate the billowing-sail effect of the shells. "'This is Utzon's masterpiece," he said. "He has improved on his original idea.'"[16] The *Sunday Mirror* found out what 'our experts' have to say on the matter. Bertram Ford, architect and president of the NSW Town Planning Association stated: 'I have never liked the Opera House design, and the changes make its appearance even worse.' An artist, Mr V. Bourlin said: 'The original design was much better than the new one. The lines are awful and the shape of the shells now is too harsh.' And another architect, Mr E.A. Towell thought 'The building is a masterpiece either way. But personally, I prefer the original design.'[17] The papers also consulted the 'man in the street.' A housewife, Mrs D. King of Kirribilli felt, 'The original design could not be bettered. Now it will look more like a bunch of mushrooms than the beautiful sails that I have always envisaged. The change is terribly disappointing.'[18] A Randwick resident, Mr R.G. Wylie, was unhappy too: 'The spontaneity of the original conception has been lost. A work of art has been "improved," and the result is hardly more happy than a poem edited for breach of syntax, or Botticelli's Venus with a straightened neck.'[19] One person said 'They put me in mind of a cricketer walking on to the field wearing white flannels and black braces.'[20] While another housewife considered 'There has been too much criticism of the Opera House by people who don't know enough about it. It was nice before and it's nice now. When it's built everyone will be satisfied with it.'[21] Three students from Bethlehem College in Ashfield wrote in on behalf of the art group. Why add the black stripes which made the Opera House look like a 'pram hood'? 'If the onlooker seeks linear delight, can it not be found in the Harbour Bridge?'[22]

The *Sunday Mirror* also caught up with Utzon, who said from Denmark "'Sydney people seem to be afraid of everything. Only people here can have any sound idea of what the Opera House is going to look like. We've had large sample panels made up of tiles with black borders and they look marvellous. ... The surfaces of the building are enormous and it needs these stripes to preserve the overall form of different elements.'"... He said the reason for using stripes of black tiles on the surface of the building was to outline different elements and emphasize the form of the building so its pattern would be visible even on a dull day.'[23]

When Utzon flew into Sydney on 21st August 1962 for the Cabinet sub-committee meeting, he told reporters the black stripes on the Opera House would be about a foot wide. Though three days later Utzon was saying he had not yet decided what colour they would be. '"The insecurity and uncertainty of a grey day in Sydney makes me feel I must divide the parts of the superstructure with tiles, as a leaf is divided in nature." He said that if an ordinary white tile was used to cover the shells' joints, the variation in the colour as the tiles came from the factory would give the impression that the Opera House's shape was changed or irregular. The coloured tiles over the joints were necessary to preserve the sense of shape.'[24] '"I am still not sure about the colour of the stripes," he said. "It may be black or it may be grey – or some other colour." I want something that will go with the white and with the beautiful blue-grey green of the surrounding water. We could have plastered over the stripes (i.e. the vertical joints between the ribs) but I wanted it to show like the mark of an operation".'[25]

Ashworth was overseas when the controversy blew up about the stripes, but he leapt to the defence of the new Opera House design on his return. He liked the idea of the black tiles to be used on the shells and had seen samples at Utzon's office and said it would 'hardly show.' 'The effect could be compared with the seams of a sail and they would emphasize the curve of the sails better than a vast expanse of white.'[26] Though Mr Serge at Crows Nest wrote to Ashworth that he was worried that the black outline to the ribbing, instead of giving the Opera House the 'sea shell effect' of the original idea, which was 'effective, classical, and in harmony with the setting' would instead 'give it a cheap, striped canvas "circus" effect.'[27]

On 29th November 1961 Utzon wrote to Ron Thomson of the Committee:

> The initial design of the shell envisaged a method of construction where the ceramic tiles would be fixed under a separate contract and I, therefore, thought that this should be a sub-contract in Stage III.
>
> Due, however, to the fact that we have now designed an entirely new method of construction for the roofs, it will be necessary for the ceramic tiling to be incorporated in Stage II. As we shall now be using a pre-cast element method of construction, incorporating tiles in the elements, it is

quite essential that we have the tiles available at the earliest possible date, as they are the first things to be put in the forms.

... I am now satisfied that the ideal type of tile has been found. The tiles of the correct quality, are available only in Sweden, these tiles being manufactured by Hoganas.[28]

The company of Hoganas Billesholms Aktiebolg had been founded in 1903 at Hoganas in south-west Sweden on the Baltic coast. Coal had been produced in the area since the middle of the sixteenth century and 'At an early stage various clay deposits were discovered within the area of such properties that they were suitable as a raw material for ceramic products. The coal rapidly became a by-product to the working of clay deposits and was primarily used for the production of gas which is now burned in our kilns.'[29] In 1961 the Hoganas group employed 4,000 people, at factories in Sweden, Germany, and the USA. Their tiles came with a choice of 420 different colours and were available in a deep transparent glaze. 'The tile body was extruded and not 'dry pressed' and 'The tile body and the glaze are burnt in one operation at a temperature of 1200° to 1300°C.'[30]

Hoganas had consulted on the tiles with Ove Pettersson, an Associate Professor at the Royal Institute of Technology in Stockholm, who had produced a technical report on 'Sydney Opera House, Calculations and Recommendations of the outer ceramic wall facings.' The report, published in May 1959, envisaged the tiles would be laid directly on the shell structure, and by way of introduction noted that

... glazed tiles have been used from the earliest times for the covering and decoration of monumental buildings. The remains of these structures bear witness even today of the durability and decorative beauty of ceramics... Thick, solid walls and vaulted roofs were built of natural stone or of bricks and mortar which served as a stable foundation for covering with other materials.[31]

But 'In this case, it is necessary to shape the external ceramic covering on the shells with regard to the different physical characteristics of ceramic tiles and concrete (which) originate from solar heating and from concrete shrinkage.' Pettersson's investigations resulted in certain recommendations regarding the stresses from concrete shrinkage and solar heating on the adhesion between tiles and mortar. 'The calculations... show that the distance between expansion joints increases with the age of the concrete at the time of tile setting…' because of 'the tensile stresses which then occur, it is best that the tiles should be set in a square pattern with straight joints in both directions, so that any possible cracks will appear in the joints.' Also he recommended that tile setting should be performed at the coldest period for the locality, that the tiles are set at least three months after the shells have been cast, and that a distance between expansion joints on the shells be maintained at three metres. In compiling the report Pettersson obtained maximum and minimum temperatures for Sydney from the Swedish Meteorological and Hydrological Institute in Stockholm, and took into effect the latitude of Sydney and the variation in the declination of the sun according to the season. By examining the tensile stresses between tiles and mortar at maximum and minimum surface temperatures and the influence of shrinkage (compression in the tile layer, tension in the concrete) Pettersson calculated the adhesive stresses between tiles and mortar, which were at a maximum adjacent to expansion joints.[32]

Besides the white tile for the shells Utzon was looking at using a black or a blue tile for the edge of the tile lids. All three tiles had been specially developed by Hoganas 'working in close co-operation with the architect'[33] in a 'series of experiment(s) and tile manufacturings.'[34]

> The tile developed is manufactured from an off-white clay body and intermixed with a white rather coarse chamotte. The glaze is transparent and shiny, which has the effect that the tile body is visible through the glaze. The blue and black tiles have a clay body which is coloured all through and the glaze is uncoloured.
>
> The tiles are frost-resistant. The glaze is absolutely non-crazing and will not be affected by ultraviolet light or by chemical attacks from industrial atmosphere.[35]

Utzon said later, 'We get the white colour from a very beautiful stone being made in Sweden, the Carmen stone.'[36] 'I found a certain type of clay and glaze which produced the silvery effect you get when the sun shines on water.'[37] The tiles were self-cleaning, and maintained their lustre by being washed clean every time there was a rain shower. Moses had tackled Utzon on the white tiles, as he was worried about the dazzling effect of the bright Australian sun glaring on such a large white surface. Utzon replied that he had ordered the tiles to be manufactured with a rippled surface to deflect the sun's rays and prevent blinding dazzle.

THE TILES

Even though Utzon had spent over two years working with Hoganas developing his tiles for the Opera House, the Committee insisted that 'for political reasons' the tile contract should go out to open tender 'even if only one firm would be able to tender.'[38] On 2nd February 1962 Utzon's office sent out a specification and invited tenders for 'The supply and delivery of Tiles to clad the exterior surface of the Concrete Shells of Sydney Opera House.'[39] Utzon had written to Ashworth just a week previously on 15th January:

> ... Hoganas can produce the tiles in the colour and quality that I want and deliver them early enough for Stage II. Personally, I do not think we can get the same quality in Sydney to the same low price, but of course time will show... I want more than anything to have everything made in Australia and avoid any political trouble for you and Mr Haviland... [40]

The tender documents specified '... Quotations must be delivered to Mr Ron Thomson, Secretary and Executive Officer, Sydney Opera House Executive Committee... not later than 12th February 1962 at 12.00 noon.'

Quantity: 20,000 yards of tiles.
90% off-white with a shiny glaze, 5 in x 5 in – $\frac{1}{2}$ in thick.
5% of total quantity to be black with shiny glaze, 5 in x 10 in – $\frac{3}{4}$ in thick.
5% of total quantity to be light blue with shiny glaze, 5 in x 10 in – $\frac{3}{4}$ in thick.
... delivery of tiles to building site by end of June 1962.

Approval
The final choice of the tile will be made by the Architect and the Engineer through tests and it must be understood that the lowest tender will not necessarily be accepted.

Tender "A"
(Specially made tile to Architects technical description as set out below).

The tiles shall be of stoneware and have a transparent shiny glaze so that the natural colour of the stoneware determines the colour of the tile, i.e.the off-white tile is made from off-white clay and has a completely transparent shiny surface on the exposed side, the blue is made of a blue stoneware with a transparent glaze over and the same in the case of the black.

The back surface to be keyed preferably in a manner formed where the tiles are fired in pairs and afterwards split. The tiles to be extruded and *not* pressed, in order to give a coarse structure to the stoneware, providing a living surface.

The tiles to be of waterproof quality and to have a great tensile strength. The tiles must be absolutely precise in shape, must not twist and must have uniform edges on all four sides.[41]

(Tender "B" was manufacturer's standard tile).

Jones of Rider Hunt and Partners wrote to Utzon on 13th February.

The quotations for the (tiles) were opened yesterday by Skipper Nielsen in the presence of Ron Thomson and myself. Skipper Nielsen has asked me to forward the following quotations received...

1. Hoganas
2. Commonwealth Ceramics
3. Wunderlich

You will be pleased to know that the lowest quotation was submitted by Hoganas.

... the overall price of £2.14s 2d (including duty) per square yard is still well below the lowest quotation. I am very pleased about this because the local people could have brought some pressure to bear on this account...

... I am looking forward very much to meeting you again in March. It seems that we are going to have a busy time then... Trust that both you and your family are well.[42]

Wunderlich sent a covering letter to Utzon with their quote:

... we have been compelled through extreme shortage of time to prepare a quotation based on current practice prevailing in the Australian Ceramic Industry.

... As the request to furnish a quotation was not received by our company until 5th February sufficient time has not been available to enable our Research Division to set in hand experiments to determine alternative and possibly more economical means of providing a blue and black coloured clay body.[43]

Wunderlich also quoted on a white tile size of 10 square inches, suggesting that if this was acceptable it could mean considerable economies.

Hoganas' quote sent from Sweden on 6th February also included a note to Ron Thomson offering that at no charge

... If requested we are prepared to send for a period of three weeks one of our service engineers to the building site to assist with technical advice and information in the application of the Hoganas' tiles... [44]

Utzon wrote to the Executive Committee on 28th March:

... All tenderers have submitted samples for inspection, which I have carefully examined. The samples submitted by Wunderlich were not in accordance with Specification "A" (special tile made to the Architect's description) but were samples of the manufacturers' standard tile

(Specification "B") and they are not acceptable, amongst other things because the tile is made with an uncoloured, water absorbent body with a coloured glaze which would not meet the requirements as to the durability of the colour.

... Commonwealth Ceramics have submitted samples made to match the samples from overseas, which were given as a pattern as regards the surface quality, but although they have taken great care to match the appearance required I cannot recommend this tile as the surface texture does not match the Hoganas' tile nor is the tile extruded as asked for in the specification.

I therefore wish to recommend to the Committee the acceptance of the quotation submitted by Hoganas, as their tile is the cheapest of the three as well as a product of high and even quality, which I feel confident will meet the requirements, architecturally as well as structurally.[45]

Hoganas were far cheaper on the white, blue and black tiles,

For example the cost of their white tiles, C.I.F. including the duty of $27\frac{1}{2}$ per cent, was £2 14s 2d per square yard, Wunderlich were £6 12s 3d, and Commonwealth Ceramics were £3 3s 6d. The Wunderlich quote on the black tiles was £18 15s 0d a square yard, while Hoganas were quoting £2 17s 3d CIF including duty.

Meanwhile Utzon was keeping his options open on what colour to use. Ivan Naslund of Hoganas wrote to Buus of Utzon's office on 10th April

Herewith two samples of the black tile which I have received from Skromberga (site of a Hoganas factory in Sweden). In my opinion these samples are not satisfactory either because they have used a tinted glaze instead of a transparent glaze, apparently because they could not manage to get the body completely black.

It has proved rather difficult to make a completely black body with white grain like the blue ditto, but now I have asked the factory to try to blacken the body even more if possible and put on a transparent glaze.

As you can see from the sample, the body becomes brownish... The question is now, if you would consider accepting a brownish-black tile with a transparent glaze and white grains in case we should not manage to blacken the body completely. A completely black tile with shiny glaze of course could be made with the usual black glaze but then the white grain will not show.

I have ordered new samples with transparent glaze where the grains are showing like on the blue tile and we shall see if we can manage to make the body more black than attached sample... [46]

Although the tile tender had called for delivery to Sydney by the end of June, no contracts could be placed as Hornibrooks still had not been accepted as the official contractors for Stage II, and Utzon's thoughts were still advancing on colour and finish. The architect wrote to Naslund on 2nd July:

> Apart from the two successful trial elements made in Skromberga I wish to order two more made in the same forms as follows:
> 1 – completely white tiles with edges of natural coloured tile and with clear transparent glaze.
> 2 – semi white tiles with edges of natural coloured tiles and with clear transparent glaze.
>
> These two elements represent the colour range in the side shells. The joints shall remain open, in other words, as the element on the right side at Skromberga.
>
> I would be glad to have the element placed beside the two existing ones in about 3 weeks time. I hope you can manage.
>
> Mr Zunz has promised to send you the total quantities in a weeks time and then we are all waiting for the starting signal from Sydney.
>
> We shall be away on holidays for 3 weeks from today, and when we come back everything should be ready to place a detailed order.
>
> PS. To avoid misunderstandings, what I call completely white tiles is: the type of tiles in the middle of the trial element at the right side at Skromberga.
>
> What I call a semi-white is: the tile in the middle of the trial element on the left and the natural coloured body with clear transparent glaze is the 'V' shaped row at the bottom of the trial elements.[47]

On 31st October Zunz wrote to Malcolm Nicklin, 'I spoke to Jorn on the phone on Monday and while he has now made up his mind as to colour of tiles there is still some lack of detail as to the number and variety of non standard sizes.'[48] At least this freed up Corbet Gore to send an order for the standard white tiles, who, also on the 31st, sent to Hoganas their order No. 12685 for tiles for the Opera House roof, drawing their attention 'to the rejection clause in the specification and written approval of samples should be obtained from the architect prior to commencing manufacture.'[49] Gore also requested 5,000 tiles for trial rib sections, to be sent and done 'immediately out of the total quantity mentioned above.'[50] Gore sent a note with the order 'We must apologize for the delay in placing this order but you will appreciate that the circumstances were quite beyond our control.'[51] Not long after the order went off, on 12th November, Utzon wrote to Commonwealth Ceramics and Wunderlich:

Gentlemen,

We wish to advise that the contract for the supply of roofing tiles for the Sydney Opera House has been awarded to the firm of Hoganas, Sweden, who submitted the lowest tender.

We thank you for your participation.[52]

Hoganas wrote to Hornibrooks on 30th November:

We acknowledge with thanks receipt of your letter dated 31st October with your attached official order for ceramic tiles to clad the exterior surface of the concrete shells of the Sydney Opera House.

... As regards the 5,000 tiles wanted by you for use on trial rib sections, we can inform you that these are already manufactured. However when Mr Utzon visited us on the 27th November to make his final choice of tiles... he selected a glazed tile which in texture and colour slightly deviates from the 5,000 tiles mentioned above. Consequently, these tiles cannot be regarded as part of your order... (but) can, however, in our opinion be used for trial purposes.

... We have duly noted the contents of the rejection clause in the tender, but would like to point out that certain slight variations in colour are natural for ceramic materials and this is also wanted by the Architect.[53]

Hoganas sent a second letter to Gore at Hornibrooks, also on 30th November:

We refer to our letter of to-day's date confirming your Order No. 12685.

... we must, however, point out that probably the price will not be as quoted. This is due to the fact that the quality chosen by the Architect is quite different to the one originally quoted.[54]

At the November meetings at Hoganas and at Hellebaek, Zunz had tied down with Utzon some of the details for the non-standard tiling including 'Tile lid detail at open end of shells.'[55] For the coloured tiles that would form the patterns around the tile lids, Utzon had chosen a matt cream coloured tile.[56] On the order and for subsequent identification, the standard square glass tiles were called 'G' tiles, and the standard square matt tiles 'M' tiles, although there were many other different sizes of matt tiles depending on, for example, if they were used at the open end of the shells or in the matt tile patterns that ran around the edges of the tile lids. The non-standard matt tiles were identified as 'D', 'X', 'B' and 'P' tiles depending on their size, the P tiles themselves having their own particular classification of P1, P2, P3 and so on as they were in many different lengths to fit the pattern at the edge of the lids. Some of the details of these tiles had been tied down, in October, as an Arups schedule noted:

If, in some cases, the bottom D-tile of the warped surface has less than 12 in clearance from finished floor, the tile pattern should start 2 ft 6 in along the surface...

Ridge tile pattern is agreed as Arup's suggestion, i.e.X-tiles directed against the ridge curve (for shells A1, B1 and B4 follow the direction at the open edge) with always at least one complete diagonal matt tile...

At open ends of main and louvre shells D-tiles are provided which must always be complete and uncut including the very top one...

Tile surface between shells 5 and 6 to be $1\frac{1}{4}$ in below those of both shells 5 and 6 along radial directions... [57]

Other details had been tied down when Gore made his flying visit in December 1962 in meetings with Hoganas representatives at Arups London office when various questions had been put to Utzon by phone. But there were still a host of unresolved tiling details and some of these were included on Zunz's list of 63 items of 'Matters affecting Utzon' that he took with him for the Boxing Day meeting with the architect at London Airport. John Blanchard wrote to Gore on 4th January 1963:

... Unfortunately, at our Boxing Day meeting with Mr Utzon certain decisions were made that affect the numbers off of various types of tiles. These were a) the special bottom tiles. Type B will be matt, not glossy, b) these B-tiles will also be used at the bottom of the warped surfaces, c) these B-tiles cannot now be used for Shells 10 where a special extra large site – cut tile Type Y will be required (approx. 12 in x $4\frac{3}{4}$ in) and d) double thickness tiles type D are now required on the tile lids adjacent to the ridges... [58]

Blanchard wrote to Hoganas on the same day:

... at a meeting with Mr Utzon in London on 26th December, design decisions were made that mean an increase in the number of D-tiles, a small change in the number of B-tiles, a change of shape and a change to matt finish of the B-tiles, and the necessity for a small number of tiles similar to Type X but slightly longer. We do not expect to be able to provide a complete specification of these requirements until the middle of February... [59]

Meanwhile news had just filtered down to Sydney that the coloured tiles would not be glossy black or blue but a creamy matt. On 6th January under the headline 'A CHANGE OF "SAILS"' the *Sun Herald* announced in bold type 'Opera House gets its stripes back (BUT THEY WON'T BE BLACK).' The papers 'special correspondent' reported:

THE TILES

The roof of Sydney's new Opera House WILL have stripes. But they will not be black – they will be almost invisible. The "humbug" effect, which raised a storm of public protest when it was proposed last June, will be replaced by a modest self-stripe pattern.

The seams of the great white sails rising above the Harbour will be faced with tiles of the same colour, but of a different finish.

The tiles on the main body of the roof will be glazed, while the seams will be matt, giving a difference in texture but much less of a noticeably striped effect.

The chairman of the Opera House executive committee, Mr S. Haviland, could not be contacted for comment yesterday.

"The Sun Herald" was told, however, the original black stripes proposed by the architect, Mr Joern Utzon, was only tentative. Mr Utzon evolved the idea in the belief that the structural elements of a building should be emphasised, not camouflaged. Since then, he has been experimenting with tiles of other colours to cover the seams. The final choice of a self-stripe was made for "aesthetic reasons."

Mr Bertram Ford, architect and president of the N.S.W. Town Planning Association, said yesterday: "I am very pleased they have changed their minds. The complaints that poured in at the time, probably had something to do with it. The people concerned had no right to suggest such a thing as black stripes. It was a mad idea, and destroyed the whole character of the building."

(One) of Sydney's leading architects held different views. Mr Harry Seidler said: "Personally, I have every confidence in Mr Utzon. The public should not interfere. They should leave things to him. Utzon has a very complex and exciting view of things. Why not let him get on with it?"[60]

The following day the *Daily Mirror* carried the story under the headline 'Utzon went it alone!'

The black stripes were taken out of the sail roof of the Opera House without the knowledge of the executive committee.

The decision was made by the architect, Mr Joern Utzon.

Mr Utzon is expected to discuss his decision with the committee on his arrival in Sydney next month.

After the *Sunday Mirror* revealed on June 24 last the decision to "candy-stripe" the Opera House roof there was a flood of protests from Sydney people.

The chairman of the committee, Mr S. Haviland, later said all 13 members of the committee had agreed the new design looked better...

Mr Haviland, who is ill, was not available for comment today.

The chairman of the committee's technical panel, Professor H. Ingham Ashworth, said today, he did not know officially whether or not Mr Utzon had changed his mind.

"We have certainly not decided anything here," he said.

"It is a matter of opinion, but I felt the black lines would have helped one appreciate the shape of the roof.

I saw models in Sweden recently and some had black lines and some didn't."

Mr I. R. Griffith, Liberal MLA for Cronulla, said today:

"Nobody seems to know what is going on. It appears the Opera House is still being built by trial and error."[61]

On 5th February Blanchard wrote to Hoganas enclosing 'for your information duplicate copies of our drawings Nos 1112/3251, 3252. These show the number, shape, size and finish of all the tiles required on this job for which Hornibrooks will shortly be placing an order with you...'[62] This cleared the way for Hornibrooks to send to Hoganas on the 15th their order No. 13879 for tiles for the Opera House. The total order was for 1,044,250 tiles, of which 817,700 were the standard square glossy off-white 'G' tile and the remaining 226,550 were matt. The matt tiles were in 52 different sizes, the 'D', 'M', 'X', 'Y' and 'B' tiles, as well as the 'P' tiles, which were numbered for P1 to P47.[63] The numbers of matt tiles ranged from 55,300 for the standard matt 'M' tiles which were the same square size as the standard glossy tiles to only 50 of the 'P42' tiles. The actual number needed for the job was 988,110, but including extras to allow for breakage this made up the total order of 1,044,250. The margin for breakage ranged from 5 per cent for the G tiles to 25 per cent for the P42 tiles. The order specified that

Colour and quality is to be as selected by the Architect, J. Utzon, and generally in accordance with the following extract from the minutes of your meeting dated 11th December, 1962:

Glazed tiles to be manufactured according to sample marked L090806 and marked with the signature and stamp of the Architect.

Unglazed edge tiles to be manufactured according to sample marked L090804 and marked with the signature and stamp of the Architect.

Variation in colour and iron stains – a certain natural colour variation is allowed. Samples 5684/5684T and L090805 show the utmost variation limit of glazed tiles.

Unglazed tiles should not be yellowish but are allowed to be light touching a white-grey tinge. Iron stains are allowed – a few large ones or several small ones. [64]

Delivery was 16 weeks from the date of the order with shipment to Hornibrooks in Sydney 'in suitable crates, branded externally with the code letter of the tiles contained therein.'[65]

Hoganas had produced samples of the glazed and matt tiles which would be kept at the factory at Hoganas, at Arups London and in Sydney as a colour and quality standard for the tile batches. It had been specified tiles would be 4¾ in square by 5/8 in thick made to a 'precision of ± ½ mm. in direction perpendicular to cuts and almost exact in other direction.'[66] Manufacture at Hoganas got under way in March to Utzon's instructions that

> Tiles for the main part of the lids should be of white stoneware and have a shiny transparent glaze so that the natural colour of the stoneware determined the colour of the tile. The stoneware clay was to be mixed with a rather coarse chamotte providing a living surface texture which could reflect the sun-rays in different angles.[67]
>
> Tiles for the edges of the lids should be of white unglazed stoneware with a rather smooth and dense surface.[68]

On 7th March Hoganas wrote to Hornibrooks thanking them for their order and confirming delivery, 'About 16 weeks from the date of your order, i.e.by the middle of June 1963.'[69] And noted that '... this order replaces your previous order no. 12685 dated 2nd November 1962 which we hereby confirm having cancelled.'[70] The extruded tiles would be manufactured in pairs with the finished surface at the top and the bottom, and on arrival in Sydney they would be split to give the rough key on the lower surface to bond to the mortar. For this purpose Hoganas mentioned they would supply 50 special splitting forks free of charge packed in a separate crate. Utzon had just arrived in Sydney and also on 7th March the *Herald* carried an article headed 'Opera House Roof to be Two-Tone.'

> The sail roof of the Opera House will be two-tone white, a combination of glossy and matt tiles, the Opera House designer, Mr Joern Utzon, said last night. "From a distance you will get a pattern of glossy tiles shining like finger-nails against the flesh-like texture of matt tiles," he said...
>
> Mr Utzon arched his fingers to form the shape of a shell and said: "The ribs will spread out from the base like a Spanish fan. The ridge of the ribs will be covered with glossy white tiles. In the folds between will be matt tiles. The two tiles will form a natural pattern in perfect harmony. The glossy tiles will reflect the surrounding colours of nature – the blue of the harbour, the green of the trees, the sky. Because they are in the folds, the matt tiles will not throw a shadow (i.e.reflection) over the glossy tiles."
>
> Mr Utzon said a two-tone roof was much better than a plain white roof which would have "no texture, no expression." "No matter from what angle you look at the Opera House it will stand out very clearly – as clear

411

as the Snowy Mountains," he said.

Mr Utzon described as a misconception reports last year that the Opera House would have black stripes. "We experimented with all colours, including black," he said. "Someone must have seen one of the experimental designs featuring black ribs."[71]

Later, talking from his office on the Opera House site and gesturing towards the red brick houses at Kirribilli, Utzon said 'all houses near the water should be painted off-white.'[72] Utzon said on another occasion that he was striving to achieve with his pattern of mixed matt and gloss tiles '"alpengluhen", the colour you get on snowcapped mountains when the sun is setting; the beautiful pink and violet reflection from the combination of matt snow and shiny ice.'[73]

'Thank you for your letters... confirming our order,' wrote Corbet Gore to Hoganas on 19th March, '... We would like to thank you for your co-operation and assistance in negotiating the placing of such a complicated order from such a distance and look forward to receiving your consignment in due course.'[74] And Utzon wrote to Ivan Naslund on 9th April: 'We are here safe and sound all of us, and Hornibrooks are working like devils. They have already produced the steel forms for the main shell ribs and have made some very satisfactory mock-ups of shell ribs lid elements.'[75] Utzon's agent looking after the production of the tiles in Sweden was Helge Hjertholm, who he wrote to on 6th May, '... As a principle I am happy that the glazed tiles are on the white side, so keep them there.'[76]

Naslund wrote to Utzon on 17th May:

The winter has been very severe this year – long and cold with lots of snow. You can be lucky you have not been here. Oresund has been completely frozen periodically with a very disturbing effect on shipping. Certain deliveries of raw materials to us among them some we need for the Sydney order did not come in time. Not long ago one of the plants in Skromberga burnt down and we lost some premises for drying and cutting... [77]

Utzon meantime had made some changes to the tiling. The warped surfaces would be matt tiles only instead of gloss and matt, and Utzon had made a decision to tile the shell pedestals and the interior of the side shell arches.[78] Blanchard wrote to Naslund on 24th May:

We confirm our telephone conversation of today, further to our letter of 15th May in which you agreed to make an amendment to the tile order for this job... This amendment is an increase of 4,000 in the number of P43 tiles and a decrease of approximately 2500 in the number of X tiles...

Would you please (this was not discussed on the telephone) give these additional 4,000 tiles, and these tiles only, the type no. F1...

This amendment relates to the Warped Surface Lids. We now find that many of the edge tiles repeat and that, by coincidence, they have the same shape as the P43 tiles. We have therefore taken the opportunity of reducing the number of tiles that have to be site cut.[79]

Utzon then sent three cables to Hoganas in the space of a week.

Due to amended procedure of casting, 65,000 are now required on site by end June, preferably 60,000 M tiles plus 5,000 X tiles... Please investigate earliest possible dispatch by fastgoing Liner via Italy... [80]

... Type B to be matt as correctly stated in Hornibrook's order... [81]

We confirm tile order being increased by approximately 150,000 M tiles. 60,000 M tiles required on site early August.[82]

And in a covering letter had various 'urgent questions' including

4. Will the increased amount of M tiles mean that other parts of the order will be delayed? If so which types of tiles?

A final revised order will be worked out and sent to you as soon as possible. I am sorry if this upsets your program, but I trust that some way can be found which will be satisfactory to the Opera House.[83]

Lewis sent a memo to Zunz on 12th June:

There has been a flurry of cables between Utzon and Hoganas attempting to arrive at a satisfactory delivery date for the additional matt tiles for the warped surfaces. It appears now that we will not be able to get these tiles on to the site when they are needed for the erection procedure. (Warped surfaces – then side shells, then Main shells had been the proposed procedure).[84]

Meanwhile Helge was keeping his eye on tile production, writing to Utzon on 29th May:

... have seen the first completed tiles. The tiles are now shooting out of the plant and they look marvellous. They are standing on their heads to make it as good and also as quickly as possible.

... I am always visualising how the individual tile will look in a big continuous area as it will be in the shell surfaces. On this basis, it does not seem as if any one is "outside". The glazed square tiles are generally a fraction lighter than the sample, but they are all within the tolerance. If you take one of the lighter tiles and place it in a continuous area of "normal tiles" it does not appear as being lighter, in other words it fits into the large area. Some very few of the glazed tiles have a green (or blue) spot, usually so feint that it cannot be seen at a distance. These last ones will be put aside for the time being, (see the sample enclosed) but, possibly you would actually like to have such variation?

... The matt tiles... are generally slightly larger than the sample (according to your wish) – and surely an advantage since they will weather more than the glazed ones.

... Do not let these details worry you, you have every reason to be happy. The way the tiles are placed in a large continuous area they look marvellous.

I have discussed with Naslund how I can best keep control with the production over there. Even if I stayed there constantly during the time of production, it would be impossible for me to control each and every tile since the sorting takes place in several areas at the same time. What I can do, is to to assist by setting out the numbers for sorting and take a control at regular intervals that the sorting is correct and also constantly take out samples from the production.[85]

And again three days later on 3rd June:

I have again been in Skromberga for two days and have got a very good idea of the quality of the production. It is very good, and everything seems to go well.

Generally, I will say that the percentage of rejections is lower than for ordinary Hoganas tiles.

At every sorting table, they have placed samples, corresponding to your samples which define the limit for light and dark, and also a limitation for how big possible black and grain dots can be accepted... It has been a true pleasure for me to go over there between large piles of beautiful tiles certainly the best I have seen up to date.[86]

Then two weeks later on 17th June:

... I have again been at Skromberga.

The tiles are coming out in an even flood from the plant, and as far as I can see the quality is still even and first class.

... Because of the pointed corners, the clay shrinks more along the edge where there is little body than further in where the body is larger. This results in a slightly curved edge. This is something which has been taken into consideration in the method of production and most of these difficulties have been overcome.

... On Friday, the first batch with approximately 1/3rd of the tiles was sent by train from Skromberga to Gothenberg from where they would continue by ship tomorrow.[87]

Hoganas wrote to Hornibrook on 26th June:

... 175 tons against this order were shipped by the M.S. *G. D. Kennedy* which left Gothenberg on June 22, with estimated arrival Sydney around August 12th. Another 100 tonnes will be shipped by M.S. *Tourcoing* loading on June 29.[88]

And Utzon to Hoganas on the same day:

> ... I am very happy with the work you have done up until now, and judging from Helge's enthusiastic report, we are getting the finest tile surface in the world.
>
> My warmest greetings to you and all at Hoganas.[89]

Utzon wrote to Corbet Gore on 8th July confirming instructions cabled to Sweden 'that an extra 150,000 M-tiles will be required. The alterations concerning P-tiles and M-tiles have already been confirmed by Arups on 15th and 24th May.'[90]

Helge wrote to Utzon again on 3rd July:

> After a new trip to Skromberga I have only this to report.
>
> Everything goes well over there – at least I have not been able to find any faults.
>
> ... The engineers over there say that it is almost sheer luck that so many different types of tiles have been produced with such a good result. Usually they calculate nearly one year to achieve a safe production of a new type.
>
> ... Some time ago, I noticed by chance a picture of a Norwegian ship in Sydney Harbour. In the background and near the bridge was another and conspicuous "ship" which took the whole picture. I must some time go on board this building work and see what it looks like.[91]

Once production was rolling shipments of tiles came through progressively to the site, though the final tile count still was not cut and dried. On 14th October 1964 Utzon wrote to Arups at the Opera House site:

> I refer to your letters of 18th September and 23rd September 1964 concerning the counts for the tiles.
>
> For the shell pedestals and the shell columns I intend to use X-tiles rather than P-tiles along the edges.
>
> Also I intend to reduce the number of tiles for the shell columns... [92]

And Utzon sent a revised count of M and X tiles 'with the totals adjusted accordingly.'[93] But Utzon was still keeping his options open for the tiling of those areas. 'In connection with the discussion at the last site meeting', he wrote to Arups at the Opera House site, 'I confirm that the fixings for tile lids on the (side-shell) arch and the shell pedestals should be cast into remaining sections of the works irrespective of the possibility of these pedestals being eventually left exposed. (in which case)... it is desirable to retain a high standard of finish for this work, especially as regards definition of edges and corners.'[94]

On 12th January 1965 Utzon had the final word on the quantity of tiles, writing to Ivan Naslund at Hoganas,

I am writing in connection with Hornibrook's provisional order of 9.11.1964 for extra tiles.

I have now decided to omit the tiles on the shell pedestals and the shell columns and the order will therefore be reduced considerably.

A revised figure will be given by the Contractor in due course.[95]

Complicated tables were produced by Utzon's and Arup's offices to determine tile counts, then revised tile counts after changes to tile colours, revised again when Utzon decided to tile side shell arches, and again when Utzon decided to use different tiles on the arches, and yet again when Utzon decided not to tile the arches. The tables were passed on to Hornibrooks, who, as the contractor, placed the official order. Some of the tiles after previous amended orders had already been delivered which 'has resulted in an excess quantity of G tiles... There is also a small excess quantity of X and Y tiles. The architect has indicated that these will be used in the Stage III contract...'.[96]

On 25th February Utzon wrote to Helge Hjertholm in Helsingor:

The construction here is moving rather slowly but we do proceed. The client causes us more problems than anything else, and constant industrial strife doesn't help – but one day it will be complete.[97]

Though the architect was in a more cheerful mood when he wrote to Ivan Naslund on 11th May:

Work is going well now. The structural part of four of the shells is more than half completed, and we can begin to visualise the final impression. I am sorry to say though that none of the tile panels have been placed in position yet – I am sure that (when they are) this is going to change the whole picture and I just cannot wait until it happens.[98]

CHAPTER 15

THE TILE LIDS

When the original design of the Opera House was envisaged as thin concrete shells cast in situ, the intention had been that tilers would lay the four acres of tiles directly onto the completed shell surface.

> On such a surface, the tiles would have to be laid by traditional methods involving serious risk of tiles falling off due to thermal strain and inadequate bedding of individual tiles. It was inconceivable that this vast number of small tiles could be laid in a satisfactory manner by tilers working on the surface of the roof.[1]

Initially, when the change was made to the prefabricated rib structure, the intention was that the tiles would be laid back face up in the rib forms, then the concrete poured on top – which is what Utzon wanted. But to erect the prefabricated structure with a finished tile surface cast into the surface of the rib segments would have been difficult, if not impossible. There was no way to insulate the structure, insurmountable difficulties were anticipated in waterproofing the rib joint and access to the rib structure was needed after erecting rib segments for placing the lateral stressing and lateral bolts. Zunz was with Ove Arup in a hotel room in Hellebaek talking about the tiles cast into the ribs, when Zunz said 'Look – this is nonsense, we'll have to separate them in some way.'[2] And Ove grunted 'I think you're right',[3] which led to the decision to use separate tile panels or 'tile lids' fixed to the completed rib structure.

Since the mid 1950s Hoganas had manufactured wall units faced with their tiles or 'prefab clinker panels' as they called them, which were fixed to the exterior walls of multi-storey buildings between lines of windows or used for interior walls. Hoganas outlined the advantages of their panels as 'Higher efficiency in construction as Hoganas units replace some structural units in the building... resistance to climate... As a rule, the total cost of clinker panels installed is no more than that of conventional wall tiles plus wages... saves time, and requires no scaffolding outside the building... erecting can be left to unskilled labour.'[4]

On 11th December 1961 Ove Arup wrote to the Committee,

Mr Boulton of Hornibrooks has now been here for two weeks and we have gone through the whole scheme with him. We have been to Denmark with him to visit Utzon, and with Utzon to Sweden to see the tile factory at Hoganas and for discussions with Swedish Contractors who have great experience in handling tiled precast units. During this fortnight the details of the scheme have been greatly clarified, and we are very happy about the outcome.[5]

Followed by a personal letter to Ashworth four days later.

... I would like to tell you that I now feel that our troubles are largely over. The last difficult practical problems, the fixing of the tiling and the jointing of the concrete members, were solved after we had had time to digest our impressions in Sweden, and had discussed the problems at length with the people there. Naturally all the details have to be worked out, and there is a lot to do, but I cannot see anything which should prevent the successful construction of the shells... [6]

To clad the outside surface of the Opera House shells there were a total of 4,253 tile lids including main shell lids, side shell lids and warped surface lids. There were 3,646 main shell tile lids, which, like the ribs, radiated from the podium like lines of longitude and became wider up the shell. The lids were in general 7 ft 6 in long, half the length of a rib segment, so the longest ribs of the highest shell of the Major Hall which were 13 segments long were clad with 26 tile lids. At the springing point at the shell pedestal the lids were 1 ft 6 in wide, increasing to a width of 12 ft 6 in wide at the top of the highest shell. Some of the top lids, which were all of different sizes, were up to 11 ft 6 in long to allow for the top rib cut-off segment at the ridge. Though the main shells were cast to a sphere of radius 246 ft, the tile lids sat on top of this, plus there was the thickness of the lid itself, so the finished tiled surface of the shells was a radius of 246 ft $8\frac{1}{2}$ in.[7] A pattern of cream matt tiles followed the top surface of the chevron edge of the lids 'to express the anatomy of the roof structure' surrounding the standard glossy off-white tiles laid diagonally inside.

Arups had carried out various tests on the tiles with Harry Stanger, 'Testing and Inspecting Engineer Materials Consultant', at their laboratories in Elstree Hertfordshire including 'strains of four specimens to determine the shear stress necessary to cause loss of bond between tiles and concrete.'[8] When Hornibrooks carried out their first trials at Enfield to test adhesion of tiles to panels the Hoganas tiles were not available yet[9] so they used a selection of bathroom tiles. 'The colour scheme was striking', reported Margaret Jones of the *Sun Herald,* 'with pinks, blues, yellows and browns pre-dominating.'[10]

The tile lids, $1\frac{3}{4}$ in thick including the layer of tiles and mortar, were backed by concrete with 6 in deep stiffening ribs and were suited to a repetitive system of casting like the shell rib segments, which meant in the case of the lower lids 276 could be produced from the same mould. The lids were made on the 'ferro-cement' principle that had been successfully used in the past to build the hulls of concrete boats. Hornibrooks set up their casting yard for the tile lids beneath the Opera House vehicle concourse where they carried out further trials on the tile lids. For the main shell tile lids concrete forms were built with side plates of $\frac{1}{4}$ in steel plate with a concave floor shaped to a spherical surface of radius 246 ft $8\frac{1}{2}$ in. But the first test pours of tile lids were not very successful, Utzon writing to Naslund on 24th May

> ... the standard lids will be cast in a form made of concrete as a concave dish according to the overall curvature of the sphere... I would be glad to learn what method of fixing in your experience, would be the most suitable to secure an even width in the joints.[11]

Naslund replied on the 14th June

> ... the technique we used at Skromberga... we placed the tiles in the bottom of the form with the backside upwards, without fixing the tiles in any way. Hereafter we filled in the joints with sand, using a container with a pipe and smoothing the surface of the joint with a soft brush. Then we wetted the whole area in order to stabilise the sand... after the cement was poured on top... the tiles had not moved at all during the pour. The wet sand in the joints kept the tiles well in position...
>
> ... This method of filling up the joints with sand is simple, but when the joints have to be open there is one disadvantage. Sand sets in the mortar and therefore the mortar becomes somewhat porous and uneven... This is definitely something to think about Jorn.[12]

Months of tests in pouring tile lids followed, until by 4th December 1963 trials had advanced to the stage where Hornibrooks felt confident enough to issue an instruction sheet on 'Tile Lid Manufacture' which carried the introduction, 'The only method to be discussed here is the one finally selected – all previous techniques had defects.'[13] Utzon required open recessed joints '$\frac{1}{4}$ in deep never less'[14] for the space between the tiles on the finished surface of the tile lids so a grid of $\frac{1}{4}$ in square aluminium strips was nailed to the gently dished concave surface of the bottom of the tile lid forms, the grid lines following 'the tile joint pattern.'[15] 'The aluminium strips are protected from corrosion and possible bonding either by mechanical action of tile edges or adhesion to mortar in the joints by a coating of wax. This wax is applied in an emulsion form by brush… (and) may have to be reapplied from time to time.'[16] Tiles were 'laid face down between aluminium strips in random orientation, i.e.extruded edges not necessarily lined up.'[17] Then to prevent mortar slurry penetrating to the face of the tile 'Fine white quartz sand… is run into the joints filling the gap between the $\frac{1}{4}$ in x $\frac{1}{4}$ in aluminium strip and side of tile completely and a minimum on top of the aluminium strip'[18] which was then 'compacted, after rough levelling in a dry state, by a fine spray of water.'[19] A sand and cement mortar with a cement to sand ratio of one to one was then 'poured into the joint up to the back of the tiles… After mortar has hardened sufficiently to hold tiles from movement'[20] three layers of galvanised steel mesh previously cut and bent to the correct chevron shape were placed on the tile backs and a concrete with a fine sandy aggregate that could pass through the mesh poured into the mould and gently vibrated through to the back of the tiles. A wooden trowel was used to screed the concrete to the dished shape of the mould to a thickness of one inch. After the ferro-cement slab had been cast, rib forms for the tile lid backs were positioned and the ribbed concrete backing for the lids poured. Not less than three hours later, each tile lid was covered 'with a tent-like PVC hessian hood'[21] and steam-cured that night 'to a maximum temperature of 170°F.'[22] In the morning the formwork was stripped and the lid lifted from the mould, then steam cleaned. Longer lids could flex as they were lifted so were lifted by one end first to prevent the aluminium grid locking in the tile joints.

The completed lids were hung beneath the concourse like carcasses at a knackers yard to prevent 'distortion due to stack loading'[23] as they cured. Utzon issued a site instruction that the bottom of the lids should be tied down while they were hung to prevent the panels knocking together and chipping the tiles when winds whistled underneath the concourse.

By 13th December Utzon was happy enough with the tile lid samples that 'full scale prototypes can be put in hand for erection with the trial segments. Utzon requested

Would you please arrange for the tiles to be laid in patterns as follows:

1. One panel with all tiles placed with the extruded edges in the same direction.
2. One panel with alternate tiles turned at right angles to the adjoining tile.
3. One panel with all tiles placed at random.[24]

Production of the prototype tile lids continued, Utzon issuing some notes on 30th January that tiles were to be marked on the backs to prevent misplacing the matt or glossy tiles and that 'matt edge tiles show dirty finger marks from handling.'[25] Followed by a note to Arups on 6th February: 'eleven tile lids have now been poured with repetitive faults and not one of them of a satisfactory standard',[26] and a further note on 10th March after the pouring of the 12th: '... The sand filling to the joints and preliminary mortar grouting appears to have been ineffectual. Most joints show mortar deposits on the edges of the tiles and in some cases the joint has been filled up completely near the edge of the tile...'.[27] Lewis sent a memo to Zunz two days later with news of an innovation that did away completely with the wetted sand in the forms:

If you have been following the course of a series of meetings which we have held with Hornibrooks and Utzon concerning modification to details in order to effect economies, you will have recognised a note of gloom concerning the production of tile lids. Hornibrooks have repeatedly been unsuccessful in producing a prototype full-scale tile lid which met the requirements of the architect for aesthetics, our requirements for strength and corrosion resistance and the contractors requirements for an economical production method. We were frankly getting a little desperate but can at last report a significant breakthrough.

Strangely enough this came about through the initiative of one of Hornibrook's foremen with the assistance of a chemist friend. They have concocted a gelatinous substance which is poured hot into the joints between the tiles to cover the strip aluminium former and to give the required depth of groove. As soon as the material cools it sets hard and we can therefore concrete directly without laying mortar between the tiles which is the technique we have been using up to the present. It means that the concrete between the tiles is a good dense material with a hard surface which will form a substantial corrosion barrier and I believe will give added adhesion to the tiles.

Stripping from the forms is an easy process using this material because it melts during the steam curing process and permits the removal of the tile lids with virtually no breakage on the edges of the tiles and no damage to the aluminium strip former.[28]

Lewis recalled that on the first trial lids

> ... Everything we did, left us with tiles breaking, with the joints being inaccurate, with mortar bleeding through the joints of the tiles, and we tried everything. We tried sand and we tried a whole variety of things to stop this.
>
> And I was walking onto the site with Corbet Gore and one of the... charge hand carpenters said: "Did you want to solve this problem?" – typical Australian. We said, "Yes, we do." He said, "Well, I can solve it for you." So we said, "How do you do it?" He said, "Now you gotta pay me." So we said, "Okay." So we said "How much do you want?" He said, "Fifty quid." I said, "Okay, you've got it."
>
> And he said, "Well, what you do is, you use animal glue. And you put the tiles down, you run animal glue along the joints, which sets. You can cast the concrete on it and you steam cure it and the steam melts the animal glue and nothing penetrates it, you see." And he got his fifty quid and we had our solution.[29]

Utzon's raked-out joint between the tiles extended to about half the depth of the tile, and as Lewis outlined in his memo; 'There is one snag which we are presently trying to overcome. When the (gelatin) substance is poured into the joints it obviously wets the sides of the tiles'[30] which 'hardened as a concave meniscus'[31] so when the mortar was poured, and the gelatin ran out in steam-curing, then the form was stripped, the top surface of the joint between the tiles 'was formed to a convex shape in cross section.'[32] This meant the raked joint between the tiles, instead of being square, looked a little like the top of an egg. 'A sharp re-entrant angle between the mortar and the tile edge resulted, which gave concern that water penetration to the mesh reinforcement could take place; this could lead to eventual corrosion of the galvanised mesh reinforcement and rust staining on the tile lids.'[33] 'A further round of investigations between Utzon's, Hornibrooks' and Arup's office achieved a mortar joint that was square in the recessed joint between the tiles, but any animal glue splashed on the full depth of the tile before the concrete was poured still left a space at the edge of the tile when the glue ran out in steam curing, even if the space was only wafer thin. This was particularly of concern to Arups as the lids lay at an angle on the shells and the top tile edge at the recessed joint 'would collect muck from the air which could be acid and which may eat into the very thin... eighth of an inch concrete covering the reinforcement at that point.'[34] To overcome this, after casting and curing the completed tile lids were laid face up in the workshop and a very thin epoxy compound in a plastic container with a nozzle like a cake icer was used to fill 'every joint of every tile lid... to give an additional seal on the concrete of the tiles. And that was a very tedious task for the whole lot of them. Very patient little Italians pouring epoxy resin into the joints, they got very adept at it after a while.'[35]

On 20th March Utzon wrote to Arups:

> The latest tile lid prototype, which was poured using "gelatin" instead of sand for filling the joints has been inspected and appears to be an improvement as regards the prevention of slurry runs to the edges of the tiles. Some breakage and chipped edges to the tiles are still apparent... [36]

Followed by a general instruction on 6th April:

> Referring to the discussion at Hornibrooks office on 28th February 1964, I wish to confirm the following decisions...
>
> ... Item 30: Orientation of tiles: The previous instruction to maintain an even orientation still stands. The tiles should be laid with the extrusion direction across the direction of the light as shown on the attached sketch.[37]

In manufacture, the tile clay was extruded into a mould to make two tiles, back to back. The clay remaining outside the mould was cut off, so by carefully examining the edges of the finished tile it was possible to tell the cut off edge to the opposite edge formed inside the mould. Utzon wanted the extrusion direction on the backs of the tiles to be at right angles to the direction of sunlight, and illustrated this on the sketch with a note 'ALL TILES TO LIDS FACING WEST AS ABOVE, ALL TILES TO LIDS FACING EAST HANDED.'

According to the report of the site meeting on 13th April significant matters affecting tiles were:

> 1. Tile lid... which was cast on 9.4.64 was approved as being of a satisfactory standard for production...
>   Full scale production of tile lids may commence...
> 3. (To prevent chipping of edges of tiles)
>   (a) Corners of aluminium strips to be bevelled
>   (b) More care to be taken when vibrating concrete and lifting lids...
> 7. Placing of Tiles
>   Tiles are to be placed so that the cut edges lie on parallel joint lines. These joint lines on all lids will lie in the same direction.[38]

A miscellaneous note at the end of the report directed that matt tiles should be marked in red on the back side. The following day Lewis sent a confidential memo to Zunz.

It is a great pity that I have to take this sort of action in Jorn's absence; Skipper feels that he cannot reverse any decisions which Jorn has made and I quite frankly feel that I cannot go ahead with this system which will make all the tile lids "handed" and will be a constant source of irritation to the Contractors who are already rather sensitive on the subject of tile lids.

I hope you agree with me because it virtually represents mutiny!?[39]

The same day, Lewis wrote to Utzon,

... Regarding item 30 which refers to the orientation of tiles in tile lids. We must point out that a great deal of energy has been directed at evolving a system which makes each type of tile lid interchangeable. This has a great advantage in production and eliminates many storage problems which the Contractor would have to face if tile lids can only be used on the west or east elevation as the case may be. The proposal set out by you will necessitate the casting of alternate tile lids with tiles orientated in different directions and is prone to error during production, storage and erection... we consider it undesirable to add to the complexity of an already difficult task.

Unless we hear further from you we intend to issue instructions to the Contractors for a single orientation of tiles in tile lids.[40]

Zunz wrote back to Lewis on 21st April,

I suppose one can become just as neurotic sorting tiles as sorting oranges! It seems that the camel's back has been broken, – anyway we agree with your decision.

I do not think we have heard the end of this and we are waiting with mounting excitement.[41]

Utzon had gone overseas for two months, but his office contacted him on his travels, and one of his staff wrote to Arups site office on 5th May '... I wish to inform you that all tiles may be placed with the cut edge pointing in the same direction.'[42]

Tales of the saga of tile lid production had reached the Minister's ear, who was also concerned by a comment of Gore's that Utzon's quality standards were beyond what could be realistically achieved. Ryan wrote to Utzon on 29th May pointing out that it would be disastrous

if tiles were to break away after the lids were fixed in position (and) it has been suggested that the tiles would be given a better grip and the metal reinforcement in the concrete... would receive increased cover if the joints were brought up flush, or nearly so, with the surface... of the tiles... in regard to Mr Gore's statement that he did not think it possible to produce 4,000 odd panels... required with absolute perfection for each one... one wonders whether the high degree of finish you seek can be achieved... Your comments on this... would be appreciated... [43]

Maclurcan of Utzon's office replied to the Minister,

> ... I feel sure that the situation is not as you have outlined it... as we are expecting Mr Utzon to return in June, a full appraisal by him, and an inspection by you on the site would assure you of the development of the work.[44]

But at the site meeting on 18th June, item 2.d related 'The question of adhesion for the matt tiles is still unsolved. Architects will write to Hoganas for advice.'[45]

> We have struck some problems in connection with the matt tiles... – wrote Utzon to Naslund at Hoganas – We found on one occasion that when one (broken) tile was removed and replaced, the tile next to it came loose and could be removed by hand.
>
> The back face of the tile showed no trace of mortar adhering to the tile, nor were there any chips from the tile body left in the mortar.
>
> Following this we removed a number of tiles from other lids, and although there were no cases as serious as the first one, it appears that the matt tiles generally have less adhesion than the glazed ones... the prospects of tiles falling off later on, I think you will agree is rather frightening...
>
> Apart from this, the tile lids have turned out almost beyond my expectations – they will be marvellous... [46]

To insulate the structure a polyurethane foam was sprayed onto the back of the tile lids, and Utzon asked Arups if since the introduction of lateral stressing it would be possible to do without it. Zunz replied on the 7th July:

> the effect of omitting the insulation would be that the average temperature of the top flanges and thin webs of the ribs could rise about 25°F above the average temperature of the 12in stems, with the following structural implications.
>
> (a) ... The average temperature of the main shell ribs would rise above that of the supporting structure by about 16°F...
>
> (b) ... A radial temperature gradient will be set up in the ribs...
>
> (c) ... internal stresses would be set up analogous to the stresses which cause failure of a glass vessel if it is heated or cooled too rapidly...
>
> I should also remark that any apparent resemblance of the uninsulated structure to the structure in its temporary condition during erection (which we have of course allowed for) is only superficial. In the latter there is no artificial cooling of the inside of the shell and supporting structure so that the transient temperature differences between these and the outside of the ribs are much smaller than in the former.

To sum up then, it is absolutely imperative that we retain the thermal insulation... [47]

Naslund too, replied to Utzon on 7th July:

I have met this problem once before. Panels with a surface of our dry-pressed tiles 6in x 6in in white and grey-porphyry were to be manufactured for two facades. In that case a sand and cement slurry was poured on the back of the tile before the concrete was cast, this to obtain a good adhesion. (I assume you do the same). But, you see, it was too much water in the slurry and the sand was not well graded, and so instead of good adhesion, there was none at all. White and grey-porphyry tiles are very dense and they do not soak up the water. It was found that a thin film of water had been spread on the actual tile surface which prevented any adhesion.

Another slurry was made of one part well graded sand and one part standard Portland Cement with a water content which made the slurry more plastic instead of lightly fluent... After hardening, it was impossible to separate tiles from concrete without destroying either tiles or concrete.

... I believe something similar has happened in your case. You see, your matt tiles are also very dense... [48]

Utzon replied to Ryan on 21st July:

... The question of the finish cannot be separated from the question of structural soundness... the Swedish factory has found from several years' experience that tile panels made with flush joints tend to develop tension forces in the surface and therefore the panels showed a tendency to bulge forwards... and bend the surface of the whole lid.

... The present method of production... is the most economical method to produce a structurally and aesthetically sound article. [49]

Hoganas had practical experience of this, because when they'd written to Utzon in May the previous year to tell him of the long hard winter in Sweden, they mentioned that on the test tile panels set up outside the Hoganas factory, 'The open joints have also had a good effect. Those panels have not arched a bit, the others have.' [50] So Utzon's decision to use open joints was not just an architectural decision, but also a structural one. [51]

On 1st September Hornibrooks wrote to Peter Rice, 'As requested, a production sample of 15 lids has been produced for quality approval by the Architects and yourselves. Would you please inspect at your earliest convenience...' [52] Thirty-eight of the early tile lids produced required various repairs. Utzon wrote to Arups on the 23rd 'I have closely studied these repairs and found them unsatisfactory... All of these lids should be replaced by new ones.' [53] On 9th October Utzon wrote to Arups regarding the side shell tile lids 'I have noticed on the first of these lids, that the pattern of the matt tiles does not follow the rules as set out on drawing No. SOH 1078...'.[54]

Meanwhile as a result of the problem with the loose matt tiles Arthur Crimp of Arups wrote to the School of Civil Engineering in Sydney to request adhesion tests on matt tile specimens. Each of the five samples failed at the mortar-tile interface at tension loads of from 655 lb to 2265 lb.[55]

While the battle continued for a perfect finished tile surface, Skipper Nielsen found a main shell cut off lid and a side-shell lid with misplaced 'matt tiles along the cut-off edges... The tiles will have to be removed and replaced with glazed tiles in accordance with the plan. It should be enforced that no concrete is poured until the laying of tiles has been checked and passed by the Clerk of Works.'[56] At a site meeting Utzon underlined

> The accurate lining up of the tiled surfaces from one lid to another is the most important consideration and takes priority over the accurate matching of the width of the joints... If a surface appears to be deviating beyond the possible limit for adjustment the whole range of tile lids in question should be repositioned and the deviation interpolated between them to avoid steps from one lid to another, or sudden changes of direction... The tiles have been sorted at the factory and are accepted as such in respect of variations in dimensions and colours. However, when over or under size tiles occur they should not be placed side by side but must be re-positioned as necessary... in an attempt to secure the best possible quality the Contractor will emphasize to the men the importance of lining up the tiles as accurately as possible (when placing them in the tile lids) by string or by straight-edge... [57]

A lid with all the tiles accurately lined up was stood on edge under the concourse and an instruction issued that 'this standard should be maintained on all lids.'[58] Sometimes there were repairs to repairs: on the cut-off tile lid 'the changing of matt tiles has been done incorrectly', wrote Nielsen to the resident engineer, 'there are now two rows of matt tiles too many instead of one which must be cut out and repaired.'[59]

One by one the problems were overcome and a way was found to make the matt tiles adhere to the concrete. With strenuous supervision by the Clerk of Works and the casting yard foreman it *was* possible to produce the lids to Utzon's exacting standards and

Hornibrooks soon had a production line underway, and the completed lids were stacked like decks of cards around the podium in readiness for placing on the shells. However before full-scale placing of the lids could go ahead, the warped surface tile lids had to be in position.

On the shells of the Opera House there were 358[60] warped surface tile lids. The warped surfaces were the outside edge of the side shell arches between the main and side shells. The surface curled and twisted from the pedestal to the crown like a children's slide curving from the top to the bottom of the shell at a crazy angle. There were 32 warped surfaces on the Opera House with 16 different lengths, depending on if they were on the east or west side of the building. But the rate of twist changed as the warped surface sprang from the pedestal and advanced to the crown; not only that but the warped surface lids *were* handed as they had a waterproofing detail on the bottom edge so lids from the east side of a warped surface could not be used upside down on the corresponding surface on the west side, which meant that every single warped surface tile lid was different.

The warped surface lids had been 'designed to follow the surface of the supporting structure'[61] and it had been anticipated that they would be the last of the lids to be fitted, but on 7th June 1963, following 'another session yesterday with Gore and Utzon'[62] on the subject, Lewis wrote to Zunz that Utzon now wanted 'The tile lids on the main shells and on the side shells... (to) overlap this lid, so that the warped surfaces should be tiled first.'[63] As Lewis pointed out in his letter, 'This raised a number of problems',[64] including that 'The angles of intersection between the different tile lid surfaces requires detailed investigation... The order for tiles has to be modified – Utzon wants the recessed warped surface tiled completely matt.'[65] And 'These tile lids are likely to be the first required on the job and the last to be detailed. This is brinkmanship of the worst kind, but I am sure you will help us to overcome the difficulties if the idea is a good one.'[66]

Huang wrote to Lewis 'At Jack's request... to let you know some of the serious drawbacks... with Utzon's latest scheme of placing the tiled warped surface... Do you still remember that about Christmas last year there was a great panic in the office because Mr Utzon insisted that all the tile spheres should meet neatly at a point? In trying to achieve this we have taken a lot of time and effort... even to the extent of making some radical changes in the geometry and scrapping some of the existing work at that time... There is very little or no possibility of changing either the shell geometry or the tile geometry because 95 per cent of the side shell tile lid drawings are now completed. If Utzon insists on changing the side shell tile geometry it will put us back for at least four months if not for ever... (also) this will invalidate our tile order for the warped surfaces which has already been issued...'.[67]

Not least of their problems which needed sorting out whatever happened was how Arups were to illustrate on drawings for Hornibrooks the setting out positions of the warped surface tile lid fixings, which were bolts cast into the octopus arch rib segments. 'The information that Hornibrooks require to locate the setting out point on (a plane of the warped surface for the tile fixings)', wrote John Nutt to Joe Huang, '... is the arc length from vanishing point on that plane and the arc length of the equivalent radial plane passing through this point... We have to give them this as equivalent radial planes. The... dimension contained on your schedules is of no use to them. Could you modify the schedules accordingly.'[68] 'I am not sure how to interpret the term "equivalent radial plane"', wrote Huang in reply, '... presumably it is the arc length of B from vanishing point and the distance of C from A that Hornibrooks require for locating C... John, I am sure that you realise that in order to obtain what you requested the co-ordinates of point C must first be calculated and this is by no means easy because of the complexity of the warped surface... Please send us a prompt reply if revision of the schedules is imperative.'[69] To which Nutt replied 'There seems to be quite a muddle between your thinking and our thinking on the subject, and you have not been able to interpret exactly what we have meant by "equivalent radial plane." Your explanation in your letter... was not correct. We will sort out what is necessary here, but on future schedules would you eliminate the arc length (on one of the planes).'[70]

To achieve Utzon's change of introducing a step between the junction of the warped surface and the side shell, Arups London sent Utzon two drawings. 'These solutions forcing the surface to correspond with the small circle of the ridge cannot be accepted. –

Utzon wrote back to Zunz on 13th August – The whole architecture in the shell scheme is based on surfaces being continuous, hence the warped surface has to be a continuous flow from bottom to top... (the cut-off at the ridge) will be decided by us when we have received... a drawing showing... an area starting at a distance below the ridge and continuing up until intersection with the plane for the axis of the Halls...'.[71] Concerning the warped surface tiling,'We appreciate that you want continuous surfaces and have worked hard with you to achieve this geometrically', wrote Zunz in reply, 'The present problem arises because you wish to have a step between side shell and warped surface tiling.'[72] Utzon had sent two drawings, but 'The details as shown on these two drawings are theoretically impossible because the geometry cannot satisfy three conditions simultaneously. These three conditions are:-, a) Continuous ridge line parallel to Hall axis, b) Continuous warped surface, c) Step between side shell and warped surface... as soon as possible we will provide you with the XYZ co-ordinates of the "theoretical" curves up to the centre line of the Hall on vertical planes... near the Hall axis. You can then make your choice.'[73] Gradually the intersections of the tiled surfaces were solved, though it took time, Lewis sending a memo to Zunz on 3rd December concerning side shell and warped surface tile panels 'Utzon has decided on the principle of allowing the warped surface geometry to continue beyond the vertical plane of the ridge beam so that in profile the curve on the more important shell is maintained and the profile of the less important shell is discontinuous...'.[74] Though some of the decisions went down to the wire, Nutt wrote a month later on 3rd January:

> We have been looking at the clearance between the top surface of the tile lids and the structural warped surface. This distance is satisfactory at the lower edge of the warped surface but decreases generally to a minimum at the intersection of the warped surface with the side shells...
>
> We will obviously have to obtain a greater clearance and two possible methods are:-
> 1. Place the side shell tile lids to a radius of 246 ft 8 ½ in.
> 2. Decrease the thickness of the edge of the side shell tile lids from 3¼ in to, say 2½ in or thereabouts.
>
> All this has been discovered since the site closed down for Christmas and the New Year and so we do not know the Architect's requirements. Hornibrooks are hoping to get under way with the fabrication of these

tile lid forms next Monday when they resume so we may have to make an immediate decision with the Architect. I am going to plug the second as being the one that will for certain involve no changes elsewhere... [75]

The 358 warped surface tile lids were cast on 'four identical casting beds... The warp could be formed by casting the lid with three corners on a horizontal plane, the fourth corner set at a height to this plane.'[76] The 'dimensional data'[77] for the extent of the adjustment of the form and the positions of 'small moulded crosses... fixed on the form to locate the tiles'[78] was 'produced by three-dimensional geometric analysis and programed so that the print-outs from the computer were issued to the site as working drawings.'[79] Like the main shell tile lids, the warped surface tile lids were cast with the tiles face down in the mould, but since the decision by Utzon to introduce a step between the warped surface and the main and side shell surface the warped lids had to be placed closer to the shell structure than had originally been intended and there was not enough clearance on the backs for the 6 in stiffening ribs. Consequently the warped surface lids were cast as a twisted concrete slab $2\frac{1}{4}$ in thick. According to the site meeting on 8th April 1965 following the casting of the first warped surface lids, measurements indicated 'that the edges of these tile elements have an excess curvature of up to 5/16 in... (and) that the corner tiles have a tendency to dip down... The engineer stated that this was caused by shrinkage in the concrete and it was thought that thermal conditions could have some implication too, in as much as the curvature would increase while (the lids were) submitted to sunshine and would go back when the sun disappeared... The Engineer suggested that it was a visual problem and it therefore should be solved by visual means by the Architect. The Architect found the problem was technical and could then have been realised, if not solved, by making mock-ups before starting production...'.[80]

The excess warp in the lids was due to 'differential shrinkage strain, a result of the restraint caused by the tiles on the one surface of the slab and an exposed face on the other (resulting) in bowing of the slabs by $\frac{1}{4}$ in to 3/8 in on all edges.'[81] Rice wrote to Kynaston that the extent of the shrinkage was 'predictable'[82] and though 'The magnitude of this deformation may not always be as we have found it in the past... the Architect... wishes us to preset the curvature of these lids so that the final shape shall be as close as possible to the theoretical.'[83] And Rice issued a site instruction:

> You should therefore arrange to preset the curvature at the main shell and side shell boundaries by 5/16 in. This should be done in such a way that all lids start off with 5/16 in less curvature (or negative curvature for lids which theoretically would have been straight) than is theoretically required.
>
> Great care must be taken to ensure that this is done accurately as any errors in dimensions destroy the effect being sought.[84]

Utzon wanted to see the effect on a mock up, so as a trial 11 warped surface tile lids – including some of the first bowed slabs – were erected on shell A6-2E, then surveyed. It was found that a particular lid, correct at some points on the surface, could, for example, be $\frac{1}{4}$ in high at others.[85] 'This was visually unacceptable, particularly along the side shell and main shell boundaries where a scalloped effect was evident. This had not occurred in main shell or side shell lids because of the stiffening effect of the ribs'[86] on the back of the lids. Utzon was concerned in particular that in low light any unevenness of the surface would be apparent.[87] A second survey was carried out two weeks later on the same lids which 'reveals conclusively that shrinkage effects are often reversed with an increase of humidity in the atmosphere. This is more noticeable in the older lids where most of the original shrinkage has already taken place.'[88] Lewis wrote to Rice and Utzon instructing them to '... check all warped surface tile lids approximately four months after casting but ensuring always (this was not more than) 28 days before the anticipated erection date... The present system of casting the reverse curvature of 5/16 in is to be maintained.'[89] It had been expected that lids outside the prescribed tolerances would have to be rejected and re-cast, but these 'were corrected by pre-cutting cracks in the lid, bending and repairing with epoxy.'[90]

Though at the end of 1965 Arups and Hornibrooks were still waiting for some warped surface tile lid details from Utzon. According to the Minutes of Site Conferences on 12th August,

> The warped surface tile lid erection sequence was discussed. The tile lid details at the fascia plane and lower warped surfaces is still unresolved and the Architect requested that construction of warped surface tile lids be left until this was resolved.[91]

And on 1st September:

> Warped Surface Lids adjacent to Fascia Plane – UNRESOLVED – awaiting final details from Architect.[92]

THE TILE LIDS

Finally on 24th November:

Unresolved Design and Construction Problems
2. Warped Surface lids Adjacent to Fascia Plane. The sketch issued by the Architect shows system which will not inhibit erection of first lids on first rib; however sketch is not sufficiently complete for Ove Arup & Partners to make working drawings. This can be regarded as RESOLVED.[93]

Initially a decision was made that 'All precast units of a shell have to be erected before placing tile panels'[94] but this was later revised so that work could commence placing tile lids on the partially completed structure. But the work was not straightforward as 'Applying tiles on very thin sections as well as the quality of finish required was in advance of anything that had previously been done.'[95] Also there was 'no precedent or store of experience to draw from in the erection and fixing of tile lids onto a doubly curved surface – in most building work there are plane surfaces which are easily measurable.'[96]

To fix the warped surface tile lids to the structure, brass plates were cast into the back of the lid and a single tile left out above the plate. The bolt in the structure passed through the hole in the plate and once the lid had been aligned and tightened down, the missing tile was placed and glued in with epoxy. For the main shell lids, a spigot and socket fixing arrangement was used so that one tile lid slotted directly onto the one below.[97] The phosphor bronze bolts and aluminium bronze brackets for the Opera House tile lids were designed and developed from scratch by Arups. 'These fixings had to have enough built-in tolerance to allow free adjustment'[98] and to be 'completely fatigue and corrosion resistant'[99] and were tested beforehand 'for strength and fatigue'[100] in laboratories. The brackets had to be able to be adjusted and packed so that the tile lids would duplicate the continuous curved surface Utzon desired, yet strong enough to sustain load applications in different directions caused by the near vertical to close to horizontal surface of the shells. 'Each tile lid (was) designed to be fixed independently of adjacent lids in a manner which permits thermal expansion and contraction to take place without impinging on adjacent lids... (as) Interaction between lids could result in over-stressing of fixing brackets and bolts as well as possible damage to lids and tiles.'[101]

To test the connection of the main shell tile lids a trial erection took place in July 1965 of fixing lids to part of the completed structure. But as fixing advanced up the shell, one lid on top of another with the locating spigots of the lower lid slotting into the sockets of the lid above, once a few lids had been fitted it became apparent that the attaching brackets beneath the lid simply would not line up.

> ... after four or five lids had been laid one above another up a rib, the fifth lid was perhaps an inch higher up the rib than it should have been and the waiting bolt in the rib had no hope of engaging the waiting hole in the bracket on the lid.[102]

As Arups put it, 'the lids had increased in dimension tangentially'[103] which in layman's language boiled down to the fact that the lids were too long from top to bottom between the chevrons.

Several mock-up erections of tile lids took place on the ground, where whole groups of lids were put together to the correct 246 ft 8½ in radius 'so you could get in underneath'[104] and examine the underside. Not only did there look like a problem at the chevron joint but 'oval spigots (had) been rotated out of the line of the normal ordinate... (and) small concrete projections on the lids (tended) to foul fixing brackets.'[105]

Lewis recalled 'It was a nervous moment. First you get a feeling that perhaps you're not going to get the tiles on at all and then you put this out of your mind and you settle down to calculate a way out of the trouble.'[106] Scrapping the existing tile lids and having a whole new set cast was one option considered.

Arups reported that the 'apparent "growth" of tangential and normal dimensions of the tile lid (arose) from side forms being loosely positioned prior to casting so that all lids are slightly oversize. The order of error is approximately 1/8 in to 3/16 in. The tolerance had been incorrectly defined previously (at) ± 1/16 in, this should have been + 0 in – 1/8 in.'[107] The 'original design requirement'[108] was for a 5/16 in joint between the tile lid chevrons, but this was too restrictive 'particularly in the larger main shell tile lids'[109] so on new lids 'The chevron joint will be increased from 5/16 in to 5/8 in by casting all new tile lids smaller in the tangential direction.'[110]

'Approximately 1254 (oversize) main shell lids'[111] had been cast, which would be 'erected by lowering the position of the lids tangentially'[112] on the shell, but 'only in specific positions where this is acceptable.'[113] So 'all the tile lids which had already been cast could be utilized in the structure, together with (the) smaller tile lids'[114] with the wider nominal chevron joint size.

But the size of the tile lids was only one of a host of difficulties. In construction of the shell structure 'the rib to rib joint of the main shells was expected to vary from $\frac{1}{2}$ in to $1\frac{1}{2}$ in whereas in some cases these tolerances have been exceeded significantly... Also the deformation has generally been in the nature of twisting about the axis of the rib rather than pure radial displacement. It was realised at the time of erecting the main ribs that these displacements would effect the tile lid erection, but the cost of rectifying the ribs would have been greater than adjusting tile lid fixings.'[115] In fact in mid-1964, at the start of the construction of the shells, Peter Rice wrote to London concerning the erection and tolerance of the main shell ribs, and in passing mentioned

> ... I feel that some of the fixing for the main shell tile lids may not have enough radial outward tolerance (I say this aware of its implications and delicacy), but then I may be wrong. Here the important thing is that we must know this in time, and have some available solution, for in the end the structure will go up and it will have tile lids.[116]

But there was a bigger picture involved than mere inaccuracy of erection of shell segments. The shells and tile lids were cast as part of a surface of a sphere. 'The ribs were cast as part of the sphere but they were then stressed together'[117] plus there was the effect of creep and 'the dead load of the weight of the roof... and consequently when they were in final position the deflection was such that (the shells) were not truly spherical... so you were fitting a spherical lid onto a non-spherical surface and the deflection was just sufficient... to cause some fitting problems.'[118]

> The compounding of a multiplicity of minor errors in casting of tile lids, location of fixing bolts in ribs, and distortion of the ribs during construction was such as to make it impossible to erect the tile lids to follow the surface of the structure and at the same time maintain the basic demands for a continuous surface free of steps between lids. The requirements of a minimum joint width for waterproofing, together with the desire for visual continuity of joints, had to be accommodated. This resulted in a complete loss of tolerance for adjustment after a number of consecutive lids had been erected... [119]

All this made 'the original fixing scheme impracticable... (and) a completely modified method of fixing main shell and side shell lids was evolved taking full account of fixings already ordered as well as the inaccuracies and difficulty of utilising the tile lids already cast...

The Consulting Engineers have redesigned fittings to take up greater tolerances and have set out a new Manual of Procedure for the adaptation of this system on the site... New fixing brackets, special washers and fittings will be ordered to replace the brackets where these are not usable.'[120] 'Consequently, fixing systems were adapted and erection techniques developed in order to place each tile lid in its theoretical position in space without regard to the location of adjacent lids'[121] and irrespective 'of the construction errors in the location of the fixing bolts or of the deflected or distorted position of the structural members.'[122]

> Each tile lid was checked for accuracy of casting by means of measuring templates; the surface being spherical or twisted meant that there was no easy reference plane for measurement – all templates were three-dimensinsal. Tile lid fixings were designed to allow for adjustment in any direction, and since each tile lid was located inside the envelope of acceptable tolerances the fit between adjacent lids was assured. This system of fixing necessitated a detailed and accurate survey of the actual location of all the tile lid fixing bolts on the structure.[123]

The computer program which had already been written to control the position of ribs was adapted to relate 'the spherical geometry of the theoretical shell surface and the location of stations around the site in such a way as to eliminate all the tedious calculations which would normally follow survey measurements.'[124] This gave 'The precise position in space which each tile lid *should* occupy... (and) gave the precise position in space which each of the lid's brackets should occupy.'[125] A refinement on the program meant that 'adjustments to brackets were fed out from the computer'[126] so construction teams on the ground could set and adjust brackets 'to take up the specific measured errors in bolt positions and inaccuracies in tile lid manufacture.'[127] The program gave 'nothing more or less than a store's list, telling the erection crew which kind of bracket and which types of packing pieces it should draw from the bronze store'[128] for the tile lid and rib bolts respectively. 'Often a workman had to have eight or ten little bits of metal to go with a bracket but the computer had provided the code numbers of the pieces he needed.'[129] 'In this way it became unnecessary to make adjustments to the position of lids after release from the crane and a very high level of sophisticated preplanning resulted in speedy and efficient site erection work.'[130] Gore described how

The area around the bolts was... built up by means of bronze plates epoxied to the shell or recessed as required in order to overcome the geometrical inaccuracies caused by deflection of the shells. Other inaccuracies and finer adjustments were accounted for in the tile lid fixings. These preparations paid dividends and the bulk of the tile lids were erected very quickly, approximately twenty-two per day per crane.[131]

Arups estimated the cost of the modified erection system used as

(i)	Preparation of tile lids	$16,600
(ii)	Additional Survey Work	15,000
(iii)	Additional Brackets	20,000
(iv)	Preparation of fixing bolts	4,000
		£55,600

If, on the other hand, the tile lids already manufactured were rejected and only "small" new tile used, the following cost would be incurred:-

(i)	Preparation of tile lids	$ 8,000
(ii)	Additional Survey	15,000
(iii)	Additional Brackets	20,000
(iv)	Preparation of fixing bolts	4,000
(v)	Cost of Main shell lids made to end November	75,000
		$122,000 [132]

This was a 'saving' of £66,400, though Arups did acknowledge that the cost of the new brackets and the survey work plus the 'alignment of the edges of the side shell tile lids'[133] which was expected to be 'one of the most difficult problems of erection'[134] would mean 'that the previous estimate of July 1965 for total erection cost (£370,000) will be exceeded by approximately £70,000 due to the modified system... which is now essential for the completion of the work.'[135]

Full-scale tile lid erection, which had been expected to start in August 1965, now got underway in February 1966 and was completed in March 1967. In some cases the erection *was* like that of an ancient cathedral. Where the main shells overhung the louvre shells there was no direct access for the cranes and the lids would be stacked on a platform then lifted into place with a block and tackle. The story of the top tile lid of each rib was a saga in itself. Each was a 'unique shape... supported partly at the ridge, and partly by a rib. To accommodate any possible relative error between rib and ridge'[136] and to maintain the tiled line of the ridge so it looked like a perfect arc drawn with a compass those 'lids (were) not cast until (that) portion of the structure (had) been built and surveyed.'[137]

Some of the survey operations were carried out with the structure already partially tiled and Elphick recalled

> a problem that we used to get sometimes with the sun, particularly as the tile panels came up... sometimes – you'd get a situation where the lines of sight would go close to the shells when the sun was around and it was just like being snowblinded. Everyone was walking around for weeks with red eyes, really bad cases of it. Because you just couldn't stop the flash coming in through the instrument – and you've got a 28 power telescope and it hits near the sun, it flashes into your eyes pretty bad. And that was just an unfortunate sort of thing. You put up with that at times.[138]

In November 1965, following the erection of some of the tile lids, motorists driving across the Cahill Expressway were complaining of the glare of the sun shining on the tiles, but the Committee thought it was no worse than that reflected from the water of the Harbour.[139] And when the tiling was completed, Ron Saw, a *Daily Mirror* columnist, commented 'I think it looks like an untidily sliced apple, or perhaps a bunch of toenails clipped from some large albino dog.'[140] But just about everyone who saw them thought the completed shells were magnificent, with their white sails glistening in the sunshine and the tiles arranged in subtle patterns 'the fine lines defining the form of the curve like the seams in a billowing sail.'[141] Bob Kelman of Ove Arups said 'Utzon was right about the tiles. He said they would gleam like an Islamic Mosque and they do.'[142]

When the first lids had gone up Utzon had written to Ivan Naslund at Hoganas 'We are still very pleased with the tiles and the large lids on the side shells look splendid in the sun.'[143] Then when the first main shell lids were fixed he wrote again

> Everything is going fine here with the tile elements... We have, of course, now a lot of trouble in fixing the tile lids but I think we will overcome that. We have had some six elements already sitting on the shell and they look fantastic in the sun. I think it is the best publicity for Hoganas you could dream of...
>
> I hope you are well and selling a lot of tiles.
>
> My warmest greetings to all my friends in Höganäs.[144]

John Nutt said 'Utzon had this extreme capacity of understanding what the structural engineer was all about... The great architectural strength of this building is the sure hand of the one architect through the roof structure. He wanted to do most of the things himself and took that right through to the detail. When you see this building you see Utzon.'[145]

THE TILE LIDS

But Utzon never saw it. He had gone. In February 1966, the month full-scale erection of tile lids started, he resigned as architect of the Sydney Opera House and a short time later left Australia never to return.

List of Illustrations

The illustration acknowledgment appears in italics at the end of each listing. The author is grateful to these sources for permission to reproduce photographs and drawings.

1. Bennelong. *The Mitchell Library.*
2. Macquarie in his days as an army officer in the service of the East India Company. *The Mitchell Library.*
3. Fort Macquarie. It was 'perfectly useless as a fortification' according to the editor of the Sydney Gazette. The battery in the foreground was later added in an attempt to address the Fort's shortcoming as a defence work. *The Mitchell Library.*
4. Fort Macquarie tram depot. When it was announced the depot would be the site of the new Opera House one Sydney paper reported the change would mean a swap from tram conductors to orchestra conductors. *Australian Consolidated Press Library.*
5. Charles Moses. *ABC Document Archives.*
6. Eugene Goossens on the plate of the Sydney – Newcastle Flyer, about to drive the steam locomotive to Newcastle carrying his orchestra. *ABC Document Archives.*
7. Elsinore Castle, Denmark, also known as Kroningsberg and Kronberg Castle, sited on a peninsula on a harbour, was Utzon's inspiration for his Opera House design. *David Messent.*
8. Jorn Utzon on site with Norman Ryan. *Max Dupain & Associates.*
9. The competition assessors with Utzon's podium ground plan. From *Sydney Builds an Opera House, Ziegler.*
10. An absolute furore erupted in the press when Utzon's competition winning Opera House design was announced. *Sydney Morning Herald.*
11. The model of Utzon's competition design. From *Utzon's Yellow Book.*
12. Even though Utzon's design had won the competition, there were many, including Charles Moses, who thought his conception would never become a reality. It just wasn't taken seriously. *Sydney Morning Herald.*
13. Signing the Stage I contract. Picture courtesy of *Owen Haviland.*

14. Isometric section of a concourse beam. *Ove Arup & Partners, London.*

15. Preparing the formwork for the first beams at the eastern end of the concourse. *Max Dupain & Associates.*

16. The dramatic sculptural effect of the completed concourse beams seen from below. *Max Dupain & Associates.*

17. 'Opera goes underground' was the caption in the Daily Telegraph when this picture was published. Boring the holes for the concrete piers for the Opera House foundations. *Australian Consolidated Press Library.*

18. The Opera House at the completion of the Stage I contract. When Mike Lewis of Ove Arup's first arrived on site he thought it looked marvellous, like a Greek amphitheatre by the sea. *Government Printing Office negatives, Mitchell Library.*

19. A sketch from one of Roger Rigby's letters to Jack Zunz at the start of the arbitration hearing on Stage I. *Ove Arup & Partners, London.*

20. Ron Jenkins. *Ove Arup & Partners, London.*

21. Weights hanging from a perspex model duplicated anticipated loads on the shells. Tests were carried out at Southampton University. *Ove Arup & Partners, London.*

22. The 1957 model of Utzon's competition design, photographed from the south. *Utzon's Yellow Book.*

23. South elevation of the spherical shell design in January 1962. This was close to the design that was built, except for changes to the side shells and the removal of the black ribbing on the shells. *Utzon's Yellow book.*

24. The final shell solution was disarmingly simple, segments cut from the same sphere. *Max Dupain & Associates.*

25. Utzon's model of the spherical scheme. *Government Printing Office negatives, Mitchell Library.*

26. West elevation of the Major Hall shells before tiling. The Louvre shells A 10 and A 9, are partially hidden behind shells A 3 and A 2. *Ove Arup & Partners, London.*

27. Diagrammatic cross-section through shell A 2 of the Major Hall. A decision was later made to leave in the temporary stressing cables as a 'belt and braces' approach to provide extra strength. The permanent stressing cables on their own were quite adequate for the design. The cast in situ concrete joint (12) between the special rib top segment (9) and the ridge beam segment (13) varied in thickness

from rib to rib to allow for the $\frac{1}{2}$ in tolerance in construction that was anticipated could occur at the top of a completed rib. *Sydney Opera House, Phaidon.*

28. The design of the concrete roof elements was extraordinarily complex, and the sculptural shapes were difficult to define on drawings, so dimensions for the formwork carpenters on site were frequently given direct from computer printouts. *Ove Arup & Partners, London.*

29. Cross-section through typical precast rib segments. Ducts for the lateral stressing cables are illustrated in the top two pictures. In the lower picture (B-B) note the three small ducts for the temporary stressing cables on each corner of the segment, beside the larger hole for the permanent stressing cables. *Ove Arup & Partners, London.*

30. The ingenious 'flying wedge' arrangement used on the temporary stressing cables during erection of rib segments. The 'female wedges', which were split collets, stayed behind in the top of the rib segment when the temporary stressing cable was pushed up through the next segment. This operation was carried out thousands of times during construction as there were some 2,000 rib segments with nine temporary stressing anchorages in each segment. When the decision was made to leave the temporary stressing cables in, and the ducts were grouted, it was the presence of the flying wedges which led to some problems with grout voids occurring. The temporary stressing procedure was described in David Dowrick's paper on stressing at the Opera House: 'The male wedges remained fixed to the strand and were re-used in each segment. After pushing the strand through to the top of each segment, the two-piece female wedges were inserted before stressing. When the strand was destressed, the double taper on the female wedges helped ensure the release of the male wedges which could not be lost in the duct for fear of jamming the strand. Very few wedges were lost in practice... The permanent stressing of a complete rib included the nine erection strands, plus between ten and twenty-three further strands which were threaded through three or four other ducts. Longer ribs were stressed from both top and bottom to minimise friction losses, while shorter ribs were stressed from the top only. When stressing the long ribs from the pedestal, some of the ducts had high curvature at the bottom end and to offset the consequent friction loss such strands were jacked to 85 % ultimate tensile strength.' Illustration, *The Prestressing of Sydney Opera House Roof, David Dowrick.*

31. Shell A1 showing lateral bolt and lateral stressing connections. *Ove Arup & Partners, London.*

32. An illustration of one of the changes involved in the design development of the lateral bolts. The change also meant a minor alteration to the rib segments. This was to introduce a pocket to drop in a K-Monel plate drilled with two holes at the centre-line of the rib. Illustration from a GKN report, *Bolting a Mammoth on the Move.*

33. Activity in the rib casting yard. The casting bed on the right is in the open position. A finished cast rib segment is about to be lifted out by crane. In the bed second from right, rib reinforcing steel is in place. A single precast diaphragm forms the joint between rib segments, which will be painted with bond-break oil on one side to match cast it against its mate when the concrete is poured. The last space in the bed is left empty to drop in a previously cast segment from the following bed before the concrete pour, ensuring every segment along the length of a rib is match cast against its mate. Photographed on 18th August 1964. *Max Dupain & Associates.*

34. The reinforcing alone for some of the cast in situ shell pedestals weighed over 15 tons. It was so incredibly thick, that Corbet Gore reckoned if you put a sparrow inside it wouldn't find its way out. *Max Dupain & Associates.*

35. Placing steel for one of the crown pieces. Photographed in September 1964. *Max Dupain & Associates.*

36. Lewis, Gore and Nielsen on site. November 1964. *Max Dupain & Associates.*

37. Lewis, Arup and Zunz on site, October 1964. *Max Dupain & Associates.*

38. Making a test application of epoxy resin. Later, on the main shell rib segments, care had to be taken to ensure no glue got on the flying wedge collets. *Ove Arup & Partners, London.*

39. A worker in a side shell arch segment. Possums from the Botanic Gardens also used to take up residence in the segments. *Max Dupain & Associates.*

40. The stage walls were the first part of the Stage II structure to rise above the podium. *Government Printing Office negatives, Mitchell Library.*

41. One of the side shells with the erection arch in place ready for the placing of the first rib segments. The base of the erection arch was jacked along the top of the shell pedestal for succeeding ribs and

adjusted telescopically for the increase in height of the ribs as they advanced up the shell. For the last rib of the shell the erection arch was in the 'outboard' position off the end of the shell pedestal, and was supported by external props. *Max Dupain & Associates*.

42. The first side shell arches and ribs in place. Because of changes to the shell columns, detail changes to the design, time taken to evolve precise survey procedures and industrial unrest on site, it took nearly two years for construction to advance this far after the completion of Stage I. The photograph was taken in December 1964. During 1965 and 1966 the pace of construction on the shells went ahead much more quickly. *Max Dupain & Associates*.

43. Looking down on the side shell arches of A 8 from the top of shell A 2. Accuracy of survey of the side shell arches was critical. Part of the procedure involved the surveyor climbing down inside the hollow arch to site his instrument on a scale at the top. Photographed June 1966. *Max Dupain & Associates*.

44. Placing the first segment of a rib. Each segment was numbered to ensure it was placed in its correct position on the shells. The shear pin at the centre of the base of the segment dropped into a socket in the top of the shell pedestal to act as a hinge to allow for movements of the rib during construction. Holes along the top and lower surface of the rib are for temporary stressing cables. Polythene taped around the top edge of the segment prevented epoxy from running onto the rib surface during temporary stressing. Photographed in April 1965. *Max Dupain & Associates*.

45. A rib under construction (centre) with an already completed rib on the left and the erection arch on the right. Black tape on the completed rib was to protect the surface from epoxy slurry. *Ove Arup & Partners, London*.

46. A rib segment drops into place. Note the special Hornibrook lifting gear which could orientate the segment to the correct position before lowering it to the shell. The pockets in the shells are for the lateral bolts and lateral bolt anchor plates. The ridges on the centre rib are lapping anchorages for lateral stressing cables. Photographed April 1965. *Max Dupain & Associates*.

47. The temporary stressing procedure. The special straddle jack in use passed over the cable at the anchor, saving having to thread the jack along the loose cable end for each temporary stressing operation. Hornibrooks went to manufacturers all round the world with the specification for the jacks before they found a factory in Canada

that could make one for the job. Photographed April 1965. *Max Dupain & Associates.*

48. The Major Hall shells start to take shape.'Like butterfly wings' wrote Emerson Curtis, who produced a book of colour sketches of the shells under construction called 'A Vision takes Form'. *Government Printing Office negatives, Mitchell Library.*

49. Progress on the Major Hall shells seen from the Harbour Bridge. Construction of the restaurant on the right, which was built on a birdcage scaffolding without the erection arches, is nearly complete. *Government Printing Office negatives, Mitchell Library.*

50. The dogman Jim Inman riding the top ridge segment of the highest Major Hall shell. 'Would you do this for $44 a week' was the caption on the sign, though in reality the dogmen were getting paid a lot more than that. *Government Printing Office negatives, Mitchell Library.*

51. Jockeying a ridge segment into position. Note the temporary stressing cables curling from the top of the rib below. The two holes on the face of the rib next to the cables are for the continuity stressing cables across the ridge. (Picture 27, number 14) Photographed April 1965. *Max Dupain & Associates.*

52. The completed restaurant shells. Photographed April 1967. *Max Dupain & Associates.*

53. The seat terracing and Minor Hall shells, photographed in 1967. *Max Dupain & Associates.*

54. Placing tiles back face up in a tile lid form. A job that was undertaken with great care to ensure no matt tiles were placed in the spaces for square glossy tiles and vice versa. The pockets around the base of the form were numbered so the correct pattern of matt tiles could be placed around the edge. Photographed July 1964. *Max Dupain & Associates.*

55. Tile lids were hung beneath the concourse on metal hooks like carcasses at a knackers yard. Though that was not to say they were not handled carefully, as the slightest knock would chip the tiles. Photographed August 1964. *Max Dupain & Associates.*

56. Setting out a non-standard tile lid in a concave dish to match the shell curvature. The widest lids on the tallest shells were one-offs, so there was no point in making re-useable forms. *Ove Arup & Partners, London.*

57. Tile lids stacked on the podium ready for placing. Arups instructed

Hornibrooks on the way the lids should be stacked to ensure no deformation of the thin tile lid surface could occur. The joint between ribs was sealed with lead flashing before the tile lids were placed. Photographed June 1966. *Max Dupain & Associates*.

58. The tile lids go into place. Once some initial fitting problems had been sorted out, tile lid placement went ahead very quickly. The chevron shape of the lids was supposed to mirror the shape of the structure beneath, but because some of the lids were manufactured oversize this didn't always happen. *Ove Arup & Partners, London*.

59. Full scale placing of the tile lids underway. Photographed September 1966. *Max Dupain & Associates*.

60. Surveyors on site. When surveying operations took place with the tile lids in place, surveyors suffered cases of snow-blindness when the sun flashed off the tiles through the telescope of the instrument. Photographed June 1966. *Max Dupain & Associates*.

61. Tiling nearly completed, photographed from the Harbour Bridge in 1966. *Max Dupain & Associates*.

62. Workers on site became mountain climbers. Gluing single tiles over the side shell tile lid bolt holes. Photographed March 1967. *Max Dupain & Associates*.

63. Patterns on the shells formed by the design of matt and glossy tiles. *David Messent*.

64. The temporary stressing procedure is described by David Dowrick in 'The Prestressing of Sydney Opera House Roof': 'To erect a rib, the first two segments were placed in position (Figure a) with epoxy glue in the joint, and were immediately stressed together using six erection strands in separate ducts. The next rib segment was then positioned and the remaining three erection strands were threaded up through the three segments and stressed (Figure b). Three of the strands in the first two segments were then destressed and fed further up their ducts through the third segment, whereupon they were re-used to stress the three segments together (Figure c). With the positioning of further segments this leap-frog sequence of destressing and restressing was repeated, ensuring a minimum of six stressed strands in all segments.' Illustration *The Prestressing of Sydney Opera House Roof, D.J. Dowrick*.

65&66. The ground floor and first floor plans of the podium. (The room arrangement in 1995). *Sydney Opera House, Phaidon*.

67&68. The development of the design of the shells. *Ove Arup & Partners*.

Notes and References

Abbreviations used

AOK New South Wales State Archives Office, Kingswood, Sydney
AONSW Archives Office of New South Wales
APODC Arup paper on design and construction of the Opera House
CAA Hornibrook Construction Achievement Award
DWL Dennis Wolanski Library
GKN Guest, Keen & Nettlefolds
MAN Maschinenfabrik Wiesbaden AG
M of M Minutes of meetings
ML Mitchell Library
NRMA National Roads and Motorists Association
OAP Ove Arup and Partners
OAPP (CCAC) Ove Arup's personal papers (Churchill College Archives, Cambridge)
OHC Opera House Committee
OHOH tapes. Opera House Oral History tapes (Dennis Wolanski Library)
PWP Papers of the New South Wales Department of Public Works
RAHS Royal Australian Historical Society.
RAIA Royal Australian Institute of Architects
SMH Sydney Morning Herald
SOH Sydney Opera House
SOHECP Sydney Opera House Executive Committee papers (Dennis Wolanski Library)
TAP Technical Advisory Panel
UIDA Union Internationale Des Architects

CHAPTER 1
BENNELONG POINT

1. No doubt named after Mr (later Sir) George Jackson, Secretary to the Admiralty and friend and patron of Cook.
2. Official narrative of the voyage of the *Endeavour* by Hawksworth.
3. Cook's diary.
4. Matra's letter 23rd August 1783.
5. Supplement attached to Matra's original letter.
6. Stockdale.
7. Lieutenant Philip Gidley King of the *Sirius* gave the following account of an encounter with the Aborigines:
    They wanted to know of what sex we were, which they explained by

pointing where it was distinguishable. As they took us for women not having our beard grown, I ordered one of the people to undeceive them in this particular, when they made a great shout of admiration, and pointing to the shore, which was but ten yards from us, we saw a great number of Women & Girls, with infant children on their shoulders, make their appearance on the beach – all in puris naturalibus pas même la feuille de figueur. Those natives who were round the boats made signs for us to go to them and made us understand their persons were at our service. However, I declined this mark of their hospitality, but shewed a handkerchief, which I offered to one of the women, pointing her out. She immediately put her child down & came alongside the boat and suffered me to apply the handkerchief where Eve did the Fig leaf; the natives then set up another very great shout & my female visitor returned on shore. As the evening was coming on fast and we were twelve miles from the fleet it was time to return...

8. After the Home Secretary, Lord Sydney who had despatched the First Fleet and appointed Phillip first Governor of New South Wales.

9. Letter, Phillip to Lord Sydney.

10. Since celebrated as Australia Day.

11. Letter, Phillip to Lord Sydney.

12. Later to be the site of the Sydney Opera House.

13. In a minor tragedy for the early settlement, a few weeks later four bulls and two cows strayed and were lost when their keeper failed to keep watch over them. The cattle, which at the time were assumed to have been killed by the Aborigines, eventually found their way to Cowpastures (which was named after them) on the Nepean River 60 kilometres away where they were found by Governor Hunter when he was exploring the area on 20th November 1795. By then they had multiplied to a herd of about 60 head.

14. The shore around the Point was covered with a thick deposit of shells, discarded over thousands of years by Aborigines who brought shellfish collected from around the harbour shores to eat at the Point. Convict women burnt the shells in kilns at the Point to make lime for the mortar used in Sydney's first buildings.

15. The accounts of Bennelong by Bradley are from his journal of 1786-92, *A Voyage to New South Wales*, a manuscript which was beautifully illustrated with watercolour views and charts of Sydney and his travels. One of the pictures illustrates the capture of Bennelong at the beach at Manly. Among his other duties Bradley was a cartographer with the First Fleet. Bradleys Head on the north shore of Sydney Harbour is named after him. The headland, still covered in natural bushland, is skirted by a harbourside track that has views through the trees across the harbour to the city and Opera House. Bradley went on to be promoted Rear

Admiral of the Blue in 1812, but two years later at the Winchester Assizes he was tried for a minor fraud against the Post Office and even though according to the *Salisbury and Winchester Journal* of 25th July 1814, 'Evidence was given... of his intellects having been in a disordered state', he was found guilty, and sentenced to transportation for life. The sentence was later waived and he was instead banished to live overseas, taking up residence in France.

16. Collins' *Account of the English Colony in New South Wales* published 1798 was, according to his own words, written to relieve 'the tedium of many a heavy hour.' It is the most comprehensive account of the early history of Sydney. Collins, 31 when he arrived in the Colony, served in New South Wales from 1788-96 as deputy Judge-Advocate and later also as Secretary to the Governor. After a few years back in England he returned to Australia in 1803, later establishing the English colony at Hobart in Tasmania which he commanded until his death in 1810. His observations of Bennelong and the Aborigines are the most detailed of any of the First Fleet journals.

    In 1772, as a second Lieutenant with the Marines, Collins had sailed in command of a guard of Marines aboard the frigate *Southampton* for Denmark. According to the foreword of a reprint of Collins' *Account* by editor, Brian Fletcher, the purpose of the expedition 'was to take into safe-keeping Queen Caroline-Matilda, the youngest daughter of Frederick, Prince of Wales... (whose) conduct with Struenss, the court physician, had so affronted the Danes that she was divorced and held in the Castle of (Kronberg) near Elsinore until she was released into British hands.'

17. Captain Watkin Tench, aged about 29 when he reached Australia in 1788, was a commander of a detachment of Marines in the Colony. The passages on Bennelong reproduced in this publication are from his *A Complete Account of the Settlement at Port Jackson* published in 1793.

18. John Hunter's *An Historical Journal of the Transactions at Pork Jackson and Norfolk Island* was first published in 1793. Hunter, 51 when he arrived in New South Wales, was the Captain of the First Fleet flagship, the *Sirius.* As well as commanding a seaborne expedition to Cape Town for supplies for the Colony, and ferrying convicts and supplies to Norfolk Island, Hunter performed duties as a Magistrate and Surveyor in Sydney. Hunter returned to England to face court martial for the shipwreck of the *Sirius* at Norfolk Island, but was acquitted and came back to Sydney to serve as Governor of New South Wales from 1795-1800.

19. The aborigines held Phillip in great reverance because one of his front teeth were missing. The leading men among the aborigines also often had a missing front tooth, which was knocked out at an adolescent initiation ceremony.

20. Bennelong's hut can be clearly picked out at the Point in several pictures drawn in the following years. They include *Binnllong Point Port Jackson, 1796*, auctioned at Sotheby's London in July 1993 and believed to have been painted by William White, a midshipman who sailed with the East India Company; *Vista de la Colonia, Inglesa de Sydney en la Nueva Gales Meridional*, a copy of which hangs in the Royal Australian Historical Society office at Macquarie Street, Sydney; and *Ben Long's Point*, a lithograph in the Mitchell Library, Sydney. In late 1790 or early 1791, Bennelong and Colbey organised a corroboree for the entertainment of the colonists outside his hut on the Point, the first theatrical performance witnessed by white men at the location.

21. According to Tench Yemmerrawanie was a 'slender fine looking youth... about sixteen years old.'

22. After whom Bass Strait is named.

23. A copy of the letter is in the National Library, Canberra.

24. A picture of Squire's home, with his brewery next to it, is depicted in a drawing by Josephy Lycett in a book called *Views in Australia*, published in London in 1825. Joseph Lycett was transported as a convict in 1810. The caption with the picture wrote of James Squire: 'His beverage had a general good name throughout the Colony, and he was universally respected and beloved as a friend and protector of the lower class of settlers. Had he been less liberal, he might have died more wealthy, but his (practical) assistance always accompanied his advice to the poor and unfortunate, and his name will long be pronounced with veneration by the grateful objects of his liberality.' Squire's grandson, James Squire Farnell, became Premier of New South Wales in 1877.

25. His name has since been carried by a punt, a racehorse, at least two hotels, Bennelong Cruises and Bennelong Boomerangs.

CHAPTER 2
FORT MACQUARIE

1. Macquarie's Diary. Though Macquarie makes no other mention of this first meeting with Bligh.

2. Ibid.

3. Cadman's Cottage, within the enclosing wall of the Dockyards, is Sydney's oldest remaining dwelling. Dated 1816, it is thought to have been designed by Greenway.

4. On laying the foundation stone Macquarie wrote in his diary, 'I christened this intended Erection Macquarie Tower – and we drank success to it in a glass of Cherry Brandy.'

5. Greenway based the design of the obelisk on an example by Nash in the Orange Garden at Bath. Macquarie's enthusiasm for this project was possibly inspired by 'Pompey's Pillar' in Egypt, which Macquarie once

spent an hour gazing at, penning in his diary it was 'truly the most magnificent and most beautiful object I have ever seen.'

6. '...such a Building is particularly necessary for keeping these depraved Females at Work within Walls, so as in some degree to be a check upon their Immoralities and disorderly Viscious Habits,' wrote Macquarie. The inmates nick-named it 'the Black Hole of Parramatta.'

7. Macquarie's first proposal was for a 'respectable court house and town hall' under the same roof, with a 'Grecian Doric portico at the main entrance copied from the Temple of Theseus at Athens.'

8. J.P. McGuanne in a paper on Bennelong Point to the RAHS 1901.

9. In 1806, the first white man to be struck and killed by lightning in Sydney was hit at Bennelong Point. In 1811, a black whale was harpooned off the Point.

In 1793 two Spanish Navigators, Melaspina and Guerra, first calculated the latitude and longitude of Sydney with approximate correctness at Bennelong Point. According to Collins, to erect their observatory 'they chose the Point of the cove on which a small brick hut had been built for Ben-nil-long...making use of the hut to secure their instruments. Ben-nil-long was absent from the colony at this time in England.' In 1795 Matthew Flinders fixed the latitude and longitude of Bennelong Point and used it as an opening and closing reference for his surveys of Port Jackson and the coast of Australia. Accompanying Flinders on the first circumnavigation of the continent was King Bungaree, the last King of the Cammeraygal Aboriginal tribe. A plaque on the north broadwalk of the Opera House relates that Flinders' use of the word Australia on maps was largely responsible for the adoption of that name for the continent.

10. A thought that struck a French visitor to Sydney, Monsieur Arago, who on seeing the completed stables, believed they 'seemed to be built with the purpose of being armed...in a style of architecture so unique that I cannot find phrases to describe it.'

11. Greenway in a letter to the editor of *The Australian*, 28th April 1825.

12. Though Fort Macquarie was tiny by comparison, it had several similarities to Kroningsberg Fortress at Elsinore. Each was on a peninsular surrounded on three sides by water guarding the entrance to a port. Kroningsberg was linked to the land by a drawbridge, so was Fort Macquarie. The outer ramparts of Kroningsberg facing the sea were sloping, like the walls of Fort Macquarie.

13. Greenway to Australian, 28.4.1825.

14. Wentworth.

CHAPTER 3
THE COMPETITION

1. Charles Moses OHOH tapes.

2. Ibid.
3. Bennett gave as his reason for escaping the useful first-hand knowledge he had obtained of fighting the Japanese. However, he had acted without orders, and was not given another command of men in the field during the war. The term 'Gordon Bennett' entered the English language to describe something unusual or surprising.
4. From the time he took charge of the ABC in 1935, with a staff of 389, to when he retired as General Manager in 1965, with a staff of over 4,000, Moses ruled the ABC as 'a virtual dictator... but a dictator who knew how to delegate command.' 'Many of the ABC's most significant activities were developed under his direction, the independent news service, schools and rural broadcasts, overseas shortwave broadcasts (Radio Australia) and the television service.' Moses was named as CBE in the 1954 honours list, and was knighted in 1961. When he retired from the ABC he became the first Secretary General of the recently formed Asian Broadcasting Union, a post he held for 12 years. Moses remained a 'fitness fanatic' throughout his life, and walked everywhere he could, including when he was aged 73 the 3 miles from his home at Darling Point to his office at Castlereagh Street in the city. An ABC delegate recalled, 'I remember when we were going by bus from our hotel to the conference centre in Jakarta, a distance of three miles. Halfway there we passed Sir Charles, walking at a furious pace in the 85 degree heat. He actually passed us later as we crawled along in Jakarta's notorious traffic.' 'Should we join Sir Charles?' someone asked. 'If you think you are as fit as he is', someone else replied. No one seemed to think they were! Moses was president of the Amateur Athletics Association of New South Wales from 1945-69, and of the New South Wales Rugby Club from 1957-63.

Other ABC delegates recalled Sir Charles' flair for conducting 'Program Committee meetings like a symphony orchestra, (with) an extraordinary ability to keep discussion flowing' and his immense stamina: 'Delegates who burned the midnight oil usually appeared red-eyed and comatose at the next morning's meeting... However, Sir Charles...would be up all night writing minutes, but would nevertheless arrive at the meeting clear-eyed (his) faculties as razor-sharp as ever.' Tomakazu Sakamoto of Japanese TV thought 'Sir Charles was like the sun. When he was there he was just there...'

These accounts of Charles Moses are from his CV in the PWP, AONSW; *ABC News*, Vol.7, No.2 1988; *Who's Who in Australia 1988*, *SMH* 10.2.1988 and Yeomans.
5. Moses OHOH tapes.
6. It was at Moses' suggestion that the ABC became involved in broadcasting concerts in the 1930s, and it was his personal lobbying of State governments, city councils and other organisations for funds that

led to the establishment of the SSO and other State orchestras in the 1940s. His efforts led to the ABC being one of the world's largest concert-giving agencies. The orchestras are controlled by the ABC, who organise their programs, pay their staff and bring out overseas artists to perform with them. The SSO's telephone number and address is listed in the phone book under the ABC, and SSO tickets are sold through ABC box offices.

7. Moses OHOH tapes. Goossens called music, 'a lot of lovely noise.'

8. Historical feature, *Daily Mirror* 19.7.78. Goossens was a cockney; the boarding house where he was born was within earshot of Bow Bells. A few days before he was born, both his grandfathers were presented to Queen Victoria at Balmoral Castle following a Royal Command Performance in which Eugene Goossens I was conductor and Aynsley Cook played Sir Joseph Porter.

   Eastman had built a theatre at Rochester New York and formed an orchestra to play in it to provide background music for the silent movies. He expanded the number of players, renamed it the Rochester Symphony Orchestra and offered Goossens the job of conductor after noticing him conduct on a trip to London. Hubble, *The Strange Case of Eugene Goossens.*

9. Moses OHOH tapes.

10. One of the conditions was that he could spend part of each year working as a guest conductor overseas. Also, on the OHOH tapes, Moses was asked if Goossens was earning more than the Prime Minister, he replied '...it would be true. Salaries in Australia were not high compared with America you see, and he would have been getting more than the Prime Minister, but then of course you have to remember that Mr Chifley was never ambitious to have more money. In fact he was on record as having said that he thought a thousand (pounds) a year was enough for anybody.' Chifley incidentally, started out as a locomotive engine driver.

11. 'Goossens gave his first performance with the SSO as its permanent conductor on July 17, 1947. The applause was frenetic. On his fourth recall to the stage of the Sydney Town Hall, Goossens declared: 'I look forward to making this one of the conspicuously great orchestras of the world. I feel that with the material I have, I can do it.' Vincent Smith, Sydney Opera House.

12. Hubble, *The Strange Case of Eugene Goossens.*

13. Smith, Vincent.

14. Moses OHOH tapes.

15. Hubble, *More than an Opera House.*

16. *Daily Guardian,* 2.8.28.

17. According to a letter to the *SMH* from W.Ford, 21.6.62.

18. In a policy speech on 21st April 1941, McKell had undertaken that the

Labor Party would 'do everything possible to foster a native culture which will express, in all the arts, not the feelings of other nations, but the aspirations and ideals of the Australian people… (It) is firmly determined, when it is in power, to implement the plans it has formulated for the advancement in New South Wales, of our art, our literature and our music.'

19. SOH 'Calendar of events', SOHECP.

20. Goossens was frequently credited with the idea of placing an opera house on Bennelong Point, however, by his own acknowledgment, the idea originated elsewhere. According to W. Ford's letter to the *SMH* published on 21.6.62, '…It might be true that Sir Eugene suggested to the later Premier, Mr Cahill, the selection of Bennelong Point as the appropriate site for the Sydney Opera House. However, he made this suggestion on the insistence of the late Sir Robert Garran and of Mr Pierre Stuart-Layner, who were respectively president and honorary organising secretary of the National Theatre Movement of Australia… At a conference with Sir Eugene, both Sir Robert and Mr Stuart-Layner obtained Sir Eugene's assurance that he would submit this suggestion to the Premier. In the beginning, Sir Eugene himself was not enthusiastic about the suggested site.'

Another letter to the *SMH* from R.D.L. Fraser, of Eaglemont Victoria published on 19.10.73 ran '…There is little doubt that Goossens' endorsement of the site was largely responsible for its selection years later by the New South Wales Government. But he did not find it. For this, the credit must go to the late Sidney Luker, Chief County Planner of the Cumberland County Council from 1945 to 1953.

As his closest associate during this period, I well remember him arriving at his office one morning in the late forties, delighted that he had that very day taken Goossens to Fort Macquarie and revealed to him a site for an opera house which the latter had acclaimed as incomparable.

At the time Luker had been studying the area closely with Karl Langer, architect and planner, who had been retained as a consultant by the Cumberland County Council to prepare plans for the remodelling of the Circular Quay area…'

21. *SMH* 7.10.48

22. Smith, Vincent.

23. Anzac Day, although it was not known as such at the time.

24. Messent/Molnar interviews.

25. Ibid.

26. While in Canberra, Molnar designed a block of apartments which was later converted into the Soviet Embassy.

27. 'I went…just for a term and I ended up 32 years teaching architecture.' Messent/Molnar interviews.

28. Messent/Molnar interviews.
29. Messent/Molnar interviews.
30. Ziegler, *Sydney builds an Opera House.*
31. Ibid.
32. Hubble, *The Strange Case of Eugene Goossens* and *More Than an Opera House.*

Also, Moses OHOH tapes, in response to whether Sir Eugene's idea for an Opera House was backed by the public,

'No, surprisingly enough. There was very little reaction. It was just the press reaction rather than public reaction. I think that the public were inclined to think that this was somebody's pipe dream – castles in the sky – it could never be a reality. It was just a dream. I think the public didn't take the thing realistically at all, that this could ever be feasible.

33. Moses OHOH tapes.

In the Legislative Assembly Mr Hills asked Cahill on the 3rd November 1954 'whether there is a need in the city of Sydney for the establishment of an Opera House?' He also asked Cahill to 'consider convening a meeting of interested persons to discuss sites, finance and other matters...' Cahill replied he was already having examined the aspects raised... He went on to say that the policy of the Government was to promote the cultural development of the State and that it considered an Opera House as essential. On 8th November, Cabinet approved Cahill's submission regarding '...calling a convention of all groups interested in drama, ballet, opera and music to discuss selection of a site and the construction of an Opera House.' SOH Calendar of Events, SOHEC papers.

Also , when Moses was asked by the interviewer on the OHOH tapes, 'Was his Government as a whole as supportive?' Moses replied, 'Oh no! Oh no! (laugh). I would say not! In fact I was amazed at his reaction, you see when all is said and done, one didn't expect a Labor Premier – and he came from a working background...I didn't expect his reaction to be what it was.'

34. Hubble, *More Than an Opera House*; Yeomans; Smith, Vincent.
35. 'Report of the Proceedings of a Conference convened by the Premier and held in the Lecture Room, Public Library, Sydney, on 30th November, 1954, concerning the question of the establishment of an Opera House in Sydney.' Haviland family papers. It lists all the individuals who invitations were sent out to, and contains a complete transcript of the conference. Cahill was accompanied by R.J. Heffron, Deputy Premier and Minister for Education; J.B. Renshaw, Minister for Public Works and Local Government; P.D. Hills, Labor member of Parliament and the Lord Mayor of Sydney; and P.H. Roper, Under Secretary, Premier's Department.

36. Harry Ingham Ashworth, born in Manchester, England on 20th February 1907, attended Manchester Grammar School before graduating with an honours degree in architecture from Manchester University. Starting work in 1929 as a junior professor of architecture at the Bartlett School of Architecture at London University, and running a small architectural practice in London with an American colleague from the university at the same time, he went on to write during this period two publications, *Professional Practice and Administration in Architecture* in 1933, and *Flats, the Planning and Equipment of*, in 1936.

    At the start of the Second World War, architects were initially not allowed to join up, so Ashworth worked in Hackney, London, responsible for the allocation of air-raid shelters to families in the district. When he was accepted by the army, he served as an engineer on the staff of the 14th Army in India and Burma 'building bridges and roads and so on', was twice mentioned in despatches and rose to the rank of Lieutenant Colonel.

    Following the war, unsettled and a little bored with life in London, Ashworth applied for jobs in South Africa, Melbourne and Sydney. He had once met Professor Wilkinson, Dean of the Faculty of Architecture at Sydney University, when the Dean had visited London, and when a vacancy cropped up at Sydney University he applied for and was accepted for the job. He came out to Australia in 1949 with his wife Ella to fill the University of Sydney's Chair of Architectural Design and History. He became Dean of the Faculty in 1950.

    On Ashworth's death in 1991, Professor Peter Johnson, wrote, 'Former students will have many memories of his idiosyncrasies – a clicking toy frog to instruct… his faculty factotum, to change slides; military shirts, as though he still used distant tailors from his army days in India and Burma; and his well known pungent pervasive cigars…

    He was a great committee man, but he had an amiable and entirely commendable habit at the end of meetings of tearing up agenda papers and casting them aside – a lesson for these present times of proliferating paper.'

    According to the Haviland family papers, to those who knew him, including Stan Haviland, he was thought of as a man of 'unimpeachable integrity.'

    Interviewed for *SMH* of 15.10.73, Charles Moses expressed the opinion that the inclusion of Ashworth on the Committee was 'a very brilliant stroke indeed.'

37. Hendy was a trustee of the Sydney Cricket Ground, a councillor and vice-president of the NRMA, a director of the Royal North Shore Hospital and a member of the Library Board. He died in May 1959 aged 69.

38. Stan Haviland, born in 1899, was a career public servant who had started

work for the New South Wales government at the Lands Department in 1915. Transferring to the Department of Local Government in 1920, he eventually was made permanent under-secretary of that Department in 1946. Cahill was Minister for Local Government as well as Premier of New South Wales, and had a good working relationship with Stan Haviland in his role as head of that Department.

In his position on the Opera House Committee Haviland, according to the *SMH* of 5th June 1972, 'was often a controversial figure because of his silence about matters under his control – particularly the Opera House… A dedicated public servant, he believed his function was to advise the Government instead of making public statements.' His reticence in this regard led him to be dubbed 'silent Stan' by the Sydney press.

Moses is quoted in *SMH* of 15th October 1973 as saying regarding Haviland's appointment to the Committee, 'The Premier wanted a senior public servant as chairman. He could provide the secretarial assistance so that the committee functioned and didn't have to get some honorary secretary. Also, this enabled the Government to keep its eye on what was doing, what was happening.' Also Baume, and Yeomans on Haviland.

39. The previous day, on the 29th, Cahill had secretly obtained approval from his Cabinet for the appointment of a working committee comprising: Haviland, Hendy (as nominee of the City Council), Goossens, Moses and Ashworth. SOH Calendar of Events, SOHEC papers.

40. *SMH* of 15th October 1973 reporting on the conference, wrote '…Mr Cahill and his ministers, very wisely, have not attempted to end the controversy over where the Opera House should be built. They propose to set up a broadly representative committee to argue that point still further.' Quoted in SMH 15.10.73.

41. The week before, on 22nd November, Goossens had 'conducted the world premiere of his oratorio, *The Apocalypse*, before a packed house at the Sydney Town Hall. He described this composition as a 'sort of Reader's Digest version of the Book of Revelations'. The epic oratorio is scored for two choirs, symphony orchestra, organ and soloists. Hubble, *The Strange Case of Eugene Goossens*.

42. Dr H.C. 'Nugget' Coombes, Governor of the Reserve Bank, was Chairman of the Australian Elizabethan Theatre Trust, named after the Elizabethan Theatre at Newtown in Sydney. The Trust was formed to support drama, opera and ballet companies throughout Australia. In the OHOH tapes Charles Moses recalled how the trust was founded :

'…we had a Drama Company, the John Alden Shakespeare Company which went round Australia, producing Shakespearean plays in many parts of Australia where they had never had one produced by a professional company before. This was under the management of Elsie Beyer, who had been the head of the big drama entrepreneurs in London.

457

She is very well known. She managed that, and in fact, spent a good deal of her own money on it to make sure it was a success.

After that was over, I felt, and Elsie Beyer convinced me, Australia could support a National drama company. We only needed, she said, about ten thousand pounds a year, and with the experience we'd had, we could manage to produce first class drama with a national drama company. I went up to Canberra, and I saw the Secretary to the Department of Treasury, who put me on to a member of his staff, Mr. Hewitt, later on he was the Chairman of Qantas, Sir Lennox Hewitt, and Mr Hewitt was interested – his wife was particularly interested in drama – but he said that he couldn't find any Commonwealth funds to give to a purpose like this. But he said "Look, why don't you go down to have a talk with the Commonwealth Bank, Nugget Coombes might be interested."

So I went straight down to see Dr Coombes and I told him what was in my mind, and he said : "Oh, I think that's a good idea, but why don't you go further. Why not set up a National Trust, which would be interested not only in drama, but in ballet and opera as well, and then we could get Government support for something of that sort." Well, I was excited. This was a much broader vision than I'd had and I said at once, "Well, as a matter of fact, the ABC orchestras could be used for the ballet and the opera." The Commission didn't know that I was committing them. But in fact in the early years, they did exactly that, before the separate orchestras were formed. That's how the Elizabethan Theatre Trust started. Dr Coombes was so excited about it, that he and I, we went round Australia, and he organised private lunches in the headquarters of the Commonwealth Bank in each capital city, to which a number of prominent citizens with money behind them, heads of big companies, were invited. Dr Coombes spoke about drama, and I got as excited as I could about the possibility of the ABC, what we could contribute and the way our orchestras could provide a background to opera that had never been heard before...

And, with this series of lunches, we actually got promises of – firm promises – I mean these weren't just sort of "well, I might give you so much", of £90,000, which was a lot of money. And he and I saw the Prime Minister (Menzies) who put us onto the then Treasurer, Sir Artie Fadden. Fadden, of course, was a bit of a philistine. He wasn't the one who was inclined to think of spending large sums of money on the arts. But Mr Menzies had obviously said to Fadden, that we must get in behind this, we must support it. (Chuckle). To my, I must say, astonishment, and great disappointment, Dr Coombes didn't commit himself. Fadden said: "Yes, oh yes, they would." They would give us one pound for every three that we collected. We had ninety thousand. And so the Federal Government put in thirty, which gave us then one hundred and twenty thousand pounds...

We got through our first season, almost square...and were able to put on when the Queen was here (in February 1954) a special Gala concert for her, in which it was a mixture, that I mean, musicians would generally not approve of, but we did have the Sydney Symphony Orchestra playing one third of the program, a scene from opera, provided by the National Opera Company and we had a performance of 'Corroboree', the ballet by John Antill. And so those three components formed a program which was inflicted on the Queen and the Royal party. It was hardly what you would call - it was a potpourri, but not one which musicians generally would approve of. But at least it did show what we could do, and all three parts did go well.'

43. Moses recorded on the OHOH tapes that ' everybody felt that this was a very good committee, because you've got the City Council involved, you've got a Professor of Architecture involved; you've got the man who was thinking and talking about it, Goossens, and I was the one that they realised who could play a leading part in it, because the ABC, as the body which had done more to promote music perhaps than anybody else in Australia up to that time - that perhaps I was also a useful additive as well.'

44. *SMH* 15.10.73.

45. From Yeomans.

46. Ashworth papers. 2.12.54.

47. Winston was also later Dean of the Faculty of Architecture. Winston was on the committee appointed by the RAIA to look for a site, and so was Ashworth and, among others, Bunning, who was Chairman of the State Planning Advisory Committee.

48. On 21st December 1954, at the second meeting of the Opera House Committee, the Secretary, (Ron Thomson of the Department of Local Government was appointed Secretary and Executive Officer of the Committee on 2nd December) read a letter dated 6th December 1954 from Professor Dennis Winston on various tentative sites, including:

    Fort Macquarie: Outstandingly suitable providing a setting unrivalled anywhere else in the world; typically characteristic of Sydney; would provide landmark for travellers; fulfill all requirements of size, spaciousness and beauty; ample parking space could be provided; road approaches excellent; well situated in relation to all public transport services; removal of tram depot would effect tremendous improvement to harbour foreshores, present occupation of site by tram shed an absurdity... M of M of OHC, Ashworth papers.

49. Messent/Molnar interviews.

50. *SMH.*

51. Messent/Molnar interviews.

52. *SMH.*

53. Moses OHOH tapes.

At the second Opera House Committee meeting, regarding the Fort Macquarie site, the minutes stated '...(it would) provide a landmark for travellers as memorable as the Stockholm Town Hall or the Doge's Palace in Venice....' At a meeting held on 4.2.55 at the University of Sydney, with Ashworth as Chairman and Winston, Bunning, Mansfield and Molnar present, a decision was made for the preference of the Fort Macquarie site and a report recommending its adoption was sent to Cahill. On 23rd March a deputation from the Committee went to see the Premier to talk about the site, who suggested the Committee should approach the Transport Department and he (Cahill) would speak to the Minister for Transport. Finally, at the seventh meeting of the OHC, 'The Chairman read to members the Premier's letter of 19.5.55 informing the Minister for Local Government that Cabinet had approved of the recommendation of the Committee that the Opera House be built on the Bennelong Point site....' M of M, OHC, Ashworth papers and SOH Calendar of Events SOHEC papers.

Although the Labor Cabinet approved of the Bennelong Point site on 13th May 1955, the Maritime Services Board had not relinquished their wharf space on the west side of the site. In fact they insisted on staying, saying that they did not propose to give up these wharves because of the cost of relocating elsewhere and in fact planned to spend up to £800,000 upgrading the existing wharf which was close to the end of its useful life. They also gave as a reason that a contingency plan had existed since 1946 that in a national emergency the navy could use them. The Board publicised their plans for new wharves at Circular Quay East. When Cahill suggested the possibility that wharf space could be provided west of the Harbour Bridge, they raised the objection that if there was a war and the Harbour Bridge was brought down, this would close off access to those wharves. When the Opera House competition conditions were sent out to prospective competitors, several asked about the wharves on the photographs of the site at Circular Quay East. '...It was agreed that competitors be advised that for the purpose of the competition they should assume that the wharves would be demolished.'

M of M of OHC, Ashworth papers, including minutes of meetings between the Committee and the Maritime Services Board.

54. Regarding the Bennelong Point site, Cahill said the Opera House Committee would have to see the Maritime Services Board. Moses reported in the *SMH* of 15th October 1973. '...so we did. The Chairman of the Board said "Oh, no, you can't have it." 'He showed us they had practically the working drawings of the overseas terminal on that site. After some strong talking from the Premier, Mr Cahill, the Maritime Services Board agreed to another site', Sir Charles said. Then came oppos-

ition from the Transport Department because of the depot at Bennelong Point. 'The head of the Transport Department was very reluctant' said Sir Charles. 'And again it was the Premier who put the pressure on. He damn well had to – he wasn't going to have them as a stumbling block.'

55. M of M of OHC, Ashworth papers.

This was a separate advisory committee of the NSW Chapter of the RAIA to advise the Opera House Committee on the impending competition, to ensure, among other things, that the competition would not breach the RAIA's rules and terms of reference. This architectural committee advised on the competition program and on the choice of a site. Ashworth was Chairman and the other members were Winston, Molnar, Bunning and Mansfield.

56. '...a large, calm, lumbering man with a shock of nearly grey hair; his firm, Bunning and Madden, usually had seven or eight million dollars-worth of its designs under construction annually...one of its best known projects is the ...National Library building in Canberra.' Yeomans.

57. Messent/Molnar interviews.

58. For the 1956 Melbourne Olympic Games.

59. Misspelt as 'Groplus' in the article.

60. M of M of OHC, Ashworth papers.

61. Ibid.

62. Goossens was knighted in May 1955 for his services to music in Australia.

63. The Committee's recommendation that the competition should be international '... was accepted by Mr Cahill without demur – he wanted a fine building and he was with us all the way...there were many people saying there were good architects in Australia, it should be restricted to Australian architects but no, no, Mr Cahill accepted that recommendation without question.' Moses OHOH tapes.

Also Ashworth recounted, 'If we held an international competition we could say that we had at least asked the world for ideas. There would be no question at a later date that the committee had not cast its net wide enough.' *SMH* 15.10.73.

64. Ashworth recalled: 'I felt there was something to be said for having the assessors of the same age group. It wouldn't work to have one young architect and the others much older. One man of great stature would pull the others by the nose. I also felt that it was desirable that Australians should keep control of the assessing.' *SMH* 15.10.73.

65. Martin was one of Ashworth's best friends and they had studied architecture in the same year at Manchester University. Messent/Ashworth interviews.

66. £1,000 each plus travelling expenses.

67. M of M of OHC, Ashworth papers.

68. SOH Calendar of Events, SOHEC papers.

69. '...when he was appointed to the jury of the competition for the Opera House every potential competitor architect must have had some idea of the visual style that would be most likely to win. Saarinen was not the only judge, of course (but)...He was the man of the hour, the American star, the new master architect; the man in Time magazine...' Robin Boyd, *Architecture Plus*, August 1973.

Eero Saarinen's father, Eliel, was a Finnish architect who had designed many buildings of note in his native Helsinki. The family migrated to America in 1923 when Eero was 12. Following on in his father's footsteps Eero was immensely successful as an architect in America, at the time of the Opera House Competition he was planning consultant to the City of Detroit and had won eight major prizes in architectural competitions, six for theatres or auditoriums. When invited to be a juror '...the first thing that came to my mind was that when my father was asked to be a juror in the Canberra City plan contest in 1911 he refused because he wanted to compete.' *SMH* 12.1.57. Eliel Saarinen went on to win second prize for his Canberra plan.

When he arrived in Sydney, Eero was working on the plans for the TWA terminal at Idlewild Airport, New York, which resembled a bird with its wings outstretched ready to take flight, 'It is planned as a structure in which the architecture itself would express the excitement of travel and movement.' Saarinen quoted in the *Sun-Herald*, 15.3.59.

70. The size of the competition condition booklet, and its layout and design, though not the program, were the same as the competition conditions for a 'Civic Auditorium for Vancouver', printed in 1954, for which one of the judges of the competition was also Saarinen. The Vancouver booklet is among the SOHEC papers relating to the Opera House Competition at the Dennis Wolanski Library.

71. A clause in the conditions that was considered most important as the stature of the judges was likely to reflect the standard of the competition entries. In interviews with Messent George Molnar outlined another reason. The competition for Canberra in 1911 '...was the first international competition in Australia. A competition where no member of the British Institute of Architects could participate. At that time there was no Australian Institute of Architects, so everybody was a member of the British Institute. Why? Because the Institute of Architects said, very rightly, that these conditions as presented to the world for an international competition are not right and I don't allow my members to take part. Because one of the important things about a competition is that you should name the assessors, because you want to know who are the bastards who are going to say whatever (laughing) they are going to say, and Australia didn't give that. And so the Institute told all its members not to participate.'

Q. They didn't have to take any notice of...

Molnar: 'Oh yes, I mean as a member of the institute you had to... Some of them used all sorts of subterfuge, just like the present Parliament House in Canberra (a competition announced in 1979) which was only for Australian architects, well that was all right. And the only way the Italian architect could enter (who won) was that he had in his office a little Australian boy and it was under his name.' Romaldo Guirgola was an Italian American architect working in New York. To enter the Canberra Parliament House competition he formed a consortium, Mitchell, Guirgola and Thorpe. At that time the Australian architect Graham Thorpe was an employee in his office.

72. From the original competition conditions, Dennis Wolanski Library.
73. Moses OHOH tapes.
74. M of M of OHC, Ashworth papers.
75. SOHECP.
76. *SMH* 10.3.56.
77. Moses OHOH tapes.
    Also '...I never discussed it with him at all. But he told Jack Cassidy that he didn't know what was there.'
78. Hubble, *The Strange Case of Eugene Goossens*.
79. *Daily Telegraph* 27.5.56.
80. Historical feature, *Daily Mirror* 19.7.78.
81. *Daily Telegraph* 29.5.56.
    Also, Renée Goossens, 'During an interview at the Opera House in 1986...said that she had discontinued work on a biography of her father after receiving a telephone call threatening her life if she continued with her research... Renée Goossens cannot remember her father taking a great interest in politics, but she believes that he may have been a victim of political intrigue. She said that she suspects that a man introduced to her in Sydney a few years ago as a British naval officer based in Australia may, in fact, have been a secret service man. She claims that he cultivated her friendship, continually broached the subject of her book and her father and then left Sydney suddenly, explaining he had been recalled to England.
    "People think you are mad when you start mentioning suitors who may have been secret service men", said Renée, "They think you are trying to make excuses. I wish I knew what did happen".' Hubble, *The Strange Case of Eugene Goossens*.
    Goossens apparently never divulged to his family or friends why he was carrying pornographic material in his baggage or for whom. The material itself was burnt following his trial.
82. From notes on the competition, SOHECP. They include a copy of the 470 questions and answers. Questions asked by the architects included, No.

35, Does vehicle traffic travel on the left hand side of the road... or the right...?; Answer: The left. There were also questions relating to the local building regulations. The competition conditions contained 'A Summary of Relevant Regulations to be Observed' covering two pages. In some cases the Committee wrote to disregard the regulations and do what was best. Molnar said that'... one of the conditions which is very Anglo-Saxon, we don't have it on the continent, is that there is a period when competitors can write in... and ask questions, you know, to verify things (and after some architects wrote in about the regulations)'... well (laughing) the existing Australian regulations never had any idea of what goes into an Opera House. I mean they were sort of statements that it should be only so far down from the footpath and so high, I mean based on halls or pubs, that sort of thing...'

83. *Daily Telegraph* 22.12.56. See also note 82.
The Balance Sheet from the competition was :

	£
Premiums – £5,000; second £2,000 third, £1,000	8,000
Assessor's fees (four at £1,000)	4,000
Consultation fees associated with drafting of conditions	105
Travelling expenses of overseas assessors	2,000
Exhibition of designs	1,710
Incidental expenses	3,440
	£19.255
Less : Deposits forfeited by competitors who failed to submit designs	4,430
Net cost	£13,825

From *Hansard* 25.11.58 in answer to a question in Parliament. The net cost was very close to the £14,500.00 requested by the Opera House Committee for competition expenses.

84. From a list of the entries received, OHC files, Ashworth papers.
85. *Daily Telegraph* 31.12.56.
86. *Daily Telegraph* 12.1.57.
87. Daily *Telegraph* 8.1.57.
88. Ashworth talking at Newcastle Technical College, reported in the *Newcastle Morning Herald*, 13.8.57.
89. Ashworth had tried to obtain a room at the Town Hall for the judging, but it was not available at the time. M of M of OHC, Ashworth papers.
90. Saarinen designed 'the Kresge auditorium at MIT by cutting three slices of

his breakfast grapefruit hemisphere, and rushing it to his office wrapped in a table-napkin... His means of designing these arbitrarily sculpted buildings, or of perfecting the design in his own eyes, was to have one half of them modelled, at a scale of half-inch to the foot, against a mirror. The mirror became the centerline of the building and the model was completed in the reflection.' Robin Boyd, *Architecture Plus*, August 1973.

91. 'At the time of the Opera House judging, when (Saarinen) ...took a few days off to dash to Sydney, he was building one of his most spectacular brainwaves: that structural tour de force, the Milwaukee War Memorial with its preposterous cantilevers. The builders were actually stripping the formwork at the time and Eero hurried anxiously to the phone more than once to receive progress reports from home.' Robin Boyd, *Architecture Plus*, August, 1973.

92. Yeomans.

93. *SMH* 12.1.57.

94. *Daily Telegraph* 12.1.57.

95. *Sun* 17.1.57.

96. *Daily Telegraph* 17.1.57.

97. Besides an acoustic diagram for the theatre interiors, 'a diagram or diagrams' illustrating audience sight lines and a perspective; the competition conditions called for a site plan, 'all floor plans necessary to ensure an understanding of the scheme', ...'A longitudinal and cross-section through the auditoriums... four main elevations' and one drawing of 'detail illustrating any portions of... the exterior and interior of the building... as selected by the competitor.'

Molnar recounted to Messent: '... one of the important things is that you should be able to put up all the designs... the requirements (asked for in the conditions)... were huge, it took more than that wall (gesturing to a wall in a large room in his apartment) to display them. ... and some of them were put up, some of them were not put up, there was a block of just drawings on tables, (at the Art Gallery). ... I mean the idea of any competition is that you should make it easy for the competitor to produce what they want to say, want to show, and not to do unnecessary work which just stops people who might be very good but haven't got the staff to do that.'

Concerning the amount of time taken by the judges to sift through the volume of drawings, Molnar had written, in his article in the *SMH* before the conditions were drawn up, '...To wade through such a number of entries necessitates a terrible amount of technical work. On the Continent this is done by a preliminary jury, directed by the main jury, who, thus freed from tedious technical detail, can give all its attention to the conception and artistic merits of the designs. This practice is worth considering.'

98. The drawings were done by Saarinen to 'assist the judges in their deliberations.' Ziegler. *Sydney builds an Opera House.*

99. There are some interesting anomalies concerning the drawing numbers. The competition conditions stipulated 'The Competition shall close on 3rd December 1956, and competitors must dispatch their drawings on or before this date.' On 3rd December the State government had received 45 designs (*Daily Telegraph* 4.12.56).

An article in the *Daily Telegraph* on 22nd December 1956 stated 'The State Government has received 217 entries in its worldwide competition for a design for a State Opera House... which has now closed.' Stan Haviland was quoted as saying 'To get 217 submissions from a field of 721 was an excellent result.' Entries were numbered consecutively as they were received. Yet in a 42-item questionnaire sent to the Committee by Pierre Vago of the Union Internationale des Architects after the competition, the answer given to question 10, 'The number of competitors who actually submitted schemes?' was 233. Utzon's entry was number 218. Utzon was to say later he nearly did not send his design because he was late. One English competitor who wrote in by letter dated 7.12.56 asking if the Committee could accept his late completed entry was turned down.

Pierre Vago of the Union sent Ashworth the questionnaire on 5.11.58 and it was returned by Ashworth on the 3.12.58. A copy of the 42 questions and answers is in Ashworth's papers.

100. *SMH* 30.1.57.

CHAPTER 4
ENTER UTZON

1. Hubble, *More than an Opera House.*
2. *SMH* 30.1.57.
3. *Daily Telegraph* 30.1.57.
4. *SMH* 3.8.57; Yeomans.
5. When King Frederick II built Kronborg Castle, waterdriven mills and smithies were needed. An extensive system of dams and canals were constructed and in 1576 a flour mill called the King's Mill was built at Hellebaekken (the holy brook). More mills, workshops and houses were added, and the place became known as Hellebaek. The manufacture of weapons developed into the most important activity, and from 1768 the workshops and mill were called The Kronborg Small Arms Factory. In Hellebaek most of the handweapons for the defence forces were produced, including those used in wars against the English and the Germans. In 1870 the small arms factory was closed.
6. *SMH* 3.8.57; Yeomans; Utzon's C.V.; Ashworth papers; Giedion.

A housing estate by Utzon was completed at Helsingor at about the time of the Opera House competition, and a second estate at Fredensborg about 30 miles away was completed a short time later. The author visited them both when he was in Denmark in 1990.

At Helsingor Utzon scattered the 60 houses around a natural wooded landscape without imposing on the landscape itself. The small single-storey terraced houses with their roofs of Spanish tiles in a setting of a pond surrounded by light woodland resembles a Chinese Garden, but a Chinese Garden as nature found it. As I was walking about the estate, one of the owners asked what I was doing and when I mentioned Utzon and the Opera House she asked me in for a cup of coffee. The owner, Pia Skoller, knew Utzon, and had stayed with his family at Palm Beach in 1965. She used to help around the office, folding up plans and doing the sweeping up, and left three months before he resigned. Pia mentioned that Utzon had lost the original plans for the Helsingor estate during the move to Sydney, so they were trying to locate them and there was even talk of asking Utzon to produce a new set.

The Fredensborg houses are built in a similar style, but in this case the estate is built on a field without disturbing the natural undulations and folds of the landscape. Instead of carving up the land between each house to give them a garden, Utzon gave each house a small square patio or terrace and left a large area of common land for the people of the estate to enjoy as a whole.

The estate was built as a retirement village for Danes returning from overseas. Owners can eat in a communal hall or relax together in an adjoining lounge. A Mayan sculpture sits in the outside courtyard of the hall and hanging around the inside walls of the eating hall are brightly coloured South American carved wooden masks.

According to an article in *Arkitektur* on Fredensborg:

The contrast between the town and the landscape has been achieved without losing the contact between dwelling and landscape. Garden walls and gables are growing out of the ground as in a medieval city, but from the strongholds of the courtyards unfolds above the low walls the view of a beautiful landscape, a piece of protected North Zealand. Horses, and cows are grazing outside the city wall.

A stipulation for the design of the estate by the Danish preservation authorities was to maintain the view towards the Kohave Forest seen from the highway. Utzon papers.

7. 'Monster or Miracle', TV documentary on the Opera House.
Utzon sent his C.V. to the Committee after winning the Opera House Competition.
'Details of Professional Training'
Born April 9th 1918 in Copenhagen Denmark.
1937-1942   Studied Architecture at The Royal Academy of Fine Arts of

Copenhagen and obtained a Masters Degree in 1942.

1942-45   Worked as an architect in Stockholm under Professor Poul Hedquist on school buildings.

1944-45   Graduated from The Royal Academy of Fine Arts in Copenhagen with a Gold Medal.

This is a kind of doctor's degree acquired by participation in an annually arranged competition by the Academy for architects under 35 years old.

The competition subject in 1944 was an academy of music with a concert hall. (This entitled him to use the letters A.A. after his name, Association of Architects of the Royal Academy of Fine Arts).

1945-46   Worked at the office of Professor Alvar Aalto Finland on rebuilding programs.

1946   Opened his own office and worked on various factory buildings for fish products and the chemical industry.

1948   Worked in Morocco in the planning of a cement factory and a factory for prefabricated elements.

1949   Won Scholarship for study trip to U.S.A. and Mexico.

1950   Chemical factory in Copenhagen.

1951   Designed his own private house in Morocco.

1952   Entered into partnership with Erik and Henry Anderson, S.A.R. in Helsingborg Sweden, and worked on housing, schools and town-planning. In October 1956 Utzon was asked by UNESCO in New York to accept a post in Egypt, planning rural communities in the Nile Valley.

Details of competitions entered.

1944   Bellahoej Copenhagen, housing – 3rd prize.

1944   Alborghallen, Concert Hall, Theatre and Conference Centre – Honourable mention.

1946   Falkoping, Sweden; Community Centre and Theatre – 4th prize.
Boras, Sweden : Housing – Honourable mention.
Association of Architects one family houses and townplanning – 1st and 2nd prize. Crystal Palace, London.

1947-48   'Vika' town planning for Oslo Centre, office buildings, Norway.
Cabinetmakers' competition furniture – 2nd prize.
Competition for designs in glass – 1st and 2nd prizes.

1953   Langelinie Pavilion, Copenhagen, restaurant and yacht club – 4th prize.

1954   Open Inter-Scandinavian competition for one family housing and town planning – 1st prize.

Elineberg, housing, town planning for 1200 flats, with schools, a shopping centre, etc.

Helsingborg, Sweden (a two-phase competition) – 2nd and 4th prize, then finally, 1st prize.

Marieberg, Stockholm, Sweden: Administration Centre and 1,000 flats – 1st prize.

Competition by invitation, Lund, Sweden, housing : 60 one family houses – 1st prize.

Ashworth papers.

8. 'Monster or Miracle.'

9. Kelman OHOH tapes.

10. Utzon talking to Stephen Gardiner of *The Observer* in Green Park, London, 16.7.78.

11. Utzon talking on the TV documentary '*The Building that Nearly Was.*'

12. *SMH* 'The Good Weekend', 31.10.92.

13. SOHEC papers.

14. *SMH* 'The Good Weekend', 31.10.92.

15. From the transcript of an interview by Rasmussen of Utzon for Danish TV in September 1965 in Sydney, published in the *Sydney Morning Herald,* 13.5.66.

16. 'The Building that Nearly Was', Duek Cohen quoting Utzon.

17. Transcript of Rasmussen interview.

18. Sydney Opera House, Ross and Pat Westcott.

19. Transcript of Rasmussen interview.

20. From a copy of the original competition conditions, Dennis Wolanski Library.

21. Answers to competitors questions, SOHEC papers.

22. Competition conditions. Ultimately, Utzon's drawings could also have been disqualified on other counts. The shells as constructed reached a height of over 200 feet, however the summary of regulations in the conditions stated 'No portion of the building used for any purpose other than for housing plant or for storage must exceed 150 feet in height from ground level.' As events were to turn out Utzon's design did not seat 3,000 to 3,500 for concerts, the conditions stated a design shall be disqualified if 'It does not provide substantially the accommodation prescribed.' Also, a design could be disqualified if '… in the opinion of the Assessors, the cost of the scheme, as submitted, is excessive.' The cost of the scheme, as constructed, did turn out to be excessive, although of course that was not known at the time. The conditions stated that '…the cost of the building cannot be limited to a specific amount… (though) funds are obviously not unlimited. Thus while extravagance cannot be entertained, competitors are allowed to use their discretion in submitting a design of the character and dignity associated with this type of building.' Regarding the cost, questions by intending competitors included:

55. Q. Why should a design be disqualified for excessive costs, if there is no specific limit of costs?

A. No comment.

56. Q. At what point would a scheme be rejected on the grounds of costs? And roughly what criteria will you be using to assess this?

A. No comment.

Finally, the conditions stated that dressing rooms'...shall not be placed under the stage or under the auditorium. They should be arranged in a section separated from the stage by fire-proof walls and construction.' An intending competitor had asked:

387.Q. There have recently been examples of auditoria built over public areas and dressing rooms. Provided the requisite fire precautions are taken, will this be allowed?

A. No.

Yet Utzon's design was built with dressing rooms on the floors beneath the auditoria.

Concerning the general competition requirements, Molnar recounted :

...people should be able to have a latitude because anybody who takes part in a competition like that knows more than anybody in Australia at that time knew (about Opera Houses).' And in regard to some of the competition requirements '... which were quite unnecessary. And then of course when you have a good assessor of course Utzon hasn't produced any of those things, they were very sketchy you know, his designs; beautifully drawn. And of course people don't look at those things. Those people who were assessors (Martin and Saarinen) were professionals. I mean they knew what it was and they were interested in an idea.' Messent/Molnar interviews.

23. Yeomans.
24. Saarinen presented the pictures to Cahill before leaving Sydney.
25. Parkes interviewed by *SMH* 15.10.73. Bruce Gibson of Neutral Bay wrote to the Herald on 2.2.57 '...when Sir Henry Parkes alienated the Crown Land we now know as Centennial Park and set it up for all time as a play area he was most bitterly opposed. It is indeed a strange coincidence that his son was one of the four adjudicators in the Opera House Competition.'

Centennial Park is an extensive area of playing fields, lakes, lawns, small woods and horse tracks, covering an area of about one and a half square miles, four miles south east of Sydney city centre.

26. Parkes interviewed by *The Australian* 19.10.73.
27. Utzon's report on his design from the *SMH* 30.1.57.
28. *SMH* 30.1.57.
29. Robin Boyd, *Architecture Plus*, August 1973.

Utzon telephoned Sydney when he heard the cost estimate of £3.600,000 to say that his building would cost more, but he was cheerfully told by an official, 'We will blind them with paper.' Hubble, *The Strange Case of Eugene Goossens*.

30. The quantity surveyor's notes on Utzon's design described it as an 'Unorthodox Sail Roof structure, one third cost and half volume contained in roof structure.' Although the internal volume in cubic feet of Utzon's building was not the smallest of the designs they looked at, the quantity surveyors produced an estimated cost of £3.600,000 which was £800,000 cheaper than the next cheapest design.

On 24th January 1957 Ralph Goddard of Rider Hunter and Partners wrote to Ashworth from London:

...I do hope that our fellows are giving you all the assistance required in calculating the probable cost of the opera scheme. I heard from Jones that Wexler, our Melbourne partner, sent our senior assistant to Sydney to give a second opinion on the probable cost.

It seems ages ago since we last met in Sydney and for myself I am finding an English winter particularly depressing after having so recently returned from the sun of Sydney.' Ashworth papers.

Ashworth wrote to Goddard on 12th February:

...Well, the great day has come and gone, and our award has really been the talk of the town!... I would once again as Chairman of the Assessors, like to offer your firm our thanks for the assistance Mr Jones and his colleagues rendered us prior to our making an award. They were splendid and did everything they could. Formal acknowledgement of their assistance was of course, made at the ceremony when the exhibition was opened by the Premier – but after all, the initial offer of assistance in the first instance came from you to me – again many thanks.' Ashworth papers.

31. Of the 17 designs that won prizes or were commended by the judges, 9 were from the UK and 1 from Scotland. From a list of competition entries, Ashworth papers.

32. *Daily Telegraph* 30.1.57.

Molnar recounted:

...after, (the winner was chosen) which shouldn't have been done, because that is not fair. But they said (Molnar chuckling), after all it is an Australian competition, can't we have somebody, an Australian, to at least give a mention or something like it...They had to dig and dig and dig and suddenly there was one and it wasn't an Australian but a Hungarian, Peter Kollar and his group. And that was a mention, no prize, no nothing. Then they find an Australian but he's Hungarian (Molnar chuckling). Messent/Molnar interviews.

33. *SMH* 30.1.57.

34. Yeomans. Baldwinson died before the building was completed.

35. *Daily Telegraph* 4.2.57.

36. *Daily Telegraph* 30.1.57.

37. *Daily Telegraph* 2.2.57.

38. Ibid.
39. Ibid.
40. *Daily Telegraph* 1.2.57.
41. *SMH* 1.2.57.
42. *SMH* 31.1.57.
43. Ibid.
44. *SMH* 31.1.57.
45. *Daily Telegraph* 1.2.57.
46. Ibid.
47. *Daily Telegraph* 31.1.57.
48. *SMH* 2.2.57.
49. Ibid.
50. *Daily Telegraph* 31.1.57.
51. *Daily Telegraph* 7.2.57.
52. *SMH* 31.1.57.
53. *SMH* 1.2.57
54. Ashworth wrote to Professor Martin on 25.3.57.
    ...I have addressed some 3,000 to 4,000 people at meetings over the last two months in an endeavour to ensure that as far as possible, there is at least some informed opinion with regard to the design. Ashworth papers.
55. Ashworth talking to the Australian Institute of Public Relations, quoted from *Daily Telegraph* 7.2.57; and 8.2.57.
56. Ashworth in *SMH* 2.2.57.
57. *SMH* 31.1.57.
58. Ashworth to a staff reporter; *Sun Herald* 3.2.57.
59. Utzon talked on this point in his interview with Rasmussen. Concerning the site, and his desire to make the podium of the Opera House look like a plateau, Utzon said: 'If you build a normal theatre it will be like a boot with the stagehouse as the top part of the boot, and if you put two boots here you do not use the plateau you destroy it.'
60. *The Sun* 26.2.57.
61. Ashworth/Saarinen correspondence, Ashworth papers.
62. *Daily Telegraph* quoting criticism at the time of the competition, 19.10.73.
63. *SMH* 1.2.57.
64. *SMH* 4.2.57.
65. *The Sun* 30.1.57.
66. *The Sun* 30.1.57.
67. Sydney newspapers.
68. ...one of our leading architects at that time, was Harry Seidler...a very fine architect, and he told me – and by the way, he was one of the great supporters of Utzon's design – there was a split in the architects. Now, Walter Bunning for example...was strongly opposed to it...But Seidler told me, he said 'You know, if I'd thought that the Government would

have taken on something so unorthodox, I would've submitted a very different design.' Which was very interesting. But he, as an architect, was so enthusiastic, he was one of the public supporters of Utzon, although he must have been a disappointed man…that he hadn't won the competition himself. But he was one of those that led the supporters of Utzon's design. …there was a difference of opinion, not only in the public, but amongst the architects of Sydney particularly, quite a big difference. But a lot of them, thank goodness, supported Utzon.' Moses OHOH tapes.

69. *Daily Telegraph* 30.1.57.
70. Moses OHOH tapes.
71. Sydney newspapers.
72. SOHEC papers.
73. *SMH* 16.2.57.
74. Romola Woods, *SMH* 16.2.57.
75. L.H.Peachey, *Daily Telegraph* 9.3.57.
76. J. Langtry, *SMH* 29.8.57.
77. The notorious bushranger Ben Hall and his gang instituted a reign of terror that lasted 3 years in southern NSW in the 1860s. Finally he was surrounded one night as he slept, and shot down when he got up after being called to surrender:

    'Come all you Lachlan men, and a sorrowful tale I'll tell,

    Concerning of a hero bold who through misfortune fell;

    His name it was Ben Hall, a man of high renown

    Who was hunted from his station and like a dog shot down.' John McGuire.

    Ben Hall's pistol, found on him when he died, is at the Sydney Justice and Police Museum, on Circular Quay, 300 metres from the Opera House.
78. *SMH* 19.2.57.
79. Margaret O'Neill White, *SMH* 2.2.57.
80. In a report by the Opera House Committee on means of financing the cost of the building, sent to Cahill on 27th February 1957:

    …Assuming that an appeal for public subscriptions will produce £200,000 the average annual contributions to be made over a period of six years will be:-

    Commonwealth Government

	£250,000
State Government	£250,000
Sydney City Council	£ 50,000
	£550,000

    The Committee justified its expectation of funds from the Commonwealth Government, '… based on the fact that the construction of a "National" Opera House in Sydney would be of the same stature for

Australia as the recent 1956 Melbourne Olympic Games.' M of M of OHC, Ashworth papers.

81. Newspaper reports in *The Telegraph*, *SMH* and *Sydney Truth* immediately following the competition. When it was apparent that no federal funds would be forthcoming, the word 'National' was quickly dropped from the title whenever the NSW government referred to the Opera House.

82. *Sydney Truth* 3.2.57, under an article headed 'OPERATIC GALE RISING' Labor MLA.s to hit at "unwanted luxury".'

83. *Daily Telegraph* 20.2.57.

84. Ashworth papers.

85. Ibid.

86. Newspapers, 9.5.57.

87. *The Sun* 10.5.57.

88. Cahill talking on 12.5.57, from *SMH* 13.5.57.

89. *Daily Telegraph* 7.6.57.

90. *Daily Telegraph*, *SMH* and other papers 17.6.57.

91. *SMH* 19.6.57.

92. *SMH* 4.7.57.

93. Ashworth papers. Ashworth wrote to Saarinen on the same day telling him of the news.

94. Ashworth papers.

95. *Woman's Day* magazine sent a correspondent to Denmark to write a story on the Utzons, and ran a feature on 'The Great Dane' at home, illustrated by photographs showing Utzon to be a whiz around the kitchen: 'Utzon has other talents. Here he opens a can.' Lis said later, 'We were quite unprepared for the media attention we received. We were just normal people, a normal family, not the urban sophisticates we had been made out to be by the press. It was quite a strain on our family at times, totally unexpected and at times overwhelming. It was also very funny sometimes.' *SMH* 'The Good Weekend', 31.10.92.

96. Ashworth quoted in *SMH* 27.4.57.

97. The model was photographed on top of a sheet of frosted glass, that resembled shimmering water. Interestingly, the model was lit from the south, with the shadows of the shells falling on the northern broadwalk, which would never happen in Australia. With the photographs Utzon sent a strange little sketch, of a match-stick man with the top of his skull hinged open, dipping his pen into his brain and signing the word 'Utzon'. Publications on the Opera House have frequently mistakenly reported that this sketch was sent with the competition drawings.

98. SMH 6.7.57.

At an interview with the Premier on 2nd July, the Committee recommended:

> Mr Utzon should be informed forthwith of the Government's intention to proceed with the building of the Opera House. He has already prepared a model of the building which he is willing to bring out at a fortnight's notice... it is proposed that his arrival...will occur not more than one week before the launching of the public appeal, (expected)...probably at the end of July.
>
> M of M of OHC, Ashworth papers.

99. A reporter from the *Australian Women's Weekly* thought 'lanky Jorn Utzon is a young Gary Cooper, only better looking.'

100. *Daily Telegraph* and *SMH* 30.7.57.

101. The route taken by convicts in the early days from transportation ships to Hyde Park Convict Barracks. The Tarpeian Way skirted the Tarpeian Rock, a low rock overlooking the Point which has now been mostly quarried away, which was named by the First Fleeters as a jesting reference to the Tarpeian Rock in Rome from which traitors were flung to their doom.

102. Gavin Souter, a reporter who was there that day at the Point. *SMH* 3.8.57 and 15.10.73. Also *SMH* 31.7.57.

103. Gavin Souter, *SMH* 3.8.57.

104. *SMH* and *Daily Telegraph*, 31.7.57.

105. *SMH* 31.7.57.

106. *Daily Telegraph* 3.8.57.

107. *SMH* and *Telegraph* 7.8.57.

108. *SMH* 1.8.57.

109. Buxtehude was born in Helsingor in 1637 and died in Lubeck in 1707, so 1957 was the 250th anniversary of his death. Music historians record that Bach walked two hundred miles to go to his Lubeck concerts. *Telegraph* 2.8.57. The Town Hall organ is one of the largest functioning pipe organs in the world.

110. Later to be the world-renowned soprano, Joan Sutherland. She was an accomplished violinist and three times New South Wales Woman Golf Champion. When asked on Channel 9's 'Meet the Press' on 22nd May 1960 which she would rather be remembered as, she replied laughing 'I have no doubt on that one. I would be very happy to forget I ever played golf.' In 1949 Goossens conducted one of his own opera compositions, *Judith*, at the Conservatorium of Music with Joan Sutherland (then a young stenographer) in the title role. Hubble. *The Strange Case of Eugene Goossens.*

Irving Lowens, the *Washington Star* critic once wrote, 'I do wish Miss Sutherland would take the hot potato out of her mouth and let us in on what all the excitement is about.' *SMH* 24.12.66.

111. Utzon said he had received 800 letters following the competition.

112. *SMH* and *Telegraph* 8.8.57.

113. *SMH* 8.8.57.

114. The Lord Mayor, Alderman Harold Jensen's nickname was 'Handsome Harry'. Yeomans.

115. Moses recalled, it was 'on the balcony of the Town Hall... (and was) a lot of money. My wife was disgusted with me spending so much...' Moses OHOH tapes.

116. *S.M.H* and other papers 8.8.57.

117. Earlier, during his stay in Sydney, on hearing that there had been opposition to the Opera House when houses were needed, Utzon said, 'Look what bombed-out Western Germany has done. There they have built eight new opera houses since the war ended – and are housing the people too. You can do it here.' *Telegraph* 30.7.57.

118. *SMH* and *Daily Mirror* 19.8.57.

119. *SMH* 24.8.57.

120. *SMH* 22.8.57.

CHAPTER 5
ENTER ARUP

1. Paper read before a joint meeting of the Institution of Structural Engineers, the Cement and Concrete Association and others at the Friends' Meeting House, London. *The Structural Engineer*, May 1956.

2. Ibid.

3. Arup papers. Translated from Danish.

4. From transcript of interview by James Trotter, McGraw-Hill, World News, OAPP (CCAC).

5. Ibid.

6. Arup, *Doodles and Doggerel*.

7. Arup Newsletters, Arup papers.

8. Trotter.

9. Ibid.

10. Ibid.

11. Ibid.

12. Ibid.

13. Ibid.

14. Ibid.

15. Peter Dunican on Ove Arup from an exhibition at the Opera House.

16. Ashworth papers.

17. Ibid.

18. Molnar in *SMH* 15.10.73.

19. Ibid.

20. Ibid.

21. Messent/Molnar interviews.

22. *SMH* 23.3.57.

23. Ibid.
24. Ibid.
25. Ibid.
26. Messent/Molnar interviews
27. 'The conditions of the competition did not call for any consulting engineer to be associated with the competitor when submitting his scheme...'

    Ashworth in answer to a questionnaire on the competition from the UIDA 3.12.58. Ashworth papers.
28. Arup paper on the design and construction of SOH Arup engineer John Nutt later said about the roof; 'Shell structures are difficult because they are delicate, and they don't take to sharp points, like the points of the Opera House on which they're supported; or sharp changes of direction, like happens on the ridges of the Opera House.'

    'Monster or Miracle'.
29. *Sun Herald* 4.11.62.
30. Arup papers.
31. Ove Arup on Utzon to Moses. Moses OHOH tapes.
32. Arup papers.
33. Ibid.
34. Ibid.
35. *Telegraph* 31.7.57.

CHAPTER 6
APPEAL AND LOTTERY

1. According to the OHC Meeting of 12.2.57, over the question of a name 'During discussion members expressed the view that the name "Opera House" may prejudice the view of the public regarding the use of the building in light of the launching of an appeal for funds, and that a press statement should be issued to draw attention to the fact that the building would only be used for opera two months of the year.' Ashworth papers.
2. *Telegraph* 5.8.57.

    Utzon's office also later made a drawing with '...a Notice Board idea containing platform, sign board and donation box in one.' Letter Utzon to Ashworth 29.7.59.
3. *SMH* 16.8.57.
4. *SMH* 27.8.57.
5. *Telegraph* 22.7.57.
6. *SMH* 23.7.57.
7. *SMH* 27.9.57.
8. No names were engraved on brass plates on chairs, but the names of those who made donations to the Appeal Fund are in a book in a glass case in the Opera House foyer, which is turned to a new page daily.

9. *SMH* 3.9.57. Dougherty relinquished his post on 16.12.57.
10. Sydney papers including *SMH* 25.5.58, 3.1.59, 19.6.59, 18.9.59, 3.12.59, 23.8.60; and
    Telegraph 21.8.57 and 14.9.57.
11. *Telegraph* 20.6.58.
12. *Telegraph* 19.9.58.
13. *SMH* 18.7.58.
14. *SMH* 19.9.58.
15. *Sunday Mirror* 19.10.58.
16. *SMH* 17.4.58.
17. *SMH* 8.12.59.
18 Ibid. The Danish community in Sydney helped wherever they could. A concert by members of the Danish Association of NSW of Danish music in the Great Hall of Sydney University raised £700.00. *SMH* 14.4.60.
19. *SMH* 21.11.58.
20. *SMH* 28.5.59.
21. *SMH* 19.6.59.
22. *SMH* 4.9.59, *Telegraph* 4.9.59.
23. Ultimately the amount collected was £49,750.00, with expenses for the special appeal 4 per cent of the amount raised. *SMH* 10.3.60.
24. *Telegraph* 11.11.59
25. *Sydney Truth* 17.2.57.
26. Letter to *SMH* 14.3.60.
27. The original Opera House Committee which drew up the competition guidelines. Moses OHOH tapes.
28. *Sunday Telegraph* 10.2.57.
29. Cahill talking on 12.5.57 from *SMH* 13.5.57.
30. Newspaper cutting, 30.9.57.
31. Most of whom were not worried if the Opera House was built or not but liked a gamble.
    – From a survey on cultural activities in NSW.
32. Labor Premier of NSW at the time of Harbour Bridge construction.
33. *Telegraph* 13.9.57.
34. *SMH* 26.9.57.
35. Opposition to the lotteries continued while the Opera House was under construction, the Rev. Alan Walker, superintendent of the Central Methodist Mission station saying '...built in part on the poverty which gambling creates. I believe the blessing of God is not likely to rest on this so-called cultural centre.' *SMH* 4.11.63.
36. *SMH* 25.11.57.
37. Ibid.
38. *Telegraph* 26.11.57.
39. *Sun* 1.12.57.

40. *Hansard* 26.9.57.
41. *Sun Herald* 30.3.58.
42. *SMH* 23.2.60.
43. *SMH* 2.6.60.
44. *SMH* 8.7.60.
45. *SMH* 30.3.61.

CHAPTER 7
THE PODIUM

1. H. Purdy of Chatswood, *SMH* 13.2.59.
2. *SMH* 5.5.59. Utzon talking to the Opera House Appeal Fund Committee.
3. Utzon talking in the BBC documentary 'The Building that Nearly Was.'
4. Ibid.
5. Typed article by Utzon for *Zodiac*, undated but with 1961 letters; Utzon papers.
6. *Australian* 9.10.95.
7. Utzon to Ron Iredale, *Australian* 27.12.69.
8. Utzon in 'Platforms and Plateaus', *Zodiac*.
9. Undated report, Utzon papers.
10. *Australian* 27.12.69.
11. Utzon from 'The Fifth Facade' TV film. Utzon made a black and white picture of the great expanse of stairs into a jigsaw puzzle which he used to confound his friends.
12. *Sun Herald* 9.12.62.
13. *Telegraph* 20.2.63.
14. According to an undated paper in the Utzon papers, Utzon wrote on the corridors:
     They are formed by the local carrying walls which in their turn take shape and position from the two auditoria on top of the base.
     ... because of the ever varying width and constantly altering shape of the corridors... a system of elements has been invented based on the simple fact that two elements connected by a flexible limb, can assume any position within their total length just as the human arm and hand, made of a series of elements connected with flexible limbs can assume any position within full reach of the arm. A new single, highly, versatile component within the existing family of architectural elements.
15. They were travelling without Eric Andersson who was never seen nor heard of again.
16. *SMH* 27.3.58.
17. This later became 3 stages, with stage 2 the shells and stage 3 the interiors.
18. Ashworth in *SMH* 23.7.57.
19. *SMH* 3.7.58. Apparently on Cahill's wishes for a theatre to seat 430 'to satisfy the needs of their many amateur theatrical societies.' Hubble, *The*

Strange Case of Eugene Goossens.
20. Arup papers.
21. *Sun Herald* 17.8.58.
22. Arup papers.
23. Ibid.
24. Copy of contract in Arup papers.
25. Memorandum of Agreement between Ove Arup and Partners and MacDonald Wagner and Priddle.
26. Letter Ron Jenkins to partners from Sydney, 11.11.58. Arup papers.
27. Letter Ove Arup to Utzon 15.8.58. Arup papers. Ove Arup also tried without success to have his old company Christiani and Nielsen tender for the work. According to Zunz in the OHOH tapes: MacDonald Wagner and Priddle 'knew the Australian scene, and in that context, they were very against Civil and Civic in the first place, and they tried not to have Civil and Civic appointed.'
28. Ove Arup to the Committee 29.10.58. Arup papers.
29. Letter from the Committee to tenderers. Copy in Arup papers.
30. *SMH* 19.11.58.
31. *Telegraph* 19.11.58.
32. Roy Grounds of Grounds, Romberg and Boyd, Melbourne. *SMH* 29.1.59.
33. The other tenders were:
    John Holland Constructions Pty Ltd. £1,609,707.00.
    Hornibrook, McKenzie Clark Pty Ltd, £1,616,060.00.
    Fletcher Constructions Co. Pty Ltd. £1,798,381.00.
    Electric Power Transmission Pty Ltd. £2,202,027.00.
    McDonald Constructions Pty Ltd. £2,227,781.00.
34. *SMH* 23.1.59.
35. F.J. Madigan to *SMH* 27.1.59.
36. *SMH* 4.2.59.
37. *Telegraph.*
38. *SMH* 12.6.58.
39. *Telegraph* 25.7.58.
40. Contract price for the demolition was £895.00. *Hansard* 25.11.58.
41. *Telegraph* 5.12.58. Demolition of the Fort was completed in time for the signing of the construction contract, though it was only in January 1964 that it was announced the destination signs on buses would be changed from 'Fort Macquarie' to 'Opera House.' 'Fort Macquarie has lost its identity' said Mr Berry, Commissioner for Government Transport on announcing the change.
42. Ashworth papers, quoting from *Hansard.*
43. Ashworth to Jenkins 18.3.59. Arup papers.
44. *SMH* 3.3.59.

45. After the ceremony the workers packed up and went home. The real work on site did not start until two months later.
46. *SMH* 3.3.59.
47. *Telegraph* 3.3.59.
48. *SMH* 3.3.59.
49. The position of the plaque at the opening ceremony was intended to be at the bottom of the podium steps at the point where the lines drawn through the apex of the two main sets of shells crossed over. The theatres are placed side by side on the podium, but on a converging axis. The plaque was made by Utzon from the bronze for a propeller in one of the Helsingor shipyards. As events turned out, the cross-hairs on the plaque were never used by surveyors, who established their own survey marks on other parts of the site. The plaque was moved from shed to shed until it was unearthed and put in place ready for the Opera House opening, but in a position on the landing above the first flight of steps because the Committee had decreased the rake of the stairs. It is still at the intersection of the two roof lines though.
50. *SMH* 3.3.59.
51. *SMH* 14.3.59.
52. *SMH* 6.2.59.
53. Newspapers.
54. Moses on 22.10.59. *SMH* 23.10.59.
55. *SMH* 28.10.59.
56. Moses OHOH tapes. Though the name was never used.
57. Utzon on leaving Sydney 4.2.60, reported in the *Telegraph* 5.2.60. Utzon also said 'I believe we have turned the corner on the most difficult of our problems.'
58. *SMH* 4.9.59.
59. Newspapers December 1959.
60. *Telegraph* 12.4.60.
61. *Daily Mirror* 12.4.61.
62. *New York Times* 19.2.61.
63. *Sun Herald* 28.5.61.
64. Ove Arup from 'The Building that Nearly Was.'
65. Ove Arup in an article on 'Problems and Progress in the Construction of Sydney Opera House.' *Civil Engineering*, February 1965.

    Arup wrote on this subject to Ashworth in a private and confidential letter on 14th December 1960.

    As you know, nearly all our troubles with the contractor stem from the political decision to start work on the site long before anybody had any clear conception of what was going to be built. When I was in Sydney with Jorn on the presentation of the sketch scheme in April, '58 no work at all had been done on the structure, on the heating or the services, and nobody knew what stage technique would be required. The sketch scheme was materially altered at that meeting and yet we were confronted with the proposition to get the tender documents out before Christmas and to start work early in 1959 so that the Foundation Stone could be laid in February.

I said at the time that if we divided the Contract into two parts, the first being only the structural concrete work on the sub-structure and if we had the architectural information necessary to design this structure by something like the end of July, 1958, and if, further, we could resort to the expedient of inviting tenders on the basis of an approximate bill of quantities which would give us the rates, then we would be able to start the Contract by the desired time, but I pointed out that it was a most undesirable thing to do and would undoubtedly create serious difficulties. Actually the architectural information was not forthcoming in July 1958 but more than two years later, and the whole job proved to be much more complicated than anybody had anticipated. Now it is I think evident to everybody that it was madness to start work so early, but at the time we were confronted with the choice of starting then or probably not starting at all, and we had to make the best of a bad situation, which incidentally I think both the Architects and we have done.
Arup papers.

66. Arup papers.
67. Ibid.
68. Ibid.
69. Summary of telephone call, Nicklin to Arups 1.12.59. Arup papers.
70. 16.12.59. Arup papers.
71. Arup papers.
72. Ibid.
73. *Engineers General Report No. 1*. Ashworth papers.
74. Ibid.
75. Ibid.
76. Messent/Kelman interviews.
77. Arup papers.
78. Ibid.
79. Ibid.
80. Kelman OHOH tapes.
81. Arup papers.
82. MacKenzie OHOH tapes.
83. Ashworth papers.
84. Arup cable to Committee 17.4.59. Arup papers.
85. MacKenzie went to Sydney for what he thought would be 18 months, but which in fact ran to four and a half years before he went back to London England instead of on to New Zealand. In June 1961 he committed the

dire crime of getting married without telling the London staff. 'We were shaken to hear of Ian's wedding over here' wrote Kelman from London on 16th June to Alan Levy in Sydney 'and Hobbs severely censured you for not informing us so that the firm could have taken the appropriate action on such occasions.' Ove Arup himself wrote to Ian MacKenzie a few days later 'We have just heard that you have got married, and my partners and I would like to send you our congratulations and best wishes for the future. We have asked Alan Levy if he will very kindly try to find on our behalf a present that you and your wife will like... I look forward to meeting your wife when I come again to Sydney.' Arup papers.

MacKenzie's wife Anne used to tell him that his first love was the Opera House, his second love was the dog and his third love was her. MacKenzie OHOH tapes.

86. MacKenzie to Hobbs. Arup papers.
87. MacKenzie OHOH tapes.
88. Ibid.
89. Ibid.
90. Minutes of meeting of TAP 25.9.59. Arup papers.
91. Jenkins to Nicklin 11.11.59. Arup papers.
92. *The Architects Journal* 23.2.61.
93. 'Constructing the pier foundations of Sydney Opera House', *Contracting and Construction Equipment*,
March 1962.
94. MacKenzie OHOH tapes.
95. Ibid.
96. Letters Nielsen to Utzon, Utzon papers.

CHAPTER 8
A CASE FOR ARBITRATION – THE FOLDED SLAB

1. The shape of the beams of the vehicle concourse are a work of art, and to view them from beneath the vehicle concourse and follow them up the stairs to the entrance canopies beneath the shells produces an awe-inspiring feeling.

Ian MacKenzie thought Utzon as an architect was:

Fabulous. No question. He could think in three dimensions, and a lot of architects can't. He had a marvellous creative mind, and his concept for things – and his ideas for doing things were – well they were psychological. One that I can always recall is, if you are down in the vehicle concourse there, which was... always intended that that was where he envisaged people being dropped from cars and then (finding)... their way... up to the auditoriums. And he liked clean simple things, and I remember him saying to me at one stage, that he abhorred the idea of having to have lots of signposts and notices... down there, saying 'Up here to the Concert Hall', (or) 'Up here to the restaurant'... He said he would much prefer it if people got there and... automatically went in the right direction. And I remember him telling me that he had read of some experiments that had been done with rats – they'd put rats in a large box with two exits from it, one of which was a tunnel which had parallel walls, and one which was a tunnel which had walls that tapered into a smaller opening, so that if you went down there you were going into a funnel. And the majority of rats went down that smaller one, that tapered into a funnel. And he felt, that if rats did that, mice did that, then people might do the same thing.

But in practical terms, you can't – so he thought, well, if my... access stairs that go off the vehicle concourse do that, then people will go (up) there, rather than for example, try and come in through the central passage where the Stage Door is. Because that (is a vehicle access) so it must have parallel sides. But on the other hand, you can't taper in walls like that, because if you've got crowds of people coming in, you just end up with a traffic jam.

But if you come up those stairs now, and look at them, you'll find that the roof drops down. And there is a funnel effect... there. And that was his explanation of why, in fact, that particular geometry evolved there. And he had... that sort of mind. Now, whether that was cause or effect, I don't know. MacKenzie OHOH tapes.

2. Alan Levy in his 'Design Synopsis on the Folded Slab' called this 'a high length to depth ratio.'

3. The evolution and design of the Concourse at the Sydney Opera House. By Ove Arup and Ron Jenkins.

4. Ibid.

5. '... a highly interesting and dynamic system of lines sweeping and falling at support and knee, merging and rising at centrespan.' Levy.

The Architects Journal (23.2.61) felt that 'The mathematical expressiveness of the slab design meant the shape of the folded slab seen from below was 'shaped like the hulls of racing canoes to match the change from maximum positive bending to maximum negative bending.'

6. A scale model was made by Bondaglass and cost £99 13s 0d.

7. Evolution of Concourse. Arup & Jenkins.

8. 'The original intention was to absorb the vertical and horizontal thrusts at the foot of the folded slab on stable Sydney Sandstone. Detailed soil exploration however, revealed large pockets of shale as well as clay seams (of thickness varying from one inch to six inches), incapable of absorbing the large horizontal thrust...' Levy.

9. Evolution of Concourse. Arup & Jenkins.

10. Ibid.

11. '... The prestressed force jacked into the tie beams exceeded somewhat

the maximum horizontal thrust for which the folded slab was designed... The application of the horizontal thrust using the ship-jacks permitted a folded slab design of greater flexibility.' Levy.

12. In fact it was more like 10 years!

13. This description of the folded slab is from 'The evolution and design of the Concourse at the Sydney Opera House' by Ove Arup and Ron Jenkins. The paper contains a more complete description of the technical details of the design.

   The folded slab when completed comprised of 50 adjacent folded beams, 6 ft wide up to 4 ft 6 in deep, with some spans extending up to 160 feet without support. The beams at the east end of the concourse covered a longer span than those at the west, and were slightly deeper, so that the roof level at the east end was a few inches lower. Traffic approached the concourse from the west end, and vans with a high top drove cheerfully beneath the concourse then jammed under the lower beams at the east end. Today at the Opera House gate the security guard checks all vehicles entering against a horizontal plastic height marker to ensure they can clear the concourse.

14. Arup papers.

   Stressing increases the strength of the concrete. A concrete beam under compression with stressing cables at each end can support a heavier load than one without them. The principle is similar to if one picks up a row of 5 or 6 bricks or books; as outlined by Utzon.

   'Another comparison is a bookase full of books on the shelves. If a delicate housewife pulls out, say five heavy books at the time, she will probably drop them, since she cannot support the ones in the middle. Her bigger and stronger husband, however, may be able to take more than ten books at one time since he can press them together so that they remain in one row.' Undated note in the Utzon papers.

15. MacKenzie to Jenkins, 26.5.60. Arup papers.

16. Arup papers.

17. Ibid.

18. Ibid.

19. The repairwork on the beam can be seen in the Exhibition Hall off the Opera House foyer.

20. Arup papers.

21. Ibid.

22. Ibid.

23. Utzon papers.

24. Arup papers.

25. Ibid.

26. Ibid.

27. Ibid.

28. Skead to Levy 13.4.61. Arup papers.
29. Kelman to Levy 11.4.61. Arup papers.
30. Arup papers.
31. Ibid.
32. Levy to Arups 14.6.61. Arup papers.
33. Arup papers.
34. 14.8.61. Arup papers.
35. Arup papers.
36. Ibid.
37. Arup papers.
38. *Consulting Engineers' General Report No. 1.* 1961. Ashworth papers.
39. MacKenzie to Jenkins 6.7.59. Arup papers.
40. 5.8.59. Arup papers.
41. 17.11.59. Arup papers.
42. Newspapers, December 1959.
43. 5.12.60. Arup papers.
44. 6.12.60. Arup papers.
45. Engineers' Report No. 1. Ashworth papers.
46. MacDonald Wagner & Priddle to Civil & Civic 10.8.61. Arup papers.
47. MacDonald Wagner & Priddle to Civil & Civic 20.8.62. Arup papers.
48. Utzon to Dusseldorp of Civil & Civic, 12.9.61. Arup papers.
49. Nielsen to Utzon. 21.1.61. Arup papers.
      Also, Civil & Civic to MacDonald, Wagner & Priddle 26.1.62, 'The tolerances demanded by the Engineers in line, level and angle is far in excess of that covered by the Bill of quantities and is more consistent with precision joinery or cabinet making rather than formwork.' Arup papers.
50. 27.1.61. Arup papers.
51. Minutes of meetings on Utzon's visit to Sydney, March-April 1961. Arup papers.
52. Nielsen to Utzon 13.8.61. Utzon papers.
      The question of whether Civil & Civic should complete the type 'C' work above + 42 level was discussed by Rider Hunt & Partners, Utzon and Arups on 31.8.61 at Arups. According to the Minutes of the Meeting:
      Mr Utzon said he was doubtful whether extra payment would in itself produce satisfactory workmanship.
      Mr Arup said a decision should be made as to whether Civil and Civic complete the work above + 42 level. Mr Utzon said that provided a satisfactory degree of workmanship would be guaranteed he would agree to this, provided always that a firm line would be taken on the question of extra payments. He said also that it might be necessary to supplement the site supervisory staff to ensure that the finish of work was satisfactory.
      Utzon papers.
53. Nielsen to Utzon 17.8.61. Utzon papers.

54. 17.8.61. Arup papers.

Though Civil & Civic would not necessarily have been asked to produce extra work not in the original tender where that work wasn't at economic rates. Wagner of MacDonald, Wagner & Priddle and Hobbs of Arups discussed this, Wagner writing on 29.8.61: '...Mr Hobbs and I agreed that C & C could not be asked to carry out extensive additional work at the tendered schedule rate where it can be established that this rate is not a profitable one. We consider however, that tendered rates should apply for all original scheduled work...'

Arup papers.

55. Arup papers.
56. MacKenzie to London 12.9.61.
57. Summary of Utzon/Zunz visit, Arup papers.

On 10th April at his last official meeting before leaving Sydney, Utzon saw the quantity surveyors and it was agreed 'The formwork in position but not to be used would be measured and valued at cost price.'

Summary of Utzon/Zunz visit, Arup papers.

58. Ibid.
59. Ibid.
60. Ibid.
61. Ibid.
62. Nielsen to Utzon 18.4.62. Arup papers.
63. Summary of Meeting 29.5.62. Arup papers.
64. Zunz to MacKenzie 30.5.62. Arup papers.
65. Arup papers.
66. Arup papers.
67. Rigby to Kelman, 11.9.62. Arup papers.
68. Nicklin to Kelman 7.9.62. Arup papers.
69. 21.9.62. Arup papers.
70. Arup papers.
71. Ibid.
72. Zunz to Nicklin 30.10.62. Arup papers.
73. 19.10.62. Arup papers.
74. Rigby to London 15.3.63. Arup papers.
75. Rigby-Zunz letters, Arup papers.
76. Arup papers.
77. Ibid.
78. 'It was so complicated. And the issue which was going to be arbitrated on was really only the tip of the iceberg.' Zunz OHOH tapes.
79. Kelman to Zunz. Arup papers.
80. Ibid.
81. Kelman to Arups 18.1.63. Corbet Gore the construction manager for Hornibrooks who built the shells thought the basis of the trouble in

regard to the quality of the work Civil & Civic had to produce was there was an 'incomplete understanding of what was expected of them.' Messent/Gore interviews.

82. Zunz to Utzon 21.1.63. Arup papers.
83. Nigel Bowen was later Foreign Minister in the Commonwealth government. When Bowen could not take the role of leading Counsel, it came to John Kerr, then a very successful barrister, and his junior was Tony Mason. John Kerr, later Sir John Kerr, went on to become the Governor General, and was a central figure with Fraser in the sacking of the Whitlam government. Mason, who was also knighted, became Sir Anthony Mason the Chief Justice, 'so it was a very distinguished legal team.' Zunz OHOH tapes.
84. Minutes of meeting in London on Arbitration, 6.2.63. Arup papers.
85. Bob Kelman wrote to London on 12.2.63:

   When booking in Ove Arup's name, the comment was 'sounds like a Scotsman!' 'No', I expostulated, in both Mr Arup's and Scotland's interest, 'it is a Danish name.' 'Oh,' was the reply, 'must be of Irish extraction!!'
   Arup papers.
86. Zunz OHOH tapes.
87. Zunz to Hobbs, Arup papers.
88. Rigby to London 15.3.63. Arup papers.
89. Sydney Opera House : Claims by Civil & Civic, PWP 4.4.63.
90. When the author met Jack Zunz in London in 1992, he said if the Arbitration hearing had continued 'We'd still be sitting there today.'
91. Sydney Opera House : Claims by Civil and Civic. PWP 4.4.63. On 9th April the Secretary of Public Works wrote to the Crown Solicitor '... For the purposes of settlement, I enclose herewith the executed counterpart Release, with a cheque in favour of Civil & Civic Pty Ltd. for £537,551 17s 6d.'
92. Minutes of SOHEC meeting 16.4.63. Arup papers.
93. *Telegraph* 11.4.63.
94. Rigby to Osborne, 25.4.63. Arup papers.
95. 28.3.63. Arup papers.
96. Messent/Zunz interviews.

   Though Arups had little to celebrate financially on the job so far. On 18th October 1962 Miss Mant sent an internal memo to Jack Zunz of engineering work on the Sydney Opera House with an estimate of '... a total calculated loss of £26,223 to the 31.3.62.' Zunz wrote to the Committee on 22.5.63 '... During recent discussions with the Technical Panel we referred to the financial strain to which we have been submitted as a result of this project. We stated that while we generally wished to avoid asking for fees as a result of modifications and alterations, we might be forced to do so in this instance in accordance with Clause 13 of our Agreement.' Costs sustained for which they had not claimed included fares for staff for 32 trips to Denmark and associated out-of-pocket expenses and living expenses. Arup papers.

97. Arup papers.
98. Zunz to Nicklin 29.4.63. Arup papers.
99. Dated 9.4.63. Arup papers.
100. *Arup Newsletter*, May 1963, Arup papers.
101. Utzon Descriptive Narrative, 1965, PWP.

CHAPTER 9
THE DESIGN OF THE SHELLS

1. Plato c. 428-347BC.
2. Utzon writing in *Zodiac* No. 14.
3. Utzon talking on the shells.
4. Utzon to Ron Iredale, *Australian* 27.12.69.
5. Jack Zunz talking to other partners, *Arup Newsletters*. Arup papers.
6. Ove Arup in the Danish paper Berlingske Tidende. Utzon papers.
7. Ove Arup in the BBC documentary 'The Building that Nearly Was'.
8. Arups paper on Design and Construction of the Opera House.
9. Zunz roof report.
10. Ove Arup, *Australian* 19.10.73.
11. Arups paper on Design and Construction.
12. *Australian* 19.10.73.
13. Isaacs to Ove Arup 14.10.57. Arup papers.
14. Ibid.
15. Arup papers.
16. Ove Arup to Utzon, 23.12.57. Arup papers.
17. Messent/Blanchard interviews.
18. Arup papers.
19. Ibid.
20. Arup papers.
21. *Telegraph* 2.4.58.
22. 6.8.58. Arup papers.
    Ove Arup came out to Denmark again at the end of December to see Utzon and the mechanical engineers Steensen and Varming, then wrote from London asking Utzon when he would be going out to Sydney again, the letter closing 'P.S. I lost my golden ball-pen the last day I was with you, and it must either have been left in your office or perhaps at Varmings. If you find it keep it for me because I am very used to it and I can't get one like it here.' Arup papers 29.12.58.
23. 1.10.58. Arup papers.
24 11.12.58. Arup papers.

25. Ibid.
26. Letter to Arups 5.1.59. Arup papers.
27. Zunz roof report
28. Molman to Ahm 21.8.59. Arup papers.
29. Kelman to Sydney staff, 9.2.60. Arup papers.
30. Ibid.
31. MOAP 24.8.60. Utzon papers.
32. Arup papers.
33. M of M Hellebaek 12.1.61. Arup papers.
34. Arup Report on the Roof Structure.
35. Ibid.
36. Arup papers.
37. Tenders had been called for the stage machinery in May 1960. Utzon and Arups had done some early development work on the stage machinery requirements with M.A.N., but Waagner Biro won the contract to design and build them working with the stage technique consultant, Professor Unruh.
38. Arup papers.
39. Ibid.
40. Ibid.
41. Ibid.
42. Consulting Engineers' *General Report No. 1*. Arup papers. Also, according to Jack Zunz in his roof report regarding wind tunnel tests,
The wind pressure distribution on structures is only known for simple shapes. However, in most practical structures it is reasonable to make approximations based on precedence, on interpolation or the application of standard Codes of Practice. In the case of the shells for the Sydney Opera House, however, the scale was so large, and the shape so unusual, that we thought it essential to carry out a series of tests on a model, specially constructed for the purpose, in a wind tunnel...

The model is 1/96 full size, which means it is approximately 3 ft 8 in long and the height of the tallest shell is 2 ft. It is constructed of solid wood. The details and method of testing are beyond the scope of this report. However, the method of measuring wind pressures is interesting. Small 1/8 in diameter grooves were cut in the surfaces of these shells, parallel to the ridge line. Nylon wires were laid in these grooves, which were then filled with resin and the nylon wire withdrawn, leaving small diameter holes at the bottom of the grooves. These holes were connected by rubber tubes to manometers where pressure readings were photographed.

The first series of tests were carried out in the wind tunnel of Southampton University in January and February 1960. This was a convenient location – we had a team there working on other researches for the roof structure. The tunnel size was 4 ft x 4 ft, so that the model became fairly large in relation to the cross-sectional area of the tunnel. This led us later to carry out a further series of tests at the National Physical Laboratory in a larger tunnel so that the interference between the model and the walls of the tunnel, and subsequent errors in the results could be eliminated.

The model was placed in the tunnel at various angles in relation to the wind direction and pressure and suction distribution profiles for the roof structure were plotted for each different position.

43. *Pix* magazine.
44. The quotes were from Waagner Biro in Vienna and Sir William Arrol & Company Ltd of Glasgow 'Bridge Builders, Structural & Mechanical Engineers and Crane Makers.' Arrol's price for the 16 bearings including cost, insurance and freight to Sydney was £33,878. Arup papers.
45. Waagner Biro to Arups. Utzon papers.
46. In effect this meant the contractor would complete the job at cost, plus a management fee.
47. Jenkins to the Committee, 20.4.61. Arup papers.
48. Ibid.
49. 4.5.61. Arup papers.
50. M of M Hellebaek 10.5.61. Utzon papers.
51. 23.5.61. Arup papers. Also, '...the shape of the original shells was quite unstructural – and I personally, was surprised then that we went as far as we did with that shape, because I felt that any reasonably informed engineer, would recognize that the form (the shell)... had, of the sharp curve down near... the support point of the shell would generate enormous moments, and that's exactly one of the problems that happened, that the thing had a sharp kink at the bottom and it was virtually impossible to design, we then straightened it up... with a direct thrust line down the abutment of the shell.' Kelman OHOH tapes.
52. Nicklin to Jenkins. Arup papers.
53. MacKenzie said that if the job had gone out to tender:
    '... any contractor pricing it would have... been so uncertain about how to do it, that he would... have loaded his price enormously to make allowance for the uncertainties – the problems that he was bound to have but that he couldn't foresee... We felt that that was... not going to be the right way to do it. You were going to lock the builder into a price, and if he saw that halfway through the job he was going to be losing money on it, then we were going to have a dreadful problem... So what was done, was... to convince the Client... that you should take that worry away from him, that if we worked in close co-operation with the builder... it would end up with the cheapest job. So (the builder) should be paid a management fee for his time and for his effort, and the costs would be... paid direct by the client.' MacKenzie OHOH tapes. Zunz felt the

negotiated contract with Hornibrooks 'was the best decision that was ever taken, because without it I don't think we could have ever built the Opera House roof.' Zunz OHOH tapes.

54. Arup papers.
55. Waagner Biro to Utzon 14.6.61. Utzon papers.
56. Jenkins to Ashworth 15.6.61. Arup papers. Arup's development work on the design of the shells was outlined in a report:

Early structural solutions made use of every possible source of strength in the scheme. All four sets of main shells, together with their side shells, were interconnected. The so-called louvre walls, the cross-walls closing the opening between the two shells of a pair, were a vital part of the continuity between shells. This structural interdependence, while necessary for stability, introduced gigantic analytical complications and made the model analysis necessary as a basis of establishing forces and moments as well as column and foundation loads...

As the design was developed, the geometry underwent several detailed changes. The side shell geometry was changed from parabolas to elliptic paraboloids, and then the whole shell geometry was changed to ellipsoids, after investigation into other suitable mathematical forms. These changes were generally made to facilitate calculations and had little, if any, visual effect. All schemes envisaged continuous surfaces rigidly inter-connected. Zunz roof report.

57. Arup papers.
58. Arup papers.
59. Waagner Biro to Utzon 17.8.61. Utzon papers.
60. Arup papers.
61. Some of the difficulties Arups struck on the analysis of the shells were outlined in a separate technical report. Its date and author is not known.

In the question of structural inadequacy one of the most important aspects was the presence of the louvre connections. The louvres and the vertical tangents were removed simultaneously. The vertical tangents produce overstressing on A4. The louvre walls increased the longitudinal stiffness and attracted load from A3 which led us to deduce very high shear forces at the louvre-A2 boundary. We could not measure these shears, nor could we calculate them, but the magnitude of the shears we deduced were larger than we could carry...

Apart from the strain on the structure, the column loads and the tie forces, things measured included the rotation of the hinges both in the direction parallel to the axis of the whole and a direction at right angles to the axis of the whole. Also the effect of wind load. It is worth noting that we went to considerable trouble to ensure that the column loads were realistic.

We also did quite a bit of work analysing the results that the model test gave – particularly we took cross sections through the shell, and checked for the external and internal equilibrium. In fact the two things that the model test revealed were (1) that vertical tangents at the support points were wrong and would not work – though I think we could probably have got this result from calculations in any case – and (2) that the whole structure was longitudinally very much stiffer than we had supposed. This meant that very much more load was being transferred to the back stage wall and furthermore we could not always see how this transference was taking place... Arup papers.

62. Mike Lewis explained this by saying that a pure single skin shell '... really is rather amorphous when you see it on the (inside) surface, because it's very ill-defined, it's just a sort of rounded shape – it's O.K. from the outside, but the inside tends to be rather amorphous looking. And when you look at the Eero Saarinen job that he did for the TWA Terminal in New York, it really is very unpleasing from the inside... (but) very dramatic outside.' Lewis OHOH tapes.

63. Zunz roof report.

64. Zunz OHOH tapes.

65. Ibid.

66. Jack Zunz writing in a book on Ove Arup published by the Insitution of Civil Engineers for the centenary of his birth.

67. Zunz OHOH tapes.

68. Ibid.

69. Ibid.

70. Ibid.

71. Messent/Zunz correspondence.

72. Messent/Zunz interviews.

73. Ibid. Zunz continued. 'I think it could have been simplified. I think Ronald Jenkins had got himself slightly tied up because while today (1992) it wouldn't present us with such a huge problem, but at the time the analytical work involved in solving this was in theoretically establishing how the forces were distributed over this structure and it was extremely difficult... Ronald was one of the foremost analysts of the day and he felt at the time he thought he could solve this particular problem, and I think he ran into some difficulties.'

74. This meant that, concerning the halls, instead of two structures on the top of the podium there were now six. Each set of shells for the halls were three separate structures, which did not touch and rested on their own foundations. One set of shells no longer depended on the adjoining shell for its strength, though later non-structural bronze louvres filled the spaces at the northward openings of the shells. This separation of the structures came some time after Arup first asked Zunz to look at a folded scheme: '... that is something which I introduced. I mean it is not a

question of personalising who said what and who did what. I dislike that actually. Everybody contributed to it.' Zunz/Messent interviews.

75. Arup Report on the Shells.

76. Huang, 28 at the time, was a Hong Kong Chinese Catholic with engineering degrees from the Sorbonne in Paris and from an English university. '... quite an interesting chap' and 'a very bright man' recalled Zunz.

77. Zunz/Messent interviews.

78. Ibid.

79. Ove Arup talking.

80. Messent/Zunz interviews.

81. Petersen to Waagner Biro 25.8.61. Utzon papers.

82. Zunz OHOH tapes.

83. Messent/Zunz interviews.

84. Zunz roof report.
Also : 'Utzon... was a great one for what he called integrity of material and he felt that steel was steel and concrete was concrete and that it was a betrayal of a good architectural principle to make a... steel roof and then put concrete on it and pretend it was concrete.' Messent/Gore interviews.

85. Zunz roof report.

86. Arup paper on Design and Construction of the Opera House Shells. '(But) a steel structure with a concrete face, now that would have been quicker, much cheaper to build of course.' Zunz OHOH tapes.

87. Messent/Zunz interviews.

88. *Good Weekend* 31.10.92.

89. *SMH* 15.10.73.

90. *Utzon and the Sydney Opera House.* Duek-Cohen.

91. Much was made later of just who had the idea of the spherical solution for the shells. Utzon was always quite adamant that the idea was his, and that he got the idea from looking at the curved shape of ships' hulls in the shipyard at Elsinore. Kelman too credits Utzon with coming up with the spherical solution. OHOH tapes. '... and Arups were certainly very glad when he did'. Messent/ Kelman interviews.
Lewis recalled that Utzon 'was told by a number of people, that if he would change the geometric criteria, that we could use the spherical form, which would standardise the ribs. And, you know, he said : "No, you can't do that." And then, surprise, surprise, he said, "Yes, you can." Lewis OHOH tapes. And Gore was 'told that Arup did consider a spherical solution in (the early) days, but because it was outside the brief they had from the Architect they discarded it.' Messent/Gore interviews. Ove Arup told Ron Gilling in 1966 that Arups had considered a spherical scheme two years before Utzon announced his solution on the shells. Messent/Gilling interviews. Jack Zunz said to the author concerning the

spherical solution, 'We led him to the water and he drank.'

Certainly to build the ribs with an ellipse as the geometry of the shells, each would have been different radii, and different formwork would have been needed for each, which would have been extremely difficult to construct 'so much so that I think it would have made it impossible.' Messent/Blanchard interviews.

According to a report in the Arup papers :

... all attempts at a geometry before Utzon produced the spherical solution had aimed at preserving two things. (1) Utzon's ridge outline: this was of decreasing curvature from the base and in this respect the ellipses did not exactly fit Utzon's desires. (2) that boundaries, such as 'front' end and side shell/main shell boundaries should be a straight line on elevation and planar (i.e. both halves of boundary contained in the same place). These facts precluded O.A.P. thinking of the spherical solution first.

Whatever the rights and wrongs of it, it entered popular folklore that Utzon solved the shells. A version of events that sits quite happily with Utzon who later remarked 'Arups couldn't do it.' Possibly a fair way to put it would be that Arups offered Utzon the solution and he accepted it.

But when it came down to it did it really matter *whose* idea it was? The folded spherical concrete shells were the solution Utzon wanted, the one he got, and the one that was built. According to Jack Zunz in a letter to the author on the development of the shell design.

The important points to any interested reader are :
• Utzon's competition scheme for the roofs had no geometric order – they were free shapes.
• Our firm (Arup and Jenkins) suggested that geometric order be brought to bear on these shapes. These followed as closely as possible the shapes which Utzon wanted. A definable geometry would help design and construction.
• A number of three dimensional geometrical orders were studied.
• Utzon is a very brilliant designer and quickly absorbed the possibilities of geometric order. Its aesthetic benefits appealed to him and he subsequently attempted to use all kinds of geometric interventions in the designs for the window walls and the interiors.
• Our role was to try and meet his aesthetic requirements while developing a viable structural system.
• The change to a spherical geometry could only have been made by him. It changed the appearance of the building radically to the extent that there were and probably still are a number of people who preferred the rather softer contours of the pre-spherical schemes.
• It is regrettable that he now appears to say that he had to solve our problems for us. This simply was not the case. At the time the collabo-

ration between us was creative and stimulating to the extent that he said to me how exciting it was that he and we (Arups) were able to force the best out of one another – a statement with which I agreed.

92. Some notes at Arups give an idea of how this figure of 246 ft was reached.

'The Architect first produced free hand sketches of the shells from which the relative dimensions between Crown, Springing and Upper Ridge Points were scaled.

With the conditions that all the shells were to have a common radius and that the crown and springing points were not to be shifted a great deal a series of calculations of the shells were made based on sphere radii ranging from 240 ft to 250 ft.

The results were plotted on a sketch for the Architect's reference. With greater emphasis on the shape of the ridge curves, the Architect chose the scheme with sphere radius of 246 feet...

Preliminary structural analysis of the longest rib of shell A2 indicated that the minimum depth of rib required was 8 ft 6 in at the crown and 4 ft 6 in at the base...' From an undated report on the geometry of the spherical shells.

Concerning the rib angle – effectively the angle between lines of longitude if the springing point of the shells is considered as the pole of a globe and the lines of the ribs are considered as lines of longitude as they increase in width the higher they go on the spherical surface of the shells:

'The rib angle was initially chosen as 3.7° based on the maximum practical width of a tile panel for the longest rib in shell A2. Then we received Utzon's free hand sketches of both major and minor halls showing the lower and upper boundary planes of all the shells. From the scaled dimensions of these sketches, we computed the angles contained by these planes. We also found by successive trial and error that the nearest rib angle which will form a multiple of the total shell angles was 3.65° with the adjustment of some shells, of course.' And to achieve the change in depth of rib segments between the pedestal and crown, 'The inner circle was chosen based on, firstly, a minimum structural depth of the pedestal at the springing point and, secondly, a minimum depth at the crown of the longest rib of shell A2 so that it will give a nice looking Y shape section with 45° inclined sides. Through these two points a circle of radius 246 ft was drawn, which we called the inner circle.

There was no predetermined depth of rib at any preset arc length... Later we found that some shells need not have such thick ribs structurally, such as shells 1, 4, etc. We merely increased the radius of the inner circle to 247ft or, more keeping the outer... (circle) unchanged.' Joe Huang to John Melling in London, Arup papers 30.5.66.

93. Ove Arup talking.
94. *Zodiac* No. 14.

95. Ove Arup to Utzon 25.2.66. Also : '… it's perfectly true that in 1961 there was a hiatus in this firm as to which way we should go to solve the problem (of the shells) and we came to the cross roads and we went down different routes… You know a great deal of fuss has been made about this internal problem, but every major project (involving)… people in a large organisation like this one (concerning huge technical problems leads to)… different points of view. Some say they have a sensible solution, some say they doubt them and this is the nature of the work.' Messent/Zunz interviews.

96. Kelman OHOH tapes.

97. Lewis OHOH tapes.

98. Arup papers.

99. Ashworth papers.

100. Arup papers.

101. The letter was actually sent on 21st November – see later reference on covering letter.

102. Arup papers.

103. Committee to Arups. Arup papers.

104. Hornibrook to Arups. Arup papers.

105. Ibid.

106. Arup papers.

107. Ashworth papers.

108. *Sun Herald* 4.11.62.

109. Ibid.

110. Arup papers.

111. Arup papers.

112. Zunz, summary of meetings in Hellebaek week starting 4th December. 13.12.61. Arup papers.

113. Ashworth papers.

114. Arup papers.

115. Ove Arup's personal papers, Churchill College Cambridge. Ashworth to Ove Arup. 5.1.62.

116. Ibid.

117. Copy in Utzon papers.

118. Utzon papers.

119. Ibid.

120. M of M Hellebaek 12th and 13th February 1962. Utzon papers.

121. Utzon papers.

122. Arup papers.

123. Arup papers.

124. Ashworth papers.

125. Ove Arup's personal papers, Cambridge.

126. Zunz to Boulton 6.2.62. Arup papers.

127. Boulton to Zunz 8.2.62. Arup papers.
128. Arup papers.
129. Ove Arup's personal papers.
130. Ibid.
131. Ibid
132. Messent/Zunz interviews.
133. *Telegraph* 15.3.62.
134. M of M 1962 Utzon/Zunz visit to Sydney. Arup papers.
135. 'And that was, of course, in hindsight, quite a courageous thing for us to say, because it did (involve) pulling out all the stops to really meet that commitment. Because it was very, very difficult indeed.' Zunz OHOH tapes.
136. M of M 1962 Utzon/Zunz visit to Sydney.
137. Ibid.
138. Ibid.
139. They were not as it turned out.
140. Arup papers.
141. Ibid.
142. Ibid.
143. Ibid.
144. *Telegraph* 27.6.62.
145. *SMH* 3.7.62. Zunz recalled that there were many in the industry 'architects and so on' who thought it wasn't 'anything like the competition style and won't be anything as good. I personally think it's infinitely better... it's crisper, and you can... sense the geometric order, which you would never have been able to sense in the competition scheme.' Zunz OHOH tapes.
146. Arup papers.
147. Ibid.

CHAPTER 10
PREPARING FOR CONSTRUCTION OF THE SHELLS

1. Arup papers.
2. M of M Hellebaek 28.8.58 attended by Utzon, Molman and an engineer called Kayser from Christiani and Nielsen. Utzon papers.
3. Arup papers.
4. Manuel Hornibrook to an Annual General Meeting of Shareholders, 23rd October 1958. *A Man of Achievement* Waveney Browne.
5. Browne.
6. Ibid.
7. Ibid.
8. Ibid.
9. Ibid.

10. Ibid.
11. The toll remained a shilling a car (10 cents after decimalisation) until handed over to the government debt-free in 1975. The investors got all their money back.
12. The author once asked Corbet Gore how many brothers Manuel Hornibrook had, and he replied, 'I don't know, but he had a lot of them.'
13. Ove Arup.
14. Messent/Gore interviews.
15. Gore had a slide of wild-looking New Guinea tribesmen labouring on a road in the highlands, which he used later to introduce slide shows on the Opera House, telling his listeners that 'this was the Opera House site when we moved onto it.' Messent/Gore interviews.
16. Gore OHOH tapes.
17. Messent/Gore interviews.
18. Ibid.
19. Gore to *Sunday Mail*, Queensland, 21.10.73.
20. Jack Zunz wrote to Messent concerning Lin.

    I wanted to consult T.Y. Lin in San Francisco about the use of light weight concrete. We were very concerned about the loads, both for the ties which had already been built, as well as for the foundations. Light weight reinforced concrete was not universally used at the time and its applications to prestressed concrete was limited. I had already consulted Professor Evans of Leeds University, who was the leading expert in the U.K. T.Y. Lin, who was more experienced in practical applications of light weight concrete than Evans, was a consulting engineer as well as an academic. I had arranged with Corbet Gore, when we were in Sydney to meet with Lin which we did. Lin's main contribution was to offer to design the project for us!

    In the end we decided that there were too many unknowns about prestressing light weight concrete and used it only in the precast (non-prestressed) cross braces of the roof ribs. Although its effect on weight reduction was marginal, we thought that every little helped.
21. Messent/Gore interviews 'Don't know whether they did or not' added Gore.
22. Gore saw some brown tiles he liked which he ordered for his back patio. Messent/Gore interviews.
23. Ibid.
24. Zunz roof report.
25. Arup minutes of discussions with Hornibrooks.
26. Ibid. These were just two or three of over 100 separate items looked at. They are listed in an Arup document 'Minutes of Discussions with Hornibrooks and decisions Reached,' covering the three weeks from 6.6.62 to 29.6.62.

27. Arup papers.
28. Ibid. 11.7.62.
29. Ibid. 17.7.62.
30. Ibid. 24.7.62.
31. Ibid. 25.7.62.
32. Ibid. 26.7.62.
33. Gore to Zunz 3.8.62. Arup papers.
34. Ibid.
35. MacKenzie to Zunz 7.8.62. Arup papers.
36. From a 15-page document setting out the responsibilities of the Public Works Department under the Sydney Opera House Act, prepared by the Director of Public Works 30.8.60. PWP.
37. Ibid.
38. Messent/Ryan interviews.
39. Ashworth papers.
40. Laurie was a Sydney architect advising the Opera House Committee, Roderick was a Professor of Civil Engineering at Sydney University.
41. Ashworth papers.
42. The government to Haviland, 8.8.62. concerning Parkes' and Haviland's meeting with the Cabinet sub-committee on 1st August. PWP.
43. Messent/Zunz interviews.
44. Zunz OHOH tapes.
45. Messent/Zunz interviews.
46. Jack Zunz writing in the *Architect's Journal*, February, 1995.
47. Minutes of a special meeting of the Technical Advisory Panel, 24.8.62. Those attending included Cobden Parkes, Ted Farmer, Eric Wagner, Ian MacKenzie, Skipper Nielsen, Stan Haviland, Utzon, Ove Arup and Jack Zunz. From a copy in the Arup papers.
48 *Telegraph* 18.8.62.
49. Ibid.
50. *Sun* 22.8.62.
51. Ibid.
52. Ibid.
53. *Telegraph* 25.8.62.
54. *SMH* 25.8.62.
55. *SMH* 25.8.62.
56. Ashworth papers.
57. Zunz OHOH tapes. Guyon graduated from the Ecole Poly-technique in 1919 and following wide experience in the design and construction of steelwork and reinforced concrete, joined E. Freyssinet in 1937. For the past 21 years Guyon had been chief technical adviser to Freyssinet's firm, Société Technique pour L'Utilisation de la Précontrainte.
58. Arup to Guyon 4.9.62. Arup papers.

CHAPTER 10 NOTES AND REFERENCES

59. A new bridge being constructed at that time over Sydney Harbour five miles west of the Harbour Bridge. On completion the Gladesville Bridge had the longest concrete arch span in the world.
60. Guyon to Ove Arup 28.9.62. Arup papers.
61. Zunz OHOH tapes.
62. Arup papers.
63. Arup papers. Arups asked Guyon for a statement of fees. Guyon charged £700, though he wrote to Zunz in July 1964 he wanted to be 'sure that this is paid by the Australian authorities : I hate to take money from friends, and if you would not be reimbursed, we could discuss again.' Arups made a bank transfer in Guyon's favour, and assured him that the New South Wales government would be footing the bill.
64. Arup papers. Arups calculated that 10 ins. of movement could occur in a typhoon two thirds of the way up the longest ribs.
65. 20.9.62. Arup papers.
66. 21.9.62. Arup papers.
67. Ibid.

'The bridges were designed to carry 110-ton wheel loads as the worst condition. Therefore, all supports had to be taken down through the building to rock or spread to pick up walls of the building which would withstand these forces.' Hornibrooks' submission for the 1968 Construction Achievement Award.

This submission, written by Corbet Gore, had 70 pages of text, plus drawings and photographs of the Opera House shells, to enter the Stage II contract for the 1968 Award. But the Award that year went to a welded steel pressure pipe used on the Snowy Mountains Scheme. The Chairman of the judging panel, Sir William Hudson, was also Chairman of the Snowy Mountains' Scheme. After that, Hornibrooks did not enter the shells for any other awards so the *construction* of the shells never received an award.

68. 2.10.62. Arup papers.
69. 4.10.62. Arup papers.
70. 10.10.62. Arup papers.
71. 12.10.62. Arup papers.
72. *Sunday Telegraph* 28.10.62.
73. According to the wording of the contract the agreement was made between the Honourable Phillip Norman Ryan 'The Minister for Public Works of the State of New South Wales as Constructing Authority for and on behalf of Her Majesty the Queen (hereinafter called "The Principal")' and Hornibrooks "AND WHEREAS plans and specifications for the Works have been prepared by OVE ARUP AND PARTNERS Consulting Engineers... the Principal has agreed to pay to the Contractor the actual cost of the said works... together with a total fee of... £75,000:0:0."'

This type of contract was a 'cost plus fixed fee' contract. From a copy of the contract in the Arup papers.

74. *Sun Herald* 21.10.62.
75. Ibid.
76. 18.10. 62. Arup papers.
77. 31.10.62. Arup papers.
78. Ibid.
79. 5.3.63. Arup papers.
80. Zunz to Continental Express. 24.10.62. Arup papers.
81. Arup papers.
82. 2.11.62..Arup papers.
83. 16.11.62. Arup papers.
84. Zunz to Gore, 21.11.62. Arup papers.
85. Arup papers.
86. Hornibrooks were puzzled by the difference in price. Mills could not understand how the Cyclone price could be so high. Hornibrooks made their own estimate of the scaffolding cost and reckoned Mills quote was a third low.
87. Gore OHOH tapes.
88. Ibid. On site the arch was nick-named 'the drunk prostitute.'
89. 5.9.62. Arup papers.
90. 24.9.62. Arup papers. Though Arup engineers Wymer and Rice both had doubts, neither were in a position to influence the decision to go ahead either way.
91. Gore to Blanchard, 21.2.63. Arup papers.
92. Harris was taking a year's sabbatical in Sydney from Cambridge University.
93. 30.4.65. Arup papers,
94. Jack Zunz included some notes on the erection arch in the Arup Newsletter of December 1963.

    ... The development of the design of this erection arch has taken nearly eighteen months. There are many detailed problems of considerable complexity associated with this erection arch, some of which are still being ironed out. Chief of these is the fact that a structure assembled completely on a rigid scaffold before release has an entirely different set of built-in stresses from one which is supported partially on a flexible steel arch on the one hand and on the last completed rib on the other. The repercussions on our design are therefore both extensive and formidable. Before reaching a decision we made comparative estimates between those arches and a rigid scaffold. The geometric properties of the shells make it impossible to use a very limited scaffold only because the horizontal projection of a rib would cover a large plan area so that a substantial part of the whole complex would have to be scaffolded at any one time.

S. Giedion wrote in his publication, *Space, Time and Architecture* an article entitled 'Jorn Utzon and the Third Generation': that 'The primacy of expression must always be achieved through the contemporary technical possibilities. This implies something more: the machine has to be subordinated to the creative process, not the creative process to the machine.' This was the case with Corbet Gore's erection arch, the building had been designed *then* Corbet Gore conceived the device to build it.

95. Arup papers.
96. Lewis OHOH tapes.
97. 'List of Queries & Discussion Headings' for Jack Zunz's visit to Hellebaek, 24.11.62. Arup papers.
98. 'Summary of action required after December 1962 meetings with Gore.' Arup papers.
99. Messent/Zunz interviews.
100. Ibid.
101. Arup papers.
102. Ibid.
103. Zunz to Utzon, 21.1.63. Arup papers.
104. Arup papers.
105. Zunz to Utzon, 21.1.63. Arup papers.
106. 'Summary of Preliminary Progress Report to the Executive Committee' 18.12.62. Arup papers.
107. Arup papers.
108. 5.3.63. Arup papers.
109. Arup papers.
110. Ibid.
111. Ibid.
112. 13.3.63. Arup papers.
113. Hornibrook Construction Achievement Award submission. 'The use of epoxy was Corbet's idea' Zunz told the author.
114. Arup notes to Hornibrook mentioned that the 'Glued joint is intended to assist the prestress to create a homogeneous member with compressive, tensile and shear properties continuous from segment to segment.' And that 'average thickness of glue not to exceed 1/32 in.'
115. Hornibrook Construction Achievement Award. The collets, which stayed in the anchorage pocket when the strand was released, were waxed to ensure they parted easily from the flying wedge.
116. Zunz to Lewis, 31.8.65. Arup papers.
117. Zunz report on Shell Structure.
118 The reason was because the workers 'put in a good story about bursting out in skin rashes to the Industrial Commission. With the story they came out with you'd think they were all being boiled in mustard gas. There was

the odd rash but a bit of calomine lotion seemed to fix it.' Messent/Gore interviews.

119. 19.3.63. Arup papers.
120. 5.4.63. Arup papers.
121. Nutt to Kelman, 16.4.63. Arup papers..
122. 17.4.63. Arup papers
123. 22.4.63. Arup papers.
124. Gore to Arups London, 26.4.63. Arup papers.
125. 30.4.63. Arup papers.
126. 1.5.63. Arup papers.
127. Dowrick to Gore, 7.5.63. Arup papers.
128. 8.5.63. Arup papers.
129. 9.1.63. Arup papers.
130. Mike Lewis from the TV documentary 'Monster or Miracle.'
131. *The Sun* 4.6.63.
132. 11.7.63. Arup papers. Lewis never did get his Utzon-designed house at Middle Cove. 'I think it would have been low on his list of priorities.' Utzon though did do a sketch design for Poul Ahm's house in London and Poul finished it. Messent/Lewis interviews.
133. *Telegraph* 30.5.63.
134. 18.6.63. Arup papers.
135. In practice the segments for the restaurant ribs were shallower. They were cast after dropping a false bottom into the standard rib forms.
136. 10.5.63. Arup papers.
137. Arup papers.
138. Zunz to Lewis, 23.4.63. Arup papers.
139. Zunz to Kelman, 26.4.63. Arup papers.
140. Ibid.
141. 12.6.63. Arup papers.
142. It was most disobedient of Gore to refer to them as arch ribs as the manual specifically said they did not exist!
143. 'Comments on Manual of Procedure' July 1963. Arup papers.
144. From the crown the arches trailed down like the legs of an octopus.
145. Effectively a steel rod.
146. A particular rib for a particular shell was identified by a numbering system.
147. The flat jacks ensured that the loads on the side shells during construction would not exceed those likely to occur when the building was in its completed state. They were a hydraulic device which could measure the forces coming onto the structure and control the loads coming onto the structure.
148. A summary of information from Arup's 'Manual of Procedure'. Arup papers.

CHAPTER 10 NOTES AND REFERENCES

149. The stage wall for the Major Hall was a triangular shape with curved sides, 70 ft long, 75 ft high and 2 ft 6 in thick.
150. Lewis too thought 'the resulting finish on the forms is absolutely magnificent.' In a letter to Arups 14.6.63.
151. The program for deflections to the erection arch was run through the computer used for calculations associated with the Woomera Rocket Range in South Australia.
152. 3.6.63. Arup papers.
153. 24.6.63. Arup papers.
154. 2.7.63. Arup papers.
155. Arup papers.
156. Sydney – Outstanding Work, Arup papers 1.8.63.
157. M of M in architect's office 17.7.63. Arup papers.
158. Hornibrooks CAA 'Although some localised patching was necessary, the surfaces generally were still producing a first class finish after fifty re-uses.' wrote Gore.

    Plastic-coated plywood specifically made to provide a smooth finish on concrete formwork was later commercially available but at that time it was not on the market.
159. Because of high wind stresses at the open end of the largest shells of the Major and Minor Halls, the specified cube strength of the three longest ribs on each Hall was increased from 6,000 lb/in2 to 7,500 lb/in2, though Hornibrooks routinely exceeded this cube strength anyway. In the 'interim' state, when a rib under construction was free to move in relation to its neighbour before a group of ribs had been laterally stressed together, '... the longest rib would be likely to fail under a wind of... 170 m.p.h. Such a wind would have to come from the least favourable direction and have a fairly long gust duration, perhaps 10-20 seconds, to induce complete failure of the longest rib.' *The Prestressing of Sydney Opera House Roof,* Dowrick.
160. Messent/Gore interviews.
161. Ibid.
162. Gore used them for a path round the side of his house.
163. Hornibrooks CAA.
164. Ibid.
165. Ibid.
166. Jack Zunz, *The Structural Engineer*, October 1969. John Blanchard called the shape of the outside surface of the arches a 'warped cylinder.' *The Contract Journal*, 7.11.63.
167. The slabs rested on precast beams spanning between the arches which were left exposed in construction as part of the architecture of the inside of the side shells. The beams were at 2.28 m centres parallel to the bottom boundary of the shell which is not parallel to the ground but slopes

between the springing points of the side shells.

168. Hornibrooks CAA. 'The work of producing the forms for the shell segments was 'a fairly substantial design and construction task' in itself,' recalled Gore. Gore OHOH tapes.

169. One story that never reached the papers was when some segments were being brought back from Long Bay Gaol on the back of a semi-trailer and one of them fell over and straight 'through the tray of the semi-trailer and ended up in the middle of Anzac Parade' causing a traffic jam. Elphick OHOH tapes.

170. Arup papers.

171. 6.9.63. Arup papers. An example of the immense difficulties involved in defining the side shell surfaces so they could be dimensioned for drawings. John Nutt, Jack Zunz and Peter Rice were among the leading engineers of their day, but on the design of the shells of the Sydney Opera House they really had a chance to 'show their metal.' Messent/Gore interviews.

172. 11.9.63. Arup papers.

CHAPTER 11
THE GUNPOWDER PLOT
A CHANGE TO THE SHELL COLUMNS

1. *Daily Mirror* 21.9.63.
2. Gore OHOH tapes.
3. Arup papers.
4. Arup papers. The meeting was attended by Jenkins, Hobbs, Molman and Kelman.
5. 29.9.61. Arup papers.
6. Arup papers. The summary included a reference to Column 15 Minor Hall 'to be checked but probably will require adjustment' and Column 2 and 7 Major Hall 'more or less O.K.'
7. Arup papers.
8. 24.7.62. Arup papers.
9. Committee report dated 14.9.62. Arup papers.
10. Arup papers.
11. Arup papers. This meant there would no longer be a hinge at the top of the column.
12. John Blanchard to Mr Keville of Leslie & Godwin London, 30.11.62.
13. This was for discussion during Gore's visit to London from the 10th – 17th December. Arup papers.
14. *Sunday Mirror* 17.3.63.
15. 18.3.63. Arup papers.
16. *Sun Herald* 17.3.63.
17. *SMH* 18.3.63.

18. 1.5.63. Arup papers.

19. 7.5.63. Arup papers.

20. 7.5.63. Arup papers.

21. Zunz to Lewis and Kelman 8.5.63. The letter, headed 'Explosives' commenced, 'Your diagnosis was right – I had a fit.' Arup papers.

22. 8.5.63. Arup papers.

23. 10.5.63. Arup papers.

24. Gore OHOH tapes.

25. 17.5.63. Arup papers.

26. A report on 'Demolition of Existing Columns' by R.S. Wood. Arup papers.

27. Arup papers.

28. The story was titled 'COMIC OPERA HOUSE.' *Sunday Mirror* 28.7.63. Though the *Herald* had in fact published some details of the story the day before in a less sensational way, under a heading 'Opera House Pillars Altered.' 'Hornibrook… have tightened security precautions at the site since a sub-contractor specialised in blasting was engaged… Some of (the pillars) are being blasted down to ground level. The others are being "modified" by a new blasting technique… Mr J. Bayutti, principal of the company doing the blasting… said last night he was not allowed to discuss it.' *SMH* 27.7.63.

29. *SMH* 29.7.63. A photo of a column shattered by explosives in Arups files had written on the back 'Gore Goes Guy Fawkes.'

30. Arup papers.

31. *SMH* 1.8.63.

32. *Hansard*.

33. Minutes of Site Conference 2.10.63. Utzon papers.

34. 9.6.64. Arup papers.

35. In costs to 31.5.66. Arup papers.

CHAPTER 12
LATERAL THINKING

1. *The Sun* 22.11.63.

2. 22.11.63. Arup papers.

3. From Messent/Nutt correspondence.

4. Messent/Zunz correspondence. Zunz also wrote: 'There were others who played central roles in designing and building SOH. John Blanchard for instance, who in his quiet and self effacing way probably contributed as much, if not more, as anybody and is one of the unsung heroes of this whole affair.'

5. Elphick OHOH tapes.

6. Zunz to Rice 1.11.63. Arup papers.

7. Arup papers. Later, when Kelman returned to London, he wrote to Peter

Rice, 'In general your instructions are too complicated for me to understand, so I deal only with Ian's!'

8. Arup papers. Huang's paragraph on his "exact solution" was marked by a question mark in the margin by someone at Arups.

9. Kelman OHOH tapes

10. Rice to Zunz 6.12.63. Arup papers.

11. Dowrick to Kelman 12.12.63.

12. *Construction* 22.1.64.

13. Zunz OHOH tapes.

14. Dr Alan Baker had written a PhD thesis on analysis of two-and three-dimensional steel building frameworks for the University of Leeds and this was extended to a computer program suited to sections of the Opera House structure.

15. Messent/Blanchard interviews. Once all the ribs are in place 'The whole shell is prestressed laterally. When all ribs are stressed together, they act as one continuous membrane, with improved strength and rigidity.' Arup film *Job 1112*.

   A number of us contributed to the concept of the structure. We articulated the structure at that time because we had no way of predicting the behaviour of a rigid structure, one which had all the ribs stressed together laterally. Alan Baker joined us when we were deliberating these issues. He had just completed a PhD thesis based on a computer program which quite incidentally could analyse the more rigid version which most of us preferred. This analysis gave us the needed confidence to proceed. Subsequently I had the Baker analysis checked by Livesley at Cambridge University, who, prior to Baker had written and developed a computer program capable of analysing complex three dimensional structures like the Opera House. This check gave us added assurance that our structure was safe.

   The essence is the change from an *articulated* structure on the one hand, ie one in which the ribs could move, to a *rigid* one on the other which we felt to be sounder. The articulated (Rice) structure *could* be stressed laterally. Once it was stressed it would no long be *articulated*. Up to ten members of the SOH team were involved on each scheme. Zunz/Messent correspondence.

16. The effort and investigations that took place to seal the shells, including the joint between the tile panels, is a story in itself. Utzon's files on the matter extend to 500 pages of correspondence. Arup's double that. Arups alone consulted with 32 companies in Australia and 18 in the UK during their quest. 'Waterproofing this roof is a major problem and in itself it is a story of technical and human endeavour.' wrote Zunz in the December 1963 *Arup Newsletter*.

17. 10.2.64. Arup papers.

18. GKN report on the bolts, Arup papers.
19. Blanchard to Notley Advertising, London, concerning a description of shell construction to be used in an ad for GKN. 15.2.66. Arup papers.
20. The K-Monel D and Titanium 314A lateral bolts were designed for a fatigue resistance of 300 years in the simply connected condition. This was although the tensile stresses due to temperature changes would be much less in the completed laterally stressed structure. Arup POD&C.
21. Arup papers.
22. M of M at Arups London 18.7.63. Arup papers.
23. 16.9.63. Arup papers.
24. 23.9.63. Arup papers.
25. 3.10.63. Arup papers.
26. 8.10.63. Arup papers.
27. 15.10.63. Arup papers.
28. The Opera House could not have been built without computers If the project had been attempted ten years earlier it simply could not have been done in the way it was because the computers were not available to process the vast quantities of data involved in the structural analysis of the shells. At the time the change was made of precasting the shells and cutting them out of a sphere Arups had spent 375,000 man hours and 1,800 computer hours on the problem. According to a booklet produced by the Sydney Opera House Trust in 1971, when the analysis for the shells was complete 'It is estimated that computer work undertaken would have occupied 1,000 mathematicians for more than 100 years.' For example a computer program to check the analysis of the side shell arches, it claimed, 'entailed about 25,000 equations and over a million analyses. The calculations carried out by a computer in 44 minutes would have occupied a good mathematician for 34 years.'

Ferranti Pegasus, Ferranti Sirius and Orion computers driven by thermionic valves were used. They occupied the space associated with the major air-conditioning plant of a modern building, and Arups – who did not possess their own – hired outside computers by the hour. The Opera House was one of the first large-scale applications of computers in structural engineering. According to the Arup paper on Design and Construction, 'There was not, at the beginning anyway, a complete understanding among practical engineers of which analytical approaches were best suited to the machines capabilities and the speed of computers and availability of programs was very limited.' Not only did Arups have to write the programs from scratch but the computers of the day were very slow and unreliable. Reported in the Arup papers of 14th June 1963, Zunz once wrote to Ferranti Ltd at the Computer Centre at Newman Street London,

We wish to draw your attention to the fact that we have suffered a considerable amount of inconvenience due to your Sirius computer being continually out of order.

It has been recorded on several occasions that four of our engineers had to wait over an hour before they could get access to the machine which, they were told, had developed a fault. Sometimes, even after the machine had been repaired, it still produced mysterious results which were beyond everybody's comprehension. The unpredictability and unreliability of this machine has affected the morale and confidence of our staff. We consider this matter now an extremely serious one.

We trust that you will look into it to avoid further inconvenience and losses to us, and advise us what measures you propose to take.

Zunz advised Northampton College of Advanced Technology regarding their Ferranti Pegasus computer, that typical programs could be run continuously over 'several all-night sessions' with an engineer in attendance. Shells 3 and 4, as free-standing structures on their own were anlaysed as complete units, while shells 1 and 2 had to be dealt with in two halves. The behaviour of the shells during erection with varying numbers of ribs in position had to be taken into account. Certain parts of the analysis were carried out by hand, and corrections were made for the fact that it was not possible to put the lateral connections in their exact theoretical positions. For temperature and prestress creep loadings which occurred after the ridge segments were stressed together, the bending stiffness of the ridge beam had to be included which was done by a program which analysed the ridge as a beam supported on springs.

According to the Arup paper on Design and Construction and Zunz's report on Shell Structure, geometric information 'could sensibly be provided only by the computer. The information used on computer programs was tabulated to suit rapid conversion' 'for preparing schedules of co-ordinates for all the designs so that three-dimensional surfaces could be projected on to two dimensions and therefore be drawn.' Some of the setting out by men on site was done 'directly from computer print outs.'

For the analysis of deflections of the erection arch Hornibrooks wrote their own program and used the IBM 7090 computer at the Weapons Research Establishment, Adelaide. It was the best computer available in Australia for the price at the time and the Establishment quoted £120 an hour for its use.

In 1988 Lewis asked one of the computer buffs at Arups to do a comparison to see how long a program run in the sixties would take compared with the desktop computers they now had available. To do a three-dimensional framework analysis of one of the side shell arches it took a week to get the data together to run the program in 1963, and then they had to have the Ferranti Pegasus computer at the University of London – which was the only one that size – the whole night feeding it with data as it took 12 hours to run the program. In 1988 it took a day instead of a week to assemble the data and four minutes instead of 12 hours to run the analysis on one of their desktop computers. The Ferranti Pegasus cost £1 million in 1988 money while the price of a desktop computer in 1988 was £2,500. When the author met Lewis in 1992 he said that already their desktop computers were ten times faster than the 1988 ones. At time of writing (1997) they are at least ten times faster again.

29. Rice to Zunz, 23.10.63. Arup papers.
30. Ibid.
31. Ibid.
32. Rice to Zunz, 24.10.63. Arup papers.
33. Ibid.
34. 4.11.63. Arup papers.
35. Lewis to Zunz, 8.11.63. Arup papers.
36. 8.11.63. Arup papers.
37. Minutes of site conferences. Utzon papers.
38. 19.11.63. Arup papers.
39. GKN to Elms at Arups London. GKN were just one of 18 companies that Arups consulted with on the bolts.
40. Lewis to Zunz 28.11.63. Arup papers.
41. Kelman to Elms 29.11.63.
42. 19.12.63. Arup papers.
43. Dr Layton of Mountfords to Elms 17.12.63. Arup papers.
44. Kelman to Zunz 2.1.64. Arup papers.
45. 10.1.64. Arup papers.
46. Blanchard to Rice 10.1.64. Arup papers.
47. Ibid.
48. 29.1.64. Arup papers.
49. Zunz to Lewis 19.2.64. Arups had been very lucky to get hold of any titanium at all because at that time UK supplies were earmarked to build the prototype of the TSR2 fighter-bomber.
50. Elms to Dr Layton of Mountfords in a letter which started 'I feel we owe both you and Henry Wiggins some explanation for our recent alteration to the bolt design.' 20.2.64. Arup papers.
51. Gore to Hutson 12.11.64. Arup papers.
52. Mountfords to Gore 18.11.64.
53. "A Saving!"
54. CIF Costs of Lateral Connections, Arup papers.
55. Blanchard to Lewis 21.4.66. Arup papers.
56. Copy of report dated 10.8.65. Arup papers.
57. 4.3.64. Arup papers.
58. Summary of December 1962 meetings at Arups. Utzon papers.
59. 22.4.66. Arup papers.

CHAPTER 13
WEIGHTS AND MEASURES :
CONSTRUCTING THE SHELLS

1. Messent/Nutt correspondence.
2. The effect of wind and temperature alone could make a difference of +- $\frac{1}{2}$ inch on the longer ribs.
3. 25.5.64. Arup papers.
4. 12.6.64. Arup papers.
5. Lewis OHOH tapes.
6. Lewis OHOH tapes.
7. Elphick OHOH tapes.
8. Ibid.
9. Paper on 'Surveys for the construction of the shell roofs of the Sydney Opera House' by Michael Elphick. From copy in the Arup papers.
10. Elphick OHOH tapes.
11. Ibid.
12. Ibid. 'We had a marvellous team of surveyors.' Lewis OHOH tapes.
13 Elphick paper on shell roofs.
14. Elphick OHOH tapes.
15. Ibid.
16. Ibid.
17. '...that had never been done before... the writing of that computer program and setting it up in such a way that it worked. That was a real breakthrough, and if we had to do it today (1988), it would be an absolute piece of cake, because the survey instruments now come with a computer built in.' Lewis OHOH tapes.
18. Ibid.
19. Zunz roof report.
20. Elphick OHOH tapes.
21. Ibid.
22. Ibid.
23. Ibid.
24. Ibid.
25. Ibid.
26. Elphick paper on shell roofs.
27. Elphick OHOH tapes.
28. Ibid. The interview was recorded in 1988, 25 years after Elphick started work at the Opera House.
29. Messent/Nutt correspondence.
30. Yeomans. The irregularity can still be seen from inside the south foyer of the Major Hall.
31. Hornibrook CAA.
32. Ibid.

33. Ibid.
34. 'Grouting Prestressing Ducts At the Sydney Opera House'. Talk to Australian Prestressed Concrete Group, 30th August 1967. John Nutt. Arup papers.
35. Messent/Gore interviews.
36. Nutt paper.
37. Hornibrook CAA.
38. Lewis OHOH tapes.
39. Ibid.
40. Nutt paper.
41. Hornibrook CAA.
42. Ibid.
43. Lewis OHOH tapes.
44. Nutt paper.
45. Ibid.
46. Ibid.
47. Ibid.
48. Ibid.
49. Ibid.
50. Ibid.
51. Ibid.
52. Ibid. At a meeting in Paris on 3rd November 1965 'to discuss the grouting of vertical cable ducts with Monsieur Fargeot and Monsieur Bore' the French suggested 'To inhibit void formation at the top, a glass tube 3 ft 6 in long was placed through the central hole in the top anchorage. The column of grout extends into this tube and does not fall below it even when settlement occurs.' Arup papers.
53. Hornibrook CAA.
54. Kelman in London to Arthur Crimp in Sydney 4.6.64. Arup papers.
55. Ibid. 12.6.64. Arup papers.
56. Ibid.
57. Arup papers.
58. Arup papers.
59. Zunz to Lewis 23.9.63. Arup papers.
60. MacKenzie to Dowrick 29.5.64. Arup papers.
61. Ibid.
62. Ibid.
63. 30.6.64. Arup papers.
64. Rice to London, June 1964.
65. 1.7.64. Arup papers.
66. *SMH* 23.6.64. This opinion was '… yet another example of the Australian desire for second-rate if it is available first, fast and five minutes sooner' wrote J. Fossey of Balgowlah in reply. *SMH* 27.6.64.

67. Paul Haege of Darling Point to *SMH* 3.7.64.
68. *The Sun* 4.8.64.
69. Utzon to Arups 18.8.64. Arup papers.
70. 6.10.64. Arup papers.
71. 13.10.64. Arup papers.
72. 20.10.64. Arup papers.
73. 16.10.64. Arup papers.
74. 22.10.64. Arup papers. Zunz wrote to Lewis on 18th November: 'I will ask John Blanchard where the "heavy" tile lids should be placed.'
75. 26.10.64. Arup papers.
76. Elphick OHOH tapes.
77. Ibid.
78. Ibid.
79. 28.10.64. Arup papers.
80. 28.10.64. Arup papers.
81. 4.11.64. Arup papers.
82. 3.7.64. Arup papers.
83. 6.11.64. Arup papers.
84. Schedule entitled 'Revised Erection Logic' 8.12.64. Arup papers. The slightest deviation from this schedule had to be okayed with London, John Blanchard writing to Mick Lewis on 2nd February 1964: 'Peter Rice's query on out-of-phase erection of shell 1 is receiving my urgent attention, but issue is not straightforward and will take another two days to resolve.' Arup papers.
85. 12.11.64. Arup papers.
86. Ryan to Ove Arup 27.11.64. PWP, AOK.
87. The Zunz roof report quoted elsewhere in this story.
88. Zunz roof report.
89. 24.11.64. Arup papers.
90. Though Hornibrooks had to spend a considerable sum in alterations to bring the cranes up to the Australian standard. The cranes came with the ladder inside ascending nearly the height of the crane to the driver's box. The Australian regulations required there to be a landing every so many rungs of steps. 'They weren't so worried if they lost a few Frenchmen.' Messent/Gore interviews.
91. Gore OHOH tapes.
92. Ellis OHOH tapes.
93. Gore OHOH tapes.
94. Utzon's description of this operation was '...two men would stand on an element perfectly made up on the ground and be moved up by crane 60 metres and put it into place like you put a lens in a camera, so exact.' *Good Weekend* 31.10.92.
95. Elphick OHOH tapes.

96. Messent/Gore interviews.

97. Ibid.

98. *Sunday Mail* Queensland 21.10.73.

99. *SMH* 22.2.63.

100. *SMH* 15.5.63.

101. 13.7.64 PWP, AOK.

102. *Financial Review* 3.7.64.

103. Gore to Johnson of Public Works 13.7.64 PWP, AOK.

104. Bi-monthly report of Consulting Engineers to Executive Committee 16.6.64. Arup papers.

105. Ibid.

106. Lewis OHOH tapes.

107. *SMH* 4.3.64. This restriction was later relaxed.

108. If the ridge segment was the keystone of each pair of ribs, the arch crown was the keystone of each of the seven shell structures. It was at the junction of the side shell arches, and had to withstand tremendous compressive forces as the ridges of the two shells in each shell structure rested against it. The ridge crown piece itself was lowered into place by crane. It was like an awkwardly shaped large box with thin concrete sides and legs sticking out like a truncated octopus. Each of the seven-arch crown pieces was then filled with 200 cubic yards of concrete by crane with a concrete skip.

109. *SMH* 11.6.64.

110. *Telegraph* 8.8.63.

111. Gore told the author that if Hornibrooks had done the shells to a price it would have sent them broke.

112. The canopies are beautifully sculpted pieces of concrete over the stairs leading from the box office foyer to the main southern foyers of the Major and Minor Halls. The finish on the concrete is quite superb, and they are frequently cited as an example of the difference that was achieved in the quality of the concrete finish between stages I and II because they butt directly onto the Stage I box office foyer roof beams. The author once asked Corbet Gore if they would have got into the same trouble on Stage I, i.e. if Hornibrooks *had* won the contract for the podium if they would have been battling to achieve a quality finish because of budget restraints, and Gore replied, 'We would have got a better finish than Stage I, but we wouldn't have got the finish we achieved on Stage II.'

113. Ed Perry to Kelman 7.12.64. Arup papers.

114. Huang to Kelman 4.12.64.

115. 9.12.64. Arup papers.

116. Arup papers.

117. Ibid.

118. Zunz to Lewis, 22.12.64. Arup papers.

119. Ibid. Though lightweight concrete was not used for the rib segments, it was used for the reinforced concrete cross-bracing between the arms of the Y on the upper rib segments. The cross-bracing elements were dropped in after the segment had been cast.
120. Lewiz to Zunz 22.1.65. Arup papers.
121. Arup papers.
122. Ibid.
123. Lewis to Zunz 16.2.65. Arup papers.
124. Ibid.
125. Ibid.
126. Arup papers.
127. Arup papers 9.4.65.
128. To Tom Farrell of the *SMH* 30.1.57.
129. *SMH* 7.2.57.
130. *SMH* 19.2.57. In Australia a 'schooner' is a size of beer glass.
131. A dissertation on Bar Area Finish, Amendment 'A.' 30.6.64. Utzon papers.
132. Messent/Gore interviews.
133. Ibid. Woods kept the piece of wood and still had it in 1996.
134. Messent/Gore interviews.
135. Ibid.
136. Ibid.
137. Utzon's Descriptive Narrative. PWP, AOK.
138. Littlemore OHOH tapes. 'He probably went back and roared the pants off some of his people who hadn't produced work of the same quality,' continued Littlemore.
139. The first segments of shell, A 1-5, weighed 11.9 tons and special approval was granted by the Department of Labour and Industry to lift them with the tower cranes.
140. Alan Moorehead, Australian author, October 1964.
141. John Douglas Pringle, *On Second Thoughts*.
142. V.J. Smith to *SMH* 1965.
143. *Telegraph* 24.1.65.
144. At a meeting of the Prestressed Concrete Development Group. *SMH* 16.1.65.
145. Gore OHOH tapes.
146. Kelman OHOH tapes.
147. Ibid.
148. Gore OHOH tapes.
149. Elphick OHOH tapes.
150. Ibid.
151. *SMH* 16.10.63.
152. MacKenzie OHOH tapes.

153. Ibid.
154. Ibid.
155. Lewis OHOH tapes.
156. Gore OHOH tapes 'of course they were all getting about three times that, but still', continued Gore.
157. Messent/Gore interviews.
158. Arup papers.
159. MacKenzie OHOH tapes.
160. 'The Opera House', TV documentary narrated by Stuart Wagstaff.
161. Kelman OHOH tapes. 'It would have made a wonderful ruin', Kelman told the author.

CHAPTER 14
THE TILES

1. Curtis.
2. Giedion.
3. Witnessed by the author.
4. *SMH* 1.2.57.
5. *Telegraph* 1.2.75.
6. *SMH* 4.2.57.
7. *SMH* 6.2.57.
8. The tiles eventually used on Stage III on vertical and horizontal surfaces in lavatories and washrooms *were* from the East. They were 47 mm square and made by 'Arita' of Japan.
9. Utzon wrote to Ove Arup in November 1957 of the 'Hoganas factory in Sweden, who are known all over the world for perfect concrete tiling materials'. 24.11.57. Arup papers.
10. From a description by Hoganas on the development of the tiles 14.8.64. Utzon papers.
11. Ibid. Pictures of the full-scale models of the shells made by Hoganas, with workers on the surface laying tiles, appear in the *Red Book*.
12. Hoganas on tile development.
13. *Sunday Mirror* 23.6.62.
14. *Telegraph* 26.6.62.
15. *The Sun* 27.6.62. In answer to a question on the tiles, Utzon wrote to Professor Cowan, Sydney University on 30.9.64. 'The black stripes on the shells were one of many attempts to find the best solution for expressing the big curved forms and their construction to the eye – white matt stripes were finally chosen after full size mock-ups of five different solutions had been made.' Utzon papers. Utzon wrote in *Zodiac* that 'Everything that can emphasise this idea and operation (of pre fabricated construction) must be shown, for instance, method of production, erection system, colour.'

16. *SMH* 25.6.62.
17. *Sunday Mirror* 1.7.62.
18. *Sunday Mirror* 1.7.62. Wherever you go, whoever you talk to, they have an opinion on the Opera House. When the author was in Helsingor a concierge at the hotel said the Opera House was 'like a mushroom curving towards the light.' When the author first started working on this project he had a picture of the Opera House in front of him and his seven-year-old son said 'I wouldn't like to go down that one on my skateboard'.
19. *Sun Herald* 6.1.63.
20. Ibid.
21. *Sunday Mirror* 1.7.62.
22. *SMH* 29.6.62.
23. *Sunday Mirror* 1.7.62. This was at the time Arups and Hornibrooks were sweating on the government announcing Hornibrooks as the nominated contractor for Stage II. Malcolm Nicklin sent some of the press cuttings to Zunz with a note regarding the contract: 'It certainly hasn't gone to Cabinet yet and what harm the attached publicity does remains to be seen. Quite frankly the latest sickening flare-up is not worth our comment.' 6.7.62. Arup papers.
24. *SMH* 25.8.62.
25. *Sunday Telegraph* 26.8.62.
26. *Telegraph* 27.10.62.
27. Serge to Ashworth 2.1.63. Copy in Utzon papers.
28. Utzon papers.
29. Information supplied by Hoganas to the Committee, 6.2.62. Utzon papers.
30. Ibid.
31. Pettersson report on tiles, Utzon papers.
32. Ibid.
33. From a description by Hoganas on the development of the tiles. 14.8.64. Utzon papers.
34. Ibid.
35. Hoganas notes sent with their quote 6.2.62. From copy in Arup papers.
36. Utzon in TV interview with Rasmussen; transcript published in *Sun-Herald*, 13.3.66.
37. *The Sydney Opera House*, Westcott.
38. During the Utzon/Zunz visit to Sydney, in a meeting with Haviland, Utzon emphasised the importance of having the best possible suppliers and subcontractors for certain works which could not be carried out by anybody else '... Mr Haviland referred to the tile tender and said that for political reasons tenders should be called even if only one firm would be able to tender.' Arup papers.
39. Utzon papers.

40. Ashworth papers.
41. Utzon papers.
42. Utzon papers.
43. Utzon papers.
44. Utzon papers.
45. Utzon papers.
46. Utzon papers.
47. Utzon papers.
48. Arup papers.
49. Arup papers.
50. Arup papers.
51. Arup papers.
52. Utzon papers. The news that Hoganas had won the contract was announced in the Sydney papers on 23rd November in an article entitled 'Swedish Tiles on Opera House.' Utzon was quoted as saying 'the locally produced tile had been given every chance to gain acceptance.' Though as far as the Committee were aware Thompson said 'The present order includes both the white body tiles and the black ones which will give the Opera House its redesigned striped appearance.' *SMH* 23.11.62.
53. Utzon papers.
54. Utzon papers.
55. Arup papers.
56. For which Hoganas were charging a considerably higher price. Gore wrote to them on 18th January 1963:

    Regarding the prices quoted, we note in your quotation dated 6th February, 1962, that your 5 in square shiny glazed tile was quoted at 24.45 Swedish Crowns per sq. yd. The price quoted for tiles Type M in your quotation of 21st December, 1962, is .65 Swedish Crowns per piece which we calculate is equivalent to 33.7 Swedish Crowns per sq. yd. We fail to understand how omitting the glaze from these tiles can cause the price to rise by 50 per cent. Perhaps you could check this figure...

    But they were a different quality tile and Hoganas stuck to their price. The 47 different sizes of P tiles were all charged at .85 Swedish Crowns per piece. Arup papers.
57. Arup's summary on tiles outlining tile detail decisions made in October 1962.
58. Utzon papers.
59. Utzon papers.
60. *Sun Herald* 6.1.63.
61. *Daily Mirror* 7.1.63.
62. Utzon papers.
63. All cut in the factory to pre-determined shapes according to a computer program written by Arups.

64. Arup papers.
65. Arup papers.
66. December 1962 meetings with Hoganas, Arup papers.
67. '... which reminds one of old Ming China' Ove Arup said of the glossy tiles.
68. Utzon's specification, from a description by Hoganas on the development of the tiles. 14.8.64. Utzon papers.
69. Utzon papers.
70. Utzon papers.
71. *SMH* 7.3.63.
72. *Sun Herald* 10.3.63.
73. Westcott.
74. Utzon papers.
75. Utzon papers.
76. Utzon papers.
77. 17.5.63. Utzon papers.
78. Utzon *had* asked for 'all sides of lower octopus leg tiled up to line of glazing.' M of M in Sydney, 20.5.63 attended by Utzon, Arups and Hornibrooks.
79. Utzon papers.
80. 28.5.63. Utzon papers.
81. 4.6.63. Utzon papers.
82. 5.6.63. Utzon papers.
83. Ibid.
84. Utzon papers.
85. 29.5.63. Utzon papers.
86. 3.6.63. Utzon papers.
87. 17.6.63. Utzon papers.
88. 26.6.63. Utzon papers.
89. Ibid.
90. Utzon papers.
91. 3.7.63. Utzon papers.
92. 14.10.64. Utzon papers.
93. Ibid.
94. 19.10.64. Utzon papers.
95. 12.1.65. Utzon papers. The ends of the bronze fixing bolts for the pedestal and side-shell arch tile lids can still be seen in the concrete where they were cut off nearly flush with the surface.
96. Site meeting on 15.9.64 to discuss the tile count. Utzon papers.
97. 25.2.65. Utzon papers.
98. 11.5.65. Utzon papers.

CHAPTER 15 NOTES AND REFERENCES

CHAPTER 15
THE TILE LIDS

1. 'Roof cladding of the Sydney Opera House', Michael Lewis, *Journal and Proceedings*, Royal Society of New South Wales, Vol. 106, 1973.
2. Messent/Zunz interviews.
3. Ibid.
4. Hoganas sales information on prefab clinker panels, Utzon papers.
5. 11.12.61. Arup papers.
6. 15.12.61. Arup papers.
7. Though apparently the lids themselves were cast to a circle of radius 246 ft $7\frac{1}{2}$ in. According to a letter from V.G. Towson of Arups London to Lewis on 2nd August 1963:

    'Though the radius to the tile surface is now shown as 246 ft $8\frac{1}{2}$ in to coincide with the increase in the gap between the main structure and the bottom of the ribs it should be made clear to Hornibrooks that the outline dimensions shown still refer to radius 246 ft $7\frac{1}{2}$ in. The discrepancy will be very small and should be taken up in the joints'. Arup papers.
8. 21.3.62. Arup papers.
9. The first batch of 5,000 Hoganas tiles was sent to Brisbane by mistake. Notes of Zunz/Utzon visit to Hoganas 27.11.62. Utzon papers.
10. *Sun Herald* 24.3.63.
11. Utzon papers.
12. Utzon papers.
13. Sheet on 'Tile Lid Manufacture', 4.12.63. Arup papers.
14. Minutes of December 1962 meetings at Arups' London office with Hoganas and Gore. Arup papers.
15. Sheet on 'Tile Lid Manufacture'.
16. Ibid. The additive was 'Shell Concrete Curing Membrane C' diluted with an equal volume of water.
17. Ibid.
18. Ibid.
19. Ibid.
20. Ibid.
21. Lewis, Royal Society paper on tiles.
22. Ibid.
23. Ibid.
24. Utzon to Arup's site office, 13.12.63. Utzon papers.
25. 30.1.64. Utzon papers.
26. 6.2.64. Utzon papers.
27. 10.3.64. Utzon papers.
28. 12.3.64. Arup paper.
29. Lewis OHOH tapes.
30. Arup papers.

31. Lewis, Royal Society paper.
32. Ibid.
33. Ibid.
34. Gore OHOH tapes.
35. Ibid.
36. 20.3.64. Utzon papers.
37. Utzon papers.
38. Ibid.
39. 14.4.64. Arup papers.
40. 14.4.64. Utzon papers.
41. Arup papers.
    Utzon often compared the rib structure of the Opera House to the segments of an orange and the tiled surface to the peel. These terms entered the nomenclature for the building. When Gore was in London for the December 1962 meetings with Arups, item 37 on the agenda, regarding the Side Shell Membrane, mentioned the 'Precast slabs, although theoretical orange peel slices will in fact be parallel sided (3/8 in deviation in 30 ft length), except for shells 7 where they will be taper sided.' M of M 10th-20th December 1962, Arups London. Utzon papers.
42. Arup papers. 'Utzon approves!' had written someone at Arups on the letter.
43. Utzon papers.
44. 29.5.64. Utzon papers.
45. Minutes of Site Meeting, 18.6.64. Utzon papers.
46. 23.6.64. Utzon papers.
47. 7.7.64. Utzon papers.
48. 7.7.64. Utzon papers. The concrete with the finely graded aggregate poured directly on the backs of the tiles on the Opera House tile lids probably caused the same phenomenum. A finely graded aggregate is similar to sand that is not well graded.
49. 21.7.64. Utzon papers.
50. 17.5.63. Utzon papers.
51. Also, according to the notes of a meeting at the Commonwealth Experimental Building Station in Sydney attended by Gore and Nielsen on 31.7.62 '… it was agreed that by spacing the tiles with a comparatively wide raked joint between, a lot of the foreseeable troubles in connection with tiles falling off were minimised.' Utzon papers.
52. 1.9.64. Utzon papers.
53. 23.9.64. Utzon papers.
54. 9.10.64. Utzon papers.
55. Letter from University to Lewis 13.10.64. Utzon papers. Load tests to destruction from both faces of the tile lid also took place in Sydney.
56. 27.11.64. Utzon papers.

57. Site meeting attended by, among others, Utzon, Nielsen, Nutt, Rice and Gore. 30.11.64. Utzon papers.

58. Minutes of Site Discussion 9.12.64, Utzon papers.

59. 3.2.65. Utzon papers.

60. Though at the planning stage it was thought the 'Total number of warped surface tile lids is estimated to be approximately 1200, all of them being different in shape, size and twist.' Arup's notes on making forms, June 1963. Arup papers.

61. Lewis, Royal Society paper.

62. Lewis to Zunz 7.6.63. Arup papers.

63. Ibid.

64. Ibid.

65. Ibid.

66. Ibid.

67. Huang to Lewis 7.6.63. Arup papers.

68. 20.8.63. Arup papers.

69. 28.8.63. Arup papers.

70. 3.9.63. Arup papers.

71. 13.8.63. Arup papers. There were some uncomplimentary remarks written by someone at Arups attached alongside this passage of Utzon's letter which could not go into print. They said words to the effect 'Well you're supposed to be the architect, not us.'

72. 20.8.63. Arup papers.

73. Ibid.

74. Which is the detail which can be seen today where the warped surface cuts off at the ridge. 3.12.63. Arup papers.

75. Nutt to Yuzo Mikami 3.1.64.

76. Lewis, Royal Society paper.

77. Ibid.

78. Ibid.

79. Ibid.

80. Utzon papers.

81. Lewis, Royal Society paper.

82. Rice to Kynaston 14.5.65. Utzon papers.

83. Ibid.

84. Ibid.

85. Lewis memo 30.6.65 regarding survey dated 16.6.65. Utzon papers.

86. Lewis, Royal Society paper.

87. Lewis memo 30.6.65. Utzon papers.

88. Lewis to Utzon 7.7.65. Utzon papers.

89. 13.8.65. Utzon papers.

90. Lewis, Royal Society paper.

91. Utzon papers.

92. Utzon papers.
93. Utzon papers.
94. Minutes of discussions with Hornibrooks and Arup, London, June 1962. Arup papers.
95. Zunz roof report.
96. Report to the Minister on lids, December 1965. Arup papers.
97. A decision that was reached not without some discussion. At the design stage it was realised that with an interlocking or spigot and socket arrangement...

    The problem of course is that if a leak does occur detaching the tile panels would have to be done in complete rib lengths unless the leak happened to be near the ridge. On the other hand one might argue that to break a tile panel locally is not a serious matter and that it could be patched up somehow with plaster and a little good humour. Frankly, we have not yet decided and when Bob comes back this coming week we will try and reach a conclusion and advise you accordingly.

    Zunz to Gore 10.8.62. Arup papers.
98. Zunz roof report.
99. Ibid.
100. Ibid.
101. Lewis, Royal Society paper.
102. Yeomans.
103. Ibid.
104. Elphick OHOH tapes.
105. Report on the Erection of the Tile Lids to the Minister for Public Works. 14.12.65. Arup papers.
106. Yeomans.
107. Report to the Minister.
108. Lewis, Royal Society paper.
109. Report to the Minister.
110. Ibid.
111. Ibid.
112. Ibid.
113. Ibid.
114. Lewis, Royal Society paper.
115. Report to the Minister.
116. June 1964. Arup papers.
117. Messent/Gore interviews.
118. Ibid.
119. Lewis, Royal Society paper.
120. Report to the Minister.
121. Lewis, Royal Society paper.
122. Report to the Minister.

123. Lewis, Royal Society paper.
123. Lewis, Royal Society paper.
125. Yeomans.
126. Lewis, Royal Society paper.
127. Report to the Minister.
128. Yeomans.
129. Ibid.
130. Lewis, Royal Society paper.
131. Hornibrooks CAA.
132. Report to the Minister.
133. Ibid.
134. Ibid.
135. Ibid.
136. Zunz roof report.
137. Ibid.
138. Elphick OHOH tapes.
139. M of M at Public Works, 19.11.65. Utzon papers.
140. *Daily Mirror*, February 1968.
141. Though Utzon never saw the completed building, he wrote in the Descriptive Narrative in 1965, The shapes of the shells give the building its character which is emphasised by the fine lines defining the form of the curve like the seams in a billowing sail.

   The patron or tourist will see the shells from below as an expanse of curved wall changing constantly as he moves along the broadwalk or on top of the podium, and particularly from these viewpoints the lines will assist his appreciation of the simple yet living geometrical forms which otherwise might escape his comprehension.
142. Kelman OHOH tapes.
143. 11.12.64. Utzon papers.
144. 6.9.65. Utzon papers.
145. 'The Opera House', documentary, 1984.

Bibliography

A time for action. A booklet on the proposed Opera House including information on the appeal fund. (Sydney 1957).

Architectural Review, (The). 'The Utzon Story'. (Robin Boyd, June 1966).

Architecture Plus. Article on the Opera House by Robin Boyd, August, 1973.

Arkitektur. (Journal, Denmark).

Arup (Ove & Partners). *Black Book (The),* Structural Scheme, Stage II (London, 1962). Arup Library London, also AONSW.

Doodles and Doggerel, a book of Ove Arup's drawings and poems published by the Ove Arup Partnership.

Job 1112, a film about the construction of the Opera House shells.

Manual of Procedure, Vols. 1 & 2, (John Blanchard).

Report on the Roof Structure to the Minister for Public Works (G.J. Zunz, May 1965).

Sydney revisited, (Arup Journal, Spring 1988).

The evolution and design of the Concourse at the Sydney Opera House. Ove Arup & Ron Jenkins.

The Sydney Opera House (Ove Arup & Jack Zunz, Arup Journal, October 1973).

Arup papers. Ove Arup & Partners papers on the Sydney Opera House, London.

Ashworth papers. The personal papers of Professor Harry Ingham Ashworth, National Library, Canberra.

Australian – The. (Newspaper, published in Sydney early in the nineteenth century).

Australian – The. (Newspaper, Sydney, since 1964).

Barnard, Marjorie. *Australia's first architect – Francis Greenway* (Melbourne, 1961).

Baume, Michael. *The Sydney Opera House Affair* (Sydney, 1967).

Bradley, William. *A Voyage to New South Wales* (Sydney, 1969).

Browne, Waveney. *A Man of Achievement, Sir Manuel Hornibrook,* (Brisbane,1974).

Civil Engineering. (London, February, 1965).

Collins, David. *An Account of the English Colony in New South Wales* (Sydney, 1975).

Conditions and Programme for the Opera House Competition. (Sydney, December, 1955, DWL).

Cook, Captain James. Journals of (London, 1955).

Curtis, Robert Emerson. *A Vision Takes Form,* (Sydney, 1967).

Daily Guardian. (Newspaper, Sydney).

Daily Mirror. (Newspaper, Sydney).

Daily Telegraph. (Newspaper, Sydney).

Dowrick, David. *The Prestressing of Sydney Opera House Roof.* Presented at Prague, June 1970. (Arup Library, London).

Drew, Philip. Sydney Opera House (London, 1995).

Duek-Cohen, E. *Utzon and the Sydney Opera House : A Statement in the Public Interest,* (Sydney, 1967).

Ellis, Malcolm. *Francis Greenway – his Life and Times* (Sydney, 1949).
Lachlan Macquarie, his life, adventures and times. (Sydney, 1947).

Elphick, Michael. Opera House Oral History tapes, (1988).
Surveys for the construction of the shell roofs of the Sydney Opera House.

Fifth Facade (The). T.V. documentary on Sydney Opera House.

Financial Review. (Newspaper, Sydney).

Giedion, S. *Jorn Utzon and the Third Generation.* A chapter in *Space, Time and Architecture.*

Global Architecture. *Sydney Opera House 1957-73.* (Christian Norberg-Schulz, Tokyo, 1980).

Hansard. *New South Wales Parliamentary Debates* (Sydney).

Haviland family papers. Dennis Wolanski Library.

Hawksworth, John. *Official narrative of the voyage of the Endeavour.* (London, 1773).

Hornibrook Group. *Building the Sydney Opera House,* (Sydney, 1973).

Hornibrook. *Construction Achievement Award submission for the Stage II Contract of Sydney Opera House,* (Corbet Gore's personal papers).

Hubble, Ava. *More Than An Opera House* (Sydney, 1983)
The Strange Case of Eugene Goossens and Other Tales from the Opera House (Sydney, 1988).

Hughes, Robert. *The Fatal Shore* (London, 1987).

Hunter, John. *An historical journal of the transactions at Port Jackson and Norfolk Island.* (London, 1792).

Kelman, Bob. Opera House Oral History tapes.

Kenny, John. *Bennelong first notable aboriginal* (Sydney, 1973).

King, Philip Gidley. The Journals of (Sydney, 1980).

Levy, Alan. *Design Synopsis on the Folded Slab.* Arup Library, London.

Lewis, Mike. Opera House Oral History tapes, 1987.
Royal Society paper on tiles. (See also listing under Royal Society).

Lycett, James. *Views in Australia or New South Wales* (London, 1824).

MacKenzie, Ian. Opera House Oral History tapes, (1986).

Macquarie, Governor Lachlan. Diaries (Mitchell Library).

Messent/Blanchard interviews, 1992.

Messent/Kelman interviews, 1995-1997.

Messent/Lewis interviews, 1992.

Messent/Molnar interviews, 1992-97.

Messent/Nutt correspondence, 1997.

Messent/Ryan interviews, 1990.

Messent/Zunz correspondence, 1997.

Messent/Zunz interviews, 1992-1997.

Messsent/Gore interviews, 1990-1997.

Miller, Pat. *Sydney Opera House 1973,* (Sydney 1973).

Monster or Miracle. TV documentary.

Morehead, Alan. Australian author.

Moses, Charles. Opera House Oral History tapes (Sydney, 1986).

Newcastle Morning Herald. (Newspaper, New South Wales).

Nutt, John. Grouting Prestressing Ducts at the Sydney Opera House. A paper presented at a talk to the Australian Prestressed Concrete Group, 30 August, 1967.

Observer – The. (Newspaper, London).

Pettersson, Ove. *Sydney Opera House, Calculations and Recommendations of the outer ceramic wall facings.* May, 1959.

Pix. (Magazine, Sydney).

Pringle, John. *On Second Thoughts,* (Sydney, 1971).

Ritchie, John. *The evidence to the Bigge Reports.* (Melbourne, 1971).

Royal Society of New South Wales, Journal and Proceedings. Vol. 106, 21 November 1973. Articles by M. Lewis, V.L. Jordan and P. Hall on the Opera House tiling, acoustics and design respectively.

Smith, Michael Pomeroy. *Sydney Opera House,* (Sydney, 1984).

Smith, Vincent. *Sydney Opera House* (Sydney, 1974).

Stockdale, John. *The Voyage of Governor Phillip to Botany Bay.* (London, 1789).

Structural Engineer – The. May 1956, October 1969.

Sun Herald. (Newspaper, Sydney).

Sun – The. (Newspaper, Sydney).

Sunday Mail. (Newspaper, Brisbane).

Sunday Mirror. (Newspaper, Sydney).

Sunday Telegraph. (Newspaper, Sydney).

Sydney Morning Herald. (Newspaper, Sydney).
    Souvenir to mark the official opening, 1973.

Sydney Morning Herald Good Weekend. Utzon interview by Eric Ellis, 31 October 1992.

Sydney Opera House. Sydney Opera House Trust 14 March 1971, (DWL).

Sydney Opera House. Booklet to commemorate the start of building, (Sydney, 1959, DWL).

Sydney Truth. (Newspaper, Sydney).

Sykes, Jill. *Sydney Opera House : From the outside in.* (Sydney, 1993).

Tench, Watkin. *A complete account of the settlement at Port Jackson in New South Wales,* (London, 1793).

The Building that Nearly Was. BBC TV documentary on the completion of the Opera House, 1973.

The Opera House. TV documentary narrated by Stuart Wagstaff, 1984.

Trotter, James. On Ove Arup for McGraw-Hill, Worlds News. OAPP CCAC.

Utzon papers. Jorn Utzon's papers on the Sydney Opera House 1960-66, Mitchell Library Manusacripts.

Utzon, Jorn. *Descriptive Narrative,* (Sydney, 1965) AONSW.

    Red Book (The), Denmark, 1958).

    Yellow Book (The), (Denmark, 1962).

Wentworth, William Charles. *Statistical description of the Colony of New South Wales (London, 1819).*

Westcott, Ross & Pat, *The Sydney Opera House,* (Sydney, 1965).

Yeomans, John. *The Other Taj Mahal* (London, 1968).

Ziegler, Oswald. *Sydney builds an Opera House* (Sydney, 1973).

    Sydney Has An Opera House, (Sydney, 1974).

Zodiac. Platforms and Plateaus : Ideas of a Danish architect, (No.10, 1962).

    '*The Sydney Opera House'*. (No.14, 1965).

Zunz, Jack. Opera House Oral History tapes.

Index

Notes and illustrations have not been indexed.
This index was prepared by Glenda Browne, a registered member
of the Australian Society of Indexers.

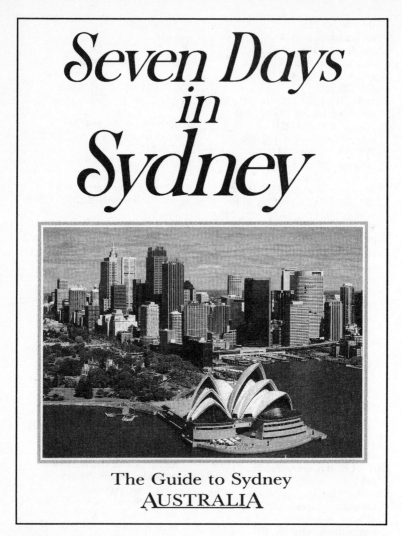

Seven Days in Sydney

The Guide to Sydney
AUSTRALIA

Sydney's best-selling tour guide now in its sixth edition. Over 100,000 in print. How to make the most of a week's stay in Sydney. 176 pages, over 200 of David Messent's pictures, with a history and descriptions of the places to visit. $19.95.

The Complete Guide to
Sydney
Harbour

New South Wales
AUSTRALIA

This *is* the complete guide to Sydney Harbour. The book contains maps of the entire 100 km coastline of the Harbour, covers the history of all the suburbs on the water, and includes descriptions of walks in the unspoilt bushland that still lines much of the shore. 160 pages illustrated with David Messent's pictures. $18.95.

Sydney's Birthplace

The Rocks

DAVID MESSENT

A guide and photographs of the historic Rocks area of Sydney.
$9.95. See the cobbled lane where the plague broke out in 1900,
climb the Harbour bridge and explore the lanes and winding
stairways of the birthplace of the nation.